ENCYCLOPEDIA *of* DRUGS, ALCOHOL & ADDICTIVE BEHAVIOR

ENCYCLOPEDIA *of* DRUGS, ALCOHOL *&* ADDICTIVE BEHAVIOR

SECOND EDITION

VOLUME 4

Appendix

Index

ROSALYN CARSON-DEWITT, M.D.

Editor in Chief
Durham, North Carolina

Macmillan Reference USA

an imprint of the Gale Group
New York • Detroit • San Francisco • London • Boston • Woodbridge, CT

Macmillan Reference USA
An imprint of the Gale Group
1633 Broadway
New York, NY 10019

Macmillan Reference USA
An imprint of the Gale Group
27500 Drake Rd.
Farmington Hills, MI 48331-3535

Printed in the United States of America

printing number
  2 3 4 5 6 7 8 9 10

Library of Congress Cataloging-in-Publication Data
Encyclopedia of drugs, alcohol, and addictive behavior / Rosalyn Carson-DeWitt, editor-in-chief.–Rev. ed.
    p. cm.
   Rev. ed. of: Encyclopedia of drugs and alcohol. c1995.
   Includes bibliographical references and index.
   ISBN 0-02-865541-9 (set)
   ISBN 0-02-865542-7 (Vol. 1)
   ISBN 0-02-865543-5 (Vol. 2)
   ISBN 0-02-865544-3 (Vol. 3)
   ISBN 0-02-865545-1 (Vol. 4)
   1. Drug abuse–Encyclopedias. 2. Substance abuse–Encyclopedias. 3. Alcoholism–Encyclopedias. 4. Drinking of alcoholic beverages–Encyclopedias. I. Carson-DeWitt, Rosalyn II. Encyclopedia of drugs and alcohol.
HV5804 .E53 2000
362.29'03–dc21

00-046068
CIP

This paper meets the requirements of ANSI-NISO Z39.48-1992 (Permanence of Paper) ∞™

Contents

APPENDIX I

Poison Control Centers for Drug Overdoses (ODs) and Emergencies

INTRODUCTION

The list of Poison Control Centers has been compiled from information furnished by the American Association of Poison Control Centers (AAPCC), 3201 New Mexico Avenue NW, Suite 310, Washington, DC, 20016.

The list includes facilities that provide information on the treatment and prevention of accidents involving ingestion of poisonous (toxic) and potentially poisonous substances, including alcohol and drugs. Alcohol and drug overdoses (ODs) often cause "blackouts," coma, and death. A call to poison control in your area, with symptoms described, can mean immediate help, first-aid suggestions, and the swift response of emergency medical services (EMS). If in doubt, call Poison Control before 911.

Household products, garden supplies, and hobby materials may be inhaled or swallowed, accidentally or on purpose. Prescription drugs and over-the-counter (OTC) medications are sometimes taken in larger doses than may be safe. "Kiddie dope"— drugs sold legally without prescription, by mail and in shops, which mimic the effects of amphetamines (speed) may be taken in great quantities; these products usually contain a combination of caffeine, phenylpropanolamine, phenylephrine, ephedrine, or pseudoephedrine. Kiddie dope is taken by youngsters who expect increased energy, weight loss, and a pleasant high— but handfuls of such pills often lead to seizures, heart failure, and cerebral bleeding (stroke). Poison control units are available to answer your questions and help out in any suspected poisoning emergency— and any chemical substance can be toxic if inhaled or taken in inappropriate quantities.

The list below is the most current provided by the AAPCC for 2000. Updates are available online at http://www.usmedicine.com/poison.html.

CERTIFIED REGIONAL POISON CENTERS

ALABAMA

Alabama Poison Center
408-A Paul Bryant Drive
Tuscaloosa, AL 35401
(205) 345-0600
(800) 282-0880 (AL only)

Regional Poison Control Center The Children's Hospital of Alabama
1600 7th Ave. South
Birmingham, AL 35233-1711
(205) 939-9201
(205) 933-4060
(800) 292-6678 (AL only)

ARIZONA

Arizona Poison and Drug Information Center
Arizona Health Sciences Center, Rm. #3204-K
1501 North Campbell Ave.
Tucson, AZ 85724
(602) 626-6016
(800) 362-0101 (AZ only)

Samaritan Regional Poison Center
Good Samaritan Regional Medical Center
Ancillary-1
1111 E. McDowell Road
Phoenix, AZ 85006
(602) 253-3334

CALIFORNIA

Central California Regional Poison Control Center
Valley Children's Hospital
3151 North Millbrook, IN31
Fresno, CA 93703
(209) 445-1222
(800) 346-5922 (Central CA only)

San Diego Regional Poison Center
UCSD Medical Center
200 West Arbor Drive
San Diego, CA 92103-8925
(619) 543-6000
(800) 876-4766 (in 619 area code only)

San Francisco Bay Regional Poison Control Center
San Francisco General Hospital
1001 Potrero Ave., Building 80, Room 230
San Francisco, CA 94110
(800) 523-2222

Santa Clara Valley Regional Poison Center
Valley Health Center, Suite 310
750 South Bascom Ave.
San Jose, CA 95128
(408) 885-6000
(800) 662-9886 (CA only)

University of California, Davis, Medical Center Regional Poison Control Center
2315 Stockton Blvd.
Sacramento, CA 95817
(916) 734-3692
(800) 662-9886 (Northern California only)

COLORADO

Rocky Mountain Poison and Drug Center
645 Bannock St.
Denver, CO 80204
(303) 629-1123

DISTRICT OF COLUMBIA

National Capital Poison Center
3201 New Mexico Avenue, NW, Suite 310
Washington, DC 20016
(202) 625-3333

FLORIDA

Florida Poison Information Center–Jacksonville
University Medical Center
University of Florida Health Science Center–Jacksonville
655 West 8th Street
Jacksonville, FL 32209
(904) 549-4480
(800) 282-3171 (FL only)

The Florida Poison Information Center and Toxicology Resource Center
Tampa General Hospital
Post Office Box 1289
Tampa, FL 33601
(813) 253-4444
(800) 282-3171 (Florida)

GEORGIA

Georgia Poison Center
Hughes Spalding Children's Hospital
Grady Health Systems
80 Butler Street SE
P.O. Box 26066
Atlanta, GA 30335-3801
(800) 282-5846 (GA only)
(404) 616-9000

INDIANA

Indiana Poison Center
Methodist Hospital of Indiana
1701 N. Senate Boulevard
P.O. Box 1367
Indianapolis, IN 46206-1367
(317) 929-2323
(800) 382-9097 (IN only)

KENTUCKY

Kentucky Regional Poison Center of Kosair Children's Hospital
P.O. Box 35070
Louisville, KY 40232-5070
(502) 629-7275
(800) 722-5725 (KY only)

MARYLAND

Maryland Poison Center
20 N. Pine St.
Baltimore, MD 21201
(410) 528-7701
(800) 492-2414 (MD only)

National Capital Poison Center (DC suburbs only)
3201 New Mexico Avenue, NW, Suite 310
Washington, DC 20016
(202) 625-3333

MASSACHUSETTS

Massachusetts Poison Control System
300 Longwood Ave.
Boston, MA 02115
(617) 232-2120
(800) 682-9211

MICHIGAN

Poison Control Center
Children's Hospital of Michigan
3901 Beaubien Blvd.
Detroit, MI 48201
(313) 745-5711

MINNESOTA

Hennepin Regional Poison Center
Hennepin County Medical Center
701 Park Ave.
Minneapolis, MN 55415
(612) 347-3141

Minnesota Regional Poison Center
St. Paul-Ramsey Medical Center
640 Jackson Street
St. Paul, MN 55101
(612) 221-2113

MISSOURI

Cardinal Glennon Children's Hospital Regional Poison Center
1465 S. Grand Blvd.
St. Louis, MO 63104
(314) 772-5200
(800) 366-8888

MONTANA

Rocky Mountain Poison and Drug Center
645 Bannock St.
Denver, CO 80204
(303) 629-1123

NEBRASKA

The Poison Center
8301 Dodge St.
Omaha, NE 68114
(402) 390-5555 (Omaha)
(800) 955-9119 (NE & WY)

NEW JERSEY

New Jersey Poison Information and Education System
201 Lyons Ave.
Newark, NJ 07112
(800) 962-1253

NEW MEXICO

New Mexico Poison and Drug Information Center
University of New Mexico
Albuquerque, NM 87131-2551
(505) 843-2551
(800) 432-6866 (NM only)

NEW YORK

Hudson Valley Regional Poison Center
Phelps Memorial Hospital Center
701 North Broadway
North Tarrytown, NY 10591
(914) 366-3030
(800) 336-6997

Long Island Regional Poison Control Center
Winthrop University Hospital
259 First Street
Mineola, NY 11501
(516) 542-2323
(516) 542-3813

New York City Poison Control Center
N.Y.C. Department of Health
455 First Ave., Room 123
New York, NY 10016
(212) POI-SONS
(212) 340-4494

NORTH CAROLINA

Carolinas Poison Center
1000 Blythe Boulevard
PO Box 32861
Charlotte, NC 28232-2861
(704) 355-4000
(800) 84TOXIN

OHIO

Central Ohio Poison Center
700 Children's Drive
Columbus, OH 43205-2696
(614) 228-1323
(614) 461-2012
(800) 682-7625

Cincinnati Drug & Poison Information Center and Regional Poison Control Center
231 Bethesda Avenue, M.L. 144
Cincinnati, OH 45267-0144
(513) 558-5111
(800) 872-5111 (OH only)

OREGON

Oregon Poison Center
Oregon Health Sciences University
3181 S.W. Sam Jackson Park Road
Portland, OR 97201
(503) 494-8968
(800) 452-7165 (OR only)

PENNSYLVANIA

Central Pennsylvania Poison Center
University Hospital
Milton S. Hershey Medical Center
Hershey, PA 17033
(800) 521-6110

The Poison Control Center serving the greater Philadelphia metropolitan area
One Children's Center
Philadelphia, PA 19104-2100
(215) 386-2100

Pittsburgh Poison Center
3705 Fifth Avenue
Pittsburgh, PA 15213
(412) 681-6669

RHODE ISLAND

Rhode Island Poison Center
593 Eddy St.
Providence, RI 02903
(401) 277-5727

TEXAS

North Texas Poison Center
5201 Harry Hines Blvd.
P.O. Box 35926
Dallas, TX 75235
(214) 590-5000

Southeast Texas Poison Center
University of Texas Medical Branch
Galveston, TX 77550-2780
(409) 765-1420 (Galveston)
(713) 654-1701 (Houston)

UTAH

Utah Poison Control Center
410 Chipeta Way, Suite 230
Salt Lake City, UT 84108
(801) 581-2151
(800) 456-7707 (UT only)

VIRGINIA

Blue Ridge Poison Center
Box 67, Blue Ridge Hospital
Charlottesville, VA 22901
(804) 924-5543
(800) 451-1428

National Capital Poison Center (Northern VA only)
3201 New Mexico Avenue, NW, Suite 310
Washington, DC 20016
(202) 625-3333

WEST VIRGINIA

West Virginia Poison Center
3110 MacCorkle Ave. S.E.
Charleston, WV 25304
(304) 348-4211
(800) 642-3625 (WV only)

WYOMING

The Poison Center
8301 Dodge St.
Omaha, NE 68114
(402) 390-5555 (Omaha)
(800) 955-9119 (NE & WY)

APPENDIX II

U.S. and State Government Drug Resources Directory

INTRODUCTION

This is a guide to state agencies that address substance abuse concerns. It begins with listings of federal agencies and goes on to state and local listings. The listings were originally compiled for a report by the U.S. Department of Justice, Bureau of Justice Statistics. Six groupings are presented here: Federal Information Centers and Clearinghouses; Other Federal Sources; Drug Abuse Resistance Education (DARE) Regional Training Centers; National Prevention Network; Treatment Alternatives to Street Crime (TASC) Programs; and the State Listings.

In Appendix III, which follows, an extensive State-by-State Directory is presented for drug abuse and alcoholism treatment and prevention programs, both public and private.

FEDERAL INFORMATION CENTERS AND CLEARINGHOUSES

CRIMINAL JUSTICE

Drugs & Crime Clearinghouse
1600 Research Boulevard
Rockville, MD 20850
(800) 666-3332
Sponsored by: Office of National
Drug Control Policy

**National Criminal Justice
Reference Service**
PO Box 6000
Rockville, MD 20849-6000
(800) 851-3420
http://www.ncjrs.org
Sponsored by: National Institute of
Justice

**Bureau of Justice Assistance
Clearinghouse**
PO Box 6000
Rockville, MD 20849-6000
(800) 688-4BJA/4252
http://bjavic.aspensys.com
Sponsored by: Bureau of Justice
Assistance

Juvenile Justice Clearinghouse
PO Box 6000
Rockville, MD 20849-6000
(800) 638-8736
http://www.ojjpd.ncrs.org
Sponsored by: Office of Juvenile
Justice and Delinquency
Prevention

Justice Statistics Clearinghouse
PO Box 179
Annapolis Junction, MD 20701-
0179
(800) 732-3277
Sponsored by: Bureau of Justice
Statistics

**Justice Technology Information
Network**
PO Box 1160
Rockville, MD 20849-1160
(800) 248-2742
http://www.nlect.org
Sponsored by: National Institute of
Justice

**National Victims Resource
Center**
PO Box 6000
Rockville, MD 20849-6000
(800) 627-6872
Sponsored by: Office for Victims of
Crime

**National Institute of Corrections
Information Center**
1860 Industrial Circle
Suite A
Longmont, CO 80501
(800) 877-1461
http://www.nicic.org
Sponsored by: National Institute of
Corrections

HEALTH

**National Clearinghouse for
Alcohol and Drug Information**
PO Box 2345
Rockville, MD 20847-2345
(800) 729-6686
http://www.health.org
Sponsored by: Office of Substance
Abuse Prevention

**National Drug Information and
Treatment Routing Service**
107 Lincoln Street
Worcester, MA 01605
(800) 662-HELP
Sponsored by: National Institute
on Drug Abuse

Drug-Free Workplace Helpline
5600 Fishers Lane
Rockville, MD 20857
(800) 843-4971
Sponsored by: National Institute
on Drug Abuse

**National AIDS Information
Clearinghouse**
PO Box 6003
Rockville, MD 20850
(800) 458-5231
Sponsored by: Centers for Disease
Control

PUBLIC HOUSING

**Drug Information and Strategy
Clearinghouse**
PO Box 6424
Rockville, MD 20850
(800) 578-3472
Sponsored by: Housing and Urban
Development

EDUCATION

ACCESS ERIC
2277 Research Boulevard
Rockville, MD 20850
(800) LET-ERIC
http://www.accesseric.org
Sponsored by: United States
Department of Education

OTHER FEDERAL SOURCES

Executive Office of the President

Office of National Drug Control
   Policy
Executive Office of the President
Washington, DC 20503
(202) 395-6700
http://
   www.whitehousedrugpolicy.gov

U.S. Department of Justice

Office of Justice Programs
810 Seventh Street, NW
Washington, DC 20531
(202) 307-0703
http://www.ojp.usdoj.gov

Bureau of Justice Assistance
810 Seventh Street, NW
Washington, DC 20531
(202) 616-6500
http://www.ojp.usdoj.gov/bja

Bureau of Justice Statistics
810 Seventh Street, NW
Washington, DC 20531
(202) 307-0765
http://www.ojp.usdoj.gov/bjs

National Institute of Justice
810 Seventh Street, NW
Washington, DC 20531
(202) 307-2942
http://www.ojp.usdoj.gov/nij

Office of Juvenile Justice and
   Delinquency Prevention
810 Seventh Street, NW
Washington, DC 20531
(202) 307-5911

Office for Victims of Crime
810 Seventh Street
Washington, DC 20531
(202) 307-5983
http://www.ojp.usdoj.gov/ovc

Executive Office for United States
   Attorneys
950 Pennsylvania Avenue, NW
Room 2261
Washington, DC 20530-0001
(202) 514-1020
http://www.usdoj.gov/eousa

Drug Enforcement Administration
700 Army Navy Drive
Arlington, VA 22202
(202) 307-7977 Public Affairs
(202) 307-8932 Library
http://www.usdoj.gov/dea

U.S. Courts

Administrative Office of the United
   States Courts
One Columbus Circle, NE
Washington, DC 20544
(202) 273-0107
http://www.uscourts.gov

Federal Judicial Center
One Columbus Circle, NE
Washington, DC 20002-8003
(202) 633-6011
http://www.fjc.gov

**U.S. Department of Health and
Human Services**

National Institute on Drug Abuse
6001 Executive Boulevard
Bethesda, MD 20892-9561
(301) 443-1124
http://www.nida.nih.gov

Office of Substance Abuse
   Prevention
Rockwall II Building
5600 Fishers Lane
Rockville, MD 20857
(301) 443-0365
http://www.samhsa.gov/csap

U.S. Department of State

Bureau of International Narcotics
   and Law Enforcement Affairs
Room 7334
2201 C Street, NW
Washington, DC 20520
(202) 647-0453
http://www.state.gov/www/global/
   narcotics_law

U.S. Department of the Treasury

Bureau of Alcohol, Tobacco, and
   Firearms
Office of Liaison and Public
   Information
Room 8290
650 Massachusetts Avenue, NW
Washington, DC 20226
(202) 927-7777
http://www.atf.treas.gov

United States Customs Service
1300 Pennsylvania Avenue, NW
Washington, DC 20229
(202) 927-1350
http://www.customs.treas.gov

**U.S. Department of
Transportation**

United States Coast Guard
2100 2nd Street, SW
Washington, DC 20593
(202) 267-2229
http://www.uscg.mil

U.S. Department of Education

Safe and Drug-Free Schools
400 Maryland Avenue, SW
Washington, DC 20202-0498
(202) 260-3954
http://www.ed.gov/offices/OESE/
   SDFS

**U.S. Department of Housing and
Urban Development**

Community Safety and
   Conservation Division
451 7th Street, SW
Room 4112
Washington, DC 20410
(202) 401-0398
http://www.hud.gov/pih/programs/
   ph/de/cscd

DRUG ABUSE RESISTANCE EDUCATION (DARE) REGIONAL TRAINING CENTERS

North Carolina State Bureau of
  Investigation
3320 Old Garner Road
P.O. Box 29500
Raleigh, NC 27626-0500
(919) 662-4500 ext. 277

Missouri State Highway Patrol
P.O. Box 568
Jefferson City, MO 65101-0568
(573) 526-6174

Virginia State Police
7700 Midlothian Turnpike
Box 27472
Richmond, VA 23261-7472
(804) 674-2238

Arizona Department of Public
  Safety
3110 North 19th Avenue
Suite 290
Phoenix, AZ 85015
(602) 223-2544

Los Angeles Police Department
3353 San Fernando Road
Los Angeles, CA 90065
(213) 485-4856

NATIONAL PREVENTION NETWORK

State Substance Abuse Coordinator
Alabama Department of Substance
  Abuse Services
PO Box 3710
Montgomery, AL 36193
(334) 242-3961

Executive Director
Alaska Council on Prevention of
  Alcohol and Drug Abuse
3333 Denali Street, Suite 201
Anchorage, AK 99503
(907) 258-6021

Manager, Office of Prevention
Department of Health Services
Behavioral Health Services
2122 East Highland
Phoenix, AZ 85016
602) 381-8996

Director, Division of Prevention
Arkansas Bureau of Alcohol and
  Drug Abuse Prevention
Freeway Medical Center, Suite 907
5800 West 10th Street
Little Rock, AR 72204
(501) 280-4511

Deputy Director
Department of Alcohol and Drug
  Programs
1700 K Street, Second Floor
Sacramento, CA 95814-4037
(916) 323-0633

Prevention Specialist
Program Services
Alcohol and Drug Abuse Division
4300 Cherry Creek Drive South
Denver, CO 80220-1530
(303) 692-2952

Prevention Director
Department of Mental Health and
  Addiction Services
410 Capitol Avenue, MS 14PIT
Hartford, CT 06134
(860) 418-6827

Director of Training
Delaware Division of Alcoholism,
  Drug Abuse and Mental Health
1901 North DuPont Highway
New Castle, DE 19720
(302) 577-4980

Administrator
Office of Prevention
Barley Mill Plaza, Building 18
4417 Lancaster Pike
Wilmington, DE 19805
(302) 892-4507

Chief
Office of Prevention and Youth
  Services
1300 First Street, NE
Washington, DC 20018
(202) 727-0092

State Prevention Coordinator
Alcohol, Drug Abuse and Mental
  Health Program Office
Office Building 5, Room 304B-1
1317 Winewood Boulevard
Tallahassee, FL 32399-0700
(904) 487-2920 ext. 105

Acting Prevention Unit Director
Substance Abuse Services
2 Peachtree Street NW, Suite 4-
  320
Atlanta, GA 30303-3171
(404) 657-2136

Prevention Coordinator
Alcohol and Drug Abuse Division
PO Box 3378
Honolulu, HI 96801
(808) 586-4007

Idaho Bureau of Substance Abuse
  and Social Services
450 West State Street
Boise, ID 83720
(208) 334-5700

Administrator for Prevention
Department of Alcoholism and
  Substance Abuse
100 West Randolph Street, Suite
  5-600
Chicago, IL 60601
(312) 814-6355

Division of Mental Health
402 West Washington Street,
  Room W353
Indianapolis, IN 46204-2739
(317) 232-7924

Prevention Consultant
Department of Public Health
Lucas State Office Building
321 East 12th Street
Des Moines, IA 50319-0075
(515) 281-4404

Public Service Executive
Alcohol and Drug Abuse Services
Biddle Building
300 Southwest Oakley
Topeka, KS 66606
(913) 296-0511

Manager
Prevention and Training Branch
Division of Substance Abuse
275 East Main Street
1R Health Services Building
Frankfort, KY 40621
(502) 564-2880

Division of Alcohol and Drug
  Abuse
1201 Capitol Access Road
P.O. Box 3868
Baton Rouge, LA 70821-3868
(504) 342-9352

Office of Substance Abuse
Division of Prevention and
  Education
State House Station 159
Augusta, ME 04333
(207) 287-8908

Assistant Director
Alcohol and Drug Abuse
Prevention and Treatment Services
201 West Preston Street, Fourth
  Floor
Baltimore, MD 21201
(410) 225-6543

Director of Prevention Services
Division of Substance Abuse
  Services
150 Tremont Street
Boston, MA 02111
(617) 727-5141

Chief, Prevention Services
Michigan Department of Public
  Health
Center for Substance Abuse
  Services
3423 North Logan
P.O. Box 30295
Lansing, MI 48909
(517) 335-8843

Prevention Coordinator
Chemical Dependency Program
  Division
444 Lafayette Road
St. Paul, MN 55155-3823
(612) 296-4711

Program Coordinator
Division of Alcohol and Drug
  Abuse
1101 Robert E. Lee Building
239 North Lamar Street
Jackson, MS 39201
(601) 359-6216

Prevention Director
Division of Alcohol and Drug
  Abuse
1706 East Elm Street
PO Box 687
Jefferson City, MO 65102
(314) 751-7814

Prevention Coordinator
Division of Addictive and Mental
  Disorders
Department of Public Health and
  Human Services
1539 11th Avenue
Helena, MT 59620
(406) 444-1202

Prevention Coordinator
Division of Alcoholism and Drug
  Abuse
P.O. Box 94728
Lincoln, NE 68509
(402) 471-2851

Prevention Specialist
Bureau of Alcohol and Drug Abuse
1830 East Sahara Avenue, Suite
  314
Las Vegas, NV 89104
(702) 486-8250

Director, Prevention, Training, and
  Education
Division of Alcoholism, Drug
  Abuse and Addiction Services
129 East Hanover Street, CN362
Trenton, NJ 08625
(609) 292-4414

Prevention Manager
Substance Abuse Bureau
1190 Saint Francis Drive
Santa Fe, New Mexico 87503
(505) 827-2601

Director, Prevention and
  Intervention
Office of Alcoholism and
  Substance Abuse Services
1450 Western Avenue
Albany, NY 12203
(518) 485-2123

Chief of Prevention
Alcohol and Drug Abuse Section
325 North Salisbury Street, Suite
  531
Raleigh, NC 27611
(919) 733-4555

Acting NPN Designee
Division of Alcoholism and Drug
  Abuse
600 South Second Street, 1-E
Bismarck, ND 58504-5729
(701) 328-8922

Chief
Prevention Services and Training
Department of Alcohol and Drug
  Addiction Services
280 North High Street, 12th Floor
Columbus, OH 43215-2357
(614) 466-3445

Director, Prevention Services
Department of Mental Health and
  Substance Abuse
P.O. Box 53277
Oklahoma City, OK 73152
(405) 522-3866

Prevention Manager
Department of Human Resources
Office of Alcohol and Drug Abuse
  Programs
500 Summer Street NE
Salem, OR 97310-1016
(503) 945-6189

Director
Bureau of Preventive Health
Pennsylvania Department of
  Health, Room 929, Health &
  Welfare Building
Seventh and Foster Streets
Harrisburg, PA 17108
(717) 787-2712

Associate Administrator
Division of Substance Abuse
Department of Health
Cannon Building, 3 Capitol Hill
Providence, RI 02908-5097
(401) 277-4680

Director, Division of Programs and
  Services
Department of Alcohol and Other
  Drug Abuse Services
3700 Forest Drive, Suite 300
Columbia, SC 29204
(803) 734-9545

Prevention Coordinator
Division of Alcohol and Drug
  Abuse
700 Governors Drive
Pierre, SD 57501
(605) 773-3123

Director, Prevention Services
Bureau of Alcohol & Drug Abuse
  Services
Cordell Hull Building
426 Fifth Avenue North, Third
  Floor
Nashville, TN 37247-4401
(615) 741-1921

Prevention Council Coordinator
Commission on Alcohol and Drug
  Abuse
710 Brazos Street
Austin, TX 78701-2576
(512) 867-8847

Prevention Coordinator
Department of Social Services
Division of Substance Abuse
120 North 200 West, Fourth Floor
Salt Lake City, UT 84103
(801) 538-3939

Chief of Prevention
Office of Alcohol and Drug Abuse
   Programs
103 South Main Street
Waterbury, VT 05676
(802) 241-2170

Program Consultant
Office of Prevention
Department of Mental Health,
   Mental Retardation, and
   Substance Abuse Services
P.O. Box 1797
Richmond, VA 23214
(804) 786-1530

Program Manager for Prevention
Division of Alcohol and Substance
   Abuse
Mail Stop: OB-21W
Olympia, WA 98504
(360) 438-8200

Program Coordinator
Division of Alcohol and Drug
   Abuse
State Capitol Complex
Building 6, Room 738
Charleston, WV 25305
(304) 558-2276

Prevention Specialist
Bureau of Substance Abuse
1 West Wilson Street, Room 434
P.O. Box 7851
Madison, WI 53707-7851
(608) 266-9485

Substance Abuse Consultant
Alcohol and Drug Abuse Programs
447 Hathaway Building
Cheyenne, WY 82002
(307) 777-6493

Department of Human Resource
Alcohol and Drug Program
Government of American Somoa
Pago Pago, AS 96799
011 (684) 633-4210

Supervisor, Prevention Branch
Guam Department of Mental
   Health and Substance Abuse
790 Gov. Carlos G. Camacho Road
Tamuning, GU 96911
011 (671) 647-5415

Department of Public Health
   Services
P.O. Box 409
Saipan, MP 96950
011 (670) 323-6560

Assistant Administrator for
   Prevention
Services and Mental Health
   Promotion
P.O. Box 21414
Rio Piedras, PR 00928-1414
(787) 763-3133

Prevention Coordinator
Virgin Islands Division of Mental
   Health,
Alcohol & Drug Dependency
One Third Street, DeCastro
   Building
Sugar Estate
St. Thomas, VI 00802
(340) 774-7700

TREATMENT ALTERNATIVES TO STREET CRIME (TASC) PROGRAMS

University of Alabama Substance
  Abuse Programs
401 Beacon Parkway West
Birmingham, AL 35209
(205) 917-3784

Treatment Assessment Screening
  Center, Inc.
North Seventh Street
Phoenix, AZ 85006
(602) 254-7328

Treatment Assessment Screening
  Center, Inc.
5270 North 59th Avenue
Glendale, AZ 85301
(602) 842-4535

Treatment Assessment Screening
  Center, Inc.
1035 North McQueen, Suite 119
Gilbert, AZ 85234
(602) 497-5602

TASC/Adult Probation
1008 Front Street
Conway, AR 72032
(501) 327-3256

S.T.E.P. Drug Court
TASC Program
715 West Second Street
Little Rock, AR 72201
(501) 374-8613

Sonoma County Drug Abuse
  Services/TASC
830 Fifth Street, Suite C
Santa Rosa, CA 95404
(707) 527-7200

Southeast TASC
25 North Spruce, Suite 301
Colorado Springs, CO 80905
(719) 444-0882

Mile High TASC
1026 Bannock
Denver, CO 80215
(303) 595-4194

Division of Youth Services
3900 South Carr
Denver, CO 80235
(303) 987-4620

Denver Juvenile Justice Integrated
  Treatment
Network
303 West Colfax Avenue
Denver, CO 80204
(303) 893-6898

Denver Juvenile Justice Integrated
  TASC Project
Denver Juvenile Court, Suite 925
303 West Colfax Avenue
Denver, CO 80204
(303) 762-3113

TASC/NCADA
136 North Seventh Street
Grand Junction, CO 81501
(970) 243-3140

Northeast TASC
7255 Irving Street, Suite 106
Westminster, CO 80030
(303) 428-5264

The Connecticut Halfway House,
  Inc.
Juvenile Drug Treatment Program
310 Collins Street
Hartford, CT 06105
(860) 543-0101

The Connecticut Prison
  Association
110 Bartholomew Avenue
Hartford, CT 06106
(203) 566-2030

Net Counseling Center
813 West Street
Wilmington, DE 19801
(302) 657-8100

TASC/Delaware Treatment Access
  Center
1602-B Jessup Street
Wilmington, DE 19802
(302) 577-2711

Department of Health and
  Rehabilitative Services
Juvenile/Adult TASC
1317 Winewood Boulevard
Tallahassee, FL 32399-0700
(904) 922-4270

Levy County (NM)
Juvenile/Adult TASC
P.O. Box 516
Bronson, FL 32621
(904) 486-5310

Operation PAR
Juvenile TASC
14500 49th Street North
Suite 135
Clearwater, FL 34622
(813) 464-1455

Stewart Marchman Treatment
  Center
Juvenile TASC
3875 Tiger Beach Road
Daytona Beach, FL 32124
(904) 947-1300

Spectrum Programs, Inc.
Juvenile TASC
2701 West Oakland Park
  Boulevard, Suite 400
Ft. Lauderdale, FL 33311
(305) 777-2977

Ruth Cooper Center
Juvenile and Adult TASC
2789 Ortiz Avenue SE
Ft. Myers, FL 33905
(941) 275-3222

Gateway Community Services, Inc.
Juvenile TASC
1283 East Eighth Street
Jacksonville, FL 32206
(904) 356-9835

Drug Abuse Treatment
  Association, Inc.
Juvenile TASC
1016 North Clemons Street, Suite
  406
Jupiter, FL 33477
(407) 743-1034

The Village/Virgin Islands TASC
Juvenile TASC
3180 Biscayne Boulevard
Miami, FL 32801
(305) 573-3784

Metro-Dade Office of
    Rehabilitative Services/TASC
Juvenile/Adult TASC
3300 Northwest 27th Avenue
    Miami, FL 33142

David Lawrence Center/Court
    Related Services
Adult and Juvenile TASC
2806 Horseshoe Drive South
Naples, FL 33942-6125

Human Services Associates
Adult and Juvenile TASC
1703 West Colonial Drive
Orlando, FL 32804
(407) 422-0880

Escambia County
Adult and Juvenile TASC
1800 West Saint Mary Avenue
Box 6
Pensacola, FL 32501
(904) 436-9855 or (904) 436-
    9856

Coastal Recovery Centers, Inc.
Juvenile TASC
2080 Ringling Boulevard
Sarasota, FL 34237
(813) 365-4469

Regional Professional Center
Juvenile TASC
4000 East Third Street, Suite
    2000
Springfield, FL 32404
(904) 872-4825

DISC Village Juvenile and Adult
    TASC Program
3333 West Pensacola Street
Tallahassee, FL 32304
(904) 575-4388

DACCO Juvenile and Adult TASC
4422 East Columbus Drive
Tampa, FL 33605
(813) 623-3500

ACTS Juvenile TASC
4211 E. Busch Boulevard, Suite H
Tampa, FL 33617
(813) 988-6096

Guidance Clinic of Upper Keys
S.C.A.T. Juvenile TASC
P.O. Box 363
Tavernier, FL 33070
(305) 852-3284

Coastal Recovery Centers, Inc.
Adult TASC
410 Cortez Road West, Suite 410
Bradenton, FL 34207
(813) 727-7719

ACT Corporation
Adult TASC
1220 Willis Avenue
Daytona Beach, FL 32114
(904) 239-6134

Stewart Marchman Treatment
    Center
Adult TASC
120 Michigan Avenue
Daytona Beach, FL 32114
(904) 947-1357

Central Florida Human Services
    Center
Program to Aid Drug Abusers
    (PAD)/Adult TASC
2920 Franklin Street
P.O. Box 1593
Eaton Park, FL 33840
(813) 665-2211

Spectrum
Adult TASC Program
2301 Wilton Drive
Ft. Lauderdale, FL 33305
(305) 563-6413

New Horizons of the Treasure
    Coast
Adult TASC
415 Avenue A, Suite 304
Ft. Pierce, FL 34950
(407) 468-5656/5663

TASC/Tri-County Services Adult
    TASC
4300 Southwest 13th Street
Gainesville, FL 32608
(904) 463-3145

Starting Place
Adult TASC
2057 Coolidge Street
Hollywood, FL 33020
(305) 925-1045

River Region Human Services
    Center
Adult TASC
330 West State Street
Jacksonville, FL 32202
(904) 359-6571

North Florida Mental Health
    Centers
Adult TASC
P.O. Box 2818
Lake City, FL 32056-2818
(904) 752-1045
Adult: (904) 758-0560

Gateway Community Services
Adult TASC
P.O. Box 502
McClenny, FL 32063

The Harbor Behavioral Health
    Care Institute
Adult TASC
P.O. Box 428
New Port Ritchey, FL 34656
(813) 943-5366

Operation PAR Adult TASC
6655 66th Street North
Pinellas Park, FL 34665
(813) 545-6416

Circles of Care/Brevard County
Adult TASC
1770 Cedar Street
Rockledge, FL 32955
(407) 632-9480

TASC/Adult
2080 Ringling Boulevard, Suite
    201B
Sarasota, FL 34237
(813) 365-4469

Operation PAR
Adult TASC
10901-C Roosevelt Boulevard,
    Suite 1000
St. Petersburg, FL 33716-2336
(813) 538-7280

TASC
State Board of Pardons and
    Paroles Special Services Unit
Two Northside 75, Suite 134
Atlanta, GA 30318
(404) 656-5651

DeKalb County Court Services
Risk Reduction Program
DeKalb Addiction Clinic
1260 Briarcliff Road NE
Atlanta, GA 30306
(404) 894-5806

Hawaii Paroling Authority/TASC
429A Walakamilo Road
Honolulu, HI 96817
(808) 832-3479

AREA I
TASC, Inc.
Adult Programs
2600 South California Avenue,
   Room 107
Chicago, IL 60608
(312) 376-0950 or 0897

TASC, Inc.
Adult Programs
1500 North Halsted, Second Floor
Chicago, IL 60622
(312) 787-0208

TASC, Inc.
Juvenile Programs
1100 South Hamilton, Room 12
Chicago, IL 66012
(312) 666-7339

AREA II
TASC, Inc.
Adult and Juvenile Programs
119 North Church Street, Suite
   202
Rockford, IL 61101
(815) 965-1106

AREA III
TASC, Inc.
Adult Programs
Regency Plaza Office Building
2525 - 24th Street, Suite 101
Rock Island, IL 61201
(309) 788-0816

AREA IV
TASC, Inc.
Adult and Juvenile Programs
Central Building
101 Southwest Adams Street, Suite
   420
Peoria, IL 61602
(309) 673-3769 or 3794

AREA V
TASC, Inc.
Adult and Juvenile Programs
Three Old Capitol Plaza West,
   Suite 8
Springfield, IL 62701
(217) 544-0842

AREA VI
TASC, Inc.
Adult Programs
104 West University
Urbana, IL 61801
(217) 344-4546

AREA VII
TASC, Inc.
Adult and Juvenile Programs
110 West Main Street
Belleville, IL 62220
(618) 277-0410

AREA VIII
TASC, Inc.
Adult and Juvenile Programs
Court Square Offices
400 West Jackson, Suite B
Marion, IL 62959
(618) 997-8181

AREA IX
TASC, Inc.
Adult and Juvenile Programs
103 Plaza Court
Edwardsville, IL 62025
(618) 656-7672

AREA X
Roosevelt Glen Corporate Center
Adult and Juvenile Programs
799 Roosevelt Road
Building 6, Suite 2
Glen Ellyn, IL 60137
(708) 858-7400

ACP (Alcohol Countermeasures/
   Probation/TASC)
226 West Wallace Street
Ft. Wayne, IN 46802
(219) 449-7134

St. Joseph's Hospital
1900 Medical Arts Drive
Huntingburg, IN 47542
(812) 683-2121

TASC Component/Municipal Court
   Probation
Marion County Municipal Courts
Room T641
200 East Washington Street
Indianapolis, IN 46204
(317) 236-3841

TASC
Dubos Superior Court Courthouse
Jasper, IN 47546
(812) 482-1661

St. Joseph County TASC
St. Joseph County Superior Court
Courthouse
South Bend, IN 46601
(219) 284-9550

Iowa TASC
Department of Corrections
Capitol Annex
523 East 12th Street
Des Moines, IA 50319
(515) 281-4592

Department of Correctional
   Services
510 Fifth Street
Ames, IA 50010
(515) 232-1511

Department of Correctional
   Services
53 Third Avenue Bridge
P.O. Box 74740
Cedar Rapids, IA 52401
(319) 398-3474

Department of Correctional
   Services
801 South 10th Street
Council Bluffs, IA 51501
(712) 325-0782

Department of Correctional
   Services
Community Resource Center
605 Main Street, Box 2A
Davenport, IA 52803-5293
(319) 322-7986

Department of Correctional
   Services
1000 Washington Avenue
Des Moines, IA 50313
(515) 242-6610

Ottumwa Residential Facility
Department of Correctional
   Services
245 Osage Drive
Ottumwa, IA 52501
(515) 682-3069

Department of Correctional
   Services
515 Water Street
Sioux City, IA 51101
(712) 252-0590

Department of Correctional
   Services
527 East Fifth Street
P.O. Box 2596
Waterloo, IA 50704
(319) 291-2091

DCCCA Center
3312 Clinton Parkway
Lawrence, KS 66047
(913) 841-4138

TASC/Early Intervention
Somerset County Jail
Five High Street
Skowhegan, ME 04976
(207) 474-9591

Health Reach Network
Eight Highwood Street
P.O. Box 1568
Waterville, ME 04903-1568
(207) 873-1127

TASC Project
105 Fleet Street
Rockville, MD 20850
(301) 279-1332

Baltimore County Alternative
   Sentencing/TASC
201 West Chesapeake
Towson, MD 21204
(410) 887-2056

Dimock Justice Resource Services
55 Dimock Street
Roxbury, MA 02119
(617) 442-6769

HSTA-TASC
174 Clark Street
Detroit, MI 48209
(313) 876-4066

Administrative Offices of the Court
Criminal Practice Division
CN982
Trenton, NJ 08625
(609) 984-0114

Warren County TASC
Warren County Court House
Belvidere, NJ 07823
(908) 475-6263

Camden County TASC
Criminal Division
Hall of Justice
Camden, NJ 08103
(609) 225-7186

Newark Target Cities
Probation Department
110 South Grove Street
East Orange, NJ 07018
(201) 677-8042

Union County TASC
Annex Building, Second Floor
Union County Court House
Elizabeth, NJ 07207
(908) 527- 4344

Union County TASC
Criminal Division/PTI
1143-1145 East Jersey Street,
   Third Floor
Union County Court House
Elizabeth, NJ 07207
(908) 527-4338

Monmouth County TASC
Monmouth County Court House
Court Street
Freehold, NJ 07728
(908) 303-7696

Hudson County TASC
P.O. Box 806
North Arlington, NJ 07037
(908) 322-6721

Atlantic County TASC
Criminal Court House
Main Street, Room 238
Mays Landing, NJ 08830
(609) 625-7000, ext. 5392

Morris County TASC
Morris County Court House
Criminal Division
P.O. Box 900
Morristown, NJ 07960-0900
(201) 829-8052

Burlington County TASC
Burlington County Courts Facility
49 Rancocas Road
Mount Holly, NJ 08060
(609) 265-5335

Middlesex County TASC
Court House
JFK Square
New Brunswick, NJ 08903
(908) 745-3873

Essex County TASC
Criminal Division
New Courts Building, Room 141
Newark, NJ 07102
(201) 621-5086

Newark Municipal Court
Probation Department
31 Green Street
Newark, NJ 07102
(201) 621-5297

Newark Target Cities
New Courts Building, Room 141
Newark, NJ 07102
(201) 621-5086

Newark Target Cities
Family Court Division
Old Court House, Room 312
470 Martin Luther King Boulevard
Newark, NJ 07102
(201) 621-5337

Passaic County TASC
Criminal Division
77 Hamilton Street
Paterson, NJ 07505
(201) 881-7689

Ocean County TASC
Criminal Division
P.O. Box 2191
Toms River, NJ 08754-2191
(908) 929-4780 ext. 2244

Gloucester County TASC
Criminal Justice Complex
Hunter Street
P.O. Box 187
Woodbury, NJ 08096
(609) 853-3588

TASC of the Capital District, Inc.
87 Columbia Street
Albany, NY 12210
(518) 465-1455

Steuben County Probation
   Department
3 East Pulteney Square
Bath, NY 14810
(607) 776-9631

EAC/Brooklyn Bridge
188 Montague Street, Room 404
Brooklyn, NY 11201
(718) 237-9404

EAC, Inc.
1 Old Country Road, Suite 420
Carle Place, NY 11514
(516) 741-5580

TASC of Orange County
224 Main Street
P.O. Box 583
Goshen, NY 10924
(914) 294-9600

EAC/Suffolk TASC
County Center North
Veterans Memorial Highway
Building 804
Hauppauge, NY 11788
(516) 853-5777

EAC/Nassau TASC.
250 Fulton Avenue
Hempstead, NY 11550
(516) 486-8944

EAC/Queens TASC
124-26 Queens Boulevard
Kew Gardens, NY 11415
(718) 268-5657

ASAC of Ulster County, Inc.
785 Broadway
Kingston, NY 12401
(914) 331-9331

Niagara County Probation
   Department
Niagara Civic Building
775 Third Street
Niagara Falls, NY 14302
(716) 284-3133

TASC/Monroe County of
   Probation
80 West Main Street
Rochester, NY 14614
(716) 428-2624

EAC/Staten Island TASC
387 Van Duzer Street
Staten Island, NY 10304
(718) 727-9722

Center for Community Alternatives
351 South Warren Street, Suite
   500
Syracuse, NY 13202
(315) 422-5638

Westchester County
Treatment Alternatives To Street
   Crime
112 East Post Road, Second Floor
White Plains, NY 10601
(914) 285-5265

Crisis Services Section
North Carolina Department of
   MH/DD/SAS
325 North Salisbury Street, Room
   1129
Raleigh, NC 27611
(919) 733-1763

Alcohol and Drug Abuse Services
North Carolina Department of
   MH/DD/SAS
325 North Salisbury Street
Raleigh, NC 27611
(919) 733-0566

Blue Ridge Area MH/MR and
   Substance Abuse Services
283 Biltmore Avenue
Asheville, NC 28801
(704) 252-8748

McLeod Center/TASC
145 Remount Road
Charlotte, NC 28203
(704) 332-9001

Durham County Substance Abuse
   Services
705 South Mangum Street
Durham, NC 27701
(919) 560-7531

Albemarle Mental Health
TASC/Substance Abuse Center
P.O. Box 326
Elizabeth City, NC 27907
(919) 331-7660

Cumberland County TASC
109 Bradford Avenue
P.O. Box 3069
Fayetteville, NC 28301
(910) 433-2712

Gaston-Lincoln Mental Health/
   DD/SA/TASC
816 Mauney Avenue
Gastonia, NC 28052
(704) 854-4882

Alamance-Coswell Area MH/DD/
   SA Program
114 South Maple Street, Suite D
Graham, NC 27253
(910) 513-4370

Alcohol & Drug Services of
   Guilford
301 East Washington Street, Suite
   101
Greensboro, NC 27401
(910) 333-6860

Pitt County Mental Health TASC
   Program
301 South Evans Street, Suite 201
Greenville, NC 27834
(919) 758-0034

Skinner House TASC/DWI
   Program
123 West Third Street
Greenville, NC 27834
(919) 758-0034

VGFW MH/DD/SAS
129 Belle Street
Henderson, NC 27536
(919) 430-3801

Albemarle Mental Health Center
   TASC Project
P.O. Box 130
Manteo, NC 27954
(919) 473-1135

TASC Project
P.O. Box 1685
Nags Head, NC 27959
(919) 441-3366

Tideland Enhanced TASC
Tideland Mental Health Center
202 East Water Street
Plymouth, NC 27962
(919) 791-1010

SouthLight
2500 Blue Ridge Road, Suite 400
Raleigh, NC 27607
(919) 787-6131

Edgecombe-Nash TASC
500 Nash Medical Arts
Rocky Mount, NC 27804
(919) 937-8141

Substance Abuse Center
417 North Main
Salisbury, NC 28144
(704) 637-9301

Coastal Horizons Center (TASC)
801 Princess Street
Wilmington, NC 28401
(910) 343-0145

Step One Inc.
Substance Abuse Services
665 West Fourth Street
Winston-Salem, NC 27101
(910) 725-8389

Ohio Department of Alcohol and
   Drug Addiction
Services
Two Nationwide Plaza
280 North High Street, 12th Floor
Columbus, OH 43215-2537
(614) 752-8330

Clermont County TASC
4440 State Route 222
Batavia, OH 45103
(513) 732-7546

Stark County TASC
218 Second Street NW, Suite 105
Canton, OH 44703
(216) 588-7180

Cuyahoga County TASC
1276 West Third Street, Suite 525
Cleveland, OH 44115
(216) 443-8250

Preble County Juvenile TASC
204 North Barron Street
Eaton, OH 45320
(513) 456-3443

Ohio Department of Alcohol and
   Drug Addiction
Services
Two Nationwide Plaza
280 North High Street, 12th Floor
Columbus, OH 43215-2537
(614) 752-8330

Clermont County TASC
4440 State Route 222
Batavia, OH 45103
(513) 732-7546

Stark County TASC
218 Second Street NW, Suite 105
Canton, OH 44703
(216) 588-7180

Cuyahoga County TASC
1276 West Third Street, Suite 525
Cleveland, OH 44115
(216) 443-8250

Preble County Juvenile TASC
204 North Barron Street
Eaton, OH 45320
(513) 456-3443

TASC of Oregon, Inc.
1733 Northeast Seventh Street
Portland, OR 97212
(503) 281-0037

Marion County Department of
   Corrections
3060 Center Street NE
Salem, OR 97301
(503) 588-5289

Office of Drug and Alcohol
   Programs
Department of Health
929 Health & Welfare Building
P.O. Box 90
Harrisburg, PA 17108
(717) 787-2712

Lehigh County TASC
521 Court Street
Allentown, PA 18101
(610) 432-6760

Centre County TASC
Keystone Community Services
111 East High Street
Bellefonte, PA 16823
(814) 353-9450

Franklin-Fulton TASC
425 Franklin Farm Lane
Chambersburg, PA 17201
(717) 263-1256

Bucks County TASC
252 West Swamp Road, Unit 33
Doylestown, PA 18901
(215) 230-8715

Clearfied-Jefferson County TASC
c/o Gateway Institute & Clinic
100 Caldwell Drive
Dubois, PA 15801
(814) 371-1100

Northampton County TASC
Treatment Trends
158-160 South Third Street
Easton, PA 18042
(610) 250-3961

Erie County TASC
GECAC Drug and Alcohol Service
809 Peach Street
Erie, PA 16501
(814) 459-4581 ext. 528

Chester County TASC
Whiteland Business Park
930 East Lancaster Avenue
Exton, PA 19341
(610) 363-7709

Venango County TASC
1283 Liberty Street
P.O. Box 1130
Franklin, PA 16323
(814) 432-9744

York/Adams County TASC
Drug and Alcohol Treatment and
   Prevention Services
108 North Stratton Street
Gettysburg, PA 17325
(717) 334-8154

Westmoreland County TASC
Comprehensive Substance Abuse
  Services of
Southwestern Pennsylvania, Inc.
203 South Maple Avenue, Room
  215
Greensburg, PA 15601
(412) 832-5880

Dauphin County TASC
25 South Front Street, Suite 825
Harrisburg, PA 17101
(717) 255-2984

C.M.P.
128 South First Street
Lehighton, PA 18235
(717) 421-1960

Mercer County TASC
Intermediate Punishment Program
403 Court Street
Mercer, PA 16137
(412) 862-3880

Montgomery County TASC
18 West Main Street
Norristown, PA 19401
(610) 279-4262

Allegheny County TASC
Ielase Institute of Forensic
  Psychology
232 First Avenue
Pittsburgh, PA 15222
(412) 261-2817

Berks County TASC
524 Washington Street
Reading, PA 19601
(610) 375-4426

Lackawanna County TASC
Drug and Alcohol Treatment
  Service
116 North Washington Avenue
Scranton, PA 18503
(717) 961-1997

Carbon County TASC
14 North Sixth Street
Stroudsburg, PA 18260
(717) 421-1960

Luzerne/Wyoming County TASC
  Catholic Social
Services
33 Northampton Street
Wilkes-Barre, PA 18701
(717) 822-7118

Green Ridge Counseling Center
829 West Fourth Street
Williamsport, PA 17701
(717) 322-1216

York/Adams County TASC
Stepping Stone Counseling and
  Education Services
211 South George Street
York, PA 17403
(717) 854-0444

Department of Substance Abuse
P.O. Box 20363
Cranston, RI 02920
(401) 464-2381

South Carolina Department of
  Alcohol and Other Drug
Abuse Services
3700 Forest Drive, Suite 300
Columbia, SC 29204
(803) 734-9520

Treatment Alternatives to
  Incarceration Program (TAIP)
Texas Commission on Alcohol and
  Drug Abuse
710 Brazos
Austin, TX 78701-2506
(512) 867-8700

Treatment Alternatives to
  Incarceration Program (TAIP)
Travis County Community
  Supervision and Corrections
Department, Suite 700
411 West 13th Street
Executive Office Building
Austin, TX 78701
(512) 473-9540

Dallas County Treatment
  Alternatives to Incarceration
  Program (TAIP)
38 Trailview Drive
Carrollton, TX 75007

Treatment Alternatives to
  Incarceration Program (TAIP)
Rio Grande Council on
  Government
1100 North Stanton, Suite 1610
El Paso, TX 79902
(915) 533-0998

Treatment Alternatives to
  Incarceration Program (TAIP)
200 West Belknap Street
Fort Worth, TX 76196
(817) 884-2449

Central Texas Treatment Center/
  Adult Probation
P.O. Box 662
Georgetown, TX 78627
(512) 869-0643

Treatment Alternatives to
  Incarceration Program (TAIP)
Houston Council on Alcohol and
  Drug Abuse
3333 Eastside, Suite 111
Houston, TX 77098
(713) 520-5502

Treatment Alternatives to
  Incarceration Program (TAIP)
200 Main Plaza, Suite 300
San Antonio, TX 78200
(210) 978-0443

Behavioral Education Associates
  and TASC Associates
1823 Stadium Road, #209
P.O. Box 213
Wharton, TX 77488-0213
(409) 282-2813

Richmond TASC
Richmond Mental Health
Mental Retardation/Substance
  Abuse Services
2930 West Broad Street, Suite 3
Richmond, VA 23230
(804) 780-4536

Snohomish County TASC/Pacific
  Treatment
Alternatives
1114 Pacific Avenue
Everett, WA 98201
(206) 259-7142

King County TASC/Drug Free
 Systems
811 First Avenue, Suite 610
Seattle, WA 98104
(206) 467-0338, ext. 111

NorthEast Washington Treatment
 Alternative/TASC
1224 North Ash
Spokane, WA 99201
(509) 326-7740

Tacoma TASC/Pierce County
 Alliance
510 Tacoma Avenue S
Tacoma, WA 98402-5416
(206) 572-4750

Pacific Crest Consortium/Clark
 County TASC
2402 Broadway
Vancouver, WA 98663
(206) 693-2243

Yakima County TASC
Yakima County Alcohol/Drug
 Assessment & Referral Center
Yakima County Courthouse
128 North Second Street, Room B-
 18
Yakima, WA 98901
(509) 575-4472

Rock Valley Treatment
 Alternatives Program
431 Olympian Boulevard
Beloit, WI 53511
(608) 362-5592

Treatment Alternatives Program
Triniteam, Inc.
202 Graham Avenue
Eau Claire, WI 54701
(715) 836-8114

Treatment Alternatives Program
 (TAP)
Wisconsin Department of Health &
 Social Services
1 West Wilson Street
P.O. Box 7851
Madison, WI 53707-7851
(608) 266-3145

Dane County Treatment
 Alternatives Program
702 West Main Street
Madison, WI 53715
(608) 256-4502

Department of Human Services
1206 North Port Drive
Madison, WI 53704
(608) 242-6474

Wisconsin Correctional Service
436 West Wisconsin Avenue
Milwaukee, WI 53203
(414) 271-2512

Programa TASC DSCA (NM)
Apartado 1190
Arecibo, PR 00613
(787) 879-2021

TASC Departamento de Servicios
 Contra La Adiccion
414 Barbosa Avenue
Hato Rey, PR 00912
(787) 763-7575

Ponce TASC (NM)
P.O. Box 7321
Ponce, PR 00732

STATE LISTINGS

State Office Functions

STATE POLICY OFFICES

Office of the Governor

Establishes policy priorities and issues executive orders; responsible for the implementation of legislation; responsible for designating the state agency that applies for federal drug law enforcement, education, treatment, and prevention funds.

State Legislature

Enacts enabling legislation and provides oversight of executive agency activities; sets funding levels for statewide drug law enforcement, treatment, and prevention.

State Drug Program Coordinator

Establishes a statewide drug abuse action plan and coordinates the activities of executive branch agencies; helps to establish program priorities.

STATE CRIMINAL JUSTICE OFFICES

Attorney General's Office

Establishes legal guidelines for the implementation of legislation and the prosecution of offenders; helps coordinate statewide drug task force activities.

Law Enforcement Planning Office

Executive branch agency responsible for coordinating statewide criminal justice initiatives.

Crime Prevention Office

Monitors statewide crime prevention efforts between law enforcement agencies and the community; disseminates drug and crime prevention literature to schools and the general public.

Statistical Analysis Centers

Assembles statewide criminal justice statistics and issues periodic reports; acts as a clearinghouse for statewide crime information and statistics.

Uniform Crime Reports

Assembles statewide UCR offense and arrest data and produces annual report; submits statewide arrest statistics to the FBI's National Uniform Crime Reports for inclusion in the annual *Crime in the United States*.

BJA Strategy Preparation Agency

Prepares and submits to the Bureau of Justice Assistance (BJA) a State drug strategy; distributes BJA grant funds in accordance with the strategy; performs other analyses of statewide drug problems and appropriate interventions.

Judicial Agency

The administrative office of the state court system coordinates the activities of the various judicial districts, gathers state court data, and issues periodic reports.

Corrections Agency

Operates the state prison system; establishes in-prison programs; collects statistics on correctional populations.

STATE HEALTH OFFICES

RADAR (Regional Alcohol and Drug Awareness Resource) Network Agency

State office responsible for distributing alcohol and drug abuse prevention and education materials. Established by the U.S. Department of Health and Human Services' Office of Substance Abuse Prevention, these activities are coordinated by the National Clearinghouse for Alcohol and Drug Information.

HIV-Prevention Program

Coordinates state AIDS prevention activity and oversees state AIDS prevention funding.

Drugs and Alcohol Agency

Sets prevention and treatment priorities and administers state and federal funds, particularly those from the U.S. Department of Health and Human Services' Office of Substance Abuse Prevention.

STATE EDUCATION OFFICE

State Coordinator For Drug-Free Schools

Establishes school-based drug and alcohol prevention/education programs and administers federal Drug-Free Schools and Communities funds.

States

Alabama

STATE POLICY OFFICES

Governor's Office
Office of the Governor
State Capitol
600 Dexter Avenue
Montgomery, AL 36104
(334) 242-7100
E-mail: govjames@asnmail.asc.edu

State Legislative Contact
Legislative Reference Service
State House
Room 613
11 South Union
Montgomery, AL 36130-6701
(334) 242-7560

State Drug Program Coordinator
Alabama Department of Public Safety
2720-A Gunter Park Drive West
Montgomery, AL 36109-1014
(334) 260-1100

STATE CRIMINAL JUSTICE OFFICES

Attorney General's Office
Attorney General's Office
State House
11 South Union Street
Montgomery, AL 36130-1801
(334) 242-7300
E-mail: alattgen@counsel.com

Law Enforcement Planning
Alabama Department of Economic and Community Affairs
Law Enforcement Planning
401 Adams Avenue
P.O. Box 5690
Montgomery, AL 36103-5690
(334) 242-5803

Statistical Analysis Center
Alabama Criminal Justice Information Center
770 Washington Avenue, Suite 350
Montgomery, AL 36130
(334) 242-4900

Uniform Crime Reports Contact
Uniform Crime Reports Program
Alabama Criminal Justice Information Center
770 Washington Avenue, Suite 350
Montgomery, AL 36130
(334) 242-4900

BJA Strategy Preparation Agency
Alabama Department of Economic and Community Affairs
Law Enforcement/Traffic Safety Division
P.O. Box 5690
401 Adams Avenue
Montgomery, AL 36103-5690
(334) 242-5891

Judicial Agency
Judicial Agency
Administrative Office of Courts
300 Dexter Avenue
Montgomery, AL 36104-3741
(334) 242-0300

Corrections Agency
Department of Corrections
Treatment Division
1400 Lloyd Street
Montgomery, AL 36130-1501
(334) 240-9586

STATE HEALTH OFFICES

RADAR Network Agency
Alabama Department of Mental Health/Mental Retardation
Division of Substance Abuse Services
100 North Union Street
P.O. Box 301410
Montgomery, AL 36130-1410
(334) 242-3966

HIV-Prevention Program
Department of Public Health
Disease Control Bureau
HIV/AIDS Division
434 Monroe Street
Montgomery, AL 36130-1410
(334) 613-5364

Drug and Alcohol Agency
Drug and Alcohol Agency
Alabama Department of Mental Health and Mental Retardation
Substance Services Division
P.O. Box 301410
Montgomery, AL 36130-1410
(334) 242-3961

STATE EDUCATION OFFICE

State Coordinator For Drug-Free Schools
Drug Education Program
State Department of Education
50 North Ripley Street, Room 5348
Montgomery, AL 36130-3901
(334) 242-8199

Alaska

STATE POLICY OFFICES

Governor's Office
Office of the Governor
P.O. Box 110001
Juneau, AK 99811-0001
(907) 465-3500

State Legislative Contact
Legislative Affairs Agency
130 Seward Street, Suite 313
Juneau, AK 99801-2197
(907) 465-4648
E-mail:
juneau-lio@legis.state.ak.us

State Drug Program Coordinator
Alaska Division of Alcohol and Drug Abuse
P.O. Box 110607
Juneau, AK 99811-0607
(907) 465-2071

STATE CRIMINAL JUSTICE OFFICES

Attorney General's Office

Attorney General
Department of Law
P.O. Box 110300
Juneau, AK 99811-0300
(907) 465-2133
E-mail: bruce-
botelho@law.state.ak.u

Law Enforcement Planning

Alaska Department of Public
Safety
P.O. Box 111200
Juneau, AK 99811-1200
(907) 465-4322
E-mail:
pestocka@psafety.state.ak.us

Crime Prevention Office

Alaska Crime Prevention
Association
P.O. Box 210-127
Anchorage, AK 99521-0127
(907) 338-5548

Statistical Analysis Center

The Justice Center
University of Alaska Anchorage
3211 Providence Drive
Anchorage, AK 99508
(907) 786-1810
E-mail: ayjust@uaa.alaska.edu

Uniform Crime Reports Contact

Uniform Crime Reporting Section
Department of Public Safety
Information System
5700 East Tudor Road
Anchorage, AK 99507
(907) 269-5708

BJA Strategy Preparation Agency

Department of Public Safety
Alaska State Troopers
5700 East Tudor Road
Anchorage, AK 99507
(907) 269-5082
E-mail:
ackatsel@psafety.state.ak.us

Judicial Agency

Administrative Office of the Courts
Alaska Court System
303 K Street
Anchorage, AK 99501
(907) 264-0547

Corrections Agency

Department of Corrections
4500 Diplomacy Drive, Suite 207
Anchorage, AK 99502
(907) 269-7350

STATE HEALTH OFFICES

RADAR Network Agency

Alaska Council on Prevention of
Alcohol and Drug Abuse
3333 Denali Street, Suite 201
Anchorage, AK 99503
(907) 258-6021

HIV-Prevention Program

AIDS/STD Program Section of
Epidemiology
Division of Public Health
P.O. Box 240249
Anchorage, AK 99524-0249
(907) 269-8000

Drug and Alcohol Agency

Division of Alcoholism and Drug
Abuse
P.O. Box 110607
Juneau, AK 99811-0607
(907) 465-2071
E-mail: ljones%health@state.ak.us

STATE EDUCATION OFFICE

State Coordinator For Drug-Free Schools

Alaska Department of Education
Drug-Free Schools Program
801 West 10th Street, Suite 200
Juneau, AK 99801-1894
(907) 465-8730

Arizona

STATE POLICY OFFICES

Governor's Office

Office of the Governor
1700 West Washington Street
Phoenix, AZ 85007
(602) 542-4331

State Legislative Contact

Legislative Council
State Capitol
Legislative Services Wing
Room 100
1700 West Washington Street
Phoenix, AZ 85007
(602) 542-4236

State Drug Program Coordinator

Governor's Division of Drug Policy
Suite 101-G
1700 West Washington Street
Phoenix, AZ 85007
(602) 542-3456
E-mail: gvboehl@ad.state.as.us

STATE CRIMINAL JUSTICE OFFICES

Attorney General's Office

Office of the Attorney General
1275 West Washington Street
Phoenix, AZ 85007
(602) 542-4266

Law Enforcement Planning

Office of the Attorney General
1275 West Washington Street
Phoenix, AZ 85007
(602) 542-4266

Statistical Analysis Center

Arizona Criminal Justice
Commission, Suite 207
1501 West Washington Street
Phoenix, AZ 85007
(602) 542-1928
E-mail: acjc@goodnet.com

Uniform Crime Reports Contact

Uniform Crime Reports Program
Arizona Department of Public
Safety
P.O. Box 6638
Phoenix, AZ 85005
(602) 223-6638

BJA Strategy Preparation Agency

Arizona Criminal Justice
Commission, Suite 207
1501 West Washington Street
Phoenix, AZ 85007
(602) 542-1928

Judicial Agency
Administrative Office of the Courts
Supreme Court
1501 West Washington Street,
Suite 411
Phoenix, AZ 85007
(602) 542-9301

Corrections Agency
Department of Corrections
1601 West Jefferson
Phoenix, AZ 85007
(602) 542-5497

STATE HEALTH OFFICES

RADAR Network Agency
Arizona Prevention Resource
Center
641 East Van Buren, Suite B-2
Phoenix, AZ 85004
(602) 727-2772

HIV-Prevention Program
Office of HIV/STD Services
Bureau of Epidemiology and
Disease Control Services
Arizona Department of Health
Services
3815 North African American
Canyon Highway
Phoenix, AZ 85015-5351
(602) 230-5819
E-mail: acjc@goodnet.com

Drug and Alcohol Agency
Bureau of Substance Abuse and
Mental Health
Arizona Department of Health
Services
2122 East Highland Avenue
Phoenix, AZ 85016
(602) 381-8999

STATE EDUCATION OFFICE

**State Coordinator For Drug-
Free Schools**
Arizona Department of Education
Title IV - Safe & Drug Free
Schools
1535 West Jefferson
Phoenix, AZ 85007
(602) 542-8728
E-mail:
colson@macpo.ade.state.az.us

Arkansas

STATE POLICY OFFICES

Governor's Office
Office of the Governor
State Capitol, Room 250
Little Rock, AR 72201
(501) 682-2345

State Legislative Contact
Bureau of Legislative Research
Legislative Council
State Capitol, Room 315
Fifth and Woodlane
Little Rock, AR 72201
(501) 682-1937

**State Drug Program
Coordinator**
State Drug Director
State Capitol, Suite 250
Little Rock, AR 72201
(501) 682-2345

STATE CRIMINAL JUSTICE OFFICES

Attorney General's Office
Office of the Attorney General
200 Tower Building
323 Center Street
Little Rock, AR 72201
(501) 682-2007

Law Enforcement Planning
Law Enforcement Standards and
Training Commission
P. O. Box 3106
East Camden, AR 71701
(501) 574-1810

Crime Prevention Offices
Arkansas Crime Information
Center
Office of Crime Prevention
One Capitol Mall 4D-200
Little Rock, AR 72201
(501) 682-2222
E-mail: acic@acic.org

Statistical Analysis Center
Special Services Section
Arkansas Crime Information
Center
One Capitol Mall, 4D-200
Little Rock, AR 72201
(501) 682-2222
E-mail: rthomas@acic.org

Uniform Crime Reports Contact
Arkansas Crime Information
Center
One Capitol Mall, 4D-200
Little Rock, AR 72201
(501) 682-2222

**BJA Strategy Preparation
Agency**
Department of Finance and
Administration
Office of Intergovernmental
Services
1515 Building, Suite 417
Little Rock, AR 72203
(501) 682-1074

Judicial Agency
Administrative Office of the Courts
Supreme Court of Arkansas
Justice Building
Little Rock, AR 72201
(501) 682-9400

Corrections Agency
Department of Corrections
P.O. Box 8707
Pine Bluff, AR 71611
(501) 247-6200

STATE HEALTH OFFICES

RADAR Network Agency
Bureau of Alcohol and Drug Abuse
Prevention
Freeway Medical Center
5800 West 10th Street, Suite 907
Little Rock, AR 72204
(501) 280-4506
E-mail: adap@aristotle.net

HIV-Prevention Program
Arkansas Department of Health
Division of AIDS/STD
4815 West Markham, Slot #33
Little Rock, AR 72205
(501) 661-2408

Drug and Alcohol Agency

Bureau of Alcohol and Drug Abuse
   Prevention
Department of Health
Freeway Medical Center
5800 West 10th Street, Suite 907
Little Rock, AR 72204
(501) 280-4505

STATE EDUCATION OFFICE

**State Coordinator For Drug-
   Free Schools**

Arkansas Department of Education
Drug Education Program
#4 Capitol Mall, Room 202B
Little Rock, AR 72201-1071
(501) 682-5170
E-mail: osmith@lokik12.ar.us

California

STATE POLICY OFFICES

Governor's Office

Office of the Governor
State Capitol Building
Sacramento, CA 95814
(916) 445-2841

State Legislative Contact

Legislative Analyst's Office
925 L Street, Suite 1000
Sacramento, CA 95819
(916) 445-4660
E-mail: craig.cornett@lao.ca.gov

**State Drug Program
   Coordinator**

State Department of Alcohol and
   Drug Programs
1700 K Street, Fifth Floor
Sacramento, CA 95814-4037
(916) 445-0834

STATE CRIMINAL
JUSTICE OFFICES

Attorney General's Office

California Attorney General's
   Office
Division of Law Enforcement
Bureau of Narcotic Enforcement
P.O. Box 161089
Sacramento, CA 95816-1089
(916) 227-4044

Law Enforcement Planning

Division of Law Enforcement
4949 Broadway
Sacramento, CA 95820
(916) 227-2222

Crime Prevention Offices

Crime and Violence Prevention
   Center
California Department of Justice
Office of the Attorney General
P.O. Box 944255
Sacramento, CA 94244-2550
E-mail: agcvpc@ns.net

Statistical Analysis Center

Criminal Justice Statistics Center
4949 Broadway, Room E-231
P.O. Box 903427
Sacramento, CA 94203-4270
(916) 227-3382
E-mail: dlesac@ns.net

Uniform Crime Reports Contact

Uniform Crime Reports Program
Law Enforcement Information
   Center
Department of Justice
P.O. Box 903427
Sacramento, CA 94203-4270
(916) 227-3473

**BJA Strategy Preparation
   Agency**

Office of Criminal Justice Planning
Anti-Drug Abuse Branch
1130 K Street, Suite 300
Sacramento, CA 95814
(916) 324-9163

Judicial Agency

Administrative Office of the Courts
303 Second Street, South Tower
San Francisco, CA 94107
(415) 396-9100

Corrections Agency

Department of Corrections
P.O. Box 942883
Sacramento, CA 94283-0001
(916) 445-7688

STATE HEALTH OFFICES

RADAR Network Agency

Department of Alcohol and Drug
   Programs
1700 K Street, First Floor
Sacramento, CA 95814-4022
(916) 327-3728
http://www.adp.cahwnet.gov
E-mail:
   adp.drepace@hwl.cahwnet.gov

HIV-Prevention Program

Director of Office of AIDS
   Programs and Policy
Los Angeles County Department of
   Health Services
600 South Commonwealth
   Avenue, Sixth Floor
Los Angeles, CA 90005
(213) 351-8000

Drug and Alcohol Agency

Department of Alcohol and Drug
   Programs
1700 K Street
Sacramento, CA 95814
(916) 445-0834

STATE EDUCATION OFFICE

**State Coordinator For Drug-
   Free Schools**

California Department of
   Education
Healthy Kids Programs Office
721 Capitol Mall, Third Floor
Sacramento, CA 95814
(916) 657-2810
E-mail: gkilbert@cde.ca.gov

Colorado

STATE POLICY OFFICES

Governor's Office

Office of the Governor
State Capitol, Room 136
Denver, CO 80203
(303) 866-2471
E-mail:
   romer@governor.state.co.us

State Legislative Contact
Legislative Council
State Capitol, Room 029
200 East Colfax Avenue
Denver, CO 80203
(303) 866-3521

STATE CRIMINAL JUSTICE OFFICES

Attorney General's Office
Office of the Attorney General
Department of Law
1525 Sherman Street, Fifth Floor
Denver, CO 80203
(303) 866-4500

Law Enforcement Planning
Division of Criminal Justice
Department of Public Safety
700 Kipling Street, Suite 3000
Lakewood, CO 80215
(303) 239-4442
E-mail:
william.woodward@safety.state.co
.us

Statistical Analysis Center
Colorado Division of Criminal
Justice
700 Kipling Street, Suite 1000
Denver, CO 80215
(303) 239-4453
E-mail: kenglis8@aol.com

Uniform Crime Reports Contact
Uniform Crime Reports Section
Colorado Bureau of Investigation
690 Kipling Street
Denver, CO 80215
(303) 239-4300

BJA Strategy/Preparation Agency
Division of Criminal Justice
700 Kipling Street, Suite 3000
Denver, CO 80215
(303) 239-4442
E-mail: tregn@aol.com

Judicial Agency
Administrative Office of the Courts
Judicial Department
1301 Pennsylvania, Suite 300
Denver, CO 80203-2416
(303) 861-1111 ext. 125

Corrections Agency
Department of Corrections
2862 South Circle Drive, Suite 400
Colorado Springs, CO 80906
(719) 579-9580

STATE HEALTH OFFICES

RADAR Network Agency
Colorado Department of Human
Services
Alcohol and Drug Abuse Division
Prevention-Intervention Section
4300 Cherry Creek Drive South
Denver, CO 80222-1530
(303) 692-2956
E-mail: linda.garrett@state.co.us

HIV-Prevention Program
Department of Health
STD/AIDS Section
4300 Cherry Creek Drive South
Denver, CO 80222-1530
(303) 692-2500

Drug and Alcohol Agency
Alcohol and Drug Abuse Division
Health Office
4300 Cherry Creek Drive South
Denver, CO 80222-1530
(303) 692-2930

STATE EDUCATION OFFICE

State Coordinator For Drug-Free Schools
Colorado Department of Education
Prevention Initiatives Unit
201 East Colfax Avenue
Denver, CO 80203
(303) 866-6869
E-mail: jackson_k@ade.state.co.us

Connecticut

STATE POLICY OFFICES

Governor's Office
Office of the Governor
Executive Chambers
210 Capitol Avenue
Hartford, CT 06106
(860) 566-4840

State Legislative Contact
Office of Legislative Research
Room 5300
Legislative Office Building
Hartford, CT 06106
(860) 240-8400

State Drug Program Coordinator
Office of Policy and Management
Policy Development Planning
Division
P.O. Box 341441
450 Capitol Avenue, MS 52-CPD
Hartford, CT 06106
(860) 418-6394

STATE CRIMINAL JUSTICE OFFICES

Attorney General's Office
Office of the Attorney General
55 Elm Street
Hartford, CT 06106
(860) 566-6026

Law Enforcement Planning
Policy Development and Planning
Division
Office of Policy Management
450 Capitol Avenue, MS 52-CPD
P.O. Box 341441
Hartford, CT 06134-1441
(860) 418-6249

Crime Prevention Office
Crime Prevention Association of
Connecticut
120 Main Street
Danbury, CT 06810
(203) 797-4577

Statistical Analysis Center
Policy Development and Planning
Division
450 Capitol Avenue, MS 52-CPD
P.O. Box 341441
Hartford, CT 06134-1441
(860) 418-6376
E-mail: dolly.reed@po.state.ct.us

Uniform Crime Reports Contact
Uniform Crime Reporting Program
1111 Country Club Road
P.O. Box 2794
Middletown, CT 06457-9294
(860) 685-8030

BJA Strategy Preparation Agency
Office of Policy and Management
450 Capitol Avenue, MS 52-CPD
P.O. Box 341441
Hartford, CT 06134-1441
(860) 418-6210

Judicial Agency
Connecticut Judicial Branch
Office of the Chief Court
   Administrator
Supreme Court
231 Capitol Avenue
P.O. Drawer N, Station A
Hartford, CT 06106
(203) 566-4461

Corrections Agency
Department of Corrections
340 Capitol Avenue
Hartford, CT 06106
(860) 566-4457

STATE HEALTH OFFICES

RADAR Network Agency
Connecticut Clearinghouse
334 Farmington Avenue
Plainville, CT 06062
(860) 793-9791
E-mail: dolly.reed@po.state.ct.us

HIV-Prevention Program
Department of Public Health
AIDS Prevention & Intervention
   Programs
P.O. Box 340308
410 Capitol Avenue, MS 11APV
Hartford, CT 06134-0308
(860) 509-7801

Drug and Alcohol Agency
Division of Community Based
   Regulation
P.O. Box 340308
410 Capitol Avenue
Hartford, CT 06134-0308
(860) 509-8045

STATE EDUCATION OFFICE

State Coordinator For Drug-Free Schools
Connecticut Department of
   Education
P.O. Box 2219, Room 215
Hartford, CT 06145
(860) 566-6645

Delaware

STATE POLICY OFFICES

Governor's Office
Office of the Governor
Tatnall Building
Dover, DE 19901
(302) 739-4101
E-mail: gcarter@state.de.us

State Legislative Contact
Legislative Council
Legislative Hall
Legislative Avenue
PO Box 1401
Dover, DE 19901
(302) 736-4114

State Drug Program Coordinator
Chairman
Department of Public Safety
P.O. Box 818
Dover, DE 19901
(302) 739-4321

STATE CRIMINAL JUSTICE OFFICES

Attorney General's Office
Office of the Attorney General
Department of Justice
820 North French Street
Wilmington, DE 19801
(302) 577-3838

Law Enforcement Planning
Criminal Justice Council
Elbert N. Carvel State Office
   Building, Fourth Floor
820 North French Street
Wilmington, DE 19801
(302) 577-3466 (beeper)

Statistical Analysis Center
60 The Plaza
Dover, DE 19901
(302) 739-4626

Uniform Crime Reports Contact
Uniform Crime Reports Program
State Bureau of Identification
P.O. Box 430
Dover, DE 19903-0430
(302) 739-5875

BJA Strategy Preparation Agency
Criminal Justice Council
Elbert N. Carvel State Office
   Building
820 North French Street, 4th
   Floor
Wilmington, DE 19801
(302) 577-3466

Judicial Agency
Administrative Office of the Courts
Elbert N. Carvel State Office
   Building
820 North French Street, 11th
   Floor
Wilmington, DE 19801
(302) 577-2480
E-mail: eboulden@state.de.us

Corrections Agency
Department of Corrections
80 Monrovia Avenue
Smyrna, DE 19977
(302) 739-5601

STATE HEALTH OFFICES

RADAR Network Agency
Office of Prevention Resource
   Clearinghouse
Delaware Youth and Family
   Center
1825 Faulkland Road
Wilmington, DE 19805-1195
(302) 892-4500

HIV-Prevention Program
Division of Public Health
AIDS/HIV Program Office
Jesse Cooper Building
P.O. Box 637
Dover, DE 19903
(302) 739-3032

Drug and Alcohol Agency

Division of Alcoholism, Drug Abuse and Mental Health
Department of Health and Social Services
1901 North DuPont Highway
New Castle, DE 19720
(302) 577-4461

STATE EDUCATION OFFICE

State Coordinator For Drug-Free Schools

Department of Public Instruction
Health Education and Services
P.O. Box 1402
Dover, DE 19903
(302) 739-4676
E-mail: evincent@state.de.us

District of Columbia

POLICY OFFICES

Mayor's Office

Executive Office of the Mayor
Office of Communications
One Judiciary Square
441 Fourth Street NW, Suite 1100
Washington, DC 20001
(202) 727-6224

Legislative Contact

Office of the Corporation Council
441 Fourth Street NW, Suite 1060N
Washington, DC 20001
(202) 727-6248

Drug Program Coordinator

Office of Criminal Justice Plans and Analysis
717 14th Street NW, Suite 500
Washington, DC 20005
(202) 727-9472

CRIMINAL JUSTICE OFFICES

Attorney General's Office

Office of the Corporation Counsel, D.C.
One Judiciary Square
441 Fourth Street NW, Suite 1060N
Washington, DC 20001
(202) 727-6248

Law Enforcement Planning

Office of Grants Management and Development
717 14th Street NW, Suite 400
Washington, DC 20001
(202) 727-6537

Statistical Analysis Center

Office of Grants Management & Development
717 14th Street NW, Suite 400
Washington, DC 20005
(202) 727-6537

Uniform Crime Reports Contact

Uniform Crime Reports Program
Information Services Division
Metropolitan Police Department, Room 5054
300 Indiana Avenue NW
Washington, DC 20001
(202) 727-4301

BJA Strategy Preparation Agency

Office of Grants Management and Development
717 14th Street NW, Suite 400
Washington, DC 20001
(202) 727-6554

Judicial Agency

Administrative Office of the Courts
District of Columbia Courts Room 1500
500 Indiana Avenue NW
Washington, DC 20001
(202) 879-1700

Corrections Agency

Department of Corrections
1923 Vermont Avenue NW
Washington, DC 20001
(202) 673-7316

HEALTH OFFICES

RADAR Network Agency

Addiction Prevention and Recovery Administration
(APRA)
Office of Prevention and Youth Services
1300 First Street NE, Third Floor
Washington, DC 20002
(202) 727-0716

HIV-Prevention Program

HIV/AIDS Agency
717 14th Street NW
Washington, DC 20005
(202) 727-2500

Drug and Alcohol Agency

Department of Human Services
Addiction Prevention and Recovery Administration
1300 First Street NE
Washington, DC 20002
(202) 727-9393

EDUCATION OFFICE

Coordinator For Drug-Free Schools

District of Columbia Public Schools
Substance Abuse Prevention Education Program
Giddings Administrative Unit
315 G Street SE
Washington, DC 20003
(202) 724-3610

Florida

STATE POLICY OFFICES

Governor's Office

Office of the Governor
The Capitol
Tallahassee, FL 32399-0001
(904) 488-4441
http://www.eog.state.fl.us

State Legislative Contact

Division of Legislative Library Services
State Legislature
The Capitol, Room 701
Tallahassee, FL 32399
(904) 488-2812

State Drug Program Coordinator
Policy Coordinator
Governor's Drug Policy Office
1501 The Capitol
Tallahassee, FL 32399-0001
(904) 922-4020

STATE CRIMINAL JUSTICE OFFICES

Attorney General's Office
Office of the Attorney General
Department of Legal Affairs
The Capitol, Plaza Level 01
Tallahassee, FL 32399-1050
(904) 487-1963

Law Enforcement Agency
Florida Department of Law Enforcement
P.O. Box 1489
Tallahassee, FL 32302-1489
(904) 488-8771

Law Enforcement Planning
Office of Planning and Budgeting
Carlton Building
Room 415
Calhoun Street
Tallahassee, FL 32301
(904) 488-0090

Crime Prevention Offices
Attorney General's Office
Bureau of Criminal Justice Programs
The Capitol
Tallahassee, FL 32399-1050
(904) 487-3712
http://legal.firn.edu

Statistical Analysis Center
Florida Department of Law Enforcement
2331 Phillips Road, 32208
Tallahassee, FL 32208
(904) 487-4808
E-mail: fsac@freenet.fsu.edu

Uniform Crime Reports Contact
Uniform Crime Reports Section
Florida Crime Information Center
P.O. Box 1489
Tallahassee, FL 32302-1489
(904) 487-1179

BJA Strategy Preparation Agency
Florida Department of Community Affairs
Bureau of Community Assistance
Criminal Justice Section
2555 Shumard Oak Boulevard
Tallahassee, FL 32399-2100
(904) 488-8016
E-mail: wilderc@dca.state.fl.us

Judicial Agency
State Courts Administrator
Supreme Court Building
500 South Duval Street
Tallahassee, FL 32399-1900
(904) 922-5082

Corrections Agency
Department of Corrections
2601 Blairstone Road
Tallahassee, FL 32399-2500
(904) 488-7480

STATE HEALTH OFFICES

RADAR Network Agency
Florida Alcohol and Drug Abuse Association
1030 East Lafayette Street, Suite 100
Tallahassee, FL 32301-4547
(904) 878-2196
E-mail: fadaa@polaris.net

HIV-Prevention Program
Office of Disease Intervention
HIV Patient Care
Building 6, Suite 403
1317 Winewood Boulevard
Tallahassee, FL 32399-0700
(904) 413-0674

Drug and Alcohol Agency
Alcohol and Drug Abuse Program
Alcohol, Drug Abuse and Mental Health Office
Florida Department of HRS
1317 Winewood Boulevard
Tallahassee, FL 32399-0700
(904) 487-2920

STATE EDUCATION OFFICE

State Coordinator For Drug-Free Schools
Florida Department of Education
Florida Drug-Free Schools Program
325 West Gaines Street, Suite 322
Tallahassee, FL 32399-0400
(904) 488-6304

Georgia

STATE POLICY OFFICES

Governor's Office
Office of the Governor
State Capitol, Room 203
Atlanta, GA 30334
(404) 656-1776

State Legislative Contact
House Research
18 Capitol Square, Suite 205A
Atlanta, GA 30334
(404) 656-3206

State Drug Program Coordinator
State Director for Substance Abuse Services
Department of Human Resources
Division of MHMRSA
2 Peachtree Street, Suite 4-550
Atlanta, GA 30303
(404) 657-6400
E-mail: rmurf@dmh.dhr.state.ga.us

STATE CRIMINAL JUSTICE OFFICES

Attorney General's Office
Office of the Attorney General
Department of Law
40 Capitol Square SW
Atlanta, GA 30334-1300
(404) 656-4585

Law Enforcement Planning
Office of the Attorney General
Department of Law
40 Capitol Square SW
Atlanta, GA 30303-1300
(404) 656-4585

Crime Prevention Offices

Georgia Crime Prevention Program
40 Marietta Street NW
Suite 800
Atlanta, GA 30303
(404) 679-4950

Georgia Crime Prevention
    Association
4400 Memorial Drive
Decatur, GA 30032
(404) 294-2574

Statistical Analysis Center

Statistical Analysis Center
Georgia Criminal Justice
    Coordinating Council
503 Oak Place, Suite 540
Atlanta, GA 30349
(404) 559-4949

Uniform Crime Reports Contact

Uniform Crime Reports
Georgia Crime Information Center
Georgia Bureau of Investigation
P.O. Box 370748
Decatur, GA 30037
(404) 244-2840

BJA Strategy Preparation Agency

Georgia Criminal Justice
    Coordinating Council
503 Oak Place, Suite 540
Atlanta, GA 30349
(404) 559-4949

Judicial Agency

Administrative Office of the Courts
State Office Building Annex, Room
    550
224 Washington Street SW
Atlanta, GA 30334
(404) 656-5171

Corrections Agency

Department of Corrections
2 Martin Luther King Jr. Drive SE
East Tower
Atlanta, GA 30334
(404) 656-6002

STATE HEALTH OFFICES

RADAR Network Agency

Georgia Prevention Resource
    Center
Substance Abuse Services Suite
    320
2 Peachtree Street, Fourth Floor
Atlanta, GA 30303
(404) 657-21364

HIV-Prevention Program

Epidemiology and Prevention
    Branch
Division of Public Health
Georgia Department of Human
    Resources
2 Peachtree Street NW
Atlanta, GA 30303
(404) 657-2700

Drug and Alcohol Agency

Division of Mental Health, Mental
    Retardation and
Substance Abuse
2 Peachtree Street NW
Atlanta, GA 30303
(404) 657-2135

STATE EDUCATION OFFICE

State Coordinator For Drug-Free Schools

Georgia Department of Education
Policy and Communications
1854 Twin Towers East
Atlanta, GA 30334-5040
(404) 651-9406

Hawaii

STATE POLICY OFFICES

Governor's Office

Office of the Governor
State Capitol
415 Beretania Street
Honolulu, HI 96813
(808) 586-0034

State Legislative Contact

Department of the Attorney
    General
425 Queen Street
Honolulu, HI 96813
(808) 548-1282

State Drug Program Coordinator

Department of the Attorney
    General
425 Queen Street
Honolulu, HI 96813
(808) 548-1282

STATE CRIMINAL JUSTICE OFFICES

Attorney General's Office

Attorney General's Office
Office of the Attorney General
425 Queen Street
Honolulu, HI 96813
(808) 586-1500

Law Enforcement Planning

Crime Prevention and Justice
    Assistance Division
Department of the Attorney
    General
425 Queen Street
Honolulu, HI 96813
(808) 586-1150
E-mail: 1koga@lava.net

Statistical Analysis Center

Crime Prevention Division
Department of the Attorney
    General
City Center Building
810 Richards Street, Suite 701
Honolulu, HI 96813
(808) 586-1416

Uniform Crime Reports Contact

Uniform Crime Reports
Crime Prevention and Justice
    Assistance Division
Department of the Attorney
    General
425 Queen Street
Honolulu, HI 96813
(808) 586-1416
E-mail: lkoga@lava.net

BJA Strategy Preparation Agency
Department of the Attorney General
Crime Prevention and Justice Assistance Division
425 Queen Street
Honolulu, HI 96813
(808) 586-1150
E-mail: lkoga@lava.net

Judicial Agency
Hawaii Drug Court Program
Circuit Court of the First Circuit
850 Richards Street
Honolulu, HI 96813
(808) 599-3700

Corrections Agency
Corrections Program Services Division
Department of Public Safety
919 Ala Moana Boulevard, Fourth Floor
Honolulu, HI 96814
(808) 587-1266

STATE HEALTH OFFICES

RADAR Network Agency
Drug-Free Hawaii Prevention Resource Center
425 Queen Street
Honolulu, HI 96813
(808) 545-3228

HIV-Prevention Program
Department of Health
STD/AIDS Branch
3627 Kilawea Avenue, #306
Honolulu, HI 96816
(808) 733-9010

Drug and Alcohol Agency
Health Department
Alcohol and Drug Abuse Division, Room 706
1270 Queen Emma Street
Honolulu, HI 96813
(808) 586-3962

STATE EDUCATION OFFICE

State Coordinator For Drug-Free Schools
Hawaii Department of Education
Safe and Drug-Free Schools and Communities Program
Special Programs Management Section, Second Floor
3430 Leahi Avenue, Building D
Honolulu, HI 96815
(808) 733-4496

Idaho

STATE POLICY OFFICES

Governor's Office
Office of the Governor
P.O. Box 83720
Boise, ID 83720-0034
(208) 334-2100
E-mail: governor@40gov.state.id.us

State Legislative Contact
Legislative Services
State Capitol Building
P.O. Box 83720
700 West Jefferson Street
Boise, ID 83720-0054
(208) 334-2475
http://www.state.id.us/legislat/legislat.html

State Drug Program Coordinator
Department of Law Enforcement
P.O. Box 700
Meridian, ID 883680-0700
(208) 884-7000

STATE CRIMINAL JUSTICE OFFICES

Attorney General's Office
Office of the Attorney General
P.O. Box 83720
Boise, ID 83720-0010
(208) 334-2400

Law Enforcement Planning
Peace Officer Standards and Training
Department of Law Enforcement
P.O. Box 700
Meridian, ID 83680-0700
(208) 884-7250
E-mail: mbecar@dle.state.id.us

Crime Prevention Office
Idaho Crime Prevention Association
7200 Barrister Driver
Boise, ID 83704
(208) 377-6622

Statistical Analysis Center
Idaho Department of Law Enforcement
Support Services Bureau
700 South Stratford
P.O. Box 700
Meridian, ID 83680-0700
(208) 884-7044
E-mail: ruhlenko@dle.state.id.us

Uniform Crime Reports Contact
Uniform Crime Reports
Idaho Department of Law Enforcement
Bureau of Criminal Identification
P.O. Box 700
Meridian, ID 83680
(208) 884-7156

BJA Strategy Preparation Agency
Idaho Department of Law Enforcement
P.O. Box 700
Meridian, ID 83680-0700
(208) 884-7040
E-mail: rsilva@dle.state.id.us

Judicial Agency
Administrative Director
Office of the Courts
Supreme Court Building
451 West State Street
Boise, ID 83720-0101
(208) 334-2246
E-mail: ptobias@jsc.state.id.us

Corrections Agency
Department of Corrections
P.O. Box 83720
Boise, ID 83720-0018
(208) 334-2318

STATE HEALTH OFFICES

RADAR Network Agency
Idaho RADAR Network Center
Boise State University
1910 University Drive
Boise, ID 83725
(208) 385-3471
E-mail: psawyer@bsu.idbsu.edu

HIV-Prevention Program
Department of Health and Welfare
Bureau of Clinical & Preventive
    Services
P.O. Box 83720
Boise, ID 83720-0036
(208) 334-6526

Drug and Alcohol Agency
Department of Health and Welfare
Division of Family and
    Community Services, Fifth
Floor
P.O. Box 83720
Boise, ID 83720-0036
(208) 334-5700

STATE EDUCATION OFFICE

**State Coordinator For Drug-
    Free Schools**
Drug Education Coordinator
Idaho Department of Education
P.O. Box 83720
Boise, ID 83720-0027
(208) 332-6960
E-mail: tbgetty@sde.state.id.us

Illinois

STATE POLICY OFFICES

Governor's Office
Office of the Governor
207 Statehouse
Springfield, IL 62706
(217) 782-7355
E-mail: governor@state.il.us

State Legislative Contact
Legislative Information Bureau
705 Stratton Building
Springfield, IL 62706
(217) 782-3944

**State Drug Program
    Coordinator**
Illinois Department of Alcoholism
    and Substance
Abuse
100 West Randolph Street, Suite
    5-600
Chicago, IL 60601
(312) 814-2291
http://www.state.il.us/agency/dhs

STATE CRIMINAL
JUSTICE OFFICES

Attorney General's Office
Office of the Attorney General
500 South Second Street
Springfield, IL 62706
(217) 782-1090

Law Enforcement Planning
Illinois Criminal Justice
    Information Authority
Suite 1016
120 South Riverside Plaza
Chicago, IL 60606
(312) 793-8550

Statistical Analysis Center
Illinois Criminal Justice
    Information
Authority, Suite 1016
120 South Riverside Plaza
Chicago, IL 60606
(312) 793-8550

Uniform Crime Reports Contact
Uniform Crime Reports
Crime Studies, Illinois State Police
100 Iles Park Place
Springfield, IL 62708
(217) 782-5791
http://www.state.il.us/isp/
    isphpage.htm

**BJA Strategy Preparation
    Agency**
Illinois Criminal Justice
    Information Authority
Suite 1016
120 South Riverside Plaza
Chicago, IL 60606-3997
(312) 793-8550

Judicial Agency
Administrative Office of the Illinois
    Courts
160 North LaSalle Street, 18th
    Floor
Chicago, IL 60601
(312) 793-8191

Corrections Agency
Department of Corrections
P.O. Box 19277
Springfield, IL 62794-9277
(217) 522-2666

STATE HEALTH OFFICES

RADAR Network Agency
Prevention First Inc. Library
720 North Franklin, Suite 500
Chicago, IL 60610
(312) 988-4646
(800) 572-5385 (IL only)

HIV-Prevention Program
Illinois Department of Public
    Health
AIDS Activity Section
525 West Jefferson Street
Springfield, IL 62761
(217) 524-5983

Drug and Alcohol Agency
Illinois Department of Alcoholism
    and Substance Abuse
James R. Thompson Center Room
    5-600
100 West Randolph Street
Chicago, IL 60601
(312) 814-3840

STATE EDUCATION OFFICE

State Coordinator For Drug-Free Schools
Illinois State Board of Education
Grants Management Division
100 North First Street
Springfield, IL 62777
(217) 782-3810

Indiana

STATE POLICY OFFICES

Governor's Office
Office of the Governor
206 State House
Indianapolis, IN 46204
(317) 232-4567
E-mail:
evanbayh@ideanet.doe.state.in.us

State Legislative Contact
Legislative Services Agency
State House, Room 302
Indianapolis, IN 46204
(317) 232-9856

State Drug Program Coordinator
Governor's Commission for a Drug-Free Indiana
Ista Building, Suite 320
150 West Market Street
Indianapolis, IN 46204
(317) 232-4219

STATE CRIMINAL JUSTICE OFFICES

Attorney General's Office
Office of the Attorney General
Indiana Government South, Fifth Floor
402 West Washington Street
Indianapolis, IN 46204-2770
(317) 232-6201

Law Enforcement Planning
Indiana Criminal Justice Institute
302 West Washington Street, Room E209
Indianapolis, IN 46204
(317) 232-1233
E-mail: cjilan@2ma.isd.state.in.us

Statistical Analysis Center
Indiana Criminal Justice Institute
302 West Washington Street, Room E209
Indianapolis, IN 46204-2767
(317) 232-1233
E-mail:
smeagher@ideanet.doe.state.in.us

BJA Strategy Preparation Agency
Indiana Criminal Justice Institute
302 West Washington Street, Room E209
Indianapolis, IN 46204
(317) 232-1233
E-mail: cjilan@2ma.isd.state.in.us

Judicial Agency
Administrative Office of the Courts
Supreme Court
115 West Washington, Suite 1080
Indianapolis, IN 46204-3417
(317) 232-2542

Corrections Agency
Department of Correction
E334 Indiana Government Center South
302 West Washington Street
Indianapolis, IN 46204
(317) 232-5766

STATE HEALTH OFFICES

RADAR Network Agency
Indiana Prevention Resource Center for Substance Abuse
Indiana University, Room 110
840 State Road, 46 Bypass
Bloomington, IN 47405
(812) 855-1237
E-mail: drugs@indiana.edu

HIV-Prevention Program
Department of Health
HIV/AIDS Program
1330 West Michigan Street
P.O. Box 1964
Indianapolis, IN 46202-1964
(317) 383-6851

Drug and Alcohol Agency
Bureau for Chemical Addictions
Division of Mental Health
Family and Social Services Administration, Room W353
402 West Washington Street
Indianapolis, IN 46204-2739
(317) 232-7800
E-mail: jmeegan@fssa.state.in.us

STATE EDUCATION OFFICE

State Coordinator For Drug-Free Schools
Department of Education
Office of Student Services
State House, Room 229
Indianapolis, IN 46204-2798
(317) 232-9111
E-mail: sdavis@doe.state.in.us

Iowa

STATE POLICY OFFICES

Governor's Office
Office of the Governor
State Capitol Building
Des Moines, IA 50319
(515) 281-5211

State Legislative Contact
Legislative Information Office
Legislative Service Bureau
State Capitol Building
Des Moines, IA 50319
(515) 281-4961

State Drug Program Coordinator
Governor's Alliance on Substance Abuse
Lucas State Office Building, Fourth Floor
Des Moines, IA 50319
(515) 281-3784

STATE CRIMINAL JUSTICE OFFICES

Attorney General's Office
Iowa Department of Justice
Second Floor
Hoover State Office Building
Des Moines, IA 50319
(515) 281-5164

Law Enforcement Planning
Department of Public Safety
Division of Criminal Investigation
Wallace State Office Building
Des Moines, IA 50319
(515) 281-6203

Statistical Analysis Center
Division of Criminal Justice and
Juvenile Planning
Lucas State Office Building
Des Moines, IA 50319
(515) 242-5816
E-mail: cjjp@max.state.ia.us

Uniform Crime Reports Contact
Uniform Crime Reports
Iowa Department of Public Safety
Wallace State Office Building
Des Moines, IA 50319
(515) 281-8494
E-mail: dps@state.ia.us

**BJA Strategy Preparation
Agency**
Governor's Alliance on Substance
Abuse
Lucas State Office Building
Des Moines, IA 50309
(515) 242-6379

Judicial Agency
Administrative Office of the Courts
Supreme Court of Iowa
State House
Des Moines, IA 50319
(515) 281-5241

Corrections Agency
Department of Corrections
Capitol Annex
523 East 12th Street
Des Moines, IA 50319
(515) 281-4811

STATE HEALTH OFFICES

RADAR Network Agency
Iowa Substance Abuse Information
Center
Cedar Rapids Public Library
500 First Street SE
Cedar Rapids, IA 52401
(319) 398-5133
E-mail: isaic@crpl.cedar-
rapids.lib.ia.us

HIV-Prevention Program
Department of Public Health
Division of Health Protection
Lucas State Office Building
321 East 12th Street
Des Moines, IA 50319
(515) 242-5838

Drug and Alcohol Agency
Department of Public Health
Division of Substance Abuse and
Health Promotion
Lucas State Office Building Third
Floor
321 East 12th Street
Des Moines, IA 50319
(515) 281-4417

STATE EDUCATION OFFICE

**State Coordinator For Drug-
Free Schools**
Substance Education Consultant
Iowa Department of Education
Grimes State Office Building
Des Moines, IA 50319
(515) 281-3021

Kansas

STATE POLICY OFFICES

Governor's Office
Office of the Governor
State Capitol, Second Floor
Topeka, KS 66612-1590
(913) 296-3232

State Legislative Contact
Legislative Research Department
State House, Room 545-N
Topeka, KS 66612
(913) 296-23181
E-mail:
kslegres@lr.01.wpo.state.ks.us

**State Drug Program
Coordinator**
Kansas Criminal Justice
Coordinating Council
Jayhawk Tower
700 Southwest Jackson, Suite 501
Topeka, KS 66603
(913) 296-2584

STATE CRIMINAL JUSTICE OFFICES

Attorney General's Office
Office of the Attorney General
Kansas Judicial Center
301 Southwest 10th Street
Topeka, KS 66612
(913) 296-2215

Crime Prevention Office
Kansas Bureau of Investigation
Crime Prevention Unit
1620 Southwest Tyler Street
Topeka, KS 66612
(913) 296-8239

Statistical Analysis Center
Kansas Criminal Justice
Coordinating Council
Kansas Sentencing Commission
Jayhawk Tower, Suite 501
700 Southwest Jackson
Topeka, KS 66603
(913) 296-0923

Uniform Crime Reports Contact
Crime Data Information Center
Kansas Bureau of Investigation
1620 Tyler Street
Topeka, KS 66612-1837
(913) 296-8200

**BJA Strategy Preparation
Agency**
Kansas Criminal Justice
Coordinating Council
700 Southwest Jackson, Room 501
Topeka, KS 66603
(913) 296-0923

Judicial Agency
Administrative Office of the Courts
Kansas Judicial Center
301 West 10th Street
Topeka, KS 66612
(913) 296-4873

Corrections Agency
Department of Corrections
900 Southwest Jackson Street,
#451
Topeka, KS 66612-1284
(913) 296-3998

STATE HEALTH OFFICES

RADAR Network Agency
Department of Social and
    Rehabilitation Services
Biddle Building, Second Floor
300 Southwest Oakley
Topeka, KS 66606-1861
(913) 296-3925

HIV-Prevention Program
AIDS Program
Kansas Department of Health and
    Environment
109 Southwest Ninth, Suite 605
Topeka, KS 66612-1271
(913) 296-6173

Drug and Alcohol Agency
Kansas Alcohol and Drug Abuse
    Services
Biddle Building, Second Floor
300 Southwest Oakley
Topeka, KS 66606
(913) 296-3925

STATE EDUCATION OFFICE

**State Coordinator For Drug-
    Free Schools**
Kansas Department of Education
120 East 10th Street
Topeka, KS 66612
(913) 296-6714

Kentucky

STATE POLICY OFFICES

Governor's Office
Office of the Governor
The Capitol
700 Capitol Avenue
Frankfort, KY 40601
(502) 564-2611

State Legislative Contact
Legislative Research Commission
State Capitol, Room 300
Frankfort, KY 40601
(502) 564-8100

**State Drug Program
    Coordinator**
Champions for a Drug Free
    Kentucky
Capitol City Airport
90 Airport Road, Suite 3
Frankfort, KY 40601
(502) 564-7889
E-mail: lcarrico@mail.state.ky.us

STATE CRIMINAL JUSTICE OFFICES

Attorney General's Office
Office of the Attorney General
P.O. Box 2000
Frankfort, KY 40602-2000
(502) 564-7600

Law Enforcement Planning
Kentucky Justice Cabinet
Law Enforcement Council
403 Wapping Street
Frankfort, KY 40601
(502) 564-3251

Statistical Analysis Center
Office of the Attorney General
Capitol Building
700 Capitol Avenue, Suite 116
Frankfort, KY 40601
(502) 564-7600

Uniform Crime Reports Contact
Uniform Crime Reports
Information Services Branch
Kentucky State Police
1250 Louisville Road
Frankfort, KY 40601
(502) 227-8783

**BJA Strategy Preparation
    Agency**
Kentucky Justice Cabinet
Division of Grants Management
Bush Building, Second Floor
403 Wapping Street
Frankfort, KY 40601
(502) 564-7554

Judicial Agency
Administrative Office of the Courts
100 Millcreek Park
Frankfort, KY 40601-9230
(502) 573-2350

Corrections Agency
Department of Corrections
State Office Building, Fifth Floor
Frankfort, KY 40601
(502) 222-9441

STATE HEALTH OFFICES

RADAR Network Agency
Drug Information Service for
    Kentucky
Division of Substance Abuse
275 East Main Street
Frankfort, KY 40621
(502) 564-2880
(800) 432-9337 (KY only)

HIV-Prevention Program
Cabinet for Health Services
Division of State and Local
    Administration
STD Control (CTS)
275 East Main Street
Frankfort, KY 40621
(502) 564-4990

Drug and Alcohol Agency
Division of Substance Abuse
Department of Mental Health and
    Mental Retardation
275 East Main Street
Frankfort, KY 40621
(502) 564-2880

STATE EDUCATION OFFICE

**State Coordinator For Drug-
    Free Schools**
State Department of Education
Division of Program Resources
Title Programs
825 Capitol Plaza Tower
500 Mero Street
Frankfort, KY 40601
(502) 564-3791

Louisiana

STATE POLICY OFFICES

Governor's Office
Office of the Governor
P.O. Box 94004
Baton Rouge, LA 70804-9004
(504) 342-7015

State Legislative Contact

Legislative Research Library
P.O. Box 94012
Baton Rouge, LA 70804
(504) 342-2456
http://www.house.state.la.us

State Drug Program Coordinator

Office of the Attorney General
P.O. Box 94005
Baton Rouge, LA 70804-9005
(504) 339-5192

STATE CRIMINAL JUSTICE OFFICES

Attorney General's Office

Office of the Attorney General
Department of Justice
P.O. Box 94005
Baton Rouge, LA 70804-9005
(504) 342-7013

Law Enforcement Planning

Law Enforcement Commission
1885 Woodfale Boulevard, Suite 708
Baton Rouge, LA 70806
(504) 925-4418

Statistical Analysis Center

Louisiana Commission on Law Enforcement and Administration of Criminal Justice Room 708
1885 Woodfale Boulevard
Baton Rouge, LA 70806-1511
(504) 925-4429

Uniform Crime Reports Contact

Uniform Crime Reports
Louisiana Commission on Law Enforcement
1885 Woodfale Boulevard, Seventh Floor
Baton Rouge, LA 70806
(504) 925-4847

BJA Strategy Preparation Agency

Louisiana Commission on Law Enforcement, Room 708
1885 Woodfale Boulevard
Baton Rouge, LA 70806
(504) 925-3513

Judicial Agency

Judicial Administrator
Supreme Court Building
301 Loyola Avenue, Room 109
New Orleans, LA 70112
(504) 568-5747

Corrections Agency

Department of Public Safety and Corrections
P.O. Box 94304
Baton Rouge, LA 70804-9304
(504) 342-6741

STATE HEALTH OFFICES

RADAR Network Agency

Louisiana Office of Alcohol and Drug Abuse
P.O. Box 3868
Baton Rouge, LA 70821-3868
(504) 342-9354

HIV-Prevention Program

HIV/AIDS Services Program
P.O. Box 60630
325 Loyola Avenue
New Orleans, LA 70160
(504) 568-5050

Drug and Alcohol Agency

Office of Alcohol and Drug Abuse
P.O. Box 2790 - Bin 18
Baton Rouge, LA 70821
(504) 342-6717

STATE EDUCATION OFFICE

State Coordinator For Drug-Free Schools

Louisiana Department of Education
Bureau of Student Services
P.O. Box 94064
Baton Rouge, LA 70804-9064
(504) 342-3480
E-mail: dfrost@mail.doe.state.la.us

Maine

STATE POLICY OFFICES

Governor's Office

Office of the Governor
1 State House Station
Augusta, ME 04333
(207) 287-3531

State Legislative Contact

Legislative Information
100 State House Station
Augusta, ME 04333
(207) 287-1692

STATE CRIMINAL JUSTICE OFFICES

Attorney General's Office

Office of the Attorney General
6 State House Station
Augusta, ME 04333
(207) 626-8800

Crime Prevention Office

Maine Criminal Justice Academy
Maine Department of Public Safety
93 Silver Street
Waterville, ME 04901
(207) 877-8000

Statistical Analysis Center

Maine Criminal Justice Data Center
Department of Corrections
State House Station #111, Fourth Floor
Augusta, ME 04333
(207) 287-4343
E-mail: colcunn@state.me.us

Uniform Crime Reports Contact

Uniform Crime Reporting Division
Maine State Police
36 Hospital Street, Station #42
Augusta, ME 04333-0042
(207) 624-7004

BJA Strategy Preparation Agency

Department of Public Safety
State House Station #42
Augusta, ME 04333
(207) 624-8758

Judicial Agency

Administrative Office of the Courts
P.O. Box 4820
Portland, ME 04112-4820
(207) 822-0792

Corrections Agency
Department of Corrections
State House Station #111
Augusta, ME 04333
(207) 287-2711
E-mail: joseph.lehman@state.me.us

STATE HEALTH OFFICES

RADAR Network Agency
Office of Substance Abuse
Information Resource Center
State House Station #159
A.M.H.I. Complex
Marguardt Building
Augusta, ME 04333
(207) 287-8900

HIV-Prevention Program
Department of Human Services
State House Station #11
Augusta, ME 04333-0011
(207) 287-37470

Drug and Alcohol Agency
Office of Substance Abuse
State House Station #159
A.M.H.I. Complex
Marguardt Building
Augusta, ME 04333
(207) 287-2595

STATE EDUCATION OFFICE

State Coordinator For Drug-Free Schools
Department of Education
Station #161
24 Stone Street
Augusta, ME 04333
(207) 287-4729
E-mail: roger.richards@state.me.us

Maryland

STATE POLICY OFFICES

Governor's Office
Office of the Governor
State House
Annapolis, MD 21404
(410) 974-3901
E-mail: governor@Gov.state.md.us

State Legislative Contact
Department of Legislative
  Reference
Legislative Services Building
90 State Circle
Annapolis, MD 21401
(410) 841-3886

State Drug Program Coordinator
Governor's Office of Crime and
  Prevention Control
300 East Joppa Road, Suite 1105
Baltimore, MD 21286-3016
(410) 321-3521

STATE CRIMINAL JUSTICE OFFICES

Attorney General's Office
Office of the Attorney General
200 Saint Paul Place
Baltimore, MD 21202-2020
(410) 576-6300

Crime Prevention Offices
Maryland Community Crime
  Prevention Institute
Police Training Commission
3085 Hernwood Road
Woodstock, MD 21163
(410) 442-2706
(800) 303-8802

Maryland Crime Prevention
  Association
PO Box 20397
Baltimore, MD 21284-0397

Statistical Analysis Center
Maryland Justice Analysis Center
Institute of Criminal Justice and
  Criminology
College of Behavioral and Social
  Sciences
2220 Samuel J. LeFrak Hall
University of Maryland
College Park, MD 20742-8235
(301) 405-4701
E-mail: cwellford@bss2.umd.edu

Uniform Crime Reports Contact
Uniform Crime Reporting Section
Central Records Division
Maryland State Police Department
1711 Belmont Avenue
Baltimore, MD 21244
(410) 298-3883

BJA Strategy Preparation Agency
Governor's Office of Crime Control
  and Prevention
300 East Joppa Road, Suite 1105
Baltimore, MD 21286
(410) 321-3521

Judicial Agency
Administrative Office of the Courts
Courts of Appeal Building
361 Rowe Boulevard
Annapolis, MD 21401
(410) 974-2141

Corrections Agency
Division of Correction
Department of Public Safety and
  Correctional Services
6776 Reisterstown Road, Suite
  310
Baltimore, MD 21215-2341
(410) 764-4100

STATE HEALTH OFFICES

RADAR Network Agency
Alcohol and Drug Abuse
  Administration
Department of Health and Mental
  Hygiene, Fourth Floor
201 West Preston Street
Baltimore, MD 21201
(410) 225-6916
E-mail: frjones@prevline.health.org

HIV-Prevention Program
AIDS Administration
Department of Health and Mental
  Hygiene
500 North Calvert Street, Fifth
  Floor
Baltimore, MD 21202
(410) 767-5132

Drug and Alcohol Agency

Governor's Crime Control and
    Prevention Commission
300 East Joppa Road, Suite 1105
Baltimore, MD 21286-3016
(410) 321-3521

STATE EDUCATION OFFICE

**State Coordinator For Drug-
    Free Schools**

State Department of Education
Drug-Free Schools Program
200 West Baltimore Street
Baltimore, MD 21201
(410) 767-0301

Massachusetts

STATE POLICY OFFICES

Governor's Office

Executive Office
State House, Room 360
Boston, MA 02133
(617) 727-3600

**State Drug Program
    Coordinator**

Governor's Alliance Against Drugs
John W. McCormack State Office
    Building
One Ashburton Place, Room 611
Boston, MA 02108
(617) 727-0786

STATE CRIMINAL
JUSTICE OFFICES

Attorney General's Office

Office of the Attorney General
Narcotics and Special
    Investigations Division
One Ashburton Place, Room 1910
Boston, MA 02108
(617) 727-2200

Law Enforcement Planning

Division of Programs
100 Cambridge Street, Room 2100
Boston, MA 02202
(617) 727-6300

Crime Prevention Offices

Massachusetts Criminal Justice
    Training Council
Massachusetts Crime Watch
411 Waverly Oaks Road, Suite
    325
Waltham, MA 02154
(617) 727-7827

Statistical Analysis Center

Director of Research &
    Development
Executive Office of Public Safety
100 Cambridge Street, Room 2100
Boston, MA 02202
(617) 727-6300
E-mail: rkohl@state.ma.us

Uniform Crime Reports Contact

Massachusetts State Police
Crime Reporting Unit
470 Worcester Road
Framingham, MA 01701
(508) 820-2110

**BJA Strategy Preparation
    Agency**

Massachusetts Committee on
    Criminal Justice
Executive Office of Public Safety
100 Cambridge Street, Room 2100
Boston, MA 02202
(617) 727-6300
E-mail: jpetuchowski@state.ma.us

Judicial Agency

The Commonwealth of
    Massachusetts
Administrative Justice of Trial
    Court
Two Center Plaza, Room 540
Boston, MA 02108
(617) 742-8575

Corrections Agency

Department of Corrections
100 Cambridge Street
Boston, MA 02202
(617) 727-3300

STATE HEALTH OFFICES

RADAR Network Agency

Prevention Support Services
The Medical Foundation
95 Berkeley Street, Suite 201
Boston, MA 02116
(617) 451-0049

HIV-Prevention Program

AIDS Office
Massachusetts Department of
    Public Health
250 Washington Street
Boston, MA 02108-4619
(617) 624-6000

Drug and Alcohol Agency

Bureau of Substance Abuse
Department of Public Health
250 Washington Street
Boston, MA 02108
(617) 624-5111

STATE EDUCATION OFFICE

**State Coordinator For Drug-
    Free Schools**

Massachusetts Department of
    Education
Learning Support Services
350 Main Street
Malden, MA 02148-5023
(617) 388-3300 ext. 415
E-mail: jbynoe@doe.mass.edu

Michigan

STATE POLICY OFFICES

Governor's Office

Office of the Governor
P.O. Box 30013
Lansing, MI 48909
(517) 373-3400
E-mail: migov@aol.com

State Legislative Contact

Legislative Service Bureau
Michigan National Tower Fourth
    Floor
P.O. Box 30036
Lansing, MI 48909-7536
(517) 373-0170

**State Drug Program
  Coordinator**
Office of Drug Control Policy
124 West Allegan
Lansing, MI 48913
(517) 373-4700

STATE CRIMINAL
JUSTICE OFFICES

Attorney General's Office
Office of the Attorney General
P.O. Box 30212
Lansing, MI 48909
(517) 373-1110

Law Enforcement Planning
Investigative Services Bureau
Michigan State Police
714 South Harrison Road
East Lansing, MI 48823
(517) 336-6531

Crime Prevention Office
Detroit Police Department
Crime Prevention Association
2110 Park Avenue, Suite 332
Detroit, MI 48201
(313) 596-2520

Statistical Analysis Center
Michigan State University School
  of Criminal Justice
560 Baker Hall
East Lansing, MI 48824-1118
(517) 355-2197
E-mail: tim.bynum@ssc.msu.edu

Uniform Crime Reports Contact
Uniform Crime Reporting Section
Michigan State Police
7150 Harris Drive
Lansing, MI 48913
(517) 322-1150

**BJA Strategy Preparation
  Agency**
Office of Drug Control Policy
1200 Michigan National Tower
124 West Allegan
Lansing, MI 48913
(517) 373-4700

Judicial Agency
State Court Administrative Office
309 North Washington Square
P.O. Box 30048
Lansing, MI 48909
(517) 373-0130

Corrections Agency
Michigan Department of
  Corrections
Grandview Plaza Building
P.O. Box 30003
Lansing, MI 48909
(517) 373-0720

STATE HEALTH OFFICES

RADAR Network Agency
Michigan Resource Center
111 West Edgewood Boulevard,
  Suite 11
Lansing, MI 48911
(517) 882-9955
E-mail: mrc@voyager.net

HIV-Prevention Program
HIV/AIDS Prevention and
  Intervention Section
Michigan Department of Public
  Health
P.O. Box 30035
3500 North Martin Luther King
  Boulevard
Lansing, MI 48909
(517) 335-8371

Drug and Alcohol Agency
Center for Substance Abuse
  Services
Michigan Department of Public
  Health
3423 North Martin Luther King
  Boulevard
P.O. Box 30195
Lansing, MI 48909
(517) 335-8810

STATE EDUCATION OFFICE

**State Coordinator For Drug-
  Free Schools**
Department of Community Health
Office of Drug Control Policy
Drug Education Division
124 West Allegan, Suite 1200
Lansing, MI 48913
(517) 373-4700

Minnesota

STATE POLICY OFFICES

Governor's Office
Office of the Governor
Room 130, State Capitol
75 Constitution Avenue
St. Paul, MN 55155-1099
(612) 296-3391
E-mail: governor@state.mn.u

State Legislative Contact
Legislative Reference Library
State Office Building, Room 645
100 Constitution Avenue
St. Paul, MN 55155
(612) 296-3398

**State Drug Program
  Coordinator**
Minnesota Department of Public
  Safety
Office of Drug Policy
444 Cedar Street, 100-D
St. Paul, MN 56101
(612) 297-7311

STATE CRIMINAL
JUSTICE OFFICES

Attorney General's Office
Office of the Attorney General
State Capitol, Room 102
St. Paul, MN 55155
(612) 296-6196
E-mail:
  attorney.general@state.mn.us

Crime Prevention Offices
Minnesota Crime Watch
Minnesota Department of Public
  Safety
Bureau of Criminal Apprehension
1246 University Avenue
St. Paul, MN 55104
(612) 643-2576

Statistical Analysis Center
Minnesota Planning Agency
Centennial Office Building
658 Cedar Street, Room 300
St. Paul, MN 55155
(612) 297-7518
E-mail:
  susan.roth@mnplan.state.mn.us

Uniform Crime Reports Contact
Uniform Crime Reports
Minnesota Department of Public
Safety
Criminal Justice Information
Systems 1246
University Avenue
St. Paul, MN 55104
(612) 642-0610

**BJA Strategy Preparation
Agency**
Minnesota Department of
Children, Families and Learning
Office of Drug Policy and Violence
Prevention
550 Cedar Street, #409
St. Paul, MN 55101
(612) 297-7311
E-mail: jeri.bolsvert@state.mn.us

Judicial Agency
Administrative Office of the Courts
Supreme Court
25 Constitution Avenue
St. Paul, MN 55155
(612) 296-2474

Corrections Agency
Department of Corrections
1450 Energy Park Drive, Suite
200
St. Paul, MN 55108-5219
(612) 642-0282

STATE HEALTH OFFICES

RADAR Network Agency
Minnesota Prevention Resource
Center
2829 Verndale Avenue
Anoka, MN 55303
(612) 427-5310
E-mail: mprc@niph.org

HIV-Prevention Program
AIDS/STD Prevention Services
Section
Minnesota Department of Health
P.O. Box 9441
717 Southeast Delaware Street
Minneapolis, MN 55440-944
(612) 623-5698

Drug and Alcohol Agency
Chemical Dependency Program
Division
Department of Human Services
444 Lafayette Road
St. Paul, MN 55155-3823
(612) 296-4610

STATE EDUCATION OFFICE

**State Coordinator For Drug-
Free Schools**
Drug Abuse Program
State Department of Education
550 Cedar Street, Room 976
St. Paul, MN 55101
(612) 296-8023
E-mail: carol.thomas@State.mn.us

Mississippi

STATE POLICY OFFICES

Governor's Office
Office of the Governor
P.O. Box 139
Jackson, MS 39215
(601) 359-3100

State Legislative Contact
Legislative Reference Bureau
P.O. Box 1018
Jackson, MS 39215-1018
(601) 359-3135

STATE CRIMINAL JUSTICE OFFICES

Attorney General's Office
Office of the Attorney General
P.O. Box 220
Jackson, MS 39205
(601) 359-3680
E-mail: mmoore@ago.state.ms.us

Statistical Analysis Center
Department of Criminal Justice
Planning
401 North West Street, Eighth
Floor
P.O. Box 23039
Jackson, MS 39225-3039
(601) 359-7896

**BJA Strategy Preparation
Agency**
Division of Public Safety Planning
Department of Public Safety
401 North West Street, Eighth
Floor
P.O. Box 23039
Jackson, MS 39201
(601) 359-7880

Judicial Agency
Administrative Office of the Courts
Supreme Court
P.O. Box 117
Jackson, MS 39205
(601) 354-7408

Corrections Agency
Department of Corrections
723 North President Street
Jackson, MS 39202-3097
(601) 359-5600

STATE HEALTH OFFICES

RADAR Network Agency
Mississippi Department of Mental
Health
Division of Alcoholism and Drug
Abuse
1101 Robert E. Lee Building, 9th
Floor
239 North Lamar Street
Jackson, MS 39207
(601) 359-1288

HIV-Prevention Program
Mississippi Department of Health
Division of STD/HIV
P.O. Box 1700
Jackson, MS 39215-1700
(601) 960-7723

Drug and Alcohol Agency
Department of Mental Health
Division of Alcohol and Drug
Abuse Services
1101 Robert E. Lee Building
Jackson, MS 39201
(601) 359-1288

STATE EDUCATION OFFICE

State Coordinator For Drug-Free Schools

Drug-Free Schools Programs
Mississippi Department of
   Education
P.O. Box 771, Suite 205
637 North President
Jackson, MS 39205
(601) 359-3793

Missouri

STATE POLICY OFFICES

Governor's Office
Office of the Governor
P.O. Box 720
Jefferson City, MO 65102
(573) 751-3222
E-mail: constit@services.state.mo.u

State Legislative Contact
Committee on Legislative Research
State Capitol, Room 117A
Jefferson City, MO 65101
(573) 751-4223

State Drug Program Coordinator
Department of Public Safety
Truman State Office Building
P.O. Box 749
Jefferson City, MO 65102
(573) 751-5432
E-mail: khiggins@mail.state.mo.us

STATE CRIMINAL JUSTICE OFFICES

Attorney General's Office
Office of the Attorney General
P.O. Box 899
Jefferson City, MO 65102
(573) 751-3321

Law Enforcement Planning
Missouri Department of Public
   Safety, Room 870
Truman State Office Building
Jefferson City, MO 65102-5432
(573) 751-4905
E-mail: khiggins@mail.state.mo.us

Crime Prevention Offices
Crime Prevention/DARE Unit
Springfield Police Department
2825 South Glenstone F-1
Springfield, MO 65804
(417) 891-1500

Missouri Department of Public
   Safety
Statewide Crime Prevention
   Resource Center, Room 870
Truman State Office Building
301 West High Street, P.O. Box
   749
Jefferson City, MO 65102
(573) 751-4905
http://www.dps.state.mo.us

Statistical Analysis Center
Information Systems Division
Missouri Highway Patrol
1510 East Elm Street
Jefferson City, MO 65102
(573) 751-4026

BJA Strategy Preparation Agency
Missouri Department of Public
   Safety, Room 870
Truman State Office Building
P.O. Box 749
Jefferson City, MO 65102-0749
(573) 751-4905
E-mail: khiggins@mail.state.mo.us

Judicial Agency
Office of the State Courts
   Administrator
Supreme Court
P.O. Box 104480
Jefferson City, MO 65110
(573) 751-3585

Corrections Agency
Department of Corrections
P.O. Box 236
Jefferson City, MO 65102
(573) 751-2389

STATE HEALTH OFFICES

RADAR Network Agency
Missouri Division of Alcohol and
   Drug Abuse
1706 East Elm Street
P.O. Box 687
Jefferson City, MO 65102
(573) 751-4942

HIV-Prevention Program
Missouri Department of Health
Bureau of STD/AIDS Care
P.O. Box 570
Jefferson City, MO 65102
(573) 751-6107

Drug and Alcohol Agency
Missouri Division of Alcohol and
   Drug Abuse
Department of Mental Health
1706 East Elm Street
P.O. Box 687
Jefferson City, MO 65102
(573) 751-4942

STATE EDUCATION OFFICE

State Coordinator For Drug-Free Schools
State Department of Elementary
   and Secondary Education
P.O. Box 480
Jefferson City, MO 65102
(573) 751-9053
E-mail:
   sbarr@mail.dese.state.mo.us

Montana

STATE POLICY OFFICES

Governor's Office
Office of the Governor
Capitol Station
Helena, MT 59620-0801
(406) 444-3111

State Legislative Contact
Legislative Services Division
State Capitol, Room 138
Helena, MT 59620-1706
(406) 444-3064
E-mail: sfox@mt.gov

State Drug Program Coordinator

Department of Public Health and Human Services
Addictive & Mental Disorders Division
P.O. Box 202951
1400 Broadway
Helena, MT 59620-2951
(406) 444-3964

STATE CRIMINAL JUSTICE OFFICES

Attorney General's Office

Office of the Attorney General
Department of Justice
Justice Building
215 North Sanders Street
Helena, MT 59620
(406) 444-2026

Law Enforcement Planning

Division of Law Enforcement Services
P.O. Box 201417
Helena, MT 59620-1417
(406) 444-3874

Statistical Analysis Center

Board of Crime Control
Montana Department of Justice
303 North Roberts Street, Fourth Floor
Helena, MT 59620
(406) 444-4298
E-mail: tmurphy@mt.gov

Uniform Crime Reports Contact

Uniform Crime Reports
Montana Board of Crime Control
303 North Roberts Street
Helena, MT 59620
(406) 444-2077

BJA Strategy Preparation Agency

Montana Board of Crime Control
Scott Hart Building
303 North Roberts Street
Helena, MT 59620
(406) 444-3604

Judicial Agency

Administrative Office of the Courts
Supreme Court
Justice Building, Room 315
215 North Sanders Street
Helena, MT 59620
(406) 444-2621

Corrections Agency

Department of Corrections
1539 11th Avenue
P.O. Box 201301
Helena, MT 59620-1301
(406) 444-3930

STATE HEALTH OFFICES

RADAR Network Agency

Department of Public Health and Human Services
Addictive & Mental Disorders Division
P.O. Box 202951
1400 Broadway
Helena, MT 59620-2951
(406) 444-3964

HIV-Prevention Program

Montana Department of Public Health and Human
Services - STD/HIV Section
Cogswell Building
P.O. Box 202951
Helena, MT 59620-2951
(406) 444-3565

Drug and Alcohol Agency

Department of Public Health and Human Services
Addictive & Mental Disorders Division
P.O. Box 202951
1400 Broadway
Helena, MT 59620-2951
(406) 444-3964

STATE EDUCATION OFFICE

State Coordinator For Drug-Free Schools

Office of Public Instruction
Capitol Building
P.O. Box 202501
Helena, MT 59620-2501
(406) 444-4434
E-mail: jbirch@opi.mt.gov

Nebraska

STATE POLICY OFFICES

Governor's Office

Office of the Governor
P.O. Box 94848
Lincoln, NE 68509-4848
(402) 471-2244

State Legislative Contact

Legislative Research Division
State Capitol
P.O. Box 94945
Lincoln, NE 68509
(402) 471-2221

State Drug Program Coordinator

Governor's Policy Research Office
P.O. Box 94601
Lincoln, NE 68509-4601
(402) 471-2414
E-mail: pro1@pro:state.ne.us

STATE CRIMINAL JUSTICE OFFICES

Attorney General's Office

Attorney General's Office
Office of the Attorney General
Drug and Violent Crime Unit
2115 State Capitol Building
Lincoln, NE 68509
(402) 471-2682

Law Enforcement Planning

Nebraska Commission on Crime
P.O. Box 94946
Lincoln, NE 68509-4946
(402) 471-2194

Statistical Analysis Center

Nebraska Commission on Law Enforcement and Criminal Justice
301 Centennial Mall South, Third Floor
P.O. Box 94946
Lincoln, NE 68509-4946
(402) 471-2194
E-mail:
crime01@vmhost.cdp.state.ne.us

Uniform Crime Reports Contact

Uniform Crime Reporting Section
Nebraska Commission of Law
  Enforcement and Criminal
  Justice
P.O. Box 94946
Lincoln, NE 68509
(402) 471-3982

**BJA Strategy Preparation
  Agency**

Nebraska Commission on Law
  Enforcement and Criminal
  Justice
P.O. Box 94946
Lincoln, NE 68509
(402) 471-3416

Judicial Agency

Administrative Office of the Courts
Supreme Court
State Capitol, Room 1220
Lincoln, NE 68509
(402) 471-3730

Corrections Agency

Department of Correctional
  Services
P.O. Box 94661
Lincoln, NE 68509-4661
(402) 471-2654

STATE HEALTH OFFICES

RADAR Network Agency

State RADAR Network Center
Nebraska Council to Prevent
  Alcohol and Drug Abuse
650 J Street, Suite 215
Lincoln, NE 68510
(402) 474-1992
E-mail: nebraskacouncil@ltec.net

HIV-Prevention Program

Department of Health
P.O. Box 95007
Lincoln, NE 68509-5007
(402) 471-2937

Drug and Alcohol Agency

Division on Alcoholism and Drug
  Abuse
Department of Public Institutions
P.O. Box 94728
Lincoln, NE 68509-4728
(402) 471-2851

STATE EDUCATION OFFICE

**State Coordinator For Drug-
  Free Schools**

Nebraska State Department of
  Education
Drug Free Programs
P.O. Box 94987
301 Centenial Mall South
Lincoln, NE 68509-4987
(402) 471-2448

Nevada

STATE POLICY OFFICES

Governor's Office

Office of the Governor
Capitol Complex
Carson City, NV 89710
(702) 687-5670

State Legislative Contact

Legislative Counsel Bureau
401 South Carson Street
Carson City, NV 89710
(702) 687-6800

**State Drug Program
  Coordinator**

Chief Legal Counsel
Office of the Governor
Capitol Complex
Las Vegas, NV 89710
(702) 687-6602

STATE CRIMINAL
JUSTICE OFFICES

Attorney General's Office

Office of the Attorney General
Capitol Complex
198 South Carson Street
Carson City, NV 89710
(702) 687-4170

Law Enforcement Planning

Department of Motor Vehicles and
  Public Safety
555 Wright Way
Carson City, NV 89711-0900
(702) 687-4412

Crime Prevention Offices

Nevada Crime Prevention
Association
P.O. Box 578
Las Vegas, NV 89101
(702) 229-3507

Attorney General's Office
Community Crime Prevention
Capitol Complex
Carson City, NV 89710
(702) 687-4170

Statistical Analysis Center

Records and Identification Services
Nevada Highway Patrol
555 Wright Way
Carson City, NV 89711-0525
(702) 687-5713

Uniform Crime Reports Contact

Criminal Information Services
Nevada Highway Patrol
555 Wright Way
Carson City, NV 89711
(702) 687-5713

**BJA Strategy Preparation
  Agency**

Department of Motor Vehicles and
  Public Safety
Office of Criminal Justice
  Assistance
107 Jacobsen Way/Stewart Facility
Carson City, NV 89711-0910
(702) 687-5282

Judicial Agency

Administrative Office of the Courts
Capitol Complex
Carson City, NV 89710
(702) 687-5076

Corrections Agency

Department of Prisons
P.O. Box 7011
Carson City, NV 89702
(702) 887-3216

STATE HEALTH OFFICES

RADAR Network Agency

Bureau of Alcohol and Drug Abuse
505 East King Street, Suite 500
Carson City, NV 89710
(702) 687-4790
E-mail:
  mlwalker@prevline.health.org

HIV-Prevention Program
Nevada State Health Division
505 East King Street, Room 304
Carson City, NV 89710
(702) 687-4800

Nevada AIDS Hotline
505 East King Street, Room 304
Carson City, NV 89710
(800) 842-AIDS
E-mail: nvhotline@aol.com

Drug and Alcohol Agency
Bureau of Alcohol and Drug Abuse
Department of Employment,
    Training & Rehabilitation
505 East Third Street
Carson City, NV 89713
(702) 687-4790
E-mail:
    mlwalker@prevline.health.or

STATE EDUCATION OFFICE

**State Coordinator For Drug-
    Free Schools**
State Department of Education
Office of Public Instruction
Capitol Complex
400 West King Street
Carson City, NV 89710
(702) 687-3187

New Hampshire

STATE POLICY OFFICES

Governor's Office
Office of the Governor
State House
107 North Main, Room 208
Concord, NH 03301
(603) 271-2121

State Legislative Contact
Office of Legislative Services
State House, Room 109
107 North Main Street
Concord, NH 03301
(603) 271-3435

**State Drug Program
    Coordinator**
Bureau of Substance Abuse
    Services
State Office Park South
105 Pleasant Street
Concord, NH 03301
(603) 271-6104

STATE CRIMINAL JUSTICE OFFICES

Attorney General's Office
Department of Justice
33 Capitol Street
Concord, NH 03301-6397
(603) 271-365

Law Enforcement Planning
Judicial Council
State House Annex
25 Capitol Street, Room 424
Concord, NH 03301
(603) 271-3592

Statistical Analysis Center
Office of the Attorney General
33 Capitol Street
Concord, NH 03301
(603) 271-3658

Uniform Crime Reports Contact
New Hampshire Department of
    Public Safety
Division of State Police
Uniform Crime Report Unit
10 Hazen Drive
Concord, NH 03305
(603) 271-2509

**BJA Strategy Preparation
    Agency**
Department of Justice
33 Capitol Street
Concord, NH 03301
(603) 271-1297

Judicial Agency
Administrative Office of the Courts
Supreme Court Building
Noble Drive
Concord, NH 03301
(603) 271-2521

Corrections Agency
Department of Corrections
P.O. Box 1806
105 Pleasant Street
Concord, NH 03302

STATE HEALTH OFFICES

RADAR Network Agency
New Hampshire Bureau of
    Substance Abuse Services
State Office Park South
105 Pleasant Street
Concord, NH 03301
(603) 271-6100
E-mail:
    mdube@prevline.health.org

HIV-Prevention Program
STD/HIV Program
Division of Public Health Services
Bureau of Disease Control
6 Hazen Drive
Concord, NH 03301
(603) 271-4576

Drug and Alcohol Agency
New Hampshire Bureau of
    Substance Abuse Services
Department of Health and Human
    Services
Division of Mental Health &
    Developmental Services
State Office Park South
105 Pleasant Street
Concord, NH 03301

STATE EDUCATION OFFICE

**State Coordinator For Drug-
    Free Schools**
Department of Education
State Office Park South
101 Pleasant Street
Concord, NH 03301
(603) 271-2717

New Jersey

STATE POLICY OFFICES

Governor's Office
Office of the Governor
125 State Street, CN 001
Trenton, NJ 08625-0001
(609) 292-6000

State Legislative Contact
Office of Legislative Services
Legislative Information and Bill
  Room
State House Annex, CN 068
Trenton, NJ 08625
(609) 292-4840
(800) 792-8630 (NJ only)
http://www.njleg.state.nj.us

State Drug Program
  Coordinator
Office of the Attorney General
Department of Law and Public
  Safety
CN 080
Trenton, NJ 08625
(609) 292-4925

STATE CRIMINAL
JUSTICE OFFICES

Attorney General's Office
Office of the Attorney General
Department of Law and Public
  Safety
Justice Complex, CN 080
Trenton, NJ 08625
(609) 292-4925

Law Enforcement Planning
State Law Enforcement Planning
  Agency and Coordination
  Section
State Police
P.O. Box 7068
Trenton, NJ 08628
(609) 882-2000

Crime Prevention Offices
New Jersey Crime Prevention
  Officers Association
3515 Bargaintown Road
Egg Harbor Two, NJ 08234-8321
(609) 926-4039

Statistical Analysis Center
Research and Evaluation Section
Criminal Justice Division
25 Market Street, CN 085
Trenton, NJ 08625
(609) 984-2737

Uniform Crime Reports Contact
Uniform Crime Reporting
Division of State Police
Box 7068
West Trenton, NJ 08628-0068
(609) 882-2000, ext. 2392

BJA Strategy Preparation
  Agency
Department of Law and Public
  Safety
Division of Criminal Justice
25 Market Street, CN 085
Trenton, NJ 08625-0085
(609) 292-5939

Judicial Agency
Administrative Office of the Courts
Hughes Justice Complex, CN 037
Trenton, NJ 08625
(609) 984-0275
E-mail: aoc@ix.netcom.com

Corrections Agency
Department of Corrections
Whittlesey Road
CN 863
Trenton, NJ 08625-0863
(609) 292-4036

STATE HEALTH OFFICES

RADAR Network Agency
New Jersey Department of Health
  and Senior Services
Division of Addiction Services
129 East Hanover Street, CN-362
Trenton, NJ 08625-0362
(609) 984-6961
E-mail:
  dadaas@prevline.health.org

HIV-Prevention Program
Department of Health
AIDS Program
50 East State Street, CN369
Trenton, NJ 08625-0369
(609) 984-5874

Drug and Alcohol Agency
Division of Addiction Services
129 East Hanover Street, CN 362
Trenton, NJ 08625-0362
(609) 292-5760

STATE EDUCATION OFFICE

State Coordinator For Drug-
  Free Schools
Manager
New Jersey State Departrment of
  Education
Division of Student Services
Office of Safe and Drug-Free
  Schools
100 Riverview Plaza, CN500
Trenton, NJ 08625
(609) 292-0321

New Mexico

STATE POLICY OFFICES

Governor's Office
Office of the Governor
State Capitol, Room 400
Santa Fe, NM 87501
(505) 827-3000
E-mail: gov@gov.state.nm.us

State Legislative Contact
Legislative Council Service
State Capitol, Room 311
Santa Fe, NM 87503
(505) 986-4600

State Drug Program
  Coordinator
Cabinet Secretary
Department of Public Safety
P.O. Box 1628
Santa Fe, NM 87504-1628
(505) 827-3370

STATE CRIMINAL
JUSTICE OFFICES

Attorney General's Office
Office of the Attorney General
P.O. Drawer 1508
Santa Fe, NM 87504-1508
(505) 827-6000

Statistical Analysis Center
Institute for Social Research
University of New Mexico
2808 Central Avenue SE
Albuquerque, NM 87106
(505) 277-2501
E-mail: lafree@unm.edu

BJA Strategy Preparation Agency
Office of Grants Management
Department of Public Safety
P.O. Box 1628
Santa Fe, NM 87504-1628
(505) 827-3338
E-mail: dfarrell@ops.state.nm.us

Judicial Agency
Administrative Office of the Courts
Supreme Court Building, Room 25
Santa Fe, NM 87501
(505) 827-4800

Corrections Agency
Department of Corrections
P.O. Box 27116
Santa Fe, NM 87502-0116
(505) 827-8645

STATE HEALTH OFFICES

RADAR Network Agency
Department of Health
Division of Substance Abuse
1190 St. Francis Drive, Room N3200
Santa Fe, NM 87502
(505) 827-2601

HIV-Prevention Program
Department of Health
Public Health Division
AIDS Prevention Program
525 Camino de los Marquez, Suite 1
Santa Fe, NM 87502-6110
(505) 476-8475

Drug and Alcohol Agency
Department of Health
Division of Substance Abuse
P.O. Box 26110
1190 St. Francis Drive
Santa Fe, NM 87502-6110
(505) 827-2601
E-mail: tie@nmbhsdl

STATE EDUCATION OFFICE

State Coordinator For Drug-Free Schools
State Department of Education
Director of Safe and Drug-Free Schools
120 South Federal Place, Room 206
Santa Fe, NM 87501
(505) 827-1827
E-mail: xfzv65a@prodigy.com

New York

STATE POLICY OFFICES

Governor's Office
Office of the Governor
Executive Chambers, State Capitol
Albany, NY 12224
(518) 474-8390

STATE CRIMINAL JUSTICE OFFICES

Attorney General's Office
Office of the Attorney General
Department of Law
State Capitol, Room 220
Albany, NY 12224
(518) 474-7330

Law Enforcement Planning
Commissioner
Division of Criminal Justice Services
Executive Park Tower
Stuyvesant Plaza
Albany, NY 12203-3764
(518) 457-1260

Crime Prevention Offices
New York State Crime Prevention Coalition
563 New Scotland Avenue
P.O. Box 8633
Albany, NY 12208-0633
(518) 344-3748
(800) NYS-CPCC

Statistical Analysis Center
Bureau of Statistical Services
New York State Division of Criminal Justice Services
Executive Park Tower, Eighth Floor
Stuyvesant Plaza
Albany, NY 12203
(518) 457-8381
E-mail: elyr@crisny.org

Uniform Crime Reports Contact
Uniform Crime Reports
Bureau of Statistical Services
New York State Division of Criminal Justice Services
Executive Park Tower Building, Eighth Floor
Stuyvesant Plaza
Albany, NY 12203
(518) 457-8381

BJA Strategy Preparation Agency
New York State Division of Criminal Justice Services
Office of Funding and Program Assistance
Executive Park Tower
Stuyvesant Plaza
Albany, NY 12203-3764
(518) 457-8462

Judicial Agency
Administrative Office of the Courts
270 Broadway, Room 1400
New York, NY 10007
(212) 417-2007

Corrections Agency
Commission on Corrections
Stuyvesant Plaza
Executive Park Tower, Second Floor
Albany, NY 12203-3764
(518) 485-2346

STATE HEALTH OFFICES

HIV-Prevention Program
Department of Health
AIDS Institute
Corning Tower, Room 308
Empire State Plaza
Albany, NY 12237
(518) 473-4229

Drug and Alcohol Agency
Office of Alcohol and Substance
  Abuse Services
1450 Western Avenue
Albany, NY 12203-8200
(518) 457-2061

STATE EDUCATION OFFICE

**State Coordinator For Drug-
  Free Schools**
State Education Department
Drug-Free Schools & Communiy
ACT Program, Room 318-MEB
Washington Avenue
Albany, NY 12234
(518) 486-6090

North Carolina

STATE POLICY OFFICES

Governor's Office
Office of the Governor
116 West Jones Street
Raleigh, NC 27603-8001
(919) 733-5811

State Legislative Contact
Department of Administration
116 West Jones
Raleigh, NC 27603-8003
(919) 733-6887

**State Drug Program
  Coordinator**
Department of Crime Control and
  Public Safety
P.O. Box 29591
Raleigh, NC 27626-0591
(919) 733-2126

STATE CRIMINAL JUSTICE OFFICES

Attorney General's Office
Office of the Attorney General
Department of Justice
P.O. Box 629
Raleigh, NC 27602-0629
(919) 733-3377

Law Enforcement Planning
Governor's Crime Commission
3824 Barrett Drive, Room 100
Raleigh, NC 27609
(919) 571-4736
E-mail: markj@gcc.dcc.state.nc.us

Crime Prevention Offices
North Carolina Crime Prevention
  Division
P.O. Box 29591
Raleigh, NC 27626-0591
(919) 733-5522

Statistical Analysis Center
Criminal Justice Analysis Center
Governor's Crime Commission
3824 Barrett Drive, Suite 100
Raleigh, NC 27609-7220
(919) 571-4736
E-mail: jimk@gcc.dcc.state.nc.us

Uniform Crime Reports Contact
Crime Reporting and Field
  Services
State Bureau of Investigation
Division of Criminal Information
407 North Blount Street
Raleigh, NC 27601
(919) 733-3171
E-mail:
  jnipper@mail.jus.state.nc.us

**BJA Strategy Preparation
  Agency**
Governor's Crime Commission
3824 Barrett Drive, Suite 100
Raleigh, NC 27609
(919) 571-4736
E-mail: markj@gcc.dcc.state.nc.us

Judicial Agency
Administrative Office of the Courts
P.O. Box 2448
Raleigh, NC 27602
(919) 733-7107

Corrections Agency
Department of Corrections
P.O. Box 29540
Raleigh, NC 27626-0540
(919) 733-4926

STATE HEALTH OFFICES

RADAR Network Agency
North Carolina Alcohol/Drug
  Resource Center
3109-A University Drive
Durham, NC 27707-3703
(919) 493-2881

HIV-Prevention Program
HIV/STD Control Section Chief
Department of Environment,
  Health and Natural Resources
Communicable Disease Control
HIV/STD Prevention Branch
P.O. Box 27687
Raleigh, NC 27611-7687
(919) 733-7301

Drug and Alcohol Agency
Department of Public Instruction
Division of School Improvement
Safe and Drug-Free Schools
  Section
301 North Wilmington Street
Raleigh, NC 27601-2825
(919) 715-1635

STATE EDUCATION OFFICE

**State Coordinator For Drug-
  Free Schools**
Director
Department of Public Instruction
Division of Alcohol & Drug
  Defense
210 North Dawson Street
Raleigh, NC 27603-1712
(919) 733-6615

North Dakota

STATE POLICY OFFICES

Governor's Office
Office of the Governor
600 East Boulevard Avenue
Bismarck, ND 58505-0001
(701) 328-2200

State Legislative Contact
Legislative Council
State Capitol
600 East Boulevard Avenue
Bismarck, ND 58505-0360
(701) 328-2916

**State Drug Program
Coordinator**

Division of Mental Health &
Alcohol and Drug Abuse
600 South Second Street, Suite 1E
Bismarck, ND 58504-5729
(701) 328-8920

STATE CRIMINAL
JUSTICE OFFICES

Attorney General's Office

Office of the Attorney General
600 East Boulevard Avenue
Bismarck, ND 58505-0040
(701) 328-2210

Law Enforcement Planning

Criminal Justice Training and
Statistics
Office of the Attorney General
State Capitol
Bismarck, ND 58505
(701) 224-2594

Statistical Analysis Center

Information Services Section
Bureau of Criminal Investigation
4205 State Street
P.O. Box 1054
Bismarck, ND 58502-1054
(701) 328-5514
E-mail:
c01125as.judyv@ranch.state.nd.u
s

Uniform Crime Reports Contact

Uniform Crime Reports
Attorney General's Office
Bureau of Criminal Investigation
P.O. Box 1054
Bismarck, ND 58502-1054
(701) 328-5500

**BJA Strategy Preparation
Agency**

Attorney General's Office
Bureau of Criminal Investigation
P.O. Box 1054
Bismarck, ND 58502
(701) 328-5500

Judicial Agency

Administrative Office of the Courts
Supreme Court
600 East Boulevard Avenue
Bismarck, ND 58505
(701) 328-4216

Corrections Agency

Department of Corrections and
Rehabilitation
P.O. Box 1898
Bismarck, ND 58502-1898
(701) 328-6390
E-mail: elittle@pioneer.state.nd.us

STATE HEALTH OFFICES

RADAR Network Agency

North Dakota Prevention Resource
Center
Division of Alcohol and Drug
Abuse
600 South Second Street, Suite 1-
E
Bismarck, ND 58504-5729
(701) 328-8919
E-mail: charolso@sendit.nodak.edu

HIV-Prevention Program

HIV/AIDS Program Manager
Division of Disease Control
North Dakota Department of
Health
600 East Boulevard Avenue
Bismarck, ND 58505-0200
(701) 328-2378
(800) 472-2180
E-mail:
msmail.pamv@ranch.state.nd.us

Drug and Alcohol Agency

Department of Public Instruction
Drug-Free Schools
State Capitol, Ninth Floor
Bismarck, ND 58505-0440
(701) 328-2254

STATE EDUCATION OFFICE

**State Coordinator For Drug-
Free Schools**

Department of Public Instruction
Drug-Free Schools
State Capitol, Ninth Floor
Bismarck, ND 58505-0440
(701) 328-2254

Ohio

STATE POLICY OFFICES

Governor's Office

Office of the Governor
77 South High Street, 30th Floor
Columbus, OH 43266-0601
(614) 644-0813

State Legislative Contact

Legislative Information Office
State House
Columbus, OH 43215
(614) 466-8842

**State Drug Program
Coordinator**

Department of Alcohol and Drug
Addiction Services
Two Nationwide Plaza, 12th Floor
280 North High Street
Columbus, OH 43215
(614) 466-3445

STATE CRIMINAL
JUSTICE OFFICES

Attorney General's Office

Office of the Attorney General
30 East Broad Street
Columbus, OH 43215-3428
(614) 466-4320

Law Enforcement Planning

Criminal Justice Services Office
400 East Town Street, Suite 120
Columbus, OH 43215
(614) 466-0280

Crime Prevention Office

Ohio Crime Prevention Association
6543 Commerce Parkway, Suite R
Dublin, OH 43017
(614) 761-0500

Statistical Analysis Center

Research and Statistics
Office of Criminal Justice Services
400 East Town Street, Suite 120
Columbus, OH 43215
(614) 466-5126
E-mail: knowles@ocjs.state.oh.us

**BJA Strategy Preparation
   Agency**
Governor's Office of Criminal
   Justice Services
400 East Town Street, Suite 120
Columbus, OH 43215
(614) 466-7782
E-mail: info@ocjs.state.oh.us

Judicial Agency
Administrative Office of the Courts
Supreme Court
30 East Broad Street
Columbus, OH 43266-0419
(614) 466-2653
E-mail: stovers@sconet.ohio.gov

Corrections Agency
Department of Rehabilitation and
   Correction
1050 Freeway Drive North
Columbus, OH 43229
(614) 752-1162

STATE HEALTH OFFICES

RADAR Network Agency
Department of Alcohol and Drug
   Addiction Services
Two Nationwide Plaza, 12th Floor
280 North High Street
Columbus, OH 43215-2537
(614) 466-6379

HIV-Prevention Program
Prevention Division
AIDS/STD Prevention Program
Ohio Department of Health
35 East Chestnut Street, Seventh
   Floor
P.O. Box 118
Columbus, OH 43266-0118
(614) 466-5480

Drug and Alcohol Agency
Department of Alcohol and Drug
   Addiction Services
280 North High Street, 12th Floor
Columbus, OH 43215-2537
(614) 466-3445
E-mail: ada@state.oh.us

STATE EDUCATION OFFICE

**State Coordinator For Drug-
   Free Schools**
Ohio Department of Education
Student Development Division
65 South Front Street, Room 611
Columbus, OH 43215-4183
(614) 466-2471
E-mail: sd_airhart@ode.ohio.gov

Oklahoma

STATE POLICY OFFICES

Governor's Office
Office of the Governor
State Capitol, Room 212
Oklahoma City, OK 73105
(405) 521-2342
E-mail: governor@oklaoss.ok.us

**State Drug Program
   Coordinator**
Oklahoma Health Care Authority
4545 North Lincoln Boulevard,
   Suite 124
Oklahoma City, OK 73105
(405) 530-3439

STATE CRIMINAL
JUSTICE OFFICES

Attorney General's Office
Office of the Attorney General
112 State Capitol Building
Oklahoma City, OK 73105
(405) 521-3921

Law Enforcement Planning
Department of Public Safety
P.O. Box 11415
Oklahoma City, OK 73136-1415
(405) 425-2001

Statistical Analysis Center
Oklahoma Criminal Justice
   Resource Center
5500 North Western, Suite 245
Oklahoma City, OK 73118
(405) 858-7025
E-mail: fferrari@oklaosf.state.ok.us

Uniform Crime Reports Contact
Uniform Crime Reporting Unit
Oklahoma Bureau of Investigation
6600 North Harvey, Suite 300
Oklahoma City, OK 73116
(405) 848-6724

**BJA Strategy Preparation
   Agency**
District Attorney's Training and
   Coordination Council
2200 Classen Boulevard, Suite
   1800
Oklahoma City, OK 73106-5811
(405) 557-6707

Judicial Agency
Administrative Office of the Courts
1915 North Stiles Avenue, Suite
   305
Oklahoma City, OK 73105
(405) 521-2450

Corrections Agency
Department of Corrections
P.O. Box 11400
Oklahoma City, OK 73136
(405) 425-2505

STATE HEALTH OFFICES

RADAR Network Agency
Oklahoma State Department of
   Mental Health and Substance
   Abuse Services, Second Floor
1200 Northeast 13th Street
P.O. Box 53277
Oklahoma City, OK 73117
(405) 522-3810

HIV-Prevention Program
Department of Health
Personal Health Services
HIV/STD Services
1000 Northeast 10th Street
Oklahoma City, OK 73117-1299
(405) 271-4636

Drug and Alcohol Agency
Department of Mental Health and
   Substance Abuse Services
P.O. Box 53277
Oklahoma City, OK 73152-3277
(405) 522-3908

STATE EDUCATION OFFICE

State Coordinator For Drug-Free Schools

Comprehensive Health
Oklahoma Department of
Education
2500 North Lincoln Boulevard
Oklahoma City, OK 73105-4599
(405) 521-4507

Oregon

STATE POLICY OFFICES

Governor's Office

Office of the Governor
State Capitol Building, Room 254
Salem, OR 97310
(503) 378-3111

State Legislative Contact

Legislative Library
State Capitol, Room 347
Salem, OR 97310
(503) 986-1668

State Drug Program Coordinator

Drug Program Coordinator
Criminal Justice Services Division
Department of State Police
400 Public Service Building
Salem, OR 97310
(503) 378-3720

STATE CRIMINAL JUSTICE OFFICES

Attorney General's Office

Office of the Attorney General
Department of Justice
1162 Court Street NE
Salem, OR 97310
(503) 378-6002

Law Enforcement Planning

Division of Civil Enforcement
Office of the Attorney General
Department of Justice
1162 Court Street NE
Salem, OR 97310
(503) 378-4732

Crime Prevention Offices

Oregon Board on Police Standards
and Training
Oregon Crime Watch
550 North Monmouth Avenue
Monmouth, OR 97361-0070
(503) 378-2100

Statistical Analysis Center

Oregon Criminal Justice
Commission
Statistical Analysis Center
155 Cottage Street NE
Salem, OR 97310
(503) 378-2053
E-mail: phil.m.lemman@state.or.us

Uniform Crime Reports Contact

Law Enforcement Data System
Section
Oregon State Police
400 Public Service Building
Salem, OR 97310
(503) 378-3057

BJA Strategy Preparation Agency

Criminal Justice Services Division
Department of State Police
400 Public Service Building
Salem, OR 97310-0310
(503) 378-3720

Judicial Agency

Office of the State Court
Administrator
Supreme Court Building
Salem, OR 97310
(503) 986-5500

Corrections Agency

Department of Corrections
2575 Center Street NE
Salem, OR 97310
(503) 945-0920

STATE HEALTH OFFICES

RADAR Network Agency

RADAR Network Agency
Oregon Prevention Resource
Center
Office of Alcohol and Drug Abuse
Programs
Department of Human Resources
555 24th Place NE
Salem, OR 97310
(503) 378-8000

HIV-Prevention Program

HIV Program Manager
Oregon Department of Human
Resources
Health Division
800 Northeast Oregon Street, Suite
745
Portland, OR 97232
(503) 731-4029
E-mail:
robert.o.mcalister@state.or.us

Drug and Alcohol Agency

Office of Alcohol and Drug Abuse
Programs
500 Summer Street NE, Third
Floor
Salem, OR 97310-1016
(503) 945-5763

STATE EDUCATION OFFICE

State Coordinator For Drug-Free Schools

Coordinator for Drug-Free Schools
State Department of Education
255 Capitol Street NE
Salem, OR 97310
(503) 378-5585

Pennsylvania

STATE POLICY OFFICES

Governor's Office

Office of the Governor
Main Capitol, Room 225
Harrisburg, PA 17120
(717) 787-2500
E-mail: tridge@gois.state.pa.us

State Legislative Contact
Legislative Reference Bureau
Main Capitol Building, Room 641
Harrisburg, PA 17120
(717) 787-422323

**State Drug Program
Coordinator**
Director of Criminal Justice Policy
Office of the Governor
506 Finance Building
Harrisburg, PA 17120
(717) 787-1854
E-mail: mwoolley@gois.state.pa.us

STATE CRIMINAL JUSTICE OFFICES

Attorney General's Office
Office of the Attorney General
Strawberry Square, 16th Floor
Harrisburg, PA 17120
(717) 787-3391

Law Enforcement Planning
Pennsylvania State Police
Bureau of Drug Law Enforcement
Strawberry Square, 16th Floor
Harrisburg, PA 17120
(717) 783-8514

Crime Prevention Offices
Pennsylvania Commission on
Crime and Delinquency
Crime Prevention Division
P.O. Box 1167
Harrisburg, PA 17108-1167
(717) 787-1777
E-mail: willough@pccd.state.pa.us

Statistical Analysis Center
Bureau of Statistics and Policy
Research
Pennsylvania Commission on
Crime and Delinquency
P.O. Box 1167
Harrisburg, PA 17108
(717) 787-5152
E-mail: renninge@pccd.state.pa.us

Uniform Crime Reports Contact
Uniform Crime Reports
Bureau of Research and
Development
Pennsylvania State Police
1800 Elmerton Avenue
Harrisburg, PA 17110
(717) 783-5536

**BJA Strategy Preparation
Agency**
Pennsylvania Commission on
Crime and Delinquency
P.O. Box 1167
Harrisburg, PA 17108-1167
(717) 787-2040
E-mail: Thomas@pccd.state.pa.us

Judicial Agency
Administrative Office of
Pennsylvania
Supreme Court of Pennsylvania
1515 Market Street, Suite 1414
Philadelphia, PA 19102
(215) 560-6300

Corrections Agency
Department of Corrections
P.O. Box 598
Camp Hill, PA 17001-0598
(717) 975-4860

STATE HEALTH OFFICES

RADAR Network Agency
PennSAHIC
652 West 17th Street
Erie, PA 16502
(814) 459-0245
(800) 582-7746
http://www.pennsahic.org
E-mail: pensahic@moose.erie.net

HIV-Prevention Program
Pennsylvania Department of
Health
Bureau of HIV/AIDS
Division of Education and
Training
P.O. Box 90, Room 912
Harrisburg, PA 17108
(717) 783-0572

Drug and Alcohol Agency
Office of Drug and Alcohol
Programs
Room 933
P.O. Box 90
Harrisburg, PA 17108
(717) 787-8200

STATE EDUCATION OFFICE

**State Coordinator For Drug-
Free Schools**
Division of Student Services
Pennsylvania Department of
Education
333 Market Street
Harrisburg, PA 17126-0333
(717) 772-2429

Rhode Island

STATE POLICY OFFICES

Governor's Office
Office of the Governor
143 State House
Providence, RI 02903
(401) 277-2080
E-mail: linc01a@prodigy.com

State Legislative Contact
Legislative Council
State House, Room 101
82 Smith Street
Providence, RI 02903
(401) 277-3757

**State Drug Program
Coordinator**
Department of Health
Division of Substance Abuse
Cannon Building, Room 105
3 Capitol Hill
Providence, RI 02908-5097
(401) 277-4680

STATE CRIMINAL JUSTICE OFFICES

Attorney General's Office
Office of the Attorney General
150 South Main Street
Providence, RI 02903
(401) 274-4400

Law Enforcement Planning

Rhode Island State Police
Headquarters
311 Danielson Pike
North Scituate, RI 02850
(401) 444-1000

Crime Prevention Office

Warwick Police Department
99 Veterans Memorial Drive
Warwick, RI 02886
(401) 737-2244

Statistical Analysis Center

Governor's Justice Commission
One Capitol Hill, Fourth Floor
Providence, RI 02908-5803
(401) 277-4499

Uniform Crime Reports Contact

Uniform Crime Reports
Rhode Island State Police
P.O. Box 185
North Scituate, RI 02857
(401) 444-1120

BJA Strategy Preparation Agency

Rhode Island Governor's Justice
Commission
222 Quaker Lane
Suite 100
West Warwick, RI 02893
(401) 277-2620

Judicial Agency

Office of the State Court
Administrator
Providence County Courthouse
250 Benefit Street
Providence, RI 02903
(401) 277-3263

Corrections Agency

Department of Corrections
40 Howard Avenue
Cranston, RI 02920
(401) 464-2611

STATE HEALTH OFFICES

RADAR Network Agency

Office of Substance Abuse
Cannon Building, Suite 105
Capitol Hill
Providence, RI 02908-5097
(401) 277-4680

HIV-Prevention Program

Department of Health
Disease Prevention and Control
3 Capitol Hill
Providence, RI 02908-5097
(401) 277-1171

Drug and Alcohol Agency

Office of Substance Abuse
Cannon Building, Suite 105
Capitol Hill
Providence, RI 02908-5097
(401) 277-4680

STATE EDUCATION OFFICE

State Coordinator For Drug-Free Schools

Rhode Island Department of
Education
Safe & Drug-Free Schools and
Communities Act
Program
225 Westminster Street, Sixth
Floor
Providence, RI 02903-3400
(401) 277-4600 ext.2372
E-mail: ride0039@ride.ri.net

South Carolina

STATE POLICY OFFICES

Governor's Office

Office of the Governor
P.O. Box 11369
Columbia, SC 29211
(803) 734-9818
E-mail: governor@state.sc.us

State Legislative Contact

Code Commissioner and Director
Legislative Council
State House
Columbia, SC 29211
(803) 734-2145

State Drug Program Coordinator

DESIP Project Administrator
South Carolina Department of
Public Safety
5400 Broad River Road
Columbia, SC 29210-4088
(803) 896-8708
E-mail: lan@scdps.state.sc.us

STATE CRIMINAL JUSTICE OFFICES

Attorney General's Office

Office of the Attorney General
P.O. Box 11549
Columbia, SC 29211
(803) 734-3970
E-mail:
   abcmcondon@ag.state.sc.us

Law Enforcement Planning

South Carolina Law Enforcement
Division
P.O. Box 21398
Columbia, SC 29221
(803) 737-9000

Statistical Analysis Center

Department of Public Safety
5400 Broad River Road
Columbia, SC 29210
(803) 896-8717
E-mail:
   rfm@mail06.scdps.state.sc.us

Uniform Crime Reports Contact

Uniform Crime Reports
South Carolina Law Enforcement
Division
P.O. Box 21398
Columbia, SC 29221-1398
(803) 896-7162

BJA Strategy Preparation Agency

Office of Safety and Grants
Department of Public Safety
5400 Broad River Road
Columbia, SC 29201-4088
(803) 896-8708

Judicial Agency

South Carolina Court
Administration
1015 Sumter Street, Second Floor
Columbia, SC 29201
(803) 734-1800

Corrections Agency

Department of Corrections
P.O. Box 21787
Columbia, SC 29221-1787
(803) 896-8555

STATE HEALTH OFFICES

RADAR Network Agency

South Carolina Commission on
    Alcohol and Drug Abuse
The Drugstore Information
    Clearinghouse
3700 Forest Drive, Suite 300
Columbia, SC 29204
(803) 734-9559
E-Mail:
    epeters@prevline.health.org

HIV-Prevention Program

Health and Environmental Control
STD/HIV Division
Jarrett Complex, Box 101106
2600 Bull Street
Columbia, SC 29201
(803) 734-4110

Drug and Alcohol Agency

Department of Alcohol and Other
    Drug Abuse Services
3700 Forest Drive, Suite 300
Columbia, SC 29204
(803) 734-9520
E-mail:
    epeters@prevline.health.org

STATE EDUCATION OFFICE

State Coordinator For Drug-Free Schools

Safe & Drug-Free Schools and
    Communities
South Carolina Department of
    Education
1429 Senate Street, Room 1108
Columbia, SC 29201
(803) 734-8566

South Dakota

STATE POLICY OFFICES

Governor's Office

Office of the Governor
500 East Capitol Avenue
Pierre, SD 57501
(605) 773-3212
E-mail: cathys@gov.state.sd.us

State Legislative Contact

Legislative Research Council
State Capitol Annex
500 East Capitol Avenue
Pierre, SD 57501
(605) 773-3251
E-mail: clarec@lrc.state.sd.us

State Drug Program Coordinator

Office of the Attorney General
500 East Capitol
Pierre, SD 57501
(605) 773-3212

STATE CRIMINAL JUSTICE OFFICES

Attorney General's Office

Office of the Attorney General
State Capitol Building
500 East Capitol Avenue
Pierre, SD 57501-5070
(605) 773-3215

Law Enforcement Planning

Division of Criminal Investigation
500 East Capitol Avenue
Pierre, SD 57501-5070
(605) 773-3331

Statistical Analysis Center

South Dakota Statistical Analysis
    Center
500 East Capitol Avenue
Pierre, SD 57501-5070
(605) 773-6310
E-mail: wandaf@atg.state.sd.us

Uniform Crime Reports Contact

State Statistical Analysis Center
500 East Capitol Avenue
Pierre, SD 57501
(605) 773-6310

BJA Strategy Preparation Agency

Office of Operations
State Capitol Building
500 East Capitol Avenue
Pierre, SD 57501-5070
(605) 773-6313

Judicial Agency

Administrative Office of the Courts
Unified Judicial System of South
    Dakota
500 East Capitol Avenue
Pierre, SD 57501
(605) 773-3474

Corrections Agency

Department of Corrections
115 East Dakota
Pierre, SD 57501
(605) 773-3478

STATE HEALTH OFFICES

RADAR Network Agency

Division of Alcohol and Drug
    Abuse
Hillsview Plaza
500 East Capitol Avenue
Pierre, SD 57501-5070
(605) 773-3123

HIV-Prevention Program

Department of Health
615 East Fourth Street
Pierre, SD 57501
(605) 773-3737
E-mail: davem@doh.state.sd.us

Drug and Alcohol Agency

Division of Alcohol and Drug
    Abuse
Department of Human Services
Hillsview Plaza
500 East Capitol Avenue
Pierre, SD 57501-5070
(605) 773-4828

STATE EDUCATION OFFICE

State Coordinator For Drug-Free Schools

State Department of Education
700 Governors Drive
Pierre, SD 57501-3182
(605) 773-4670

Tennessee

STATE POLICY OFFICES

Governor's Office
Office of the Governor
State Capitol, First Floor
Nashville, TN 37243-0001
(615) 741-2001
E-mail:
dsundquist@mail.state.tn.us

State Legislative Contact
Office of Legislative Information
Services
General Assembly
Rachel Jackson Building, First
Floor
Nashville, TN 37243
(615) 741-3511

State Drug Program Coordinator
Safe & Drug Free Schools
Community Program
Andrew Johnson Tower, Sixth
Floor
710 James Robertson Parkway
Nashville, TN 37243-0375
(615) 741-3248

STATE CRIMINAL JUSTICE OFFICES

Attorney General's Office
Office of the Attorney General
Enforcement Division
Nashville, TN 20494
(615) 741-4081

Law Enforcement Planning
Department of Safety
1150 Foster Avenue, Room 292
Nashville, TN 37249-1000
(615) 251-5166
E-mail: akimbrou@mail.state.tn.us

Statistical Analysis Center
Tennessee Bureau of Investigation
1148 Foster Avenue
Nashville, TN 37210-4406
(615) 726-7970
E-mail:
jvandercook@mail.state.tn.us

BJA Strategy Preparation Agency
Office of Criminal Justice
Programs
Department of Finance and
Administration
1400 Andrew Jackson Building
500 Deaderick Street
Nashville, TN 37243-1700
(615) 741-3784

Judicial Agency
Administrative Office of the Courts
Nashville City Center
511 Union Street, Suite 600
Nashville, TN 37243-0607
(615) 741-2687

Corrections Agency
Department of Corrections
320 Sixth Avenue North, Fourth
Floor
Nashville, TN 37243-0465
(615) 741-2071
http://www.state.tn.us

STATE HEALTH OFFICES

RADAR Network Agency
Tennessee Alcohol and Drug
Association
Statewide Clearinghouse
545 Mainstream Drive, Suite 404
Nashville, TN 37228
(615) 244-7066
1-800-889-9789

HIV-Prevention Program
Department of Health
STD/HIV Program
Health Services Bureau
426 Fifth Avenue North, Fourth
Floor
Nashville, TN 37247-4501
(615) 741-7247

Drug and Alcohol Agency
Tennessee Bureau of Alcohol and
Drug Abuse Services
Third Floor Cordell Hull
426 Fifth Avenue North
Nashville, TN 37247-0101
(615) 741-1921
E-mail: sperry@mail.state.tn.us

STATE EDUCATION OFFICE

State Coordinator For Drug-Free Schools
Tennessee Department of
Education
Safe and Drug-Free Schools
Program
Andrew Johnson Tower, Sixth
Floor
710 James Robertson Parkway
Nashville, TN 37243-0375
(615) 741-3248

Texas

STATE POLICY OFFICES

Governor's Office
Office of the Governor
Capitol Station
P.O. Box 12428
Austin, TX 78711
(512) 463-2000
http://www.governor.state.tx.us

State Legislative Contact
Legislative Council
State Capitol, 1W15
Austin, TX 78711
(512) 463-1151

State Drug Program Coordinator
Texas War on Drugs
7600 Chevy Chase Drive, Suite
115
Austin, TX 78752
(512) 452-0141
E-mail: twod@cris.com

STATE CRIMINAL JUSTICE OFFICES

Attorney General's Office
Office of the Attorney General
P.O. Box 12548
Austin, TX 78711-2548
(512) 463-2100
(800) 252-8011 (TX only)
http://www.oag.state.tx.us

Law Enforcement Planning

Criminal Justice Division
Office of the Attorney General
P.O. Box 12548
Austin, TX 78711-2548
(512) 463-2080

Crime Prevention Office

Office of Court Administration of
the Texas
Judicial System
P.O. Box 12066
Austin, TX 78711-2066
(512) 463-1625

Statistical Analysis Center

Criminal Justice Policy Council
P.O. Box 13332
Austin, TX 78711-3332
(512) 463-1810
E-mail: cjpc@access.texas.gov

Uniform Crime Reports Contact

Uniform Crime Reporting
Texas Department of Public Safety
P.O. Box 4143
Austin, TX 78765
(512) 424-2091

**BJA Strategy Preparation
Agency**

Criminal Justice Division
Office of the Governor
P.O. Box 12428
Austin, TX 78711
(512) 463-1952
E-mail:
    rbodisch@governor.texas.gov

Judicial Agency

Administrative Office of the Courts
Tom C. Clark State Courts
    Building
205 West 14th Street, Suite 600
Austin, TX 78701
(512) 463-1625

Corrections Agency

Criminal Justice Agency
Department of Criminal Justice
P.O. Box 99
Huntsville, TX 77342-0099
(409) 295-6371
E-mail: wscott.@access.texas.gov

STATE HEALTH OFFICES

RADAR Network Agency

Texas Commission on Alcohol and
    Drug Abuse
9001 North IH 35, Suite 105
Austin, TX 78753-5233
(512) 349-6644
E-mail: mstanfie@tcada.state.tx.us

HIV-Prevention Program

Texas Department of Health
Disease Control and Prevention
HIV/STD Prevention Bureau
1100 West 49th Street
Austin, TX 78756-3199
(512) 490-2505

Drug and Alcohol Agency

Texas Commission on Alcohol and
    Drug Abuse
9001 North IH 35, Suite 105
Austin, TX 78753-5233
(512) 349-6600

STATE EDUCATION OFFICE

**State Coordinator For Drug-
Free Schools**

Safe and Drug-Free Schools and
    Communities
Coordinator
Texas Education Agency
Division of Accelerated Instruction
1701 North Congress Avenue
Austin, TX 78701-1494
(512) 463-9374

Utah

STATE POLICY OFFICES

Governor's Office

Office of the Governor
State Capitol, Room 210
Salt Lake City, UT 84114
(801) 538-1000
E-mail: governor@state.ut.us

State Legislative Contact

Office of Legislative Research and
    General Counsel
State Capitol, Room 436
Salt Lake City, UT 84114
(801) 538-1032

**State Drug Program
Coordinator**

Commission on Criminal and
    Juvenile Justice
State Capitol, Room 101
Salt Lake City, UT 84114
(801) 538-1031

STATE CRIMINAL
JUSTICE OFFICES

Attorney General's Office

State Capitol
Room 236
Salt Lake City, UT 84114
(801) 533-5261

Law Enforcement Planning

Utah Department of Public Safety
5272 South College Drive, Room
    200
Murray, UT 84123
(801) 284-6240
E-mail:
    psdomain.psudi.bmunson@state.u
    t.us

Statistical Analysis Center

101 State Capitol
Salt Lake City, UT 84114
(801) 538-1031
E-mail: jhemenwa@state.ut.us

Uniform Crime Reports Contact

Uniform Crime Reports
Utah Department of Public Safety
4501 South 2700 West
Salt Lake City, UT 84119
(801) 965-4445

**BJA Strategy Preparation
Agency**

Commission on Criminal and
    Juvenile Justice
State Capitol, Room 101
Salt Lake City, UT 84114
(801) 538-1031
E-mail: jhemenwa@state.ut.us

Judicial Agency

Office of Court Administrator
230 South 500 East, Suite 300
Salt Lake City, UT 84102
(801) 578-3800
E-mail: ericl@aoc.utcourts.gov

Corrections Agency
Department of Corrections
6100 South Fashion Boulevard
Murray, UT 84107
(801) 265-5500
E-mail: crdept.jford@state.ut.us

STATE HEALTH OFFICES

RADAR Network Agency
Utah State Division of Substance
Abuse
120 North 200 West, Second Floor
Salt Lake City, UT 84103
(801) 538-3939

HIV-Prevention Program
HIV/AIDS Drug Therapy Program
Utah Department of Health
Bureau of HIV/AIDS
P.O. Box 142867
Salt Lake City, UT 84114-2867
(801) 538-6096

Drug and Alcohol Agency
Division of Substance Abuse
Department of Human Services
P.O. Box 45500
Salt Lake City, UT 84145-0500
(801) 538-3938

STATE EDUCATION OFFICE

**State Coordinator For Drug-
Free Schools**
Drug-Free School Coordinator
Utah State Office of Education
Drug-Free Schools Program
250 East 500 South
Salt Lake City, UT 84111
(801) 538-7713

Vermont

STATE POLICY OFFICES

Governor's Office
Office of the Governor
Pavilion Office Building
109 State Street
Montpelier, VT 05609-0101
(802) 828-3333
E-mail: jbagalio@state.vt.us

State Legislative Contact
Legislative Council
State House
115 State Street, Drawer 33
Montpelier, VT 05633-5301
(802) 828-2231

**State Drug Program
Coordinator**
Director of State Police
Department of Public Safety
103 South Main Street
Waterbury, VT 05671-2101
(802) 244-8718
E-mail: jwalton@dps.vt.us

STATE CRIMINAL JUSTICE OFFICES

Attorney General's Office
Office of the Attorney General
109 State Street
Montpelier, VT 05609-1001
(802) 828-3171
E-mail:
syoung@ag10.atg.state.vt.us

Law Enforcement Planning
Department of Public Safety
103 South Main Street
Waterbury, VT 05671-2101
(802) 244-8718
E-mail: jwalton@dps.vt.us

Statistical Analysis Center
Vermont Center for Justice
Research
33 College Street
Northfield, VT 05602
(802) 828-8511
E-mail: clemmey@norwich.edu

Uniform Crime Reports Contact
Uniform Crime Reports
Support Services
Department of Public Safety
103 South Main Street
Waterbury, VT 05671-2101
(802) 244-8786

**BJA Strategy Preparation
Agency**
Department of Public Safety
Waterbury State Complex
103 South Main Street
Waterbury, VT 05676-0850
(802) 244-8781
E-mail: jwalton@dps.vt.u

Judicial Agency
Office of the Court Administrator
Supreme Court
109 State Street
Montpelier, VT 05609-0701
(802) 828-3278
E-mail: supreme.crt@state.vt.us

Corrections Agency
Department of Corrections
Agency of Human Services
State Complex
103 South Main Street
Waterbury, VT 05671-0201
(802) 241-2263

STATE HEALTH OFFICES

RADAR Network Agency
Office of Alcohol and Drug Abuse
Programs
P.O. Box 70
108 Cherry Street
Burlington, VT 05402-0070
(802) 651-1550

HIV-Prevention Program
Department of Health
VD Control Program
P.O. Box 70
108 Cherry Street
Burlington, VT 05402
(802) 863-7245

Drug and Alcohol Agency
Office of Alcohol and Drug Abuse
Programs
P.O. Box 70
108 Cherry Street
Burlington, VT 05402-0070
(802) 651-1550

STATE EDUCATION OFFICE

State Coordinator For Drug-Free Schools

Department of Education
Safe and Drug-Free Schools &
    Communities Program
120 State Street
Montpelier, VT 05620-2703
(802) 828-3125
E-mail: smahoney@doe.state.ut.us

Virginia

STATE POLICY OFFICES

Governor's Office

Office of the Governor
Capitol Building, Third Floor
Richmond, VA 23219
(804) 786-2211
E-mail:
    jerry.kilgore@lms.state.va.us

State Legislative Contact

Division of Legislative Services
General Assembly Building
910 Capitol Street, Second Floor
Richmond, VA 23208
(804) 786-3591

State Drug Program Coordinator

Office of the Secretary of Public
    Safety
202 North Ninth Street, Suite 613
Richmond, VA 23219
(804) 786-5351

STATE CRIMINAL JUSTICE OFFICES

Attorney General's Office

Office of the Attorney General
Commonwealth of Virginia
900 East Main Street
Richmond, VA 23219
(804) 786-2071
E-mail: vaattygen@aol.com

Law Enforcement Planning

State Police
P.O. Box 27472
Richmond, VA 23261-7472
(804) 674-2087

Crime Prevention Offices

Department of Criminal Justice
    Services
Virginia Crime Prevention Center
805 East Broad Street
Richmond, VA 23219
(804) 786-8467

Virginia Crime Prevention
    Association, Inc.
4914 Redford Avenue, Suite 306
Richmond, VA 23230
(804) 359-8120

Statistical Analysis Center

Department of Criminal Justice
    Services
805 East Broad Street
Richmond, VA 23219
(804) 371-0532
E-mail:
    jmcdonough.dcjs@state.va.us

Uniform Crime Reports Contact

Uniform Crime Reports
Records Management Division
Department of State Police
P.O. Box 27472
Richmond, VA 23261-7472
(804) 674-2023

BJA Strategy Preparation Agency

Department of Criminal Justice
    Services
805 East Broad Street, 10th Floor
Richmond, VA 23219
(804) 786-1577
E-mail: jmarshall.dcjs@state.va.us

Judicial Agency

Administrative Office of the Courts
Supreme Court
100 North Ninth Street, Third
    Floor
Richmond, VA 23219
(804) 786-6455

Corrections Agency

Department of Corrections
P.O. Box 26963
Richmond, VA 23261-6963
(804) 674-3119

STATE HEALTH OFFICES

RADAR Network Agency

Office of Prevention
Department of Mental Health
P.O. Box 1797
Richmond, VA 23214
(804) 371-75649

HIV-Prevention Program

Office of Health & Human
    Resources
Health Department
P.O. Box 2448
Richmond, VA 23218
(804) 786-6267
E-mail: elam.vdh@state.va.us

Drug and Alcohol Agency

Division of Substance Abuse
    Services
Department of Mental Health,
    Mental Retardation,
and Substance Abuse Services
P.O. Box 1797
Richmond, VA 23218
(804) 786-3906

STATE EDUCATION OFFICE

State Coordinator For Drug-Free Schools

State Coordinator for Drug-Free
    Schools
Virginia Department of Education
Youth Risk Prevention Program
P.O. Box 2120
Richmond, VA 23216-2120
(804) 225-2871

Washington

STATE POLICY OFFICES

Governor's Office

Office of the Governor
Legislative Building, Room AS-13
Olympia, WA 98504-0002
(360) 753-6780
http://www.wa.gov/governor

State Legislative Contact

Office of Program Research
House of Representatives
House Office Building, Room 230
Olympia, WA 98504
(360) 786-7102

**State Drug Program
  Coordinator**
Executive Policy Legal Counsel
Office of the Governor
P.O. Box 43113
Olympia, WA 98504-3113
(360) 753-1022

STATE CRIMINAL
JUSTICE OFFICES

Attorney General's Office
Office of the Attorney General
P.O. Box 40100
Olympia, WA 98504-0100
(360) 753-6200

Law Enforcement Planning
Research & Planning Section
Budget & Fiscal Services
Washington State Patrol
P.O. Box 42602
Olympia, WA 98504-2602

Statistical Analysis Center
Office of Financial Management
Information and Forecasting
  Services
Insurance Building
P.O. Box 43113
Olympia, WA 98504-3113
(360) 586-2501
E-mail: glenn@ofm.wa.gov

Uniform Crime Reports Contact
Uniform Crime Reporting Program
Washington Association of Sheriffs
  and Police Chiefs
P.O. Box 826
Olympia, WA 98507
(360) 586-3221

**BJA Strategy Preparation
  Agency**
State Department of Community,
  Trade and Economic
Development
906 Columbia Street SW
P.O. Box 48300
Olympia, WA 98504-8300
(360) 586-0665

Judicial Agency
Administrative Office of the Courts
Supreme Court - Temple of Justice
P.O. Box 41174
Olympia, WA 98504-1174
(360) 357-2121

Corrections Agency
Department of Corrections
P.O. Box 41100
Olympia, WA 98504-1100
(360) 753-2500

STATE HEALTH OFFICES

RADAR Network Agency
Washington State Substance Abuse
  Coalition, Suite 18
12729 Northeast 20th Street
Bellevue, WA 98005
(206) 637-7011
E-mail: wssac@halcyon.com

HIV-Prevention Program
HIV-AIDS Office of Prevention
  and Education Services
Airdustrial Park, Building 9
P.O. Box 47890
Olympia, WA 98504-7840
(360) 586-0426

Drug and Alcohol Agency
Division of Alcohol and Substance
  Abuse
Department of Social and Health
  Services
Health and Rehabilitative Services
P.O. Box 45330
Olympia, WA 98504-5060
(360) 438-820

STATE EDUCATION OFFICE

**State Coordinator For Drug-
  Free Schools**
Safe & Drug-Free Schools
  Program, OSPI
P.O. Box 47200
Old Capitol Building
Olympia, WA 98504-7200
(360) 753-5595

West Virginia

STATE POLICY OFFICES

Governor's Office
Office of the Governor
Capitol Building
1900 Kanawha Boulevard East
Charleston, WV 25305-0370
(304) 558-2000

State Legislative Contact
Legislative Services
State Capitol, Room E-132
Charleston, WV 25305
(304) 347-4830

**State Drug Program
  Coordinator**
Department of Public Safety
State Capitol Complex
P.O. Box 50155
Charleston, WV 25305
(304) 348-2930

STATE CRIMINAL
JUSTICE OFFICES

Attorney General's Office
Office of the Attorney General
Building 1, Room E-26
1900 Kanawha Boulevard East
Charleston, WV 25305-0220
(304) 558-2021

Law Enforcement Planning
Division of Criminal Justice and
  Highway Safety
Department of Military Affairs and
  Public Safety
1204 Kanawha Boulevard East
Charleston, WV 25304-0311
(304) 348-8814
E-mail: wvcjhs@citynet.net

Statistical Analysis Center
Criminal Justice & Highway Safety
  Division
1204 Kanawha Boulevard East
Charleston, WV 25301
(304) 558-8814

Uniform Crime Reports Contact

Uniform Crime Reporting Program
West Virginia State Police
725 Jefferson Road
South Charleston, WV 25309
(304) 746-2159

BJA Strategy Preparation Agency

Criminal Justice and Highway
Safety Division
Department of Military Affairs and
Public Safety
1204 Kanawha Boulevard East
Charleston, WV 25301
(304) 558-8814
E-mail: wvcjhs@citynet.net

Judicial Agency

Administrative Office of the Courts
Supreme Court of Appeals
E-400 State Capitol Building
1900 Kanawha Boulevard East
Charleston, WV 25305-0833
(304) 558-0145

Corrections Agency

Division of Corrections
State Office Building 4, Room 300
112 California Avenue
Charleston, WV 25305
(304) 558-2036

STATE HEALTH OFFICES

RADAR Network Agency

West Virginia Library Commission
Cultural Center
1900 Kanawha Boulevard East
Charleston, WV 25305-0620
(304) 558-2041

HIV-Prevention Program

Department of Health and Human
Resources
Bureau for Public Health
AIDS Program
1422 Washington Street East
Charleston, WV 25301
(304) 558-2195

Drug and Alcohol Agency

Division on Alcoholism and Drug
Abuse
Bureau of Community Support
State Office Building 6, Room 717
Charleston, WV 25305
(304) 558-2276

STATE EDUCATION OFFICE

State Coordinator For Drug-Free Schools

State Department of Education
Student Services and Assessment
Capitol Complex, Building 6, B-057
1900 Kanawha Boulevard East
Charleston, WV 25305-0330
(304) 558-2546

Wisconsin

STATE POLICY OFFICES

Governor's Office

Office of the Governor
P.O. Box 7863
Madison, WI 53707-7863
(608) 266-1212
http://www.wisgov.state.wi.us

State Legislative Contact

Reference Staff
Legislative Reference Bureau
P.O. Box 2037
Madison, WI 53701-2037
(608) 266-0341

State Drug Program Coordinator

Alliance for a Drug-Free Wisconsin
1 West Wilson Street, Room 851
Madison, WI 53702
(608) 266-9354

STATE CRIMINAL JUSTICE OFFICES

Attorney General's Office

Office of the Attorney General
114 East, State Capitol
Madison, WI 53707-7857
(608) 266-1221

Law Enforcement Planning

Division of Law Enforcement
Services
Department of Justice
P.O. Box 7857
Madison, WI 53707-7858
(608) 266-7751

Crime Prevention Office

Attorney General's Crime
Prevention Resource Center
2 East Mifflin, Suite 100
Madison, WI 53703
(608) 267-6736
E-mail: perretzda@doj.state.wi.us

Statistical Analysis Center

Office of Justice Assistance
222 State Street, Second Floor
Madison, WI 53702
(608) 266-7185

Uniform Crime Reports Contact

Uniform Crime Reports
Office of Justice Assistance
222 State Street, Second Floor
Madison, WI 53703
(608) 266-3323

BJA Strategy Preparation Agency

Office of Justice Assistance
222 State Street, Second Floor
Madison, WI 53702
(608) 266-7282
(608) 266-7282

Judicial Agency

Director of State Courts
State Capitol, Room 213 NE
P.O. Box 1688
Madison, WI 53701-1688
(608) 266-6828

Corrections Agency

Department of Corrections
P.O. Box 7925
Madison, WI 53707-7925
(608) 266-4548

STATE HEALTH OFFICES

RADAR Network Agency

Wisconsin Clearinghouse for
Prevention Resources
1552 University Avenue
Madison, WI 53705
(608) 262-9157
http://www.uhs.wisc.edu/wch
E-mail: wchpr@www.uhs.wisc.edu

HIV-Prevention Program

AIDS/HIV Program
Bureau of Public Health
Division of Health, Room 96
1414 East Washington Avenue
Madison, WI 53703-3044
(608) 267-5287

Drug and Alcohol Agency

Bureau of Substance Abuse
Services
Supportive Living Division
P.O. Box 7851
Madison, WI 53707-7851
(608) 266-3719
E-mail: mcculps@dhfs.state.wi.us

STATE EDUCATION OFFICE

State Coordinator For Drug-Free Schools

Department of Public Instruction
Student Services/Prevention and
Wellness Team
125 South Webster Street
P.O. Box 7841
Madison, WI 53707-7841
(608) 266-3390
E-mail: trudebk@mail.state.wi.us

Wyoming

STATE POLICY OFFICES

Governor's Office

Office of the Governor
State Capitol Building, Room 124
200 West 24th Street
Cheyenne, WY 82002-0010
(307) 777-7434
E-mail:
governor@missc.state.wy.us

State Legislative Contact

Legislative Service Office
State Capitol, Room 213
200 West 24th Street
Cheyenne, WY 82002
(307) 777-788

State Drug Program Coordinator

Governor's State Drug Policy
Board
316 West 22nd Street
Cheyenne, WY 82002-0001
(307) 777-7181

STATE CRIMINAL JUSTICE OFFICES

Attorney General's Office

Office of the Attorney General
123 Capitol Building
Cheyenne, WY 82002
(307) 777-7841

Law Enforcement Planning

Office of the Attorney General
123 Capitol Building
200 West 24th Street
Cheyenne, WY 82002
(307) 777-7841

Crime Prevention Office

Wyoming Crime Prevention
Coalition
45 West 12th Street
Sheridan, WY 82801
(307) 672-2413

Statistical Analysis Center

Division of Criminal Investigation
Office of the Attorney General
316 West 22nd Street
Cheyenne, WY 82002
(307) 777-7523

Uniform Crime Reports Contact

Uniform Crime Reports
Criminal Justice Information
Section
Division of Criminal Investigation
316 West 22nd Street
Cheyenne, WY 82002
(307) 777-7625

BJA Strategy Preparation Agency

Division of Criminal Investigation
316 West 22nd Street
Cheyenne, WY 82002
(307) 777-7181

Judicial Agency

Court Administrator
Wyoming Supreme Court
Supreme Court Building
Cheyenne, WY 82002
(307) 777-7480
E-mail:
ajohnson@courts.state.wy.us

Corrections Agency

Department of Corrections
1 East Herschler Building
Cheyenne, WY 82002
(307) 777-7405
E-mail: jlight@missc.state.wy.us

STATE HEALTH OFFICES

RADAR Network Agency

Wyoming CARE Program
Box 3374, University Station
Room 35, College of Education
Laramie, WY 82071-3374
(307) 766-4119

HIV-Prevention Program

Department of Health
Division of Public Health
Hathaway Building, Fourth Floor
Cheyenne, WY 82002-0480
(307) 777-6186

Drug and Alcohol Agency

Office of Substance Abuse
Division of Behavioral Health
451 Hathaway Building
2300 Capitol Avenue
Cheyenne, WY 82002-0480
(307) 777-7094
E-mail: jdefra@missc.state.wy.us

STATE EDUCATION OFFICE

State Coordinator For Drug-Free Schools

Wyoming Department of
Education
Hathaway Building
2300 Capitol Avenue
Cheyenne, WY 82002
(307) 777-7168
E-mail:
psoumoki@educ.state.wy.us

American Samoa

POLICY OFFICES

Governor's Office

Office of the Governor
Pago Pago, AS 96799
011-684-633-4116

CRIMINAL JUSTICE OFFICES

Attorney General's Office

Department of Legal Affairs
Fagatogo
Pago Pago, AS 96799
011-684-633-4163

Law Enforcement Planning

Criminal Justice Planning Agency
Utulei
Pago Pago, AS 96799
011-684-633-5221

Uniform Crime Reports Contact

Uniform Crime Reports
Department of Public Safety
PO Box 1086
Pago Pago, AS 96799
011-684-633-1111

BJA Strategy Preparation Agency

Government of American Samoa
Office of Legal Affairs
P.O. Box 7
Pago Pago, AS 96799
011-684-633-1838

Judicial Agency

High Court and District Court
Court House
Fagatogo
Pago Pago, AS 96799
011-684-633-4131

Corrections Agency

Department of Public Safety
PO Box 1086
Pago Pago, AS 96799
011-684-633-1111

HEALTH OFFICES

RADAR Network Agency

Department of Human Resources
Social Services Division
Drugs and Alcohol Program
Government of American Samoa
P.O. Box 5051
Pago Pago, AS 96799
011-684-633-2696

HIV-Prevention Program

Government of American Samoa
Department of Public Health
Pago Pago, AS 96799
011-684-633-4606
E-mail: dr_lorac@msn.com

Drug and Alcohol Agency

Division of Social Services
Department of Human Resources
American Samoa Government
Pago Pago, AS 96799
011-684-699-2696

EDUCATION OFFICE

Coordinator For Drug-Free Schools

Department of Education
Drug-Free Schools Program
American Samoa Government
P.O. Box 1923
Pago Pago, AS 96799
011-684-633-5244

Guam

POLICY OFFICES

Governor's Office

Office of the Governor
Executive Chambers
P.O. Box 2950
Agana, GU 96910
011-671-472-8931

CRIMINAL JUSTICE OFFICES

Attorney General's Office

Office of the Attorney General
Prosecution Division
2-200E Judicial Center
120 West O'Brien Drive
Agana, GU 96910
011-671-475-3406
E-mail: smaxwell@ns.gov.gu

Uniform Crime Reports Contact

Uniform Crime Reports
Guam Police Department
Planning, Research and
Development
Pedro's Plaza
287 West O'Brien Drive
Agana, GU 96910
011-671-472-8911

BJA Strategy Preparation Agency

Bureau of Planning
The Ricardo J. Bordallo
Governor's Complex
P.O. Box 2950
Agana, GU 96932
011-671-472-4201

Judicial Agency

Administrative Office of the Courts
Superior Court of Guam
Guam Judicial Center
120 West O'Brien Drive
Agana, GU 96910
011-671-475-3544

HEALTH OFFICES

RADAR Network Agency
Department of Mental Health and
  Substance Abuse
709 Governor Carlos G. Camacho
  Road
P.O. Box 9400
Tamuning, GU 96911
011-671-647-5441

HIV-Prevention Program
STD/HIV Supervisor
Bureau of Communicable Disease
  Control Unit
Department of Public Health and
  Social Services
P.O. Box 2816
Agana, GU 96932
011-671-734-2437

Drug and Alcohol Agency
Drug & Alcohol Treatment
  Services Branch
Department of Mental Health and
  Substance Abuse
790 Governor Carlos G. Camacho
  Road
Tamuning, GU 96911
011-671-647-5445/5440/5325

EDUCATION OFFICE

**Coordinator For Drug-Free
  Schools**
Department of Education
DFSC Coordinator
Guam Public School System
P.O. Box DE
Agana, GU 96910
011-671-472-8524 ext. 307

Northern Mariana Islands

STATE POLICY OFFICES

Governor's Office
Office of the Governor
Capitol Hill
Saipan, MP 96950
(670) 322-5191

STATE CRIMINAL JUSTICE OFFICES

Attorney General's Office
Attorney General
Administration Building
Capitol Hill
Saipan, MP 96950
(670) 322-4311

Law Enforcement Planning
Executive Director
Capitol Hill
P.O. Box 1133
Saipan, MP 96950
(670) 322-9350

Statistical Analysis Center
Criminal Justice Planning Agency
Commonwealth of the Northern
  Mariana Islands
Criminal Justice Statistical
  Analysis Center
P.O. Box 1133
Saipan, MP 96950
(670) 664-4550

Uniform Crime Reports Contact
Uniform Crime Report
Director of Public Safety
Civic Center
Saipan, MP 96950
(670) 234-6823

Judicial Agency
Commonwealth Supreme Court
Nauru Building, Second Floor
P.O. Box 2165
Saipan, MP 96950
(670) 234-5175

Corrections Agency
Director of Division of Corrections
Department of Public Safety
Commonwealth of the Northern
  Mariana Islands
P.O. Box 10007
Saipan, MP 96950
(670) 234-7254

Puerto Rico

POLICY OFFICES

Governor's Office
Office of the Governor
Public Safety Area
P.O. Box 902-0082
San Juan, PR 00902-0082
(787) 721-2840

Legislative Contact
Legislative Reference Library
Office of Legislative Services
P.O. Box 3986
San Juan, PR 00902-3986
(787) 723-4112

CRIMINAL JUSTICE OFFICES

Attorney General's Office
Attorney General
Department of Justice
P.O. Box 902192
San Juan, PR 00902-0192
(787) 721-7700

Law Enforcement Planning
Crime Commission
P.O. Box 82
San Juan, PR 00901
(787) 793-1234

Statistical Analysis Center
Criminal Justice Information
  Center
Statistical Analysis Center
Office of the Attorney General
601 Olimpo Street, Miramar
P.O. Box 192
San Juan, PR 00902
(787) 729-2445

Uniform Crime Reports Contact
Uniform Crime Reports
Statistics Division
Puerto Rico Police
P.O. Box 70166
San Juan, PR 00936-8166
(787) 793-1234

**BJA Strategy Preparation
   Agency**
Attorney General
Department of Justice
Commonwealth of Puerto Rico
P.O. Box 902192
San Juan, PR 00902
(787) 721-7700

Judicial Agency
Office of Court Administration
General Court of Justice
P.O. Box 190917, Hato Rey
   Station
Hato Rey, PR 00919
(787) 763-3358

HEALTH OFFICES

RADAR Network Agency
Department of Anti-Addiction
   Services
414 Barbosa Avenue
Hato Rey, PR 00918
(787) 767-5990

Drug and Alcohol Agency
Mental Health, Drug, and Alcohol
   Agency
Mental Health and Anti-addiction
   Services
Administration
P.O. Box 21414
San Juan, PR 00928-1414
(787) 764-3670

EDUCATION OFFICE

**Coordinator For Drug-Free
   Schools**
Department of Education
Office of Federal Affairs
P.O. Box 759
Hato Rey, PR 00919
(787) 759-8910

Virgin Islands

POLICY OFFICES

Governor's Office
Office of the Governor
Government House
St. Thomas, VI 00802
(340) 774-0001

Legislative Contact
Legislative Counsel's Office
Veterans Drive
Charlotte Amalie
St. Thomas, VI 00801
(340) 774-0739

Drug Program Coordinator
Law Enforcement Planning
   Commission
Office of the Governor
8172 Sub Base, Suite 3
St. Thomas, VI 00802-5803
(340) 774-6400

CRIMINAL JUSTICE OFFICES

Attorney General's Office
Department of Justice, 48B-50C
Gers Complex, 2nd Floor
St. Thomas, VI 00802
(340) 774-5666

Law Enforcement Planning
Law Enforcement Planning
   Commission
8172 Sub Base, Suite 3
St. Thomas, VI 00802-5803
(340) 774-6400

Statistical Analysis Center
Law Enforcement Planning
   Commission
8172 Sub Base, Suite 3
St. Thomas, VI 00802-5803
(340) 774-6400

Uniform Crime Reports Contact
Records Bureau Uniform Crime
   Reports
Virgin Islands Police Department
Criminal Justice Complex
Charlotte Amalie
St. Thomas, VI 00802
(340) 774-2211

**BJA Strategy Preparation
   Agency**
Law Enforcement Planning
   Commission
Office of the Governor
8172 Sub Base, Suite 3
St. Thomas, VI 00802-5803
(340) 774-6400

Judicial Agency
Administrative Office of the Courts
Territorial Court of the Virgin
   Islands
P.O. Box 70
Charlotte Amalie
St. Thomas, VI 00804
(340) 774-6680

Corrections Agency
Department of Justice
Bureau of Corrections
3008 Orange Grove
Christian Stead
St. Croix, VI 00820
(340) 773-6309

HEALTH OFFICES

RADAR Network Agency
Division of Mental Health
Prevention Unit
Charles Harwood Hospital
   Complex, Richmond
St. Croix, VI 00820
(340) 774-7700

HIV-Prevention Program
Department of Health
PO Box 1026
Christiansted
St. Croix, VI 00820
(340) 773-1059

Drug and Alcohol Agency
Division of Mental Health,
   Alcoholism and Drug
Dependency Services
Charles Harwood Memorial
   Hospital
Christian Stead
St. Croix, VI 00820
(340) 774-7400

EDUCATION OFFICE

**Coordinator For Drug-Free
   Schools**
Department of Education
44-46 Kongens Gade
Charlotte Amalie
St. Thomas, VI 00802
(340) 774-0100

APPENDIX III

State-by-State Directory of Drug Abuse and Alcoholism Treatment and Prevention Programs

INTRODUCTION

This directory is a compilation of U.S. public and private facilities responsible for providing alcoholism and drug-abuse treatment and prevention services. The information was collected by the Substance Abuse and Mental Health Administration (SAMHSA), Office of Applied Studies, and last published in print version in 1998. An online, searchable version is available at http://www.samhsa.gov

The directory is provided as a resource for program managers, treatment personnel, researchers, education officials, parents, and students interested in the location of such facilities. Licensed treatment centers in the Federated States of Micronesia, Guam, Puerto Rico, the Republic of Palau, and the Virgin Islands appear at the end of the list, starting on page 1796. Phone numbers have not been provided since they may change—check your local telephone directory for new listings or contact your information operator service for current listings.

ALABAMA

ALEXANDER CITY

Lighthouse of Tallapoosa County, Inc.
36 Franklin Street
Alexander City, AL 35010

ANNISTON

Anniston Fellowship House, Inc.
106 East 22nd Street
Anniston, AL 36201

Calhoun/Cleburne Mental Health Center New Directions
331 East 8th Street
Anniston, AL 36202

BIRMINGHAM

Alcoholism Recovery Services, Inc.
2701 Jefferson Avenue SW
Birmingham, AL 35211

Aletheia House, Inc.
201 Finley Avenue West
Birmingham, AL 35204

Birmingham Health Care for the Homeless
712 25th Street North
Birmingham, AL 35203

Fellowship House, Inc.
1625 12th Avenue South
Birmingham, AL 35205

Bradford Health Services
Birmingham Regional Office
Jefferson
631 Beacon Parkway West, Suite 211
Birmingham, AL 35209

Department of Veterans Affairs Medical Center
1717 11th Avenue South
Birmingham, AL 35205

Hill Crest Behavioral Health Services
Chemical Dependency Track
6869 5th Avenue South
Birmingham, AL 35212

Jefferson County Economic Opportunity Alcoholism Outreach/Aftercare Program
3040 Ensley Avenue
Birmingham, AL 35208

Oakmont Center
1915 Avenue H
Ensley
Birmingham, AL 35218

Saint Anne's Home, Inc.
2772 Hanover Circle
Birmingham, AL 35205

Tri-County Treatment Center
500 Gene Reed Road, Suite 220
Birmingham, AL 35215

University of Alabama Substance Abuse Programs
401 Beacon Parkway West
Birmingham, AL 35209

University of Alabama in Birmingham Hospital Center for Psychiatric Medicine
1713 6th Avenue South
Birmingham, AL 35294-0018

CALERA

Chilton/Shelby Mental Health Center Substance Abuse Division
1822 17th Street
Highway 25
Calera, AL 35040

CENTRE

Lifeline Services Inc.
Cherokee County Location
423 East Main Street
Centre, AL 35960

CLAYTON

Ventress Correctional Facility Substance Abuse Services
State Road 239
Clayton, AL 36016

DECATUR

Mental Health Center of North Central Alabama
Quest Recovery Center Substance Abuse Treatment
Highway 31 South
Decatur, AL 35601

DEMOPOLIS

West Alabama Mental Health Center Substance Abuse Program
1215 South Walnut Avenue
Demopolis, AL 36732

DOTHAN

Spectra Care
831 John D Odom Road
Dothan, AL 36303

FAIRHOPE

Baldwin County Mental Health Center
372 South Greeno Road
Fairhope, AL 36532

FLORENCE

Riverbend Center for Mental Health
635 West College Street
Florence, AL 35630

GADSDEN

Cherokee/Etowah/De Kalb Mental Health Center Substance Abuse Services
901 Goodyear Avenue
Gadsden, AL 35903

The Bridge, Inc.
3232 Lay Springs Road
Gadsden, AL 35901

GUNTERSVILLE

Marshall/Jackson Mental Health Authority
Mountain Lakes Behavioral Health Care
22165 U.S. Highway 431
Guntersville, AL 35976

HUNTSVILLE

Crestwood Medical Center of Huntsville Behavioral Services
1 Hospital Drive
Huntsville, AL 35801

Huntsville Metro Treatment Center
2227 Drake Avenue
Suite 10-D
Huntsville, AL 35805

Madison County Mental Health Center New Horizons Recovery Center
600 Saint Clair Street
Number 9 Suite 23
Huntsville, AL 35801

The Pathfinder, Inc.
3104 Ivy Avenue SW
Huntsville, AL 35805

JASPER

Northwest Alabama Mental Health Center
1100 7 Avenue
Jasper, AL 35501

MAXWELL AFB

Maxwell Air Force Base Substance Abuse Program
42MDOS/SGOMH
330 Kirkpatrick Avenue E
Maxwell AFB, AL 36113-6334

MOBILE

Bradford Health Services Mobile Outreach
1000 Hillcrest Road, Suite 304
Mobile, AL 36695

Dauphin Way Lodge
1009 Dauphin Street
Mobile, AL 36604

ECD Program
2950 Springhill Avenue
Mobile, AL 36607

Oasis
4211 Government Blvd.
Mobile, AL 36693

MONTGOMERY

Bradford Health Services Montgomery Outreach
100 Mendel Parkway
Montgomery AL, 36117

Chemical Addictions Program, Inc.
1153 Air Base Boulevard
Montgomery, AL 36108

Jackson Hospital Psychiatric Unit
1235 Forest Avenue
Montgomery, AL 36106

Lighthouse Counseling Center, Inc. Intensive Outpatient Unit
1415 East South Boulevard
Montgomery, AL 36116

Meadhaven Addictive Disease Program
2105 East South Boulevard
Montgomery, AL 36116

Montgomery Metro Treatment Center
4303 Norman Bridge Road
Montgomery, AL 36105

MUSCLE SHOALS

Shoals Treatment Center
520 Louise Street
Muscle Shoals, AL 35661

PELHAM

Bradford Health Services
Oak Mountain Shelby
2280 Highway 35 South
Pelham, AL 35124

PHENIX CITY

Lifeline Services Inc.
Russell County Location
1602 Broad Street
Phenix City, AL 36867

ROANOKE

Self Discovery Inc.
59928 Highway 22
Roanoke AL 36274

ROGERSVILLE

The Freedom House
Route 4
Rogersville, AL 35652

RUSSELLVILLE

**Sunrise Lodge Substance Abuse
Treatment Center**
1163 Washington Avenue SW
Russellville, AL 35653

SELMA

**Cahaba Cares Substance Abuse
Services**
912 Jeff Davis Avenue
Selma, AL 36701

SPANISH FORT

The Shoulder
4901 Battleship Parkway
Spanish Fort, AL 36577

SYLACAUGA

Cheaha Regional Mental Health
Mental Retardation Board Inc.
1721 Old Birmingham Highway
Sylacauga, AL 35150

TUSCALOOSA

**Indian Rivers Mental Health
Center Alcohol and Drug
Abuse Program**
505 19 Avenue
Tuscaloosa, AL 35401

Phoenix House, Inc.
700 35 Avenue
Tuscaloosa, AL 35401

Tuscaloosa Treatment Center
535 River Road NE
Suite G3
Tuscaloosa, AL 35404

**Veterans Affairs Primary Car
Substance Abuse Clinic**
3701 Loop Road East
Tuscaloosa, AL 35404

TUSKEGEE

**Central Alabama Veteran
Health Care System**
2400 Hospital Road
Tuskegee, AL 36083

WARRIOR

Bradford Health Services
Warrior Lodge/Jefferson
1189 Allbritton Road
Warrior, AL 35180

WETUMPKA

**Bradford Health Services at
Elmore Community Hospital**
500 Hospital Drive
Wetumpka, AL 36092

ALASKA

ANCHORAGE

Akeela Treatment Services
2805 Bering Street, Suite 4
Anchorage, AK 99503

**Alaska Human Services Inc.
Outpatient Alcohol/Substance
Abuse Treatment Program**
4050 Lake Otis Parkway
Suite 111
Anchorage, AK 99508

**Alaska North Addictions
Recovery Center**
4330 Bragaw Street
Anchorage, AK 99508

**Booth Memorial Youth and
Family Services**
3600 East 20th Avenue
Anchorage, AK 99508

**Charter North Behavioral
Health System**
2530 Debarr Road
Anchorage, AK 99508

Genesis House Inc.
2825 West 42nd Place
Anchorage, AK 99517

**Narcotic Drug Treatment
Center, Inc. Center for Drug
Problems**
520 East 4th Avenue
Suite 102
Anchorage, AK 99501

Pacific Rim Counseling Inc.
4141 B Street, Suite 210
Anchorage, AK 99503

**Providence Alaska Medical
Center Project Breakthrough**
2401 East 42nd Avenue, Suite 103
Anchorage, AK 99508

RITE Inc.
301 East Fireweed Lane
Suite 102
Anchorage, AK 99503

Salvation Army Clitheroe Center
1709 South Bragaw Street
Point Woronzof/West End Road,
Suite B
Anchorage, AK 99503

Southcentral Foundation
Dena A Coy
3916 East 9th Avenue
Anchorage, AK 99508

Veterans Affairs and ROC Anchorage
2925 Debarr Road, Suite 116
Anchorage, AK 99508

Volunteers of America ARCH/ ASSIST
441 West 5th Street
Suite 301
Anchorage, AK 99501

ANIAK

Kuskokwim Native Association Community Counseling Program
P.O. Box 155
Aniak, AK 99557

BARROW

North Slope Borough Health Substance Abuse Treatment Services
579 Kingosak Street
Barrow, AK 99723

COPPER CENTER

Copper River Mental Health Center Substance Abuse Services
Mile 104 Old Richardson Highway
Copper Center, AK 99573

CORDOVA

Sound Alternatives
Cordova Community Medical Center
602 Chase Avenue
Cordova, AK 99574

DILLINGHAM

Bristol Bay Area Health Corporation Alcohol/Drug Abuse Program
Dillingham, AK 99576

DUTCH HARBOR

Aleutian Counseling Center
Dutch Harbor, AK 99692

EAGLE RIVER

Volunteers of America of Alaska ARCH
HC 85
Eagle River, AK 99577

EIELSON AFB

Eielson Air Force Base Substance Abuse Program
354 MDOS/SGOMH
3349 Central Avenue, Suite 1
Eielson AFB, AK 99702-2325

ELMENDORF AFB

Elmendorf AFB Substance Abuse Office
3 MDOS/SGOMH
24800 Hospital Drive
Elmendorf AFB, AK 99506

FAIRBANKS

Fairbanks Memorial Hospital Family Recovery Center
1650 Cowles Street
Fairbanks, AK 99701

Graf Rheeneenhaanjii Substance Abuse Services
2550 Lawlor Road
Fairbanks, AK 99701

Regional Center for Alcohol and other Addictions
3100 South Cushman Street
Fairbanks, AK 99707

Tanana Chiefs Conference Inc. Old Minto Recovery Camp
1221 1st Avenue, Suite 600
Fairbanks, AK 99707

Tanana Chiefs Conference, Inc. Ukon Tanana Counseling Servces
1302 21st Avenue
Fairbanks, AK 99701

FORT RICHARDSON

Community Counseling Center
600 Richardson Drive
Fort Richardson, AK 99505

FORT WAINWRIGHT

Fort Wainwright Alcohol and Drug Abuse Prevention Control Program (ADAPCP)
1060 Gaffney Road, Suite 6600
MCUC/CCC Building 1064
Fort Wainwright, AK 99703

HEALY

Railbelt Mental Health and Addiction
Dry Creek and Coal Street
Healy, AK 99743

JUNEAU

Gastineau Human Services
5597 Aisek Street
Juneau, AK 99801

Tongass Community Counseling Center
222 Seward Street, Suite 202
Juneau, AK 99801

KENAI

Cook Inlet Council on Alcohol and Drug Abuse
10200 Kenai Spur Highway
Kenai, AK 99611

Kenaitze Indian Tribe
Nakenu
150 North Willow Street
Kenai, AK 99611

KETCHIKAN

Gateway Center for Human Services Substance Abuse Services Division
3050 5th Avenue
Ketchikan, AK 99901

Ketchikan General Hospital Recovery Center
126 Washington Street
Ketchikan, AK 99901

Ketchikan Indian Corporation
355 Carlanna Lake Road
Ketchikan, AK 99901

KODIAK

Kodiak Council on Alcoholism, Inc.
115 Mill bay Road
Kodiak, AK 99615

KOTZEBUE

Maniilaq Addictions and Support
Maniilaq Association
Frank Ferguson Building
D and E Wings
Kotzebue, AK 99752

MCGRATH

Four Rivers Counseling Services
McGrath/Anvik Education MH
   Association
229 Joaquin Street
McGrath, AK 99627

METLAKATLA

Annette Island Service Unit
Family Services
Metlakatla, AK 99926

NOME

Northern Lights Recovery Center
5 Avenue and Division Streets
Community Health Services
   Building
Nome, AK 99762

PETERSBURG

Changing Tides Counseling Services
201 North Nordic Street
Suites 204 and 205
Petersburg, AK 99833

SAINT PAUL ISLAND

Pribilof Counseling Center
Saint Paul Island, AK 99660

SAND POINT

Eastern Aleutian Tirbes Inc.
Main Street
Sand Point, AK 99661

SELDOVIA

Seldovia Village Tribe/SKIAP
274 Main Street
Seldovia, AK 99663-0197

SEWARD

Seward Life Action Council
504 Adams Street
Seward, AK 99664

SITKA

Ravens Way/SEARHC Adolescent Residential Treatment Program
222 Tongass Drive
Sitka, AK 99835

Sitka Prevention and Treatment Services Inc.
509 Lincoln Street
Sitka, AK 99835

Southeast Alaska Regional Health Consortium Community Family Services Program
222 Tongass Avenue
Sitka, AK 99835

TOK

Upper Tanana Alcohol Program
Tok Clinic Building
Tok Cut-Off
Tok, AK 99780

VALDEZ

Valdez Counseling Center
337 Egan Avenue
Valdez, AK 99686

WASILLA

Alaska Addiction Rehab Services
Nugens Ranch
3701 Palmer-Wasilla Highway
Wasilla, AK 99687

MAT/SU Recovery Center Inc.
2801 Bogard Road
Wasilla, AK 99654

WRANGELL

Avenues
406 Alaska Avenue
Wrangell, AK 99929

AMERICAN SAMOA

PAGO PAGO

**LBJ Tropical Medical Center
Alcohol and Drug Program
Human Services Clinic**
Pago Pago, AS 96799

ARIZONA

APACHE JUNCTION

**SMMHC Inc. Mental Health
Center/Substance Abuse
Services**
564 North Idaho Road, Suite 9
Apache Junction, AZ 85220

BENSON

**Southeastern Arizona
Behavioral Health Services
(SEABHS)**
Administrative Unit
590 South Ocotillo Avenue
Benson, AZ 85602

BULLHEAD CITY

**Mohave Mental Health Clinic
Outpatient and Day
Treatment**
2135 Highway 95
Suites 125 and 241
Bullhead City, AZ 86442

CAMP VERDE

**Camp Verde Yavapai/Apache
Alcohol/Substance Abuse
Program**
Camp Verde, AZ 86322

**Verde Valley Guidance Clinic
Inc.**
497 Main Street, Suite 4
Camp Verde, AZ 86322

CASA GRANDE

Against Abuse Inc.
Casa Grande, AZ 95230-0733

**Behavioral Health Agency of
Central Arizona**
120 West Main Street
Casa Grande, AZ 85222-4820

**PGBHA BHACA Casa Grande
Outpatient**
120 West Main Street
Casa Grande, AZ 85222

PGBHA Helping Associates Inc.
1901 North Trekell Road, Suite A
Casa Grande, AZ 85222

CHANDLER

Centro de Amistad Inc
100 West Boston Street, Suite 5
Chandler, AZ 85224

**Chandler Valley Hope and Drug
Treatment Center**
501 North Washington Street
Chandler, AZ 85225

COTTONWOOD

**Verde Valley Guidance Clinic,
Inc.**
19 East Beech Street
Cottonwood, AZ 86326

DILKON

Dilcon Agency
Department of Behavioral Health
Services
Old Preschool Building
Next Chapter House
Dilkon, AZ 86047

ELOY

**PGBHA Pinal County Hispanic
Council**
712 North Main Street
Eloy, AZ 85231

FLAGSTAFF

**Aspen Hill Behavioral Health
Systems**
305 West Forest Avenue
Flagstaff, AZ 86001

Community Medical Services
2559 East 7th Avenue
Flagstaff, AZ 86004

The Guidance Center
2187 North Vickey Street
Flagstaff, AZ 86004

GLENDALE

**Community Care Network (CCN)
Jewish Family and Children's
Services**
6376 West Bell Road
Glendale, AZ 85308

Maverick House
7022 North 48th Avenue
Glendale, AZ 85301

**Thunderbird Samaritan
Behavioral Health**
5555 West Thunderbird Road
Glendale, AZ 85306

GREEN VALLEY

La Frontera Center
BLNA
1151 South La Canada
Suite 105
Green Valley, AZ 85614

HOLBROOK

Community Counseling Centers, Inc.
105 North 5th Avenue
Holbrook, AZ 86025

KAYENTA

Kayenta outpatient Treatment Center
Kayenta, AZ 86033

KEARNY

Copper Community Resource and Development Inc.
1116 Tilbury Street
Kearny, AZ 85237

KINGMAN

Mohave Mental Health Clinic Substance Abuse Services
1750 Beverly Street
Kingman, AZ 86401

LAKE HAVASU CITY

Mohave Mental Health Clinic
Substance Abuse Services
2187 Swanson Street
Lake Havasu City, AZ 86403

LUKE AFB

Luke Air Force Base Substance Abuse Program
52 MDOS/SGOMH
7219 North Litchfield Road
Luke AFB, AZ 85309-1525

Mental Health Clinic Substance Abuse Control
56 MDOS/SGOMH
7219 North Litchfield Road
Luke AFB, AZ 85309-1525

MESA

Centro de Amistad, Inc. Mesa Office
734 East Broadway
Suite C
Mesa, AZ 85204

East Valley Addiction Council Inc.
554 South Bellview Street
Mesa, AZ 85204

East Valley Catholic Social Services
430 North Dobson Road
Mesa, AZ 85204

New Hope Behavioral Health Center, Inc.
6550 Broadway
Suite 101
Mesa, AZ 85208

Prehab of Arizona, Inc.
Center for Family Enrichment
1655 East University Drive
Mesa, AZ 85203

Helaman House
2613 South Power Road
Mesa, AZ 85206

Homestead Residence
1131 East University Drive
Mesa, AZ 85203

Samaritan Behavioral Health Desert
2225 West Southern Avenue
Mesa, AZ 85202

Women in New Recovery
540 West 1st Street
Mesa, AZ 85202

MORENCI

SEABHS
Administrative Office
Burro Alley and Coronado Boulevard
Morenci, AZ 85540

NOGALES

Santa Cruz Family Guidance Center Division Inc.
489 North Arroyo Boulevard
Nogales, AZ 85621

ORACLE

PGBHA Tri Community Resource Center
98 Mount Lemmon Road
Oracle, AZ 85623

PAGE

Kaibeto Outpatient Treatment Center
DBHS
337 North Navajo Street
Page, AZ 86040

PARKER

Colorado River Indian Tribes Behavioral Health Services
Route 1
Parker, AZ 85344

New Life Guidance Center
1200 Arizona Avenue
Parker, AZ 85344

Public Health Service
Indian Hospital Substance Abuse Services
Route 1
Parker, AZ 85344

PAYSON

Rim Guidance Center
404 West Aero Drive
Payson, AZ 85547

PEACH SPRINGS

Hualapai Health Department Alcoholism and Drug Abuse Program
960 Rodeo Way
Peach Springs, AZ 86434

PHOENIX

Behavioral Systems Southwest
2846 East Roosevelt Street
Phoenix, AZ 85008

Calvary Rehabilitation Center
720 East Montebello Avenue
Phoenix, AZ 85014

**Carl T Hayden VA Medical
Center Substance Abuse
Treatment Program**
650 East Indian School Road,
Suite 11-A9
Phoenix, AZ 85012

Casa De Amigas
1648 West Cotler Street, Suite 8
Phoenix, AZ 85015

Chicanos por la Causa, Inc.
Centro de la Familia
4622 West Indian School Road,
Suite D-12
Phoenix, AZ 85009

Community Medical Services
Larkspur Medical Center
12426 North 28th Drive
Phoenix, 85029

Corazon/CPLC
3639 West Lincoln Street
Phoenix, AZ 85009

Crossroads
1845 East Ocotillo Road
Phoenix, AZ 85016

**Drug and Alcohol Treatment
Institute Clarence Lawson
Foundation**
2230 North 24th Street
Phoenix, AZ 85008

Ebony House, Inc.
6222 South 13th Street
Phoenix, AZ 85040

Family Service Agency
1530 East Flower Street
Phoenix, AZ 85014

Hohokam Room
1501 East Washington Street
Phoenix, AZ 85034

Indian Rehabilitation, Inc.
650 North 2nd Avenue
Phoenix, AZ 85003

**Intensive Treatment Systems
Inc.**
651 West Coolidge Street
Phoenix, AZ 85013

**Jewish Family and Children's
Service**
2033 North 7th Street
Phoenix, AZ 85006

**National Council on Alcohol
and Drug Dependency/
Central and Northern Arizona**
2701 North 16 Street
Suite 103
Phoenix, AZ 85006

New Arizona Family I
3301 East Pinchot Avenue
Phoenix, AZ 85018

**New Arizona Family II SMI Dial
Diagnosis Program**
302 East Southern Avenue
Phoenix, AZ 85040

New Life for Girls
6216 North 27th Avenue
Phoenix, AZ 85017

**Phoenix LARC Meta Center
Public Inebriate Program**
2770 East Van Buren Street
Phoenix, AZ 85008

Phoenix Indian Center
2601 North 3rd Street
Suite 100
Phoenix, AZ 85004

Progress Valley Phoenix
4430 North 23rd Avenue
Phoenix, AZ 85015

**Saint Luke's Behavioral Health
Center**
1800 East Van Buren Street
Phoenix, AZ 85006

Salvation Army Recovery Center
2707 East Van Buren Street
Treatment Center
Phoenix, AZ 85008

Adult Rehabilitation Center
1625 South Central Avenue
Phoenix, AZ 85004

**Southwest Behavioral Health
Inc.**
1714 East Broadway
Phoenix, AZ 85040

1424 South 7th Avenue
Phoenix, AZ 85007

5116 East Thomas Road
Phoenix, AZ 85018

Terros, Inc.
320 East Virginia Street
Phoenix, AZ 85004

**Treatment Assessment
Screening Center**
TASC Inc.
2234 North 7th Street, Suite A
Phoenix, AZ 85006

**Valle Del Sol, Inc. Behavioral
Health Program**
1209 South First Avenue
Phoenix, AZ 85003

PRESCOTT

Veterans' Affairs Medical Center
500 Highway 89 North, Room 208
Prescott, AZ 86313

West Yavapai Guidance Clinic
Hillside Center
642 Dameron Drive
Prescott, AZ 86301

**Yavapai/Prescott Tribe Social
Services Department**
530 East Merritt Street
Prescott, AZ 86301

SACATON

**Gila River Indian Community
Alcohol and Drug Abuse
Program**
315 West Casa Blanca Road
Sacaton, AZ 85247

SAFFORD

SEABHS Graham/Greenlee Counseling Center
Safford Outpatient
620 Central Avenue
Safford, AZ 85546

SAINT JOHNS

Little Colorado Behavioral Health Center, Inc.
470 West Cleveland Street
Saint Johns, AZ 85936

SAN CARLOS

San Carlos Apache Tribe Alcohol Program
San Carlos, AZ 85550

SCOTTSDALE

Jewish Family and Children's Services
7770 East Roosevelt Street
Scottsdale, AZ 85257

New Foundation
Scottsdale, AZ 85271

Salt River Pima/Maricopa Behavioral Health Program
10005 East Osborn Road
Scottsdale, AZ 85256

Samaritan Behavioral Health
7575 East Earl Drive
Scottsdale, AZ 85251

Teen Ranch
5718 East Sharron Drive
Scottsdale, AZ 85254

SECOND MESA

Hopi Behavioral Health and Social Services Program
Second Mesa, AZ 86043

SEDONA

Verde Valley Guidance Clinic Inc.
2880 Hopi Drive
Sedona, AZ 86336

SELLS

Tohono Oodham Human Services Alcoholism and Substance Abuse Branch
Sells, AZ 85634

SHOW LOW

Community Counseling Centers
Outpatient Unit
2350 Show Low Lake Road
Show Low, AZ 85901

SIERRA VISTA

SEABHS Coronado Behavioral Health Division Sierra Vista Outpatient
185 South Moorman Street
Sierra Vista, AZ 85635

SOMERTON

Cocopah Alcohol and Drug Abuse Prevention Program
County 15th and Avenue G
Somerton, AZ 85350

SPRINGERVILLE

Little Colorado Behavioral Health Center, Inc.
50 North Hopi Street
Springerville, AZ 85938

TEMPE

Center for Behavioral Health
Special Services
2123 East Southern Avenue
Suite 2
Tempe, AZ 85282

Contact
1400 East Southern Street
Suite 301
Tempe, AZ 85282

Tempe Saint Luke's Hospital
1500 South Mill Avenue
Tempe, AZ 85281

Valle Del Sol, Inc. East Clinic
509 South Rockford Drive
Tempe, AZ 85281

TUBA CITY

Tuba City Outpatient Treatment Center Behavioral Health Services/DBHS
Main Street
Building 25
Tuba City, AZ 86045

TUCSON

Amity, Inc.
10500 East Tanque Verde Road
Tucson, AZ 85749

CODAC Behavioral Health Services of Pima County, Inc.
CODAC Counseling Center
333 West Fort Lowell Street
Tucson, AZ 85705

Wildflowers
700 North 7th Avenue
Tucson, AZ 85705

Compass Health Care
2475 North Jack Rabbit Street
Tucson, AZ 85745

Cope Behavioral Services
101 South Stone Street, Suite 200
Tucson, AZ 85745

Cottonwood de Tucson
4110 Sweetwater Drive
Tucson, AZ 85745

Davis Monthan Air Force Base ADPB
355 MDOS/SGOHA
Tucson, AZ 85707

Haven, Inc.
1107 East Adelaide Drive
Tucson, AZ 85719

La Frontera Center
East Clinic
2222 North Craycroft Road
Suite 120
Tucson, AZ 85712

Hope Center
260 South Scott Street
Tucson, AZ 85701

Substance Abuse Outpatient Service
502 West 29th Street
Tucson, AZ 85711

**Mark Youth and Family Care
Campus Inc.**
4653 East Pima Street
Tucson, AZ 85712

**Pascua Yaqui Chemical
Dependency Program**
7490 south Camino De Oeste
Tucson, AZ 85746

**Portable Prep Behavioral
Health Services Alcoholism
Treatment Unit**
806 East 46th Street
Tucson, AZ 85713

**Saint Josephs Hospital O'Reilly
Care Center**
350 North Wilmont Road
Tucson, AZ 8711

**Salvation Army Adult
Rehabilitation Center**
2717 South 6th Avenue
Tucson, AZ 85713

Sierra Tucson LLC
Lago Del Oro Parkway
Tucson, AZ 85739

**Tucson Alcoholic Recovery
Home, Inc.**
1809 East 23 Street
Tucson, AZ 85713

**Veterans Affairs Medical Center
Substance Abuse Program**
3601 South 6th Avenue
Tucson, AZ 85723

Westcenter
2105 East Allen Road
Tucson, AZ 85719

WHITERIVER

Rainbow Center
White Mountain Apache Tribe
White River, AZ 85941

WICKENBURG

Meadows Holdings
1655 North Tegner Road
Wickenburg, AZ 85390

WILLIAMS

The Guidance Center, Inc.
301 South 7th Street
Williams, AZ 86046

WINSLOW

**Community Counseling Centers
Outpatient Clinic**
211 East 3rd Street
Winslow, AZ 86047

**Navajo Nation Dilkon
Outpatient Treatment Center**
Dilkon Chapter House
Winslow, AZ 86047

ARKANSAS

ARKADELPHIA

Quapaw House, Inc.
401 Crittenden Street
Arkadelphia, AR 71923-6139

BENTON

**Counseling Clinic, Inc.
Outpatient Abuse Program**
307 East Servier Street
Benton, AR 72015

**Department of Corrections
Benton Unit Substance Abuse
Treatment Program**
6701 Highway 67
Benton, AR 72015

BRICKEYS

East Arkansas Regional Unit
Route 1 Highway 131
Brickeys, AR 72320

CALICO ROCK

SATP North Central Unit
HC 62
Calico Rock, AR 72519

CAMDEN

**Ouachita County Hospital
Chemical Dependency Unit**
638 California Street
Camden, AR 71701

CLARKSVILLE

Counseling Associates
1021 Poplar Street
Clarksville, AR 72830-4428

CONWAY

Counseling Associates, Inc.
350 Salem Road Suite 1
Conway, AR 72032-6135

DERMOTT

**Department of Corrections
Delta Reg Unit Substance
Abuse Treatment Program**
880 East Gaines Street
Dermott, AR 71638

EL DORADO

**South Arkansas Regional Health
Center Recovery Center**
710 West Grove Street
El Dorado, AR 71730

FAYETTEVILLE

**Charter Behavioral Health
Systems of Northwest
Arkansas**
4253 Crossover Road
Fayetteville, AR 72703

Veterans Affairs Medical Center
1100 North College Street 116-A
Fayetteville, AR 72703

FORT SMITH

Gateway House, Inc. June Bailey Center
3900 North Armour Avenue
Fort Smith, AR 72904

Harbor House, Inc.
615 North 19th Street
Fort Smith, AR 72901

Harbor View Mercy Hospital Chemical Dependency Program
10301 Mayo Drive
Fort Smith, AR 72917

Horizon
3113 South 70th Street
Fort Smith, AR 72903

Sparks Care for Alcoholic and Drug Addiction
1311 South I Street
Fort Smith, AR 72901

Western Arkansas Counseling and Guidance Center/Horizon Adolescent Program
3113 South 70th Street
Fort Smith, AR 72903

GASSVILLE

Omart Inc
116 Snowball Drive
Gassville, AR 72635

GRADY

Dept. of Correction/Cummins Unit Substance Abuse Treatment Program (SATP)
Grady, AR 71644

Dept. of Correction/Cummins Unit Substance Abuse Treatment Program (SATP)
Grady, AR 71644

Dept. of Correction/Varner Unit Substance Abuse Treatment Program (SATP)
Grady, AR 71644

HARRISON

Omart
218 East Ridge Avenue
Harrison, AR 72601-4307

HOPE

Southwest Arkansas Counseling and Mental Health Center
201 North 20th Street
Hope, AR 71801

HOT SPRINGS

Quapaw House, Inc.
812 Mount Pine Road
Hot Springs, AR 71913

HOT SPRINGS NATIONAL PARK

Barbs Place
276 Linden Avenue
Hot Springs National Park, AR 71901-3308

JONESBORO

Crowleys Ridge Development Council Northeast Arkansas Womens Recovery
417 West Jefferson Street
Jonesboro, AR 72401

Mid/South Health Systems
2920 McClellan Drive
Jonesboro, AR 72401

Saint Bernards Behavioral Health
Substance Abuse Treatment Unit
2712 East Johnson Avenue
Jonesboro, AR 72401

LITTLE ROCK

Addiction Treatment Centers
2021 Main Street
Little Rock, AR 72206

BHC Pinnacle Pointe Hospital Substance Abuse Services
11501 Financial Center Parkway
Little Rock, AR 72211

Baptist Medicla Center
9601 Interstate 630 Exit 7
Little Rock, AR 72205

Catar Clinic
1401 South University Avenue
Little Rock, AR 72204

Gyst House
8101 Frenchman Lane
Little Rock, AR 72219

Living Hope Institute
600 South McKinley Street
Suite 400
Little Rock, AR 72205-5583

Serenity Park, Inc.
2801 Roosevelt Road
Little Rock, AR 72204

Mid Arkansas Substance Abuse Services
4601 West 7th Street
Little Rock, AR 72205

Recovery 2005, Inc.
1920 South Broadway
Little Rock, AR 72204

Serenity Park, Inc.
2801 Roosevelt Road
Little Rock, AR 72204

Supervised Treatment and Education Program
715 West 2nd Street
Little Rock, AR 72201

UAMS/Substance Abuse Treatment Clinic
4313 West Markham Street Unit 3
Lower North Side
Little Rock, AR 72205

Univ of Arkansas for Medical Sciences Arkansas Cares
5821 West 20th Street
Little Rock, AR 72204

Women and Childrens Recovery Center Arkansas CARES
2002 South Fillmore Street
Cottage 6
Little Rock, AR 72204-4909

LUXURA

Department of Corrections Mississippi County Work Release
Luxura, AR 72358

MAUMELLE

Charter Behavioral Health Systems
1601 Murphy Drive
Maumelle, AR 72113

The Bridgeway
21 Bridgeway Road
Maumelle, AR 72113

MOUNTAIN HOME

Ozark Counseling Services
8 Medical Plaza
Mountain Home, AR 72653

NORTH LITTLE ROCK

Central Arkansas Veterans Healthcare Special Treatment Section
2300 Fort Roots Drive
North Little Rock Division
North Little Rock, AR 72214

Family Service Agency of Central Arkansas
628 West Broadway, Suite 300
North Little Rock, AR 72114

Riverbend Recovery Center
1201 River Road
North Little Rock, AR 72114

Central Arkansas Veterans Healthcare Special Treatment Section
2300 Fort Roots Drive
North Little Rock Division
North Little Rock, AR 72114

PARAGOULD

Crowley's Ridge Development Council Northeast Arkansas Regional Recovery Center
5882 Highway 135 South
Paragould, AR 72401

PARIS

Western Arkansas Counseling
415 South 6th Street
Paris, AR 72855-4511

PINE BLUFF

Dept. of Corrections
8001 West 7th Street
Pine Bluff, AR 71603

Human Development and Research Services, Inc.
6841 West 13th Street
Pine Bluff, AR 71602

Human Development and Research Services Pregnant Parenting Women Living Center
3100 West 34th Avenue
Pine Bluff, AR 71603-5504

Human Development and Research Services
2801 Olive Street, Suite 23
Pine Bluff, AR 71611

Southeast Arkansas Behavioral Health Care, Inc.
2500 Rike Drive
Pine Bluff, AR 71613

POCAHONTAS

Black River Area Development Corp. Substance Abuse Treatment Program
1403 Hospital Drive
Pocahontas, AR 72455

RUSSELLVILLE

Arkansas River Valley Area Council Freedom House
400 Lake Front Drive
Russellville, AR 72801

Counseling Associates/ Russellville
110 Skyline Drive
Russellville, AR 72802

SEARCY

Wilbur D. Mills Center
3204 East Moore Avenue
Searcy, AR 72143

SPRINGDALE

A Little Bit of Recovery
640 North Mill Street
Springdale, AR 72764

Decision Point, Inc.
301 Holcomb Street
Springdale, AR 72764

Ozark Guidance Center
219 South Thompson Street
Springdale, AR 72766-6430

TEXARKANA

Southwest Arkansas Counseling Mental Health Center, Inc
2904 Arkansas Boulevard
Texarkana, AR 71854

TUCKER

Arkansas Department of Corrections Tucker Maximum Security Unit
2501 State Farm Road
Tucker, AR 72168

WRIGHTSVILLE

Arkansas Department of Correction Boot Camp
Wrightsville, AR 72183

CALIFORNIA

ACTON

Department of Health Services Acton Rehabilitation Center
30500 Arrastre Canyon Road
Acton, CA 93510

ALAMEDA

Xanthos
1335 Park Avenue
Alameda, CA 94501

ALHAMBRA

San Gabriel Valley Driver Improvement
25 South Raymond Avenue
Suite 301
Alhambra, CA 91801

ALISO VIEJO

Orange County Health Care Agency Aliso Viejo Alcohol/ Drug Abuse Servicess
5 Mareblu Street Suite 100
Aliso Viejo, CA 92656

ALTURAS

Modoc County alcohol and Drug Services
128 Henderson Street
Alturas, CA 96101

ANAHEIM

California Hispanic Commission on Alcohol/Drug Abuse
Casa Elena
832 South Anaheim Boulevard
Anaheim, CA 92805

Counseling Concepts
1815 East Center Street
Anaheim, CA 92805

Hope House
707 North Anaheim Boulevard
Anaheim, CA 92805

Oasis Counseling Centers
500 Melissa Street
Barstow, CA 92311

West Coast Detox
956 South Flore Street
Anaheim, CA 92805

Western Medical Center
1025 South Anaheim Boulevard
Anaheim, CA 92805

ANGELS CAMP

Changing Echoes
7632 Pool Station Road
Angels Camp, CA 95222

ANTIOCH

Criminal Justice Service, East Location
2400 Sycamore Drive
Suite 36
Antioch, CA 94509

Reach Project
1915 D Street
Antioch, CA 94509

APPLE VALLEY

Starting Point
11726 Deep Creek Road
Apple Valley, CA 92308

APTOS

Acacia Associates
9057 Soquel Drive
Suite E
Aptos, CA 95003

ARCATA

Mad River Community Hospital/ Chemical Dependency
3800 Janes Road
Arcata, CA 95521

ARROYO GRANDE

Life Steps Pasos De Vida
1431 Pomeroy Road
Arroyo Grande, CA 93420

San Luis Obispo County Drug and Alcohol Services
1106 Grand Avenue
Arroyo Grande, CA 93420

ARVIN

Traffic and Alcohol Awareness School of Kern (TAASK)
525 Bear Mountain Boulevard
Arvin, CA 93203

ATASCADERO

Aegis Medical Systems, Inc.
6500 Morro Road
Suite D
Atascadero, CA 93422

San Luis Obispo County Drug and Alcohol Services
3556 El Camino Real
Atascadero, CA 93422

ATWATER

Community and Social Model Advocates Tranquility Village
599 Mendocino Court
Atwater, CA 95301

AUBURN

Eagle Recovery Programs
12183 Locksley Lane
Auburn, CA 95602

Pacific Educational Services
11795 Education Street, Suite 220
Auburn, CA 95603

Sierra Council on Alcohol and Drug Dependency Auburn Service Center
610 Auburn Ravine Road
Suite A
Auburn, CA 95603

South Placer Residential Treatment Program
11417 D Avenue
Auburn, CA 95603

Sierra Family Services/Auburn
991 Lincoln Way
Auburn, CA 95603

AZUSA

Social Model Recovery Systems River Community
23701 East Fork Road
Azusa, CA 91702

Stepping Stones Home Colby House II
18417 Orkney Street
Azusa, CA 91702

BAKERSFIELD

Aegis Medical Systems, Inc.
1018 21st Street
Bakersfield, CA 93301

Citizens for the Betterment of Community and Country
Capistrano Women
3316 Laverne Street
Bakersfield, CA 93309

Jasons Retreat
504 Bernard Street
Bakersfield, CA 93305

Community Service Organization (CSO) Brotherhood
715 Lake Street
Bakersfield, CA 93305

Desert Counseling
Teen Recovery Program
1617 30th Street
Bakersfield, CA 93301

Womens Services
2913 South H Street
Bakersfield, CA 93304

Ebony Counseling Center
1301 California Avenue
Bakersfield, CA 93304

Family and Substance Abuse Counseling Agency
1009 Chester Avenue
Bakersfield, CA 93301

Kern County Hispanic Commission on Alcohol/Drug Abuse
Casa Serena
2300 18th Street
Bakersfield, CA 93303

Kern County Dept. of Mental Health Services Judicial Services
1401 L Street
Bakersfield, CA 93301

Recovery Network Biofeedback Center
2100 24th Street Suite 4
Bakersfield, CA 93301

Salvation Army Adult Rehabilitation Center
200 19th Street
Bakersfield, CA 93301

Sierra Tribal Consortium
1527 19th Street Suite 418
Bakersfield, CA 93301

Substance Abuse Alternatives
1101 Union Avenue Suite 100
Bakersfield, CA 93304

Traffic and Alcohol Awareness School of Kern (TAASK)
324 Oak Street, Suite A
Bakersfield, CA 93304

Vinesman Ponderosa Christian Recovery Ranch
3231 East Panoma Lane
Bakersfield, CA 93307

BALDWIN PARK

Aegis Medical Systems, Inc.
14418 East Pacific Avenue
Baldwin Park, CA 91706

Ettie Lee Homes
4100 Baldwin Park Boulevard
Baldwin Park, CA 91706

Industry Community Interface Enterprises
13922 East Ramona Street
Suite B
Baldwin Park, CA 91706

BANNING

Soroptomist House of Hope
628 8th Street
Banning, CA 92220

Koalacare of California Ace Program
455 1st Street
Banning, CA 92220

Riverside San Bernadino County Indian Health
11555 1/2 Potrero Road
Banning, CA 92220

Riverside County Substance Abuse Program Second Chance
1626 Hargrave Street
Banning, CA 92220

BARSTOW

Civilian Employee Assistance Programs Family Services Center B-170
Marine Corps Logistics Base
Barstow, CA 92311

Jackson/Bibby Awareness Group
222 Main Street
Suite 218
Barstow, CA 92311

Oasis Counseling Centers
500 Melissa Street
Barstow, CA 92311

BELL GARDENS

Southern California Alcohol/ Drug Program Casa Libre
6635 Florence Avenue
Suites 101 and 102
Bell Gardens, CA 90201

BERKELEY

Berkeley Addiction Treatment Services
2975 Sacramento Street
Berkeley, CA 94702

Berkeley Mental Health Court Program
2640 Martin Luther King Jr Way
Berkeley, CA 94704

Bonita House Resident Treatment Facility for Dual Diagnosis
1410 Bonita Avenue
Berkeley, CA 94709

New Bridge Foundation
1820 Scenic Avenue
Berkeley, CA 94709

BEVERLY HILLS

A Los Angeles Driver Education Center of Beverly Hills
147 North San Vicinte Avenue
Beverly Hills, CA 90211

BIG BEAR LAKE

Operation Breakthrough
40880 Pedder Road
Big Bear Lake, CA 92315

BISHOP

Inyo County Substance Abuse Services
162 H Grove Street
Suite J
Bishop, CA 93514

Toiyabe Indian Health Project Family Service Department
52 Tu Su Lane
Bishop, CA 93514

BLOOMINGTON

Cedar House Rehabilitation Center
18612 Santa Ana Avenue
Bloomington, CA 92316

BLYTHE

Riverside County Substance Abuse Program
1267 West Hobson Way
Blythe, CA 92225

Veterans Alcoholic Rehabilitation Program
9826 18 Street
Blythe, CA 92225

BOULEVARD

La Posta Substance Abuse Center
8 Crestwood Place
Boulevard, CA 91905

BRISBANE

Latino Commission on Alcohol and Drug Abuse Services of San Mateo County/Casa Maria
105 McLain Avenue
Brisbane, CA 94005

BURBANK

New Way Foundation
Aware Program
207 North Victory Boulevard
Burbank, CA 91502

Padre, Inc.
2410 West Olive Avenue
Burbank, CA 91506

BURLINGAME

Insights Youth and Family Assistance
1860 El Camino Real, Suite 400
Burlingame, CA 94010

Mills Peninsula Hospital Chemical Dependency Center
1783 El Camino Real
Burlingame, CA 94010

Radiant Recovery
530 El Camino Real, Suite B
Burlingame, CA 94010

Women's Recovery Association Residential and Outpatient
1450 Chapin Street
1st Floor
Burlingame, CA 94010

BURNEY

Crossroads Clinic
20597 Commerce Way
Burney, CA 96013

Pit River Health Services Substance Abuse Services
36977 Park Avenue
Burney, CA 96013

CALEXICO

Imperial Valley Methadone Clinic
535 Cesar Chavez Boulevard
Calexico, CA 92231

CALISTOGA

Duffy's Myrtledale, Inc. Alcohol Recovery Facility
3076 Myrtledale Road
Calistoga, CA 94515

CAMARILLO

Gateway Recovery and Intervention Program
200 Horizon Circle
Camarillo, CA 93010

Palmer Drug Abuse Program of Ventura County
155 Granada Street, Suite K
Camarillo, CA 93010

CAMPBELL

Camp Recovery Centers Outpatient Services
65 West Hamilton Avenue
Campbell, CA 95008

Office of Children Adolescent and Family Services (OCAFS)
595 Millich Drive Suite 100
Campbell, CA 95008

Support Systems Homes Inc
Support Systems Homes I
2000-A White Oaks Drive
Campbell, CA 95008

Support Systems Homes II
2015 White Oaks Drive
Campbell, CA 95008

CAMPO

San Diego Freedom Ranch
1777 Buckman Springs Road
Campo, CA 91906

CAMP PENDLETON

Consolidated Substance Abuse Counseling Center
Marine Corps Base Building 16105
Camp Pendleton, CA 92055-5016

Naval Hospital Naval Addictions Rehab/Education Department
Building H-49
Camp Pendleton, CA 92055

CANOGA PARK

Cabrito Foundation
Cabrito House
7552 Remmet Avenue
Canoga Park, CA 91303

Pine Grove Hospital
7011 Shoup Avenue
Canoga Park, CA 91307

CANYON COUNTRY

I-ADARP
27225 Camp Plenty Road, Suite 4
Canyon Country, CA 91351-2654

CAPISTRANO BEACH

Community Counseling Center of San Juan Capistrano/Casa Del Cerro I
26882-26884 Avenida Las Palmas South
Capistrano Beach, CA 92624

CARMICHAEL

Associated Rehab Program for Women
8400 Fair Oaks Boulevard
Carmichael, CA 95608

Bivalley Medical Clinic Carmichael
6127 Fair Oaks Boulevard
Carmichael, CA 95608

CARPINTERIA

Salvation Army Adult Rehabilitation Center
6410 Cindy Lane
Carpinteria, CA 93013

CARSON

Fred Brown Recovery Services
Carson House
329 West 218th Street
Carson, CA 90745

Kaiser Permanente Chemical Dependency Recovery Program/Carson
23621 South Main Street
Carson, CA 90745

CASTAIC

Antelope Valley Rehabilitation Centers Warm Springs Rehabilitation Center
38200 North Lake Hughes Road
Castaic, CA 91310

CASTRO VALLEY

HAART/Castro Valley
2457 Grove Way Suite 103A
Castro Valley, CA 94546

CATHEDRAL CITY

Charter Behavioral Health System of Southern California/Palm Springs
69696 Ramon Road
Cathedral City, CA 92234

Riverside County Substance Abuse Program Cathedral Canyon Clinic
68-615 Perez Road Suite 8
Cathedral City, CA 92234

CERRITOS

Southeast California Alcoholism and Drug Programs, Inc.
13205 South Street
Cerritos, CA 90701

CHICO

Aegis Medical Systems
1166 Esplanade Street, Suite 1
Chico, CA 95926

Butte County Department of Behavioral Health
Adult Services
584 Rio Lindo Avenue
Chico, CA 95926

Youth Services
564 Rio Lindo Avenue Suite 103
Chico, CA 95926

Chico Recovery Center
2565 Zanella Way Suite E
Chico, CA 95928

EAP Addiction Recovery
1224 Mangrove Avenue Suite 7
Chico, CA 95926

Solutions
2095 Forest Avenue, Suite 2
Chico, CA 95928

Touch Stone
1390 East Lasser Avenue
Chico, CA 95926

CHINO

Jericho Outreach
Men's Home
5151 F Street
Chino, CA 91710

Women's Home
12591 Benson Avenue
Chino, CA 91710

San Bernardino County Chino Multiple Diagnosis Clinic
6180 Riverside Drive
Suite H
Chino, CA 91710

CHULA VISTA

Acupuncture Institute for Addiction Free Life
236 F Street
Chula Vista, CA 91910

MAAC Project Health Services Division
1180 3rd Avenue
Chula Vista, CA 91910

Nosotros
73 North 2nd Avenue
Building B
Chula Vista, CA 91910

McAlister Institute for Treatment and Education (MITE) Options for Recovery/ South Bay
251 Palomar Street
Suite A
Chula Vista, CA 91911

Mental Health Systems Kinesis South
835 3rd Avenue, Suite E
Chula Vista, CA 91911

San Diego Treatment Services Third Avenue Clinic
1161 3 Avenue
Chula Vista, CA 91911

Bayview Hospital Medical Health System
330 Moss Street
Chula Vista, CA 91911

CITRUS HEIGHTS

Oak House Corporation
Oak House I and II
7919 Oak Avenue
Citrus Heights, CA 95610

CLAREMONT

Crossroads
1269 North Harvard Avenue
Claremont, CA 91711

CLAYTON

Bi Bett Corporation Diablo Valley Ranch Male Recovery Community
11540 Marsh Creek Road
Clayton, CA 94517

CLEARLAKE

Alcohol and Other Drug Services Southshore
7000 B South Center Drive
Clearlake, CA 95422

Drug Abuse Alternatives Center
14709 Lakeshore Drive
Clearlake, CA 95422

CLOVIS

Central Valley Indian Health Program Substance Abuse Services
20 North Dewitt Street
Clovis, CA 93612

COLOMA

Progress House/Men's Facility
838 Beach Court Road
Coloma, CA 95613

COLTON

Western Clinical Health Services (WCHS) Inland Health Services
2275 East Cooley Drive
Colton, CA 92324-6324

COLUSA

Colusa County Behavioral Health Services
85 East Webster Street
Colusa, CA 95932

COMPTON

Compton Special Services Center
404 North Alameda Street
Compton, CA 90221

Get Off Drugs Women's Home
1416 South Tamarind Street
Compton, CA 90220

Kazi House Residential Drug Program
930 West Compton Boulevard
Compton, CA 90220

King/Drew Substance Abuse Treatment Program
3221 North Alameda Street
Building 4, Suite J
Compton, CA 90222

Mini Twelve Step House The Solution Drop-In Center
200 North Long Beach Boulevard
Compton, CA 90221

Shields for Families Exodus
1500 East Kay Street
Compton, CA 90221

CONCORD

Affordable Detox
2481 Pacheco Street
Concord, CA 94520

Bi Bett Corporation
Frederic Ozanam Center
2931 Prospect Street
Concord, CA 94518

Shennum Center
2090 Commerce Avenue
Concord, CA 94520

Mount Diablo Medical Pavilion Center for Recovery
2740 Grant Street
Concord, CA 94520

New Connections The Keller House
1760 Clayton Road
Concord, CA 94520

New Leaf Treatment Center
2151 Salvio Street, Suite T
Concord, CA 94520-2458

Recovery Management Services
Crossroads Recovery Center II
2480 Pacheco Street
Concord, CA 94520

Crossroads Recovery Center III
2118 East Street
Concord, CA 94520

Crossroads Recovery Center IV
2080 East Street
Concord, CA 94520

Crossroads Treatment Center I
2449 Pacheco Street 2nd Floor
Concord, CA 94520

Sunrise House
135 Mason Circle
Unit M
Concord, CA 94520

CORNING

Tehama Alcohol Recovery Center
Right Road
275 Solano Street
Corning, CA 96021

CORONA

Charter Behavioral Health System of Southern California/Corona
2055 Kellogg Avenue
Corona, CA 91719

Riverside County Substance Abuse Program/Corona
623 North Main Street
Suite D-11
Corona, CA 91719

CORONADO

Coronado Recovery Center
830 Orange Avenue
Coronado, CA 92118

COSTA MESA

Addiction Institute
3151 Airway Building
Suite C-1
Costa Mesa, CA 92626

Breakaway Health Corporation Breakthrough
3151 Airway Avenue, Suite D-1
Costa Mesa, CA 92626

Cope Center
440 Fair Drive
Suite K
Costa Mesa, CA 92626

First Step House of Orange County
2015 Charle Street
Costa Mesa, CA 92627

Gold Coast Counseling Center, Inc.
2950 Airway Avenue, Suite B-3
Costa Mesa, CA 92626

Hope Institute Center for Recovery and Family Education Inc
2900 Bristol Street, Suite C-206
Costa Mesa, CA 92626

Matrix Center at Costa Mesa
275 Victoria Street Suite 2-F
Costa Mesa, CA 92627

New Directions for Women
2601 Willo Lane
Costa Mesa, CA 92627

Newport Mesa Halfway House
1865 Anaheim Street
Costa Mesa, CA 92627

Orange County Health Care Agency Newport Mesa Drug Abuse Service
3115 Redhill Avenue
Costa Mesa, CA 92626

Rap Center
666 West Baker Street
Suite 421
Costa Mesa, CA 92626

South Coast Counseling Center
693 Plumer Street
Costa Mesa, CA 92627

Southern California Alcohol and Drug Programs Heritage House
2212 Placentia Avenue
Costa Mesa, CA 92627

COTATI

A Step Up
420 East Cotati Avenue
Cotati, CA 94931

COVELO

Yuki Trails Substance Abuse Program
Covelo, CA 95428

COVINA

National Council on Alcohol/ Drug Dependency of East San Gabriel and Pomona Valleys
754 East Arrow Highway
Suite F
Covina, CA 91722

Santa Anita Family Services Pathways
716 North Citrus Avenue
Covina, CA 91723

Stepping Stones Home I and II
17727 East Cypress Street
Covina, CA 91722

CRESCENT CITY

Del Norte County Drug and Alcohol Services
384 Elk Valley Road
Crescent City, CA 95531

Humboldt Addictions Services Programs (HASP) Del Norte County
200 Marine Way
Crescent City, CA 95531

CULVER CITY

Driver Safety Schools AM/PM Culver City Budget School
4244 Overland Avenue
Culver City, CA 90230

DALY CITY

Asian American Recovery Services Project ODASA
244 92nd Street
Daly City, CA 94015

DANA POINT

Witts Inn
24901 Dana Point Harbor Drive
Suite 220 and 230
Dana Point, CA 92629

Christina House
33025 Christina Street
Dana Point, CA 92629

DANVILLE

San Ramon Valley Discovery Center
530 La Gonda Way
Suite A
Danville, CA 94526

DEER PARK

Crutchers Serenity House
50 Hillcrest Street
Deer Park, CA 94576

Saint Helena Hospital Alcohol and Chemical Recovery
650 Sanitarium Road
Deer Park, CA 94576

DELANO

Aegis Medical Systems, Inc.
1019 Jefferson Street
Delano, CA 93215

Traffic and Alcohol Awareness School of Kern (TAASK)
623 Main Street
Delano, CA 93215

DESCANSO

Phoenix House San Diego Residential Drug Free Program
23981 Sherilton Valley Road
Descanso, CA 91916

DESERT HOT SPRINGS

Desert Rehabilitation Services
Hacienda Valdez
12890 Quinta Way
Desert Hot Springs, CA 92240

The Ranch
7885 Annandale Avenue
Desert Hot Springs, CA 92240

Soroptimist House of Hope
13525 Cielo Azul Way
Desert Hot Springs, CA 92240

DIXON

Dixon Family Services
155 North 2 Street
Dixon, CA 95620

DOWNEY

Kaiser Permanente/Bellflower Med Ctr Imperial Outpatient Clinic
9449 East Imperial Highway
Downey, CA 90242

Southern California Alcohol and Drug Programs
Awakenings Program
11500 Paramount Boulevard
Downey, CA 90241

La Casita De Las Mamas of Downey
10615 Downey Avenue
Downey, CA 90241

DUBLIN

Occupational Health Services Drinking Driver Program
6670 Amador Plaza Road
Suite 203
Dublin, CA 94568

DULZURA

Rancho L Abri
18091 Bee Canyon Road
Dulzura, CA 91917

EAST PALO ALTO

Free at Last/Intensive Outpatient Unit
1946 University Avenue
East Palo Alto, CA 94303

EL CAJON

El Cajon Drug Court
1357 Broadway, Suite 100
El Cajon, CA 92021

McAlister Institute for Treatment and Education (MITE)
East County Center
1365 North Johnson Avenue
Suite 108
El Cajon, CA 92020

Pregnant Inmates Program
1365 North Johnson Avenue
Suite 111
El Cajon, CA 92020

San Diego Health Alliance East Office
234 North Magnolia Avenue
El Cajon, CA 92020

EL CENTRO

Imperial County MH Alcohol and Drug Programs
Outpatient Clinic
1030 Broadway
Suite 104
El Centro, CA 92243

Healthy New Life/Perinatal Treatment Program
1331 Clark Road
Building 3
El Centro, CA 92243

Sober Roads
395 Broadway
Suite 111
El Centro, CA 92243

Sure Helpline Center
120 North 6th Street
El Centro, CA 92243

Volunteers of America Alcohol and Drug Program
1331-B Clark Road
El Centro, CA 92243

EL MONTE

California Hispanic Commission on Alcohol/Drug Abuse Casa Blanca Service Center
12042 Ramona Boulevard
El Monte, CA 91732

Community Health Projects Medical Group
11041 Valley Boulevard
El Monte, CA 91731

Mid Valley Alcohol Recovery Service
3430 Cogswell Road
El Monte, CA 91732

Twin Palms Recovery Center
3574 Lexington Avenue
El Monte, CA 91731

ENCINITAS

Phoenix House Impact Program
345 Saxony Road, Suite 104
Encinitas, CA 92024

Phoenix House
335 Saxony Road
Encinitas, CA 92024

San Luis Rey Hospital
335 Saxony Road
Encinitas, CA 92024

ESCONDIDO

Fellowship Center Alcohol and Other Drug Services
736 East Grand Avenue
Escondido, CA 92025

Mental Health Systems Kinesis North
474 West Vermont Avenue
Escondido, CA 92027

Mental Health Systems North Inland Regional Recovery Center
620 North Ash Street
Escondido, CA 92025

North County Serenity House
123 South Elm Street
Escondido, CA 92025

Serenity Too
117 West Elm Street
Escondido, CA 92027

Vietnam Veterans of San Diego New Resolve Program
1207 South Escondido Boulevard
Escondido, CA 92025

EUREKA

Alcohol/Drug Care Services
1335 C Street
Eureka, CA 95501

Healthy Moms Program
2944 D Street
Eureka, CA 95501

Humboldt County Alcohol and Drug Programs
2922 I Street
Eureka, CA 95501

North Coast Substance Abuse Council Crossroads
1205 Myrtle Avenue
Eureka, CA 95501

Saint Joseph Hospital Family Recovery Services
2700 Dolbeer Street
Eureka, CA 95501

United Indian Health Child and Family Services
2120 Campton Road
Eureka, CA 95501

United Indian Lodge
116 9th Street
Eureka, CA 95501

EXETER

Courage to Change
1230 North Anderson Street
Exeter, CA 93321

FAIRFIELD

Solano County Health and Social Services Freedom Outreach
1735 Enterprise Drive
Building 1, Suite 104
Fairfield, CA 94533

Youth and Family Services Womens Substance Abuse Programs
934 Missouri Street, Suite A
Fairfield, CA 94533

FAIR OAKS

Messenger Clinic
4009-A Bridge Street
Fair Oaks, CA 95628-7503

Social Health and Addiction Recov Prog Fair Oaks Recovery Center
8312 Madison Avenue
Fair Oaks, CA 95628

FONTANA

Kaiser Permanente Hospital Chemical Dependency Recovery Program/Fontana
17046 Marygold Avenue
Marygold Annex
Fontana, CA 92335

Merrill Community Services, Inc.
16846 Merrill Avenue
Suite 202
Fontana, CA 92335

San Bernardino Mental Health Fontana Perinatal Treatment
8621 Juniper Avenue, Suite 101
Fontana, CA 92335

FOREST KNOLLS

Serenity Knolls Chemical Dependency Recovery Program
145 Tamal Road
Forest Knolls, CA 94933

FORT BRAGG

Growth Advocates Healing Center Whole Person/Growth for Adv Healing
200 South Franklin Street
Fort Bragg, CA 95437

Mendocino County Alcohol and Other Drug Programs/Fort Bragg
120 West Fir Street
Fort Bragg, CA 95437

FORTUNA

Center for Individual Recovery Services
173 South Fortuna Boulevard
Fortuna, CA 95540

Fortuna Community Services Humboldt Alcohol Recovery Treatment
2331 Rohnerville Road
Fortuna, CA 95540

FOSTER CITY

Avalon Family Counseling
225 Bonita Lane
Foster City, CA 94404

FOUNTAIN VALLEY

Pathways to Discovery
18350 Mount Langley Street
Suite 205
Fountain Valley, CA 92708

FREMONT

BHC Fremont Hospital
39001 Sundale Drive
Fremont, CA 94538

**Carnales Unidos Reformando
Adictos (CURA) Therapeutic
Community**
37437 Glenmore Drive
Fremont, CA 94536

**Second Chance Phoinix
Women's Program**
37957 Fremont Boulevard
Fremont, CA 94536

Solidarity Fellowship
34413 Blackstone Way
Fremont, CA 94555

FRENCH CAMP

San Joaquin County
Methadone Maintenance Clinic
Office of Substance Abuse
    Recovery House
Outpatient Methadone Detox
    Clinic
Residential Treatment Center
500 West Hospital Road
French Camp, CA 95231

FRESNO

**Addiction Research/Treatment,
CAL Detox**
East Cartwright Clinic
3103 East Cartwright Street
Fresno, CA 93725

South Orange Clinic
1235 E Street
Fresno, CA 93706

Van Ness Clinic
539 North Van Ness Street
Fresno, CA 93728

Aegis Medical Systems
34 East Minarets Avenue
Fresno, CA 93650

**Alcoholism and Drug Abuse
Council**
4411 North Cedar Avenue
Suite 108
Fresno, CA 93721

**California Substance Abuse
Institute**
2913 Tulare Street
Fresno, CA 93721

Cedar Vista Hospital
7171 North Cedar Avenue
Fresno, CA 93720

**Comprehensive Alcohol
Program (CAP) Residential**
2445 West Whitesbridge Road
Fresno, CA 93706

**Eleventh Hour Residential and
Outpatient Programs**
5639 East Park Circle Drive
Fresno, CA 93727

**Family Communication Center
Fresno Youth Advocates**
1039 U Street
Fresno, CA 93721

**Focus to Life Extended Service
Program**
440 North Blackstone Street
Fresno, CA 93706

**Fresno County Hispanic
Commission on Alcohol and
Drug Abuse Services**
1444 Fulton Street
Fresno, CA 93721

**Genesis Group Home Spirit of
Woman**
728 North Echo Avenue
Fresno, CA 93728

**Kaiser Permanente Chemical
Dependency Services**
4785 North 1st Street 2nd Floor
Fresno, CA 93726

King of Kings
Men's Recovery Home
2267 South Geneva Street
Fresno, CA 93706

Pregnant Post-Partum Women's
    Program
1350 East Annadale Avenue
Fresno, CA 93706

Residential Pregnancy and Post-
    Partum Visions Program
1530 West Whitesbridge Road
Fresno, CA 93706

West Fresno Outpatient Services
2385 South Fairview Avenue
Suite 17
Fresno, CA 93706

Nuestra Casa Recovery Home
1414 West Kearny Boulevard
Fresno, CA 93706

Tower Recovery Center
1028 North Fulton Street
Suite 101
Fresno, CA 93728

**Third Floor Community
Involvement Center**
4969 east Clinton Street
Fresno, CA 93727

West Whitesbridge Klise Center
2855 West Whitesbridge Road
Fresno, CA 93706

Turning Point
Substance Abuse Treatment Unit
2904 East Belgravia Street
Fresno, CA 93701

After Care
1638 L Street
Fresno, CA 93721

**VA Central CA Health Care
System Chemical Dependence
Treatment Program**
2615 East Clinton Avenue
Room 116-D
Fresno, CA 93703

FRONTERA

California Institution for Women
16756 Chino-Corona Road
Frontera, CA 91720

FULLERTON

Addiction Treatment Center
Commonwealth Street
Fullerton, CA 92831

KC Services, Inc.
801 South Euclid Street
Suite 201
Fullerton, CA 92832

Orange County Health Care Agency North Orange County Alcohol and Drug Abuse Services
211 West Commonwealth Avenue
Suite 204
Fullerton, CA 92832

Saint Jude Medical Center Outpatient Family Recovery Services
251 East Imperial Highway
Suite 440
Fullerton, CA 92835

Western Pacific Fullerton Program Outpatient Detox and Methadone Maintenance
218 East Commonwealth Avenue
Fullerton, CA 92832

Woodglen Recovery Junction
771 West Orangethorpe Avenue
Fullerton, CA 92832

GARBERVILLE

Singing Trees Recovery Center
2061 Highway 101 South
Garberville, CA 95442

GARDENA

Behavioral Health Services Omni
15519 Crenshaw Boulevard
Gardena, CA 90249

GARDEN GROVE

California Hispanic Commission on Alcohol and Drug Abuse Unidos Recovery Home
9842 West 13 Street, Suite B
Garden Grove, CA 92844

Roque Center Residential
9842 West 13 Street, Suite A
Garden Grove, CA 92844

GARDEN VALLEY

Progress House II Women's Facility
5607 Mount Murphy Road
Garden Valley, CA 95633

Special Services for Groups Pacific Asian Alcohol and Drug Program
14112 South Kingsley Drive
Gardena, CA 90247

GEORGETOWN

El Dorado Council on Alcoholism Lifeskills/Divide Wellness Center
6065 Highway 193
Georgetown, CA 95634

GILROY

Community Solutions
8475 Forest Street
Suite A2
Gilroy, CA 95020

GLENDALE

Glendale Memorial Hospital and Health Center Alpha Addiction Center
1330 South Glendale Avenue
Glendale, CA 91205

New Insights
431 North Brand Boulevard
Suite 304
Glendale, CA 91203

Right on Programs
522 East Broadway, Suite 101
Glendale, CA 91205

Verdugo Mental Health Center
Substance Abuse Program
1540 east Colorado
Glendale, CA 91205

Positive Directions
225-D North Maryland Avenue
Glendale, CA 91206

GLENDORA

Project Info Community Prevention and Recovery Programs
1505 South Sunflower Avenue
Glendora, CA 91740

GOLETA

Aegis Medical Systems
5710 Hollister Avenue
Goleta, CA 93117

Santa Barbara Neighborhood Clinics Isla Vista Medical Clinic
970 Embarcadero Del Mar
Goleta, CA 93117

GRAND TERRACE

Drug Alternative Program Recovery House
11810 Kingston Street
Grand Terrace, CA 92313

GRASS VALLEY

Nevada County Council on Alcoholism Substance Abuse Treatment and Recovery
440 Henderson Street, Suite C
Grass Valley, CA 95945

Team III Family Council Center
256 Buena Vista Drive, Suite 210
Grass Valley, CA 95945

GREENBRAE

Ross Hospital Chemical Dependency Services
1111 Sir Francis Drake Boulevard
Greenbrae, CA 94904

GRIDLEY

Butte County Behavioral Health Gridley Family Counseling Center
995 Spruce Street
Gridley, CA 95948

GROVER BEACH

Casa Solana
383 South 13 Street
Grover Beach, CA 93433

HANFORD

Alcohol/Drug Education and Counseling Center
289 East 8th Street
Hanford, CA 93230

Cornerstone Community Alcohol/Drug Recovery Systems
Men's Recovery
801-805 West 7 Street
Hanford, CA 93230

Women's Program
817 West 7th Street
Hanford, CA 93230

HAPPY CAMP

River of Wellness and Recovery of The Karuk Tribal Health Program
64236 2nd Avenue
Happy Camp, CA 96039

HARBOR CITY

Western Health Harbor City Clinic
1647 West Anaheim Street
Harbor City, CA 90710

HAWTHORNE

Behavioral Health Services
Pacifica House
2501 West El Segundo Boulevard
Hawthorne, CA 90250

Patterns
12917 Cerise Avenue
Hawthorne, CA 90250

HAYWARD

Horizon Services Cronin House
2595 Depot Road
Hayward, CA 94545

Second Chance/Hayward Recovery Center
22297 Mission Boulevard
Hayward, CA 94541

Successful Alternatives for Addiction and Counseling Services
409 Jackson Street, Suite 201
Hayward, CA 94544

Terra Firma Diversion/ Education Services
26785 Mission Boulevard
Hayward, CA 94544

HEMET

Double Check Retreat
47552 East Florida Avenue
Hemet, CA 92544

I Am New Life Ministries
38400 San Ignacio Road
Hemet, CA 92543

Koalacare of California, Inc. Ace Program
413 East Latham Road
Suite 108
Hemet, CA 92543

Riverside County Substance Abuse Program/Hemet
1005 North State Street
Hemet, CA 92543

Riverside Recovery Resources
First Step House
40329 Stetson Avenue
Hemet, CA 92544

Our House
41040 Acacia Avenue
Hemet, CA 92544

Sun Ray Addictions
980 North State Street, Suite 2
Hemet, CA 92543

HERALD

River City Recovery
12490 Alta Mesa Road
Herald, CA 95638

HESPERIA

San Bernardino County Perinatal Treatment Program
11951 Hesperia Road
Hesperia, CA 92345

San Bernardino Dept of Behavioral Health Victor Valley Multi-Diagnosis Clinic
11951 Hesperia Road
Hesperia, CA 92345

HOLLISTER

San Benito County Substance Abuse Program
1111 San Felipe Road
Suite 108
Hollister, CA 95023

HOOPA

Hoopa Valley Tribal Council Division of Human Services
Orchard Avenue
Hoopa, CA 95546

HUNTINGTON PARK

Diversion Safety Program, Inc.
Escuela Latina De Alcohol
6606 Pacific Boulevard
Huntington Park, CA 90255

INDIO

ABC Recovery Center, Inc.
44-374 Palm Street
Indio, CA 92201

Awareness Program Drinking Driver
45-561 Oasis Street
Indio, CA 92201

Riverside Colatino Alcohol/Drug Abuse Casa Las Palmas
83844 Hopi Avenue
Indio, CA 92201

Riverside County Substance Abuse Program
83-912 Avenue 45
Suite 9
Indio, CA 92201

INGLEWOOD

Aegis Medical Systems
614 West Manchester Boulevard
Suite 104
Inglewood, CA 90301

Behavioral Health Services Inc Inglewood Prevention and Recovery Center
279 West Beach Avenue
Inglewood, CA 90302

Community Information and Resource Center
1630 Centinela Avenue Suite 1
Inglewood, CA 90302

El Dorado Community Service Center Inglewood Medical and Mental Healtt Services
4450 West Century Boulevard
Inglewood, CA 90304

Industry Community Interface Enterprises
101 North Labrea Avenue
Suite 402
Inglewood, CA 90301

Inglewood Substance Abuse Traffic Violators Agency
400 South La Brea Avenue
Suite 202
Inglewood, CA 90301

Los Angeles Vets Welfare to Work Program
733 South Hindry Avenue
Inglewood, CA 90301

Pride Health Services
8619 Crenshaw Boulevard
Inglewood, CA 90305

Working Alternatives Century Community Correctional Center
4026 West Century Boulevard
Inglewood, CA 90304

IONE

Department of Youth Authority Manzanita Substance Abuse Programs
201 Waterman Road
Ione, CA 95640

JACKSON

Amador County Alcohol and Drug Services
1001 Broadway
Suite 106
Jackson, CA 95642

JOSHUA TREE

Morongo Basin Mental Health Panorama Ranch
65675 Sullivan Road
Joshua Tree, CA 92252

LAGUNA BEACH

Brandys Friends Family Counseling Center
362 Third Street, Suite 200
Laguna Beach, CA 92651

LAGUNA HILLS

Carequest Program
25431 Cabot Road, Suite 111
Laguna Hills, CA 92653

LAGUNA NIGUEL

Gold Coast Counseling Center
28052 Camino Capistrano
Suite 214
Laguna Niguel, CA 92677

LA JOLLA

Practical Recovery Services
8950 Villa La Jolla Drive
Suite 1130
La Jolla, CA 92037

Scripps Memorial Hospital McDonald Center
9904 Genessee Avenue
La Jolla, CA 92037

LAKE ELSINORE

Riverside Recovery Resources Community Recovery Center
323 North Main Street
Lake Elsinore, CA 92530

LAKE FOREST

Chapman Counseling Adolescent Program
23361 El Toro Road
Suite 207
Lake Forest, CA 92630

LAKEPORT

Alcohol and Other Drug Services/Northlake
858 Lakeport Boulevard
Lakeport, CA 95453

Lake County Tribal Health Consortium
925 Berins Court
Lakeport, CA 95453

LAKEWOOD

Lakewood Regional Medical Center New Beginnings
3700 East South Street
Lakewood, CA 90712

LA MESA

Charter Behavioral Health Systems Alvarado Parkway Institute
7050 Parkway Boulevard
La Mesa, CA 91942

Federal Probation Program
7808 El Cajon Boulevard
Building 1 Suite H
La Mesa, CA 91941

Mental Health Systems Pegasus East
7841 El Cajon Boulevard, Suite C
La Mesa, CA 91941

Recovery Learning Centers
4670 Nebo Drive Suite 200
La Mesa, CA 91941

Vista Hill Foundation Parent Care Family Recovery Center
5360 Jackson Drive, Suite 120
La Mesa, CA 91942

LAMONT

Community Service Organization (CSO) De Colores
8000 Segrue Street
Lamont, CA 93241

LANCASTER

Alcohol Drug Abuse Center
43423 Division Street, Suite 108
Lancaster, CA 93535

Antelope Valley Council on Alcoholism and Drug Dependency
44815 Fig Avenue
Suite 206
Lancaster, CA 93534

High Road Program
44823 Date Avenue
Lancaster, CA 93534

Miracle Star Women's Recovering Community
44664 North Cedar Avenue
Lancaster, CA 93534

Tarzana Treatment Center
44447 North 10th Street
Lancaster, CA 93534

Western Pacific Medical Corporation Antelope Valley Medical Clinic
45335 Sierra Highway
Lancaster, CA 93534

LA PUENTE

Bay Area Addiction Research/ Treatment, CAL Detox
15229 East Amar Road
La Puente, CA 91744

LARKSPUR

Bay Area Community Resources
375 Doherty Drive
Larkspur, CA 94939

Marin Services for Women Outpatient Unit
444 Magnolia Avenue, Suite 101
Larkspur, CA 94939

Residential Unit
127 King Street
Larkspur, CA 94939

LAWNDALE

Lawndale Medical and Mental Health Services
4429 West 147th Street
Lawndale, CA 90260

LEMON GROVE

McAlister Institute for Treatment and Education (MITE)
Options Recovery East
2049 Skyline Drive
Lemon Grove, CA 91945

LEMOORE

Naval Air Station/Lemoore Counseling and Assistance Center
Barracks 1
Lemoore, CA 93246

LODI

Valley Community Counseling Services
301 West Locust Street
Lodi, CA 95240

LOMA LINDA

Jerry L. Pettis Memorial VA Medical Center Alcohol and Drug Treatment Program
11201 Benton Street
Room 116A1
Loma Linda, CA 92357

LOMPOC

Aegis Medical Systems Medical Group
200 East College Street
Lompoc, CA 93436

Family Life Counseling Service Inc
410 East Ocean Avenue
Lompoc, CA 93436

Vandenberg AFB Mental Health 30th Medical Group
338 South Dakota Avenue
Building 13-850
Lompoc, CA 93437

LONG BEACH

Behavioral Health Services Redgate Memorial Hospital
1775 Chestnut Avenue
Long Beach, CA 90813

Cambodian Association of America Community Prevention and Recovery Program
2501 Atlantic Avenue
Long Beach, CA 90806

Church at Long Beach House of Levi Christian Men's Home
725 Rose Avenue
Long Beach, CA 90813

Family Services of Long Beach
1043 Pine Avenue
Long Beach, CA 90813

Flossie Lewis Alcoholism Recovery Center
Alcoholism Recovery Center
351 East 6th Street
Long Beach, CA 90802

New Life Center
615 Elm Street
Long Beach, CA 90802

Transitional Sober Living Center
351 East 6th Street
Long Beach, CA 90802

Harbor Area High Gain Program, Inc.
330 East 3rd Street
Long Beach, CA 90802

Industry Community Interface Enterprises
555 East Artesia Street
Suite B
Long Beach, CA 90806

Long Beach Alcohol and Drug Rehab Program
Central Clinic
1133 East Rhea Street
Long Beach, CA 90806

Grand Avenue Clinic
2525 Grand Avenue
Long Beach, CA 90815

North Clinic
6335 Myrtle Avenue
Long Beach, CA 90805

National Council on Alcoholism and Other Drug Dependencies/Woman to Woman
3750 Long Beach Boulevard
Long Beach, CA 90807

New Found Life
2211 and 2137 East Ocean Boulevard
Long Beach, CA 90803

Palm House Alcoholism Recovery Home
2515 East Jefferson Street
Long Beach, CA 90810

Salsido Recovery Center Freedom House
250 East Louise Street
Long Beach, CA 90805

Southern California Alcohol/ Drug Problems Baby Step Inn
1755 Freeman Avenue
Long Beach, CA 90804

Substance Abuse Foundation of Long Beach
3125 East 7th Street
Long Beach, CA 90804

Tarzana Treatment Center/Long Beach
2101 Magnolia Avenue
Long Beach, CA 90806

Veterans' Affairs Medical Center Substance Abuse Treatment Program
5901 East 7 Street
Ward 116-A
Long Beach, CA 90822

West County Medical Clinic Substance Abuse Program
100 East Market Street
Long Beach, CA 90805

Western Health Long Beach Clinic
2933 East Anaheim Street
Long Beach, CA 90804

LOS ALAMITOS

Twin Town Treatment Center
10741 Los Alamitos Boulevard
Los Alamitos, CA 90720

LOS ANGELES

Addiction Alternatives
1125 South Beverly Drive
Suite 401
Los Angeles, CA 90035

Addiction Research/Treatment, CAL Detox
Hollywood Clinic
6411 Hollywood Boulevard
2nd Floor
Los Angeles, CA 90028

West Olympic
1926 West Beverly Boulevard
Los Angeles, CA 90057

Alcoholism Center for Women, Inc.
1147 South Alvarado Street
Los Angeles, CA 90006

A Los Angeles Driver Education Center
Eagle Rock
2607 Colorado Boulevard
Suite 104
Los Angeles, CA 90041

Alta Med Health Services Buena Care
1701 Zonal Avenue
Los Angeles, CA 90033

Alternative Action Programs
2511 South Barrington Avenue
Los Angeles, CA 90064

Alternatives Unit
2530 Hyperion Avenue
Los Angeles, CA 90027

American Health Services Hollywood Medical and Mental Health Services
8348 Beverly Boulevard
Los Angeles, CA 90048

Asian American Drug Abuse Program, Inc.
Therapeutic Community Residential
5318 South Crenshaw Boulevard
Los Angeles, CA 90043

Special Deliveries/Perinatal Services
3850 Martin Luther King Boulevard
Suite 201
Los Angeles, CA 90008

Avalon/Carver Community Center Drug Abuse Program
4920 South Avalon Boulevard
Los Angeles, CA 90011

Behavioral Health Services Hollywood Family Recovery Center
6838 Sunset Boulevard
Los Angeles, CA 90028

Boyle Heights
3421 East Olympic Boulevard
Los Angeles, CA 90023

Unit 2
4099 North Mission Road
Building A
Los Angeles, CA 90032

Beverlywood Mental Health Center
8926 Sawyer Street
Los Angeles, CA 90035

California Hispanic Comm. on Alcohol and Drug Abuse
Aguila Recovery Home
6157 North Figueroa Street
Los Angeles, CA 90042

Latino Alcohol and Drug Abuse Service Center
5801 East Beverly Boulevard
Los Angeles, CA 90022

Latinas Recovery Home/Saint
Louis
327 North Saint Louis Street
Los Angeles, CA 90033

Hispanic Alcohol Recovery Home
4754 East Brooklyn Avenue
Los Angeles, CA 90022

Latinos Recovery Home/Wabash
2436 Wabash Avenue
Los Angeles, CA 90033

Mujeres Recovery Home
530 North Avenue, Suite 54
Los Angeles, CA 90042

Paloma Recovery Home
328 North Avenue, Suite 59
Los Angeles, CA 90042

Vista CPRP/Sol Youth Resources
Project
109 and 111 North Avenue 56
Los Angeles, CA 90042

Canon Human Services Center
9705 South Holmes Avenue
Los Angeles, CA 90002

Casa de Hermandad
West Area Opportunity Center
11821 West Pico Boulevard
Los Angeles, CA 90064

**Chabad Residential Treatment
Center for Men**
5675 West Olympic Boulevard
Los Angeles, CA 90029

**Children's Hospital of Los
Angeles Division of
Adolescent Medicine/
Substance Abuse Services**
5000 Sunset Boulevard, 4th floor
Los Angeles, CA 90027

Childrens Institute International
711 South New Hampshire Avenue
Los Angeles, CA 90005

**Community Health Foundation
Perinatal CPRP**
1904 Bailey Street
Los Angeles, CA 90033

Covenant House
1325 North Western Avenue
Los Angeles, CA 90027

CRI Help Socorro RDF
5110 South Huntington Drive
Los Angeles, CA 90032

**Dare U to Care Outreach
Ministry**
316 West 120th Street
Los Angeles, CA 90061

**Didi Hirsch CMHC Dignity
Center**
672 South Lafayette Park Place
Suite 6
Los Angeles, CA 90057

**Do It Now Foundation of
Southern California, Inc.**
6565 Sunset Boulevard
Suite 417
Los Angeles, CA 90028

**East Los Angeles Health Task
Force Comprehensive
Substance Abuse Program**
630 South Saint Louis Street
Los Angeles, CA 90023

**East Los Angeles Womens
Health Center MELA
Counseling Service Center**
5240 East Beverly Boulevard
2nd Floor
Los Angeles, CA 90022

**El Centro De Ayuda
Corporation El Centro
Substance Abuse Treatment
Center**
1972 East Cesar Chavez Avenue
Los Angeles, CA 90033

El Centro Del Pueblo/Alvarado
2501 West 7th Street
Los Angeles, CA 90057

Felicity House
3701 Cardiff Avenue
Los Angeles, CA 90034

Higher Goals
10510 South Vermont Avenue
Los Angeles, CA 90044

His Sheltering Arms
Family Services Center
112 West 111 Street
Los Angeles, CA 90061

Recovery Home
11101 South Main Street
Los Angeles, CA 90061

**Homeless Health Care Los
Angeles**
1010 South Flower Street
Suite 500
Los Angeles, CA 90015

**Industry Community Interface
Projects**
2126 South La Brea Street
Suite 203
Los Angeles, CA 90016

**Jeff Grand Medical Group
Outpatient Methadone
Maintenance and Detox**
3130 South Hill Street
Los Angeles, CA 90007

**Jewish Family Services of Los
Angeles Alcohol and Drug
Action Program**
6380 Wilshire Boulevard
Los Angeles, CA 90048

**Kaiser Permanente Chemical
Dependency Recovery
Program**
Culver Marina
12001 West Washington
Boulevard
Los Angeles, CA 90066

Korean Community Services
4416 West Beverly Boulevard
Los Angeles, CA 90004

Living in Recovery
951 North Mariposa Avenue
Los Angeles, CA 90029

**Los Angeles Gay and Lesbian
Center Mental Health Services**
1625 North Schrader Boulevard
Los Angeles, CA 90028

Los Angeles Treatment Services
11427 South Avalon Boulevard
Los Angeles, CA 90061

**Los Angeles Centers for
Alcaohol/Drug Abuse LACADA/
Homeless Outreach Project**
333 South Central Avenue
Los Angeles, CA 90013

Lynwood Women and Children Center Watts Women and Children
8005 South Figueora Street
Los Angeles, CA 90003

Mary Lind Foundation
Bimini Recovery Home
155 South Bimini Place
Los Angeles, CA 90004

Rena B Recovery Home
4445 Burns Avenue
Los Angeles, CA 90029

Royal Palms Recovery Home
360 South Westlake Avenue
Los Angeles, CA 90057

Matrix Center/West Los Angeles
12304 Santa Monica Boulevard, Suite 200
Los Angeles, CA 90025

Matrix Institute
5220 West Washington Boulevard
Suite 101
Los Angeles, CA 90016

Mid Valley Recovery Services Mariposa Recovery Home
453 South Indiana Street
Los Angeles, CA 90063

Mini Twelve-Step House
303 East 52 Street
Los Angeles, CA 90011

MJB Transitional Recovery
11152 South Main Street
Los Angeles, CA 90061

Narcotic Educational Foundation of America
5055 Sunset Boulevard
Los Angeles, CA 90027

National Council on Alcoholism and Drug Dependency Main Directions
985 East 108th Street
Los Angeles, CA 90059

Natural High
3801 South Western Avenue
Los Angeles, CA 90062

Ness Counseling Center
8512 Whitworth Drive, Suite 102
Los Angeles, CA 90035

People in Progress Nonresidential Recovery Services
2500 Wilshire Boulevard
Suite 1155
2nd Floor
Los Angeles, CA 90057

Pizarro Treatment Center Outpatient Methadone Maintenance
1525 Pizarro Street
Los Angeles, CA 90026

Plaza Community Center The Esperanza Project
648 South Indiana Street
Los Angeles, CA 90023

Principles
510 New High Street
Los Angeles, CA 90012

Salvation Army
Harbor Light Center
809 East 5 Street
Los Angeles, CA 90013

Harmony Hall
3107 South Grand Avenue
Los Angeles, CA 90007

Safe Harbor
721 East 5th Street
Los Angeles, CA 90013

Shields for Families Project
Eden
1721 East 120th Street
Trailer 6
Los Angeles, CA 90059

Genesis Family Day Treatment Program
12021 South Wilmington Street, Lot C
Los Angeles, CA 90059

Soledad Enrichment Action Program
161 South Fetterly Avenue
Los Angeles, CA 90022

Special Service for Groups Pacific Asian Alcohol Program
5325 South Vermont Avenue
Los Angeles, CA 90020

Sunrise Community Counseling Center In/Outpatient
537 South Alvarado Street
Los Angeles, CA 90057

Union Rescue Christian Life Discipleship Program
226 South Main Street
Los Angeles, CA 90012

United American Indian Involvement
1125 West 6th Street, Suite 400
Los Angeles, CA 90017

United Women in Transition
5001 Budlong Avenue
Los Angeles, CA 90037

Van Ness Recovery House
1919 North Beachwood Drive
Los Angeles, CA 90068

Veterans Affairs Outpatient Clinic Drug Dependence Treatment Program
351 East Temple Street, 11C
Los Angeles, CA 90012-3328

Volunteers of America Screening and Evaluation Services
541 South Crocker Street
Los Angeles, CA 90013

Volunteers of America of Los Angeles
Alcohol Services
515 East 6th Street
Los Angeles, CA 90021

Central City Recovery Program
515 East 6th Street, 9th Floor
Los Angeles, CA 90021

Washington Medical Center and Recovery Center
12101 West Washington Boulevard
Los Angeles, CA 90066

Watts Health Foundation
House of Uhuru
8005 South Figueroa Street
Los Angeles, CA 90003

Weingart Center Association Stairs II Program
566 South San Pedro Street
Los Angeles, CA 90013

West Los Angeles Treatment Program Clinic I and Clinic II
2321 Pontius Avenue
Los Angeles, CA 90064

Wilshire Treatment Center
11704 Wilshire Boulevard
Suite D-228
Los Angeles, CA 90025

LOS GATOS

South Bay Teen Challenge
16735 Lark Avenue
Los Gatos, CA 95032

West Valley Treatment and Recovery Center
375 Knowles Drive
Los Gatos, CA 95030

LOYALTON

Sierra County Human Services Alcohol and Drug Department
704 Mill Street
Loyalton, CA 96118

LUCERNE VALLEY

True Vines Training Center for Men
10180 Banta Road
Lucerne Valley, CA 92356

LYNWOOD

Los Angeles Health Services Lynwood Clinic
11315 South Atlantic Avenue
Lynwood, CA 90262

One Nation Under God Christian Church Living High in the Lord Ministries
12526 Waldorf Drive
Lynwood, CA 90262

Principles California Regional Detention Facility
11705 Alameda Street
Lynwood, CA 90262

Shields for Families Ark Comprehensive Child Development Pg
11705 Deputy Yamamoto Place, Suite A
Lynwood, CA 90262

MADERA

Madera Counseling Center Substance Abuse Services
14277 Road 28
Madera, CA 93639

Yosemite Women's Center[
126 North B Street Street
Madera, CA 93637

MALIBU

Westside Sober Living Centers Promises Residential Treatment Center
20725 Rockcroft Drive
Malibu, CA 90265

MAMMOTH LAKES

Mono County Alcohol and Drug Program
Sierra Centre Mall
3rd Floor
Mammoth Lakes, CA 93546

MANHATTAN BEACH

San Pedro Penisula Hospital Chemical Dependency Treatment Center
1022 Sepulveda Boulevard
Manhattan Beach, CA 90266

MANTECA

San Joaquin Council for the American Indian/Three Rivers Lodge
13505 Union Road
Manteca, CA 95336

Valley Community Counseling Services
110 Sherman Avenue
Manteca, CA 95336

MARINA DEL RAY

Daniel Freeman Marina Hospital Exodus Recovery Center
4650 Lincoln Boulevard
Marina Del Ray, CA 90292

MARIPOSA

Kings View Community Services Mariposa Counseling Center
5085 Bullion Street
Mariposa, CA 95338

MARKLEEVILLE

Alpine County Mental Health Department Alcohol and Drug Program
260 Laramie Street
Markleeville, CA 96120

MARTINEZ

Born Free
111 Allen Street
Martinez, CA 94533

Discovery Program Discovery House
4639 Pacheco Boulevard
Martinez, CA 94553

Ujima Family Recovery
904 Mellus Street
Martinez, CA 94553

MARYSVILLE

Aegis Medical Systems
320 H Street, Suite 2
Marysville, CA 95901

Center for Behavioral Health of Marysville
1496 North Beale Road
Marysville, CA 95901

MCCHORD AFB

McChord Air Force Base Substance Abuse Program
62 MDOS/SGOMH 160 G Street
McChord AFB, CA 98438-1130

MCCLELLAN AFB

McClellan AFB Substance Abuse Program Social Actions Office
77 Medical Group/SGOHA 5727 Perrin Street
Suite 1 Bldg 1042
McClellan AFB, CA 95652-1231

MENLO PARK

Veterans' Affairs Health Care System Addiction Treatment Service Psychiatric Services
795 Willow Road
137 ATS
Menlo Park, CA 94025

MERCED

Central Valley Addiction Center
17 East Main Street
Merced, CA 95340-5044

Community/Social Model Advocates, Inc.
Hobie House
1301 Yosemite Parkway
Merced, CA 95340

Lifestyle Management Drinking Driver Program
1521 West Main Street
Merced, CA 95340

Merced Alcohol and Drug Services Recovery Assistance for Teens
1836 K Street
Merced, CA 95340

Merced County Alcohol and Drug Abuse Services Perinatal Center
658 West Main Street
Merced, CA 95340

MISSION VIEJO

Charter Behavioral Health System of Southern California/Mission Viejo
23228 Madero Street
Mission Viejo, CA 92691

MODESTO

Aegis Medical Systems, Inc.
801 17th Street, Suite E
Modesto, CA 95350

Family Service Agency of Stanislaus County
First-Step Program
707 14th Street
Modesto, CA 95351

New Hope Recovery House
1406 Fordham Avenue
Modesto, CA 95350

Recovery Crossroads
1024 J Street Suite 427
Modesto, CA 95354-0844

Recovery Systems Associates
330 McHenry Avenue Suite C
Modesto, CA 95354

Stanislaus Behavioral Health Center
1501 Claus Road
Modesto, CA 95355

Stanislaus County Dept. of Mental Health
Alcohol and Drug Treatment Program
800 Scenic Drive
Building D North
Modesto, CA 95350

Genesis Narcotic Replacement Therapy
800 Scenic Drive SW
Building D South
Modesto, CA 95350

Juvenile Drug Court
2215 Blue Gum Street
Main Building
Modesto, CA 95350

Men in Recovery
8224 West Grayson Road
Modesto, CA 95358

Substance Abuse Services
Outpatient Drug Free
1501 F Street
Modesto, CA 95354

MONROVIA

Santa Anita Family Services Pathways
605 South Myrtle Avenue
Monrovia, CA 91016

Spencer Recovery Hospital
345 West Foothill Boulevard
Monrovia, CA 91016

MONTAGUE

Next Step Perinatal Services
211 South 13th Street
Montague, CA 96064

MONTCLAIR

Inland Health Services (IHS) Montclair
4761 Arrow Highway
Montclair, CA 91763

MONTEREY

Community Hospital Recovery Center
576 Hartnell Street
Monterey, CA 93940

MONTEREY PARK

Alhambra Safety Services
926 East Garvey Avenue
Suite A
Monterey Park, CA 91754

MONTGOMERY CREEK

Wilderness Recovery Center
19650 Cove Road
Montgomery Creek, CA 96065

MOORPARK

Turning Point Counseling
3939 Hitch Boulevard
Moorpark, CA 93021-8706

MOUNTAIN VIEW

Community Health Awareness Program
711 Church Street
Mountain View, CA 94041

El Camino Hospital Chemical Dependency Services
2500 Grant Road
ECH133
Mountain View, CA 94040

Siskiyou County Mental Health Alcohol and Drug Abuse Services
909 Ream Avenue
Mount Shasta, CA 96067

MURRIETA

Anderson and Associates Counseling Services
26811 Hobie Circle
Suite 02
Murrieta, CA 92362

Dr Raese and Associates
25095 Jefferson Avenue, Suite 202
Murrieta, CA 92562

NAPA

Alternatives For Better Living
1100 Lincoln Avenue, Suite 204
Napa, CA 94558

Napa County Drinking Driver Program
900 Coombs Street
Suite M16
Napa, CA 94559

Napa County Human Services Alcohol and Drug Program
2344 Old Sonoma Road
Napa, CA 94559

Our Family Corporation
Jefferson House
3552 Jefferson Street
Napa, CA 94558

Napa State Hospital
Evergreen Drive/D Ward
Napa, CA 94559

Redwood House
2033 Redwood Road
Napa, CA 94558

NATIONAL CITY

Healthy Beginnings/Nueva Esperanza Paradise Valley Hospital
2345 East 8th Street, Suite 110
National City, CA 91950

NEVADA CITY

Nevada County Dept. of Mental Health
Lovett Recovery Center
10075 Bost Avenue
Nevada City, CA 95959

Mental Health Services
10433 Willow Valley Road
Nevada City, CA 95959

NEWARK

Second Chance Tri-Cities Program
6330 Thornton Avenue
Newark, CA 94560

NEWBURY PARK

Ventura County DDP Conejo Valley DDP
2824 Camino Dos Rios, Suite 101
Newbury Park, CA 91320

NEWHALL

ACT Behavioral Center
24876 Apple Street, Suite C
Newhall, CA 91321

El Dorado Community Service Center Santa Clarita Medical and Mental Health Services
24625 Arch Street
Newhall, CA 91321

National Council on Alcoholism and Drug Dependence of San Fernando Valley
24779 Valley Street
Newhall, CA 91321

NEWPORT BEACH

Alternative Sentencing Relapse Prevention
Newport Boulevard, Suite 101
Newport Beach, CA 92663

Hoag Memorial Hospital Chemical Dependency Center
1 Hoag Drive
Newport Beach, CA 92658

Sober Living by the Sea
2811 Vista Way
Newport Beach, CA 92663

NORCO

Walden House Therapeutic Community at The California Rehabilitation Center
5th and Western Street
Norco, CA 91760

NORTH FORK

Sierra Tribal Consortium
57128 Road 225
North Fork, CA 93643

NORTH HIGHLANDS

Mexican American Alcoholism Program MAAP Sacramento DDP and Drug Diversion
3437 Myrtle Avenue, Suite 420
North Highlands, CA 95660

NORTH HILLS

Veterans Affairs Medical Center Chemical Dependency Treatment Program
16111 Plummer Street
Ward 41-C 116-A
North Hills, CA 91343

NORTH HOLLYWOOD

Chandler Lodge Foundation
11455 Chandler Boulevard
North Hollywood, CA 91601

Cri-Help, Inc. George T Pfleger Center
11027 Burbank Boulevard
North Hollywood, CA 91601

Western Pacific North Hollywood
11321 Camarillo Street
North Hollywood, CA 91602

NORWALK

Los Angeles Centers for Alcohol/Drug Abuse Recovery House
11400 Norwalk Boulevard
Suite 305
Norwalk, CA 90650

Southern California Alcohol/ Drug Problems Cider House
11400 Norwalk Boulevard
Building 209
Norwalk, CA 90650

Western Pacific Norwalk Medical Clinic
11902 Rosecrans Boulevard
Norwalk, CA 90650

NOVATO

Henry Ohlhoff House/North
5394 Nave Drive
Novato, CA 94949

Sunny Hill Children's Services Threshold for Change
619 Canyon Road
Novato, CA 94947

OAKDALE

Stanislaus County Dept of Mental Health East Side Counseling Center
631 West F Street
Oakdale, CA 95361

OAKHURST

Kings View Community Services Oakhurst Counseling Center
49774 Roak 426, Suite D
Oakhurst, CA 93644

OAKLAND

Thunder Road Chemical Dependency Recovery Hospital
390 40th Street
Oakland, CA 94609

Alameda County Healthy Infant Program Summit Medical Center
3012 Summer Street
Suite G-625
Oakland, CA 94609

Allen Temple Haight Ashbury Recovery Center
9925 14th Street
Oakland, CA 94621

Allied Fellowship Services
1524 29th Avenue
Oakland, CA 94606

American Indian Family Healing Center New Dawn Lodge/White Cloud Lodges
1815 39th Avenue
Suites D and C
Oakland, CA 94601

Asian Community Mental Health Services
310 8th Street
Suite 201
Oakland, CA 94607

Bi Bett Corporation
East Oakland Recovery Center
8900 International Bboulevard
Oakland, CA 94621

Orchid Women's Recovery Center
1342 East 27th Street
Oakland, CA 94606

East Bay Community Recovery Project
Project Pride
2441 San Pablo Avenue, 2nd floor
Oakland, CA 94606

First Step Alcohol and Drug Crisis Center
1531 Jefferson Street
Oakland, CA 94612

Healthy Babies Project
Harriet Tubman Recovery Center
1004 36th Street
Oakland, CA 94609

Harriet Tubman Recovery
Center II
3328 Elm Street
Oakland, CA 94609

Maudell Shirek
3229 Elm Street
Oakland, CA 94609

Maudell Shirek Recovery Village
471 34th Street
Oakland, CA 94609

Highland Hospital Substance Abuse Program Healthy Start
14ll East 31st Street
Oakland, CA 94602

Kaiser Permanente Chemical Dependency Services
969 Broadway Street
Oakland, CA 94607

Mandana House Community Recovery Center
3989 Howe Street
Oakland, CA 94611

Merritt Peralta Institute Treatment Services
3012 Summitt Street
Oakland, CA 94609

Missionary Recovery Center
1739 8th Street
Oakland, CA 94602

Narcotic Education League
El Chante Alcoholism Recovery
Home
425 Vernon Street
Oakland, CA 94610

Si Se Puede
3315 International Boulevard
Oakland, CA 94601

Native American Health Center
3124 East 14th Street
Oakland, CA 94601

Occupational Health Service DWI Education Program
340 Pendleton Way
Suite B 129
Oakland, CA 94621

Praise Fellowship Ministries Men's Recovery Facility
7400 MacArthur Boulevard
Oakland, CA 94605

Saint Marys Center Recovery 55
635 22nd Street
Oakland, CA 94612

Solid Foundation
Keller House
353 Athol Avenue
Oakland, CA 94606

Mandela I
6939 McArthur Boulevard
Oakland, CA 94601

Mandela II
3408 Andover Street
Oakland, CA 94610

Women's Center
4778 East 14th Street
Oakland, CA 94621

West Oakland Health Center
Cocaine Recovery Center East
9006 MacArthur Boulevard
Oakland, CA 94605

Wistar Redemption and Recovery
220 Wistar Road
Oakland, CA 94603

ZDK 14th Street Clinic and Medical Group
1124 International Boulevard
Oakland, CA 94703

OCEANSIDE

McAlister Institute for Treatment and Education (MITE)
North Coastal
514 North Hill Street
Oceanside, CA 92054

North Coastal Detox
4010 Via Serra Street
Oceanside, CA 92056

Mental Health Systems Pegasus West
560 Greenbrier Drive
Oceanside, CA 92054

Rebuild
2103 El Camino Real, Suite 203
Oceanside, CA 92008

Tri City Medical Center
4002 Vista Way
Oceanside, CA 92056

Turning Point Crisis Center
1738 South Tremont Street
Oceanside, CA 92054

ONTARIO

Bilingual Family Counseling Service Center for Recovery
317 West F Street
Ontario, CA 91762

Community Health Projects/ Ontario
324 North Laurel Avenue
Ontario, CA 91762

Inland Aids Project
1135 North Mountain Street
Ontario, CA 91762

Inland Valley Drug and Alcohol Recovery Services Caroline House
1646 East Caroline Street
Ontario, CA 91764

Marin Recovery Home
1636 North Marin Avenue
Ontario, CA 91764

Orange Recovery Center
1003 North Orange Avenue
Ontario, CA 91764

Valley Improvement Programs
210 West B Street
Ontario, CA 91762

ORANGE

Chapman House
3806 East Roberta Avenue
Orange, CA 92869

City of Orange Police Department Crisis Intervention Unit
1107 North Batavia Street
Orange, CA 92667

Mariposa Women's Center
812 Town and Country Road
Orange, CA 92668

Touchstones
525 North Parker Street
Orange, CA 92668

Turning Point Recovery Center
805 West LaVeta Street, Suite 103
Orange, CA 92868

ORANGEVALE

New Dawn
6043 Roloff Way
Orangevale, CA 95662

ORLAND

Glenn County Health Services/ Orland Substance Abuse Department
1187 East South Street
Orland, CA 95963

ORLEANS

River of Wellness and Recovery of The Karuk Tribal Health Program
Highway 96
Orleans, CA 95556

OROVILLE

Behavioral Health Services Feather River Indian Health
2167 Montgomery Street
Oroville, CA 95965

Butte County Behavioral Health Services
Adult Services/Oroville
18-C County Center Drive
Oroville, CA 95965

Oroville Community Counseling Center
2856 Olive Highway, Suite A
Oroville, CA 95965

OXNARD

Alternative Action Programs
2630 Saddle Avenue
Oxnard, CA 93033

Aegis Medical Systems
620 South D Street
Oxnard, CA 93030

2055 Saviers Road
Suite 10
Oxnard, CA 93033

Rainbow Recovery Centers I
1826 East Channel Island
    Boulevard
Oxnard, CA 93033

Shamrock House
1334 East Channel Islands
    Boulevard
Oxnard, CA 93033

Oxnard Center
2651 South C Street
Suite 1
Oxnard, CA 93033

New Start for Moms
315 North A Street
Oxnard, CA 93030

**Ventura County Hispanic
    Commission on Alcohol and
    Drug Services/Casa Latina**
1430 Junewood Way
Oxnard, CA 93030

Victory Outreach Oxnard
200 Pleasant Valley Road
Oxnard, CA 93030

PACIFICA

Pyramid Alternatives
480 Manor Plaza
Pacifica, CA 94044

PACIFIC GROVE

Beacon House
468 Pine Avenue
Pacific Grove, CA 93950

PACOIMA

**Didi Hirsch CMHC Via Avanta
    Program**
11643 Glenoaks Boulevard
Pacoima, CA 91331

El Proyecto Del Barrio Arleta
8902 Woodman Avenue
Pacoima, CA 91331

PALMDALE

**American Health Services
    Palmdale Medical**
2720 East Palmdale Boulevard,
    Suite 129
Palmdale, CA 93550

**Antelope Valley Council on
    Alcoholism and Drug
    Dependency**
38345 30th Street, Suite E
Palmdale, CA 93550

**Midway Ranch Sober Living
    Center**
40836 20th Street West
Palmdale, CA 93551

PALM DESERT

Crossroads Counseling
Highway 111, Suite 202
Palm Desert, CA 92260-3909

PALM SPRINGS

Lifes Journey Center
291 East Camino Monte Vista
    Street
Palm Springs, CA 92262

**Michael's House Treatment
    Center for Men**
430 South Cahuilla Street
Palm Springs, CA 92262

PALO ALTO

Daytop Village Adult Services
2560 Pulgas Avenue
Palo Alto, CA 94303

Free at Last
Malaika House
2043 Euclid Avenue
Palo Alto, CA 94303

Walker House
1095 Weeks Street
Palo Alto, CA 94303

**North County Alcohol Services
    Center**
231 Grant Avenue
Palo Alto, CA 94306

**Stanford Alcohol and Drug
    Treatment Center Dept of
    Psychiatry/Behavioral
    Sciences**
401 Quarry Road Room 1353
Palo Alto, CA 94305-5541

PANORAMA CITY

El Proyecto Del Barrio
9140 Van Nuys Boulevard
Panorama City, CA 91402

**Western Pacific Med Corp
    Western Pacific Panorama
    Med Clinic**
9462 Van Nuys Boulevard
Panorama City, CA 91402

PARADISE

**Butte County Behavioral Health
    Paradise Community
    Counseling Center**
5910 Clarke Road, Suite W
Paradise, CA 95969

Skyway House
6373 Oak Way
Paradise, CA 95967

PARAMOUNT

Creative Alternatives
8528 1/2 Rosecrans Avenue
Paramount, CA 90723

PASADENA

Aegis Medical Systems
1724 East Washington Boulevard
Pasadena, CA 91101

Bishop Gooden Home
191 North El Molino Avenue
Pasadena, CA 91101

California Drug Consultants
659 East Walnut Street
Pasadena, CA 91101

Casa de las Amigas
160 North El Molino Avenue
Pasadena, CA 91101

City of Pasadena/Dept of Public Health Pasadena Recovery Program
1845 North Fair Oaks Avenue
Pasadena, CA 91103

Grandview Foundation
1230 North Marengo Avenue
Pasadena, CA 91103

225 Grandview Street
Pasadena, CA 91104

Las Encinas Hospital Chemical Dependency Program
2900 East Del Mar Boulevard
Pasadena, CA 91107

Pasadena Council on Alcoholism and Drug Depedency/Referral Agency
181 North Hudson Avenue
Pasadena, CA 91101

Principles Impact Drug/Alcohol Treatment Center
2659 & 2661 Nina Street
Pasadena, CA 91103

1680 North Fair Oaks Avenue
Pasadena, CA 91103

145 North Vista Avenue
Suite 101
Pasadena, CA 91107

Saint Luke Medical Center Share Unit
2632 East Washington Boulevard
Pasadena, CA 91107-7021

Urban Revitalization Development Corporation/ Choices
1460 North Lake Avenue
Suite 107
Pasadena, CA 91104

Walter Moving Home
218 South Madison Avenue
Pasadena, CA 91101

PATTON

Patton State Hospital
3102 East Highland Avenue
Patton, CA 92369

PERRIS

Perris Valley Recovery Programs
236 East Third Street, Suite B
Perris, CA 92570

PETALUMA

Comprehensive Counseling Center
35 Maria Drive, Suite 861
Petaluma, CA 94952

Henry Ohlhoff Outpatient Programs Petaluma Office
35 Maria Drive, Suite 852
Petaluma, CA 94954

Saint Anthony Foundation Saint Anthony Farm
11207 Valley Ford Road
Petaluma, CA 94952

PHELAN

Aegis Medical Systems
Phelan Clinic
203777 Phelan Road
Phelan, CA 92371

PICO RIVERA

Cornerstone Health Services Outpatient Methadone Clinic
8207 Whittier Boulevard
Pico Rivera, CA 90660

Eastside Health Services
5200 San Gabriel Place
Suite B and C
Pico Rivera, CA 90660

PINOLE

Doctors Hospital of Pinole New Beginnings Program
2151 Appian Way
Pinole, CA 94564

Tri-Cities Discovery Center
2586 Appian Way
Pinole, CA 94564

PITTSBURG

Addiction Research/Treatment, CAL Detox
45 Civic Avenue
Room 128
Pittsburg, CA 94565

Bi Bett Corporation
East County Detox Center/DUI
500 School Street
Pittsburg, CA 94565

East County Wollam House/ Perinatal
510 Wollam Avenue
Pittsburg, CA 94565

Born Free East
550 School Street
Pittsburg, CA 94565

East County Wollam House for Women
498 Wollam Avenue
Pittsburg, CA 94565

New Connections/Pittsburg Bay Point
440 Railroad Avenue
Pittsburg, CA 94565

UJIMA Family Recovery Services
East Intensive Day Treatment
369 East Leland Road
Pittsburg, CA 94565

PLACERVILLE

El Dorado Council on Alcoholism (EDCA) Lifeskills
2810 Coloma Road
Placerville, CA 95667

New Morning Youth and Family Services
6765 Green Valley Road
Placerville, CA 95667

Progress House Outpatient Program
2914 A Cold Springs Road
Placerville, CA 95667

PLEASANT HILL

**Bi Bett Corporation Gregory
    Recovery Center**
270 Campbell Lane
Pleasant Hill, CA 94523

Drake House
808 Grayson Road
Pleasant Hill, CA 94523

PLEASANTON

**Valley Community Health
    Center, Inc.**
3922 Valley Avenue, Suite A
Pleasanton, CA 94566

POINT REYES STATION

**West Marin County Community
    Outreach Project**
3922 Valley Aavenue, Suite A
Point Reyes Station, CA 94956

POMONA

Aegis Medical Systems
Garey Clinic
1050 North Garey Avenue
Pomona, CA 91767

Pomona Unit
152 West Artesia Street
Pomona, CA 91768

**Behavioral Health Services
    American Recovery Center**
2180 West Valley Boulevard
Pomona, CA 91768

**Inland Valley Drug and Alcohol
    Recovery Services**
375 South Main Street, Suite 111
Pomona, CA 91766

**National Council on
    Alcoholism/Drug Dependence
    of East San Gabriel**
375 South Main Street, Suite 102
Pomona, CA 91766

**Pomona Community Crisis
    Center**
221 North Palomares Street
Pomona, CA 91766

Prototypes Women's Center
845 East Arrow Highway
Pomona, CA 91767

PORT HUENEME

**Anacapa Hospital Substance
    Abuse Services**
307 East Clara Street
Port Hueneme, CA 93041

PORTERVILLE

**Alcohol and Drug Services of
    Tulare Alternative Services**
215 North D Street
Porterville, CA 93257

**Indian Health Services Tule
    River Alcoholism Program**
Route 7
Porterville, CA 93257

**Paar Center Porterville Halfway
    House**
218-232 West Belleview Avenue
Porterville, CA 93257

237 West Belleview Avenue
Porterville, CA 93257

SRS
38 West Morton Avenue
Porterville, CA 93257

Turning Point Youth Services
288 North 2nd Street
Porterville, CA 93257

QUINCY

**Plumas County Alcohol and
    Drug Dept.**
Courthouse Annex and
    Highway 70
Quincy, CA 95971

RAMONA

Broad Horizons
1236 H Street
Ramona, CA 92065

Group Conscience/Pemarro
1482 Kings Villa Road
Ramona, CA 92065

**Mental Health Systems North
    Rural Recovery Center**
323 Hunter Street
Ramona, CA 92065

RANCHO CORDOVA

D and A Detox Center
2721 Barbera Way
Rancho Cordova, CA 95670

RANCHO CUCAMONGA

Matrix Institute on Addictions
9375 Archibald Avenue, Suite 204
Rancho Cucamonga, CA 91730

RANCHO MIRAGE

Betty Ford Center at Eisenhower
39000 Bob Hope Drive
Rancho Mirage, CA 92270

Pine Ridge Treatment Center
71650 Sahara Road Sahara Plaza
Suite 1
Rancho Mirage, CA 92270

RED BLUFF

**Tehama County Health Agency
    Alcohol and Drug Division**
447 Walnut Street
Red Bluff, CA 96080

REDDING

Cornerstone Recovery Systems
13144 Bear Mountain Road
Redding, CA 96003

Empire Recovery Center
1237 California Street
Redding, CA 96001

**Guardian Rehabilitation
    Northstate Recovery System**
2801 Eureka Way
Redding, CA 96001

Remi Vista Inc
3191 Churn Creek Road
Redding, CA 96002

**Shasta County Alcohol and
    Drug Program**
2770 Pioneer Drive, Suite 200
Redding, CA 96001

Perinatal Program
2770 Pioneer Drive, Suite 240
Redding, CA 96001

Shasta Options
2530 Larkspur Lane
Redding, CA 96002

Shasta Sierra Work Furlough Program
1727 South Street
Redding, CA 96001

Noble House Substance Abuse and Growth Recovery
15799 Nauvoo Trail
Redding, CA 96001

REDLANDS

Jackson/Bibby Awareness Group, Inc.
1200 Arizona Street
Suite B-10
Redlands, CA 92374

Loma Linda University Behavioral Medicine Center
1710 Barton Road
Redlands, CA 92373

Redlands Drug Court
802 West Colton Avenue, Suite C
Redlands, CA 92374

Redlands/Yucaipa Guidance Clinic Association Inc
1323 West Colton Avenue
Suite 200
Redlands, CA 92374

REDWOOD CITY

Avalon Family Counseling Services
915 Middle Field Road Suite 4
Redwood City, CA 94063

Daytop Village Adolescent
631 Woodside Road
Redwood City, CA 94061

El Centro de Libertad/The Freedom Center
650 Main Street, Suite 600
Redwood City, CA 94063

Professional Treatment Redwood City Treatment Clinic
500 Arguello Street
Redwood City, CA 94063

Service League of San Mateo County Hope House
3789 Hoover Street
Redwood City, CA 94063

REDWOOD VALLEY

Consolidated Tribal Health Project, Inc.
6991 North State Street
Redwood Valley, CA 95470

RESEDA

Fully Alive Center
18645 Sherman Way
Reseda, CA 91335

Kaiser Permanente Chemical Dependency Recovery Program
18040 Sherman Way
Reseda, CA 91335

Safety Education Center
18700 Sherman Way, Suite 118
Reseda, CA 91335

Western Pacific Reseda Program Outpatient Detox and Methadone Maintenance
18437 Saticoy Street
Reseda, CA 91335

RIALTO

San Bernardino County Office of Alcohol and Drug Programs and Treatment Services
850 East Foothill Boulevard
Suite E
Rialto, CA 92376

RICHMOND

Addiction Research/Treatment, CAL Detox
1313 Cutting Boulevard
Richmond, CA 94804

Born Free/Richmond
100 38 Street
Room 1608
Richmond, CA 94804

Contra Costa County Supervised Treatment and Recovery Program (STAR)
205 41st Street
Richmond, CA 94805

Criminal Justice Service West Location
205 41st Street
Richmond, CA 94805

Neighborhood House of North Richmond Hollman Detoxification and Fauerso Center
208 23rd Street
Richmond, CA 94804

Rectory Women's Recovery Center
CJ Hawkins House
1515 24th Street
Richmond, CA 94804

Sojourne Community Counseling Center
3029 Mac Donald Avenue
Richmond, CA 94804

Ujima Family Recovery Services Ujima West Intensive Day Treatment
3939 Bissell Street
Richmond, CA 94805

West GAADDS
205 41st Street
Richmond, CA 94805

RIDGECREST

College Health IPA Ridgecrest Unit
1400 North Norma Street
Suite 13
Ridgecrest, CA 93555

Traffic and Alcohol Awareness School of Kern (TAASK)
443 West Church Street
Ridgecrest, CA 93555

RIO VISTA

Rio Vista Care
125 Sacramento Street
Rio Vista, CA 94571

RIVERSIDE

Born Free
8310 Baxter Way
Riverside, CA 92504

**Knollwood Psychiatric and
    Chemical Dependency Center**
5900 Brockton Avenue
Riverside, CA 92506

Pine Ridge Treatment Center
5995 Brockton Avenue
Suite B
Riverside, CA 92506

**March AFB Social Actions Office
    Drug and Alcohol Abuse
    Control Program**
22 CSG/SLD
Building 466
Riverside, CA 92518

My Family Recovery Center
17270 Roosevelt Avenue
Riverside, CA 92508

A Woman's Place
4295 Brockton Avenue
Riverside, CA 92501

Recovery for Women
7211 Magnolia Avenue
Riverside, CA 92504

**Riverside County Substance
    Abuse Program/Alcohol**
1777 Atlantic Avenue
Riverside, CA 92507

Riverside Recovery Resources
3757 Elizabeth Street
Riverside, CA 92506

Sammon House
1420 Orange Street
Riverside, CA 92501

10 Acre Ranch, Inc.
6067 Beach Street
Riverside, CA 92509

**Western Clinical Health Service
    (WCHS)**
Inland Health Services
1021 West La Cadena Drive
Riverside, CA 92501

**Whiteside Manor Alcoholic
    Recovery Home**
2743 Orange Street
Riverside, CA 92501

9935 Challen Street
Riverside, CA 92501

**Youth Service Center of
    Riverside**
3847 Terracina Drive
Riverside, CA 92506

ROCKLIN

**Rocklin Community Counseling
    Center**
5175 Pacific Street, Suite D
Rocklin, CA 95677

ROSEMEAD

**Family Care Center Substance
    Abuse Program**
4022 North Rosemead Boulevard
Rosemead, CA 91770

ROSEVILLE

**Adolescent Intercept
    Professional Recovery
    Services**
220 Douglas Boulevard
Roseville, CA 95678

Aegis Medical Systems
360 Sunrise Boulevard
Roseville, CA 95678

Amicus Counseling Services
3017 Douglas Boulevard
Roseville, CA 95661

**Charter Behavioral Health
    System of Northern California**
101 Cirby Hills Drive
Roseville, CA 95678

**Sierra Council on Alcohol and
    Drug Dependency Roseville
    Service Center**
1A Sierragate Plaza
Suite 110
Roseville, CA 95678

Sierra Family Services/Roseville
424 Vernon Street
Roseville, CA 95678

RUNNING SPRINGS

Pine Ridge Treatment Center
2727 Highland Drive
Running Springs, CA 92382

SACRAMENTO

**American Indian Substance
    Abuse Program, Inc.
    Turquoise Indian Lodge**
2727 P Street
Sacramento, CA 95816

Another Choice Another Chance
5524 Assembly Court Suite 27
Sacramento, CA 95823

BHC Sierra Vista Hospital
8001 Bruceville Road
Sacramento, CA 95823

Bi-Valley Medical Clinic
2100 Capitol Avenue
Sacramento, CA 95816

Norwood
310 Harris Avenue
Suite A
Sacramento, CA 95838

**California Hispanic Commission
    Alcohol and Drug Abuse
    Amigas Recovery Home**
101 Southlite Circle
Sacramento, CA 95831

**Center for AIDS Research
    Education and Services
    (CARES)**
1500 21st Street
Sacramento, CA 95814

Center for Behavioral Health Inc
7225 East Southgate Drive
Suite D
Sacramento, CA 95823

Change
2701 Cottage Way, Suite 34
Sacramento, CA 95825

Chemical Dependency Center for Women
1507 21st Street, Suite 100
Sacramento, CA 95814

Options for Recovery/Passages
7000 Franklin Boulevard
Suite 110
Sacramento, CA 95823

Del Paso Heights Neighborhood Sacramento County Alcohol and Drug Bureau
3970 Research Drive
Sacramento, CA 95838

Facts
2726 Rio Linda Boulevard
Sacramento, CA 95815

Gateway Foundation, Inc. Gateway Recovery House
4049 Miller Way
Sacramento, CA 95817

Getting Sober Staying Sober/A Hand Up
2942 La Solidad Way
Sacramento, CA 95817

Kaiser Permanente Medical Center Chemical Dependency Program
6600 Bruceville Road
Sacramento, CA 95823

Mexican American Alcoholism Program
Mi Casa Recovery Home
2515 48 Avenue
Sacramento, CA 95822

National Council on Alcohol and Drug Dependency/ Sacramento County Affiliate
1300 Ethan Way, Suite 250
Sacramento, CA 95825

Oak Park Multi Service Center Alcohol and Drug Bureau
3415 Martin Luther King Jr. Boulevard
Sacramento, CA 95817

River City Recovery Center
E Street Unit
2218 E Street
Sacramento, CA 95816

G Street Unit
2217 G Street
Sacramento, CA 95816

Sacramento County Probation Drug Court
2140 Stockton Boulevard
Sacramento, CA 95817

Sacramento Black Alcoholism Center (SBAC)
2425 Alhambra Boulevard
Suite F
Sacramento, CA 95817

Sacramento Urban Indian Health Leo Camp Alcohol Program
801 Broadway
Sacramento, CA 95818

Salvation Army
Adult Rehabilitation Center
1615 D Street
Sacramento, CA 95814

The Effort
Alternative House
1550 Juliesse Avenue
Sacramento, CA 95815

Counseling Center
1820 J Street
Sacramento, CA 95816

Detoxification Program
7586 Stockton Boulevard
Sacramento, CA 95816

Volunteers of America
Options for Recovery
1001 Grand Avenue
Sacramento, CA 95838

Yale Mother/Infant Program
1009 Yale Street
Sacramento, CA 95818

SALINAS

Community Human Services
Methadone Clinic
1101 F North Main Street
Salinas, CA 93906

Proyecto Unidad
209 Pajaro Street Suite B
Salinas, CA 93901

Door to Hope
Women's Recovery Center
165 Clay Street
Salinas, CA 93901

Gente Del Sol Community Recovery Center
5 Williams Road
Salinas, CA 93905

Monterey County Health Department Perinatal Recovery Services
209 Pajaro Street, Suite A
Salinas, CA 93906

Sun Street Centers
Residential Recovery Program
8 Sun Street
Salinas, CA 93901

Women and Children Recovery Services
209 Pajaro Street, Suite A
Salinas, CA 93906

Valley Health Associates Medetrac
622 East Alisal Street, Suite 6
Salinas, CA 93905

SAN ANDREAS

Calaveras County Alcohol/Drug Abuse Program
891 Mountain Ranch Road
Government Center Department 64-66
San Andreas, CA 95249

SAN ANSELMO

Sunny Hills Childrens Services
300 Sunny Hills Drive Building E
San Anselmo, CA 94960

SAN BERNARDINO

Casa de Ayuda
7255 Garden Drive
San Bernardino, CA 92404

7274 Garden Drive
San Bernardino, CA 92404

Casa de San Bernardino
735 North D Street
San Bernardino, CA 92401

Center for Community Counseling and Education Agape House
1643 East Highland Avenue
Suite C
San Bernardino, CA 92404

Drug Court of San Bernardino
595 North Arrowhead Avenue
Suite A
San Bernardino, CA 92401

Hase and Associates Systems
353 West 6 Street
San Bernardino, CA 92401

Industry Community Interface Projects (ICI Projects)
265 East Mill Street, Suite 1
San Bernardino, CA 92408

Inland AIDS Project
186 East Highland Avenue
San Bernardino, CA 92405

Inland Behavioral Services
1963 North E Street
San Bernardino, CA 92405

Mental Health Systems
Pegasus DUI
2301 North Sierra Way
San Bernardino, CA 92405

Probationers Recovery Through Intervention and Drug Education (PRIDE)
595 North Arrowhead Avenue
San Bernardino, CA 92401

New House, Inc.
Men's Program
840 North Arrowhead Avenue
San Bernardino, CA 92401

Women with Children Under Five Years and Pregnant Women
856 North Arrowhead Avenue
San Bernardino, CA 92401

Pine Ridge Outpatient Center
1881 Commerce Center East, Suite 108
San Bernardino, CA 92408

San Bernardino County Dept of Public Health
799 East Rialto Avenue
San Bernardino, CA 92415

Veterans Alcoholic And Rehabilitation Program (VARP)
Gibson House for Men
1100 North D Street
San Bernardino, CA 92410

Gibson Recovery Home for Women
1135 North D Street
San Bernardino, CA 92410

Harris House
907 West Rialto Avenue
San Bernardino, CA 92410

SAN BRUNO

Casa Aztlan
3080 Longview Drive
San Bruno, CA 94066

SAN CARLOS

First Chance
335 Quarry Road
San Carlos, CA 94070

SAN CLEMENTE

Mainstream Support Group Recovery Home
607 Avenida Las Flores
San Clemente, CA 92672

Pacific Hills Treatment Center
217 and 219 Avenida Monterey
San Clemente, CA 92672

SAN DIEGO

Advanced Health Care
3703 Camino del Rio South, Suite 200
San Diego, CA 92108

Behavioral Health Group/ Frontier ADTC
10435 Chubb Lane
San Diego, CA 92101

Charter Behavioral Health System of San Diego/North LLC
11878 Avenue of Industry
San Diego, CA 92128

Cobar House
4318 Meade Avenue
San Diego, CA 92116

Community Connection Resource Center Solutions Outpatient Program
4080 Centre Street, Suite 207
San Diego, CA 92103

Comprehensive Health Center Project Hope
1760 Euclid Avenue
San Diego, CA 92105

Crash
Golden Hill House
2410 E Street
San Diego, CA 92102

Options for Recovery Central
5605 El Cajon Boulevard
San Diego, CA 92115

Short Term/RDF
4161 Marlborough Avenue
San Diego, CA 92105

Short Term II
4890 67 Street
San Diego, CA 92105

South City Regional Center
220 North Euclid Avenue
Suite 120
San Diego, CA 92114

Crossroads Foundation
3594 4 Avenue
San Diego, CA 92103

Episcopal Community Service (ECS) Mid-City Regional Recovery Center
2855 El Cajon Boulevard
San Diego, CA 92104

Ethridge Center Inc
2230 Logan Avenue
San Diego, CA 92113

Family Center for Substance
1959 Grand Avenue
San Diego, CA 92109-4511

Freedom House Community Connection Resource Center
4318 Louisiana Street
San Diego, CA 92104

Griffin and Wong Institute for Education and Training
2870 4th Avenue, Suite 100
San Diego, CA 92103

HHS South Bay Drug Court Treatment and Testing Program
1515 Palm Avenue, Suite A
San Diego, CA 92101

House of Metamorphosis
Parolee Partnership Program
412 30th Street
San Diego, CA 92102

Residential Center
2970 Market Street
San Diego, CA 92102

Isis Center
892 27th Street
San Diego, CA 92154

Kaiser Permanente Medical Group Chemical Dependency Recovery Program
3420 KenyonStreet
San Diego, CA 92103

Kearny Mesa Regional Recovery Center
7601 Convoy Court
San Diego, CA 92111

MAAC Project Recovery Home Casa de Milagros
1127 South 38th Street
San Diego, CA 92113

Mental Health Systems
Harmony Women's Recovery Center
6150 Mission Gorge Road
Suite 116
San Diego, CA 92120

Mid-Coast Counseling and Recovery Center
4926 Savannah Street, Suite 175
San Diego, CA 92110

Probationers in Recovery/Metro
6153 Fairmont Avenue, Suite 102
San Diego, CA 92120

Mesa Vista Hospital Chemical Dependency Program
7850 Vista Hill Avenue
San Diego, CA 92123

Naval Station Substance Abuse Rehab Department
3075 Corbina Alley
Building 268
San Diego, CA 92136-5127

New Hope Center
4324 34th Street
San Diego, CA 92104

Partners in Prevention Education and Recovery
3274 Rosecrans Street
San Diego, CA 92110

Pathfinders of San Diego
Recovery Home
2980 Cedar Street
San Diego, CA 92102

San Diego Center for Psychotherapy
600 B Street, Suite 1420
San Diego, CA 92101

San Diego Community Treatment Center
502 10th Avenue
San Diego, CA 92101

San Diego Health Alliance
West Office
7020 Friars Road
San Diego, CA 92108

San Diego Treatment Services Home Avenue Clinic
3940 Home Avenue
San Diego, CA 92105

San Diego Youth and Community Services
Teen Options
3660 Fairmount Avenue
San Diego, CA 92105

Scripps Clinic Chemical Dependency Treatment Program
4320 La Jolla Village Drive, Suite 140
San Diego, CA 92122

Stepping Stone, Inc.
Long Term Rehab
3767 Central Avenue
San Diego, CA 92105

Nonresidential Program
3425 5th Avenue
San Diego, CA 92103

Substance Abuse Counseling Center
Community Service MCAS Miramar
San Diego, CA 92145-2008

The Way Back
2516 A Street
San Diego, CA 92102

Turning Point Home of San Diego
1315 25th Street
San Diego, CA 92102

Twelve-Step House Heartland House
5855 Streamview Drive
San Diego, CA 92105

U.S. Marine Corps Substance Abuse Control Center
Marine Corps Recruit Depot
Building 6-E
San Diego, CA 92141

Union of Pan Asian Communities Pan Asian Alcohol/Drug Treatment Program
3288 El Cajon Boulevard, Suite 13
San Diego, CA 92104

Venture Day MHS, Inc.
6460 Boulder Lake Avenue
San Diego, CA 92119-3154

Veterans' Affairs Medical Center Alcohol and Drug Treatment Program
3350 La Jolla Village Drive
Suite 116A
San Diego, CA 02161

Vista Pacifica
7989 Linda Vista Road
San Diego, CA 92111

Volunteers of America Alcohol Services Center
741 11th Avenue
San Diego, CA 92101

1111 Island Avenue
San Diego, CA 92101

SAN FERNANDO

Northeast Valley Health Corporation community Prevention and Decovery Program
1053 North Maclay Street
San Fernando, CA 91340

SAN FRANCISCO

Addiction Research/Treatment CAL Detox Market Clinic
1111 Market Street 1st Floor
San Francisco, CA 94103

Alcoholics Rehabilitation Association First Step Home
1035 Haight Street
San Francisco, CA 94117

Asian American Recovery Services, Inc. Residential Program
2024 Hayes Street
San Francisco, CA 94117

Bakers Place
Acceptance Place
673 San Jose Avenue
San Francisco, CA 94110

Ferguson Place
1249 Scott Street
San Francisco, CA 94115

Bay Area Service Network Residential of Haight-Ashbury Clinics
111 Taylor Street, Suite 301
San Francisco, CA 94102

Bayview Hunters Point Foundation
Alice Griffith Clinic
43 Nichols Street
San Francisco, CA 94124

Substance Abuse Program
1625 Carrol Street
San Francisco, CA 94124

Youth Services
5015 3rd Street
San Francisco, CA 94124

Center on Juvenile and Criminal Justice Supportive Living Program
1671 25th Avenue
San Francisco, CA 94122

Epiphany Center Outpatient Treatment
100 Masonic Avenue
San Francisco, CA 94118

Fort Help Methadone Program
495 3 Street
San Francisco, CA 94107

Freedom from Alcohol and Drugs
1353 48th Avenue
San Francisco, CA 94122

Unit II
1362–1366 48th Avenue
San Francisco, CA 94122

Unit III
1569–1569A and 1569B
48th Avenue
San Francisco, CA 94122

Friendship House Association of American Indians
80 Julian Avenue
San Francisco, CA 94103

Golden Gate for Seniors
637 South Van Ness Avenue
San Francisco, CA 94110

Haight-Ashbury Free Clinics
Alcohol Treatment Services
425 Divisadero Street, Suite 201
San Francisco, CA 94117

Bill Pone Memorial Unit
1696 Haight Street
San Francisco, CA 94117

Black Extended Family Program
330 Ellis Street
San Francisco, CA 94102

Drug Detoxification Project
529 Clayton Street
San Francisco, CA 94117

Smith House
766 Stanyan Street
San Francisco, CA 94117

Henry Ohlhoff House
601 Steiner Street
San Francisco, CA 94117

Outpatient Programs
2423 Clement Street
San Francisco, CA 94121

2418 Clement Street
San Francisco, CA 94121

Iris Center Women's Counseling and Recovery Services
333 Valencia Street, Suite 222
San Francisco, CA 94103

Jelani House
1601 Quesada Avenue
San Francisco, CA 94124

Outpatient Services
1588 Quesada Avenue
San Francisco, CA 94124

Kaiser Permanente Hospital Chemical Dependency Recovery Program
1201 Fillmore Street
San Francisco, CA 94115

Laguna Honda Hospital Rehabilitation Center
375 Laguna Honda Boulevard
San Francisco, CA 94116-1499

Liberation House Programs
1724 Steiner Street
San Francisco, CA 94115

Milestones
291 10th Street
San Francisco, CA 94103

Mission Council on Alcohol Abuse for the Spanish Speaking
820 Valencia Street
San Francisco, CA 94110

Morrisania West
205 13th Street, Suite 3300
San Francisco, CA 94103

New Leaf Substance Abuse Services
1853 Market Street
San Francisco, CA 94103

North of Market
Senior Alcohol Program
333 Turk Street
San Francisco, CA 94102

Portero Hill Neighborhood House ZAP Project
953 Haro Street
San Francisco, CA 94107

Project Adapt
2020 Hayes Street
San Francisco, CA 94117

Saint Anthony's Foundation Covenant House
818 Steiner Street
San Francisco, CA 94117

Ozanam Reception Center
1175 Howard Street
San Francisco, CA 94103

Salvation Army Harborlight Center
Detox Primary Program
1275 Harrison Street
San Francisco, CA 94103

San Francisco General Hospital
Stimulant Treatment Outpatient
   Program
3180 18th Street
Suite 205
San Francisco, CA 94110

Opiate Treatment Outpatient
   Program/Methadone Detox
1001 Potrero Avenue
Building 90 Ward 93
San Francisco, CA 94110

Substance Abuse Services/
   Methadone Maintenance
1001 Potrero Avenue
Building 90 Ward 93
San Francisco, CA 94110

Swords to Plowshares Veterans Rights Organization
1063 Market Street
San Francisco, CA 94103

Twelve-Step Programs
4049 Judah Street, Suite B
San Francisco, CA 94122

Veterans Affairs Medical Center Substance Abuse Program
4150 Clement Street, Suite 116-E
San Francisco, CA 94121

Walden House
890 Hayes Street
San Francisco, CA 94117

Adult Residential Program
815 Buena Vista West
San Francisco, CA 94117

Walden Multi-Service Center
1885 Mission Street
San Francisco, CA 94110

Adolescent Program
214 Haight Street
San Francisco, CA 94102

Western Addition Recovery House
940 Haight Street
San Francisco, CA 94117

Westside Community Mental Health Center
Inner City Program
973 Market Street
San Francisco, CA 94103

Westside Methadone Treatment
   Program
1153 Oak Street
San Francisco, CA 94115

Westside Youth Awareness
   Program
1140 Oak Street
San Francisco, CA 94117

Women's Alcoholism Center
Aviva House Recovery Home
1724 Bryant Street
San Francisco, CA 94110

Florette Pomeroy House
2263 Bryant Street
San Francisco, CA 94110

Lee Woodward Counseling Center
2201 Sutter Street
San Francisco, CA 95115

Mia House
300 Holyoke Street
San Francisco, CA 94132

SAN GABRIEL

Family Counseling Services
314 East Mission Drive
San Gabriel, CA 91776

SANGER

Fresno County Hispanic Commission on Alcohol and Drug Abuse Services
2640 Jensen Avenue
Sanger, CA 93657

SAN JACINTO

Anderson Associates Counseling Services
166 East Main Street
Suite 2
San Jacinto, CA 92586

La Vista Women's Alcoholic Recovery Center
2220 Girard Street
San Jacinto, CA 92581

SAN JOSE

Adult and Child Guidance Center Comadres Program
380 North 1st Street, Suite 200
San Jose, CA 95112

950 West Julian Street
San Jose, CA 95126

Alert Driving, Inc. (ADI)
Advanced Drug Diversion
Institute
3150 Almaden Expressway
Suite 145
San Jose, CA 95118

Alexian Associates Family
Psychology and Counseling
3110 Provo Court, Suite A
San Jose, CA 95127-1034

ARH Recovery Homes
House on The Hill
9505 Malech Road
San Jose, CA 95151

Mariposa Lodge
9500 Malech Road
San Jose, CA 95151

Treatment Options
2345 and 2355 Mather Drive
San Jose, CA 95116

Asian Americans for Community
Involvement
2400 Moorpark Avenue, Suite 300
San Jose, CA 95112

Benny McKeown Center
1281 Fleming Avenue
San Jose, CA 95127

Blossoms Perinatal Center
Gardner Family
3030 Alum Rock Avenue
San Jose, CA 95127

Central Treatment and Recovery
Center
976 Lenzen Avenue, 1st Floor
San Jose, CA 95126

Central Valley Methadone
Clinic
2425 Enborg Lane
San Jose, CA 95128

Charter Behavioral Health
System of San Jose
455 Silicon Valley Boulevard
San Jose, CA 95138

Columbia Good Samaritan
Hospital Recovery Center
2425 Samaritan Drive
San Jose, CA 95124

Combined Addicts and
Professional Services (CAPS)
Outpatient Program
693 South 2nd Street
San Jose, CA 95112

Residential Unit
398 South 12th Street
San Jose, CA 95112

Drug Abuse Treatment
2220 Moorpark Avenue
San Jose, CA 95128

East Valley Treatment and
Recovery
1675 Burdette Drive, Suite B
San Jose, CA 95121

Economic Social Opportunities,
Inc. Rehab Health Services
1445–1447 Oakland Road
San Jose, CA 95112

Horizon Services Horizon South
650 South Bascom Avenue
San Jose, CA 95128

Indian Health Center of Santa
Clara Valley Inc
1333 Meridan Avenue
San Jose, CA 95125

National Traffic Safety Institute
275 North 4th Street, 2nd Floor
San Jose, CA 95112

Office of Children Adolescent
and Family Services (OCAFS)/
Foothill
230 Pala Avenue
San Jose, CA 95127

Pate House Recovery Home
35 South 12th Street
San Jose, CA 95112

Pathway House
102 South 11th Street
San Jose, CA 95112

Proyecto Primavera Garner
Family Care Corp.
614 Tully Road
San Jose, CA 95111

Sullivan Recovery Home
2345 Mather Drive
San Jose, CA 95116

Support Systems Homes III
1032 Thornton Way
San Jose, CA 95128

Willow Home
808 Palm Street
San Jose, CA 95110

SAN LEANDRO

HAART
15400 Foothill Boulevard
San Leandro, CA 94578

Horizon Community Center
1403 164 Avenue
San Leandro, CA 94578

Telecare Vida Nuvea
15750 Foothill Boulevard
San Leandro, CA 94578-1012

SAN LUIS OBISPO

Cottage Care Outpatient Center
of San Luis Obispo
555 Chorro Street, Suite D-2
San Luis Obispo, CA 93405

Life Steps Drug Alcohol Free
Living Center
1217 Mill Street
San Luis Obispo, CA 93401

San Luis Obispo County
Drug and Alcohol Services
1102 Laurel Lane
San Luis Obispo, CA 93401

SAN MARCOS

Mental Health Systems Teen
Recovery Center/North
150 Valpreda Road, Suite 104
San Marcos, CA 92069

Occupational Health Services
1637 Capalina Road
San Marcos, CA 92069

San Diego Health Alliance
North Office
1560 Capalina Street
Suite A
San Marcos, CA 92069

SAN MARTIN

Santa Clara Bureau of Alcohol and Drug Programs/South County Methadone Clinic
80 West Highland Avenue
San Martin, CA 95046

SAN MATEO

Palm Avenue Detoxification
2251 Palm Avenue
San Mateo, CA 94403

Project Ninety
15 9 Avenue
San Mateo, CA 94401

Solidarity Family Center
1668 South Norfolk Avenue
San Mateo, CA 94403

Solidarity Family Center
1668 South Norfolk Street
San Mateo, CA 94403

Womens Recovery Association Hillside House
217 North Delaware Street
Suite B
San Mateo, CA 94401

SAN PABLO

Ujima Family Recovery Services
1901 Church Lane
San Pablo, CA 94806

SAN PEDRO

Beacon House Association of San Pedro
1003 South Beacon Street
San Pedro, CA 90731

Channel View House
124 West 11th Street
San Pedro, CA 90731

Lighthouse
130 West 10th Street
San Pedro, CA 90731

Palos Verdes House
1012 South Palos Verdes Street
San Pedro, CA 90731

Fred Brown's Recovery Services
13th Street House
1235 West 13th Street
San Pedro, CA 90731

Mesa House
14th Street Services
349 West 14th Street
San Pedro, CA 90731

19th Street Services
856 West 19th Street
San Pedro, CA 90731

Women's House
270 West 14th Street
San Pedro, CA 90731

House of Hope Foundation
235 West 9th Street
San Pedro, CA 90731

Joint Efforts, Inc. Outpatient Services
505 South Pacific Avenue
Suite 205
San Pedro, CA 90731

San Pedro Peninsula Hospital Chemical Dependency Treatment Center
1386 West 7th Street
San Pedro, CA 90732

SAN RAFAEL

Bay Area Institute for Family Therapy
2400 Las Gallinas Street
Suite 260
San Rafael, CA 94903

Center Point
Lifelink Perinatal Services
1477 Lincoln Avenue
San Rafael, CA 94901

Nonresidential Services
1601 2nd Street, Suite 104
San Rafael, CA 94901

The Manor
603 D Street
San Rafael, CA 94901

Henry Ohlhoff Outpatient Programs
526 3rd Street
San Rafael, CA 94901

Kaiser Permanente Medical Group Chemical Dependency Services
820 Las Gallinas Avenue
San Rafael, CA 94903

Marin Services for Men
424 Mission Avenue
San Rafael, CA 94901

Marin Treatment Center Outpatient Services
1466 Lincoln Avenue
San Rafael, CA 94901

SAN RAMON

New Bridge Foundation of San Ramon
125 Ryan Industrial Court
Suite 202
San Ramon, CA 94583

San Ramon Regional Medical Center New Beginnings
6001 Norris Canyon Road
San Ramon, CA 94583

SANTA ANA

Addiction Alternatives
1851 East 1st Street, Suite 840
Santa Ana, CA 92705

California Treatment Services Third Street Clinic
717 East 3rd Street
Santa Ana, CA 92701

Cornerstone Adult Outpatient
2130 East 4th Street, Suite 160
Santa Ana, CA 92705-3827

Orange County Health Care Agency BHC Narcotic Treatment Program
1725 West 17th Street
Room 146-B
Santa Ana, CA 92701

Orange County Health Services Agency/Orange County Drug Court
1200 North Main Street
Suite 630
Santa Ana, CA 92701

Phoenix House Adult and Adolescent Programs
1207 East Fruit Street
Santa Ana, CA 92701

Santa Ana Alcohol and Drug Abuse Services
1200 North Main Street
Suite 100-B
Santa Ana, CA 92701

Straight Talk Gerry House
1225 West 6th Street
Santa Ana, CA 92703

Gerry House West
217 North Cooper Street
Santa Ana, CA 92703

Villa Center
910 North French Street
Santa Ana, CA 92701

SANTA BARBARA

Aegis Medical Systems
217 Camino Del Remedio Street
Santa Barbara, CA 93110

American Indian Health Services
4141 State Street Suite B-6
Santa Barbara, CA 93110

Community Counseling Center
923 Olive Street, Suite 1
Santa Barbara, CA 93101

Council on Alcoholism and Drug Abuse
232 East Canon Perdido Street
Santa Barbara, CA 93102

Drug Abuse Preventive Center
24 West Arrellaga Street
Santa Barbara, CA 93101

Gay and Lesbian Resource Center Counseling and Recovery Services
126 East Haley Street
Suite A-17
Santa Barbara, CA 93101

Sansum/Santa Barbara Medical Foundation Clinic/Foundation For Recovery
215 Pesetas Lane
Santa Barbara, CA 93110

Santa Barbara Cottage Hospital
419 Pueblo Street
Santa Barbara, CA 93102

Santa Barbara Council on Alcohol and Drug Abuse/ Project Recovery
133 East Haley Street
Santa Barbara, CA 93102

Santa Barbara Rescue Mission and Bethel House
535 Eats Yanonali Street
Santa Barbara, CA 93102

Zona Seca
Alcohol/Drug Abuse Counseling Agency
26 West Figueroa Street
Santa Barbara, CA 93103

SANTA CLARA

Pathway Society
1659 Scott Boulevard, Suite 30
Santa Clara, CA 95050

SANTA CRUZ

Community Support Services
290 Pioneer Street
Santa Cruz, CA 95060

Janus of Santa Cruz
200 7 Avenue
Suite 150
Santa Cruz, CA 95062

Narconon International/ Narconon of Northern California
8699 Empire Grade Road
Santa Cruz, CA 95060

New Life Community Services Inc
707 Fair Avenue
Santa Cruz, CA 95060

Santa Cruz Community Counseling Center
Alto Counseling Center/North
271 Water Street
Santa Cruz, CA 95060

Sobriety Works
1051 41st Avenue
Santa Cruz, CA 95062-4400

Sunflower House
125 Rigg Street
Santa Cruz, CA 95060

Youth Services North County
709 Mission Street
Santa Cruz, CA 95060

Triad Santa Cruz Clinic Outpatient Methadone Maintenance
1000-A Emeline Avenue
Santa Cruz, CA 95060

Women's Crisis Support Shelter Services
1658 Soquel Drive, Suite A
Santa Cruz, CA 95060

SANTA MARIA

Aegis Medical Systems
115 East Fesler Street
Santa Maria, CA 93454

Central Coast Headway Drugs and Alcohol Awareness Program
318 West Carmen Lane
Santa Maria, CA 93454

Charles Golodner Counseling Group
301 South Miller Street, Suite 105
Santa Maria, CA 93454

Cottage Care Outpatient Center of Santa Maria
201 South Miller Street, Suite 105
Santa Maria, CA 93454

Family Life Counseling Services
301 South Miller Street, Suite 103
Santa Maria, CA 93454

Good Samaritan Shelter
Recovery Point
406 South Pine Street
Santa Maria, CA 93454

SANTA MONICA

Alcoholism Council West Area High Gain Project
1424 4 Street
Suite 205
Santa Monica, CA 90401

Clare Foundation
Adult Recovery Home
1871 9 Street
Santa Monica, CA 90405

Drug Court Program
1002 Pico Boulevard
Santa Monica, CA 90404

Santa Monica Recovery/Detox
Center
907 Pico Boulevard
Santa Monica, CA 90405

Signs of Recovery Program
1023 Pico Boulevard
Santa Monica, CA 90405

**Saint John's Hospital and
Health Center Chemical
Dependency Center**
1328 22 Street
Santa Monica, CA 90404

**Santa Monica Bay Area Drug
Abuse Council/New Start**
2714 Pico Boulevard
Suite 210
Santa Monica, CA 90401

SANTA PAULA

Community Health Projects
625 East Main Street
Santa Paula, CA 93060

Rainbow Recovery Youth Center
15005 Faulkner Road
Santa Paula, CA 93060

**Santa Clara Valley Alcoholism
Services United**
Outpatient Program
951 East Main Street
Santa Paula, CA 93060

Recovery Home/Casa Un Paso
Adelante
222 8th Street
Santa Paula, CA 93060

SANTA ROSA

**California Human Development
Corp Athena House**
1539 Humboldt Street
Santa Rosa, CA 95404

**Campobello Chemical
Dependency Recovery Center**
3400 Guerneville Road
Santa Rosa, CA 95401

Casa Calmecac
857 Dutton Avenue
Santa Rosa, CA 95407

**Drink/Link Moderation
Programs Products and
Services**
Santa Rosa, CA 95402

Drug Abuse Alternatives Center
Outpatient Treatment
Perinatal Day Treatment
Redwood Empire Addictions
Program (REAP)
Turning Point Program
2403 Professional Drive
Santa Rosa, CA 95403

**Lower Lake Transitional Living
Center**
2403 Professional Drive, Suite 101
Santa Rosa, CA 95403

R House
Oak Park Facility
5136 Oak Park Way
Santa Rosa, CA 95409

Santa Rosa Treatment Program
1901 Cleveland Avenue
Unit B
Santa Rosa, CA 95403

**Sonoma County Alcohol, Drug,
and Tobacco Services**
2759 Bennett Valley Road
Santa Rosa, CA 95404

Drinking Driver Program
1300 Coddington Center
Santa Rosa, CA 95401

Ruth Place
1018 Ruth Place
Santa Rosa, CA 95401

Unity House
920 West 8th Street
Santa Rosa, CA 95401

**Sonoma County Indian Health
Project Behavioral Health
Department**
791 Lombardi Court
Suite 101
Santa Rosa, CA 95407

Villa Lodge
3640 Stony Point Road
Santa Rosa, CA 95407

**Womens Recovery Services/A
Unique Place**
98-140 Hendley Street
Santa Rosa, CA 95401

SANTA YNEZ

**Santa Ynez Tribal Health Clinic
Substance Abuse Services**
3410 East Highway 246
Santa Ynez, CA 93460

SAUGUS

Live Again Recovery Home
38215 North San Francisquito
Canyon Road
Saugus, CA 91350

SAUSALITO

**Bay Area Community Resources
Marin City Project**
740 Drake Avenue
Sausalito, CA 94965

SCOTTS VALLEY

Camp Recovery Center
3192 Glen Canyon Road
Scotts Valley, CA 05066

**Triad Community Services
Outpatient Drug and Alcohol
Treatment Program**
5271 Scotts Valley Drive
Suite 200
Scotts Valley, CA 95066

SEASIDE

Community Human Services
Genesis Residential Center
1152 Sonoma Avenue
Seaside, CA 93955

SHAFTER

Traffic and Alcohol Awareness School of Kern (TAASK)
511 Central Valley Highway
Shafter, CA 93263

SIERRA MADRE

Lifechanges Counseling Center
37 Auburn Street, Suite 5
Sierra Madre, CA 91024

SIMI VALLEY

Aegis Medical Systems
2943 Sycamore Drive
Suite 1
Simi Valley, CA 93065

Rainbow Recovery Centers II
3165 Tapo Canyon Road
Simi Valley, CA 93063

Ventura County Department of Public Health Simi Valley Center
4322 Eileen Street
Simi Valley, CA 93063

SKYFOREST

Rim Family Services
28545 Highway 18
Skyforest, CA 92385

SONORA

Tuolumne County Alcohol/Drug Services
12801 Cabezut Road
Sonora, CA 95370

SOUTH GATE

Southern California Alcohol and Drug Program
8627 California Avenue
South Gate, CA 90280

SOUTH LAGUNA BEACH

South Coast Medical Center Genesis Chemical Dependency Services
31872 Coast Highway
South Laguna Beach, CA 92677

SOUTH LAKE TAHOE

Sierra Recovery Center
931 Macinaw Street
South Lake Tahoe, CA 96150

2677 Reaves Street
South Lake Tahoe, CA 96150

972 Tallac Avenue, Suite B
South Lake Tahoe, CA 96150

Tahoe Turning Point Juvenile
Heavenly Treatment Center
TEHMENA
South Lake Tahoe, CA 96151

Residential Treatment Centers
562 Tehema Street
South Lake Tahoe, CA 96151

Tahoe Youth and Family Services, Inc.
1021 Fremont Avenue
South Lake Tahoe, CA 95705

SOUTH SAN FRANCISCO

First Chance Program
383 East Grand Avenue
South San Francisco, CA 94080-0007

Kaiser Permanente Medical Center Chemical Dependency Service
1200 El Camino Real
South San Francisco, CA 94080

Sitike Counseling Center
306 Spruce Avenue
South San Francisco, CA 94080

STANTON

Stanton Detox
Roque Center
10936 Dale Street
Stanton, CA 90680

Western Pacific Stanton Medical Clinic
10751 Dale Street
Stanton, CA 90680

STOCKTON

Aegis Medical Systems
8626 Lower Sacramento Road,
Suite 41
Stockton, CA 95210

Focus
322 North California Street
Stockton, CA 95202

Jesus Saves Ministries
438 South Sutter Street
Stockton, CA 95203

Maynards Chemical Dependency Recovery Center
4550 North Pershing Street
Suite 3
Stockton, CA 95207

Narrow Gate Counseling Consortium
930 North Hunter Street
Stockton, CA 95269

Saint Joseph's Behavioral Health Center
2510 North California Street
Stockton, CA 95204

Salvation Army Adult Rehabilitation Center
1247 South Wilson Way
Stockton, CA 95205

San Joaquin County Chemical Dependency Counseling Center
620 North Aurora Street
Stockton, CA 95205

Starting Point
701 East Park Street
Stockton, CA 95202

Xenia Ark Residential Treatment Center
1609 North Wilson Way
Stockton, CA 95205

STUDIO CITY

Quest Counseling
3959 Laurel Canyon Boulevard,
Suite C
Studio City, CA 91604

SUN VALLEY

People in Progress Sun Valley Community Rehab Center
8140 Sunland Boulevard
Sun Valley, CA 91352

SUSANVILLE

Lassen County Alcohol and Drug Program
476 Alexander Avenue
Susanville, CA 96130

Promises Perinatal Program
701-373 Johnstonville Road
Susanville, CA 96130

Lassen Indian Health Center Substance Abuse Services
795 Joaquin Street
Susanville, CA 96130

SYLMAR

Industry Community Interface (ICI) Enterprises
13741 Foothill Boulevard
Suite 110
Sylmar, CA 91342

MaClay House Inc
13370 Sayre Street
Sylmar, CA 91342

Oasis Women's Recovering Community
13832 Polk Street
Sylmar, CA 91342

Phoenix Houses of Los Angeles
11600 Eldridge Avenue
Sylmar, CA 91342

Shepherds Recovery
13466 Hubbard Street
Sylmar, CA 91342

TAFT

Memorial Center Taft Outpatient Clinic
401 Finley Drive
Taft, CA 93268

Traffic and Alcohol Awareness School of Kern (TAASK)
Taft College WESTEC 210 East
Center Street
Taft, CA 93268

TAHOE CITY

Sierra Family Services/Tahoe
2690 Lake Forest Road
Suite 202
Tahoe City, CA 96145

TARZANA

Center for Counseling and Education
6025 Etiwanda Street
Tarzana, CA 91356

Looking Glass Counseling Center
19318 Ventura Boulevard
Suite 206
Tarzana, CA 91356

Ronald Nicholas, Ph.D. Marriage and Family Professional Corp.
6025 Etiwanda Avenue
Tarzana, CA 91356

Tarzana Treatment Center
18646 Oxnard Street
Tarzana, CA 91356

Valley Women's Center and Family Recovery Center
5530 Corbin Avenue
Suite 325
Tarzana, CA 91356

TEMECULA

Riverside County Substance Abuse Program
41002 Country Center Drive
Temecula, CA 92590

Hill Alcohol and Drug Treatment Center
29377 Rancho California Road
Temecula, CA 92591

THERMAL

Riverside Cnty Latino Commission on Alcohol and Drug Services/Casa Cecilia Recovery Home
83-385 Rosa Avenue
Thermal, CA 92274

THOUSAND OAKS

Ventura Recovery Cente
166 Siesta Avenue
Thousand Oaks, CA 91360

Be Free Treatment Center at Conejo Counseling Center
3625 Thousand Oaks Boulevard
Suite 6
Thousand Oaks, CA 91362

TORRANCE

Childrens Institute International South County Facility
21810 Normandie Avenue
Torrance, CA 90509

Life Change Residential Treatment Center
2815 Artesia Boulevard
Torrance, CA 90504

National Council on Alcohol and Drug Dependency
1334 Post Avenue
Torrance, CA 90501

Options for Recovery The Stork Club
1124 West Carson Street
Building N33
Torrance, CA 90502

South Bay Drug Abuse Coalition
2370 West Carson Street
Suite 136
Torrance, CA 90501

Southwest Driver Benefits Program
2370 West Carson Street
Suite 150
Torrance, CA 90501

**Torrance Memorial Medical
     Center Outpatient Chemical
     Dependency Program**
3330 Lomita Boulevard, 7th Floor
Torrance, CA 90505

Twin Town Treatment Center
2171 Torrance Boulevard
Torrance, CA 90501

TRACY

**Valley Community Counseling
     Center**
19 East 6th Street
Tracy, CA 95376

TRAVIS AFB

**Alcohol and Drug Treatment
     Inpatient Program**
530 Hickam Avenue
Travis AFB, CA 94535

TRUCKEE

**Nevada County Substance
     Abuse Treatment and
     Recovery (NCSA)**
10015 Palisades Drive, Suite 1
Truckee, CA 96162

**TGIF Counseling Center
     Substance Abuse Services**
10075 Levon Avenue, Suite 102
Truckee, CA 96161

TULARE

**Alcohol Center for Teenagers
     (ACT)**
23393 Road 68
Tulare, CA 93274

**Kings View Substance Abuse
     Program Tulare County**
559 East Bardsley Avenue
Tulare, CA 93275

TUOLUMNE

**MACT Health Board Tuolumne
     Rural Indian Health Program**
19590 Mi Wu Street
Tuolumne, CA 95379

**Maynards Chemical
     Dependency Recovery Center**
19325 Cherokee Road
Tuolumne, CA 95379

TUSTIN

**Recovery Homes of America,
     Inc.**
Cornerstone
13682 Yorba Street
Tustin, CA 92680

TWENTYNINE PALMS

**Combined Drug and Alcohol
     Counseling Center (CDACC)
     Manpower Program**
Marine Corps Air Ground Combat
     Center
Twentynine Palms, CA 92278

UKIAH

Ford Street Project
139 Ford Street
Ukiah, CA 95482

Guidville Rancheria
419h Talmage Road
Ukiah, CA 95482

**Mendocino County Public
     Health Dept. Division of
     Alcohol and Other Drug
     Programs**
302 West Henry Street
Ukiah, CA 95482

**Mendocino County Youth
     Project**
776 South State Street
Ukiah, CA 95482

UNION CITY

**Kaiser Permanente Chemical
     Dependency Services**
3552 Whipple Road
Union City, CA 94587

UPLAND

Arrow House
1439 West Arrow Highway
Upland, CA 91786

**Inland Valley Drug and Alcohol
     Recovery Services Recovery
     Center**
934 North Mountain Avenue
Suite A
Upland, CA 91786

**San Antonio Community
     Hospital**
999 San Bernardino Road
Upland, CA 91786

VACAVILLE

**Latino Substance Abuse
     Program**
190 South Orchard Street
Suite B-101
Vacaville, CA 95688

VALLEJO

Bi Bett Corporation
Recovery Connection
604 Broadway
Vallejo, CA 94590

Shamia Recovery Center
126 Ohio Street
Vallejo, CA 94590

Southern Solano Alcohol Council
419 Pennsylvania Street
Vallejo, CA 94590

Genesis House
1149 Warren Avenue
Vallejo, CA 94591

**House of Acts Substance Abuse
     Program**
627 Grant Street
Vallejo, CA 94590

**Kaiser Permanente Chemical
     Dependency Services**
800 Sereno Drive
Vallejo, CA 94589

**Youth and Family Services
     Adolescent Substance Abuse
     Programs**
408 Tennessee Street
Vallejo, CA 94590

VAN NUYS

American Health Services/Van Nuys
6265 Sepulveda Boulevard, Suite 9
Van Nuys, CA 91411

High Road Program
14430 Sherman Way
Van Nuys, CA 91405-2340

I/ADARP Van Nuys Clinic
7400 Van Nuys Boulevard
Suite 207
Van Nuys, CA 91411

National Council on Alcoholism and Drug Dependency of San Fernando Valley
14557 Friar Street
Van Nuys, CA 91411

New Directions for Youth
7400 Van Nuys Boulevard
Suite 203
Van Nuys, CA 91405

Northeast Valley Health Corporation Mi Descanso
6819 Sepulveda Boulevard
Suite 102
Van Nuys, CA 91405

Western Pacific Medical Corporation/Van Nuys
14332 Victory Boulevard
Van Nuys, CA 91401

VENICE

Didi Hirsch CMHC Outpatient Drug Abuse Services
1600 Main Street, Suite B
Venice, CA 90291

Inglewood Medical and Mental Health Services/Venice
2014 Lincoln Boulevard
Venice, CA 90291

Phoenix Houses
503 Ocean Front Walk
Venice, CA 90291

Promises Residential Treatment
3743 South Barrington Avenue
Venice, CA 90291

VENTURA

Center for Creative Change
8 North Fir Street
Ventura, CA 93001

Khepra House
105 West Harrison Avenue
Ventura, CA 93001

Medical Support Services to Substance Abusers
3291 Loma Vista Road
Ventura, CA 93003

Miracle House
92 & 94 South Anacapa Street
Ventura, CA 93001

Paul Booth Addictions Education
290 Maple Court, Suite 254
Ventura, CA 93003

Prototypes Women's Center
152 North Dos Caminos Avenue
Ventura, CA 93003

4973 Terry Drive
Ventura, CA 93003

Ventura County Drinking Driver Program
702 County Square Drive
Ventura, CA 93003

Vista Del Mar Hospital Addiction Medicine Services
801 Seneca Street
Ventura, CA 93001

VICTORVILLE

High Desert Child/Adolescent and Family Service Center
16248 Victor Street
Victorville, CA 92392

Jackson/Bibby Awareness Group DUI Services
14420 Civic Drive, Suite 3
Victorville, CA 92392

Pine Ridge Treatment Center
15367 Bonanza RoadSuite A
Victorville, CA 92392

Saint John of God Health Care Services
Alpha House
Casa San Raphael
How House Men's Program
Alpha Tot House
13333 Palmdale Road
Victorville, CA 92392

VISALIA

Alcohol and Drug Services of Tulare County Alternative Services
2223 North Shirk Road
Visalia, CA 93291

Kings View Substance Abuse Program Tulare County/New Generation
1011 West Center Street
Visalia, CA 93277

Tulare County Alcoholism Council
Mothering Heights
504 South Locust Street
Visalia, CA 93277

New Visions for Women
1425 East Walnut Street
Visalia, CA 93292

Pine Recovery Center
120 West School Street
Visalia, CA 93291

Tulare County Hispanic Commission El Primer Paso
1350 South Crowe Street
Visalia, CA 93277

Turning Point of Central California Turning Point Youth Services
119 South Locust Street
Visalia, CA 93291

VISTA

Amity at Vista
2260 Watson Way
Vista, CA 92083

Choices in Recovery
733 South Santa Fe Avenue
Vista, CA 92083

Mental Health Systems
North County Drug Court
1855 East Vista Way Suite 9
Vista, CA 92084

Options for Recovery
1381 East Vista Way
Vista, CA 92083

Probationers in Recovery
1855 East Vista Way
Vista, CA 92083

WALNUT CREEK

**Criminal Justice Treatment
Program Post Conviction DDP**
2020 North Broadway, Suite 101
Walnut Creek, CA 94596

**Kaiser Permanente Chemical
Dependency Program**
1425 South Main Street
Walnut Creek, CA 94596

**Walnut Creek Hospital Dual
Diagnosis and Addiction
Services**
175 La Casa Via
Walnut Creek, CA 94598

WATSONVILLE

Fenix Services
Family Outpatient Services
406 Main Street
Suite 403
Watsonville, CA 95076

Hermanas Recovery Home
640 Rodriguez Street
Watsonville, CA 95076

**Pajaro Valley Prevention and
Student Assistance Program**
335 East Lake Avenue
Watsonville, CA 95076

Paloma House
321 East Beach Street
Watsonville, CA 95076

**Santa Cruz Community
Counseling Center**
Alto Counseling Center/South
11-D Alexander Street
Watsonville, CA 95076

Si Se Puede
161 Miles Lane
Watsonville, CA 95076

Youth Services/South
241 East Lake Street
Watsonville, CA 95076

**Watsonville Community
Hospital Alcohol and Drug
Treatment Center**
75 Nielson Street
Watsonville, CA 95076

WEAVERVILLE

**Trinity County Counseling
Center Alcohol and Drug
Program**
801 Main Street, Suite A
Weaverville, CA 96093

Rainbow to Recovery
801 Main Street, Suite P
Weaverville, CA 96093

WEST COVINA

**Community Health Projects/Los
Angeles**
West Covina Unit
1825 East Thelborn Street
West Covina, CA 91790

**Rickman Recovery Center/West
Covina**
1107 South Glendora Avenue
West Covina, CA 91790

Safety Education Center
1400 West Covina Parkway
3rd Floor
West Covina, CA 91790

**San Gabriel Valley Driver
Improvement Program**
1502 West Covina Parkway
Suite 207
West Covina, CA 91790

WEST HILLS

**Pine Grove Hospital Matrix
Center**
7011 Shoup Avenue
West Hills, CA 91307-2337

WEST HOLLYWOOD

**A Los Angeles Driver Education
Center**
8350 Santa Monica Boulevard
Suite 107
West Hollywood, CA 90069

WESTMINSTER

**Orange County Health Care
Agency Alcohol and Drug
Abuse Services**
14180 Beach Boulevard Suite 203
Westminster, CA 92683

WEST SACRAMENTO

**John H Jones Community Clinic
Drug Treatment Program**
950 Sacramento Avenue
West Sacramento, CA 95691

**Sacramento Recovery House,
Inc.**
1520 Madrone Avenue
Apartment 2
West Sacramento, CA 95691-2632

WHITTIER

**Aegis Medical Systems/Whittier
Methadone Treatment
Program**
11738 Valley View Avenue
Suite B
Whittier, CA 90604

Awakenings
12322 Clearglen Avenue
Whittier, CA 90604

**Center for Recovery from
Compulsivities HOW House**
7237 Milton Avenue
Whittier, CA 90602

**Fred C. Nelles Youth Correction
Facility**
11850 East Whittier Boulevard
Whittier, CA 90601

**Presbyterian Intercommunity
Hospital**
12401 East Washington Boulevard
Whittier, CA 90602

Southern California Alcohol and Drug Programs Foley House
10501–10519 Mills Avenue
Whittier, CA 90606

WILLITS

Lucky Deuce DUI/DDP
145 South Main Street
Willits, CA 95490

Mendocino County Alcohol and Other Drug Programs
72 West Commercial Street
Willits, CA 95490

WILMINGTON

Aegis Medical Systems
936 North Wilmington Boulevard
Wilmington, CA 90744

Behavioral Health Services Wilmington Comm. Prevention/Recovery Center
1318 Avalon Boulevard
Wilmington, CA 90744

La Clinica Del Pueblo
1547 North Avalon Boulevard
Wilmington, CA 90744

Transcultural Health Development
117 East Harry Bridges Boulevard
Wilmington, CA 90744

WINNETKA

Women's Odyssey Organization, Inc.
20830 Parthenia Street
Winnetka, CA 91306

WINTERHAVEN

Fort Yuma Alcohol and Drug Abuse Prevention Program
1888 San Pasqual Road
Winterhaven, CA 92283

WOODLAND

Beamer Street Detoxification and Residential Treatment Center
178 West Beamer Street
Woodland, CA 95695

Yolo Alcoholic Recovery Center Cache Creek Lodge
435 Aspen Street
Woodland, CA 95695

YOUNTVILLE

Veterans' Home of California Alcohol and Drug Treatment Program
200 California Avenue
Yountville, CA 94599

YREKA

Siskiyou Alcohol and Drug Abuse Services
804 South Main Street
Yreka, CA 96097

The Kuruk Tribal Health Program of River of Health and Wellness
1519 South Oregon Street
Yreka, CA 96097

YUBA CITY

First Steps
539 Garden Highway, Suite C
Yuba City, CA 95991

Philbricks Place
2250 Sanborn Road, Building 3
Yuba City, CA 95993

YUCCA VALLEY

Morongo Basin Mental Health Choices DDP
55475 Santa Fe Trail
Yucca Valley, CA 92284-0000

COLORADO

AKRON

Centennial Mental Health Center Substance Abuse Services
871 East First Street
Akron, CO 80720

ALAMOSA

Crossroads Managed Care Systems Inc
2265 Lava Lane
Alamosa, CO 81101

San Luis Valley Mental Health Addiction Services
522 Alamosa Avenue
Alamosa, CO 81101

ARVADA

Alcohol Behavior Information, Inc.
7550 Grant Place
Arvada, CO 80002

Arvada Counseling Center
7850 Vance Drive, Suite 280
Arvada, CO 80003-2128

Empowerment Counseling Services Northwest
5460 Ward Road, Suite 215
Arvada, CO 80002

ASPEN

Colorado West Aspen Counseling Center
405 Castle Creek Road, Suite 9
Aspen, CO 81611

Springs Counseling Center Youth Facility
455 Rio Grande Place
Aspen, CO 81611

AURORA

Abusive Behavior Center
509-A Sable Boulevard
Aurora, CO 80011

Anchor Counseling Inc
15290 East 6th Avenue, Suite 200
Aurora, CO 80011-8833

Aurora Center for Treatment, Ltd.
1591 Chambers Road, Suite E
Aurora, CO 80011

Countermeasures
1450 South Havana Street, Suite 712
Aurora, CO 80012

Dynamic Directions Counseling Services
2323 South Troy Street, Suite 1-226
Aurora, CO 80014-1980

Insights Counseling Service, Inc.
15200 East Girard Avenue
Aurora, CO 80014-5039

Rangeview Counseling Center
1591 Fulton Street, Suite 101
Aurora, CO 80012

AVON

Spring Counseling Center PC
0150 East Beaver Creek Boulevard Suite 207
Avon, CO 81620

BOULDER

Boulder Alcohol Education Center
1525 Spruce Street
Suite 100
Boulder, CO 80302

Boulder Clinic Inc
1317 Spruce Street
Boulder, CO 80302

Boulder Community Hospital
311 Mapleton Avenue
Boulder, CO 80302

Boulder County Health Department
Recovery Program
3450 Broadway
Boulder, CO 80304

Substance Abuse Program
1333 Iris Avenue
Boulder, CO 80302

Personal Growth Services
2305 Canyon Boulevard, Room 205
Boulder, CO 80302

Rangeview Counseling Center
1800 30th Street Suite 220
Boulder, CO 80301

Serenity Center for Personal Growth, Inc.
1800 30th Street
Sussex One Suite 220-I
Boulder, CO 80301

BRECKENRIDGE

Colorado West Detox Center
501 North Park Avenue
Breckenridge, CO 80424-0754

BRIGHTON

Educational Center for Addictions
710 South Main Street
Brighton, CO 80601

Patterns for Positive Living
14 Main Street, Suite F
Brighton, CO 80601

BUCKLEY AFB

Buckley Air Force Base Substance Abuse Program
82 MDOS/SGOMH 275 South Aspen Street
Buckley AFB, CO 80011-9547

BUENA VISTA

Rocky Mountain Behavioral Health
715 East Main Street
Buena Vista, CO 81211-9799

BURLINGTON

Centennial Mental Health Center Alcohol and Drug Outpatient Program
1291 Circle Drive
Burlington, CO 80807

CANON CITY

Covenant Counseling
503 Main Street
Canon City, CO 81212

Rocky Mountain Behavioral Health, Inc.
618 Main Street
Canon City, CO 81215

CARBONDALE

Springs Counseling Center
1101 Village Road, Suite LL-2A
Carbondale, CO 81623-1571

CASTLE ROCK

Dynamic Directions
314 Wilcox Street
Castle Rock, CO 80104

CHEYENNE WELLS

Centennial Mental Health Center, Inc.
Keefe Memorial Hospital
Cheyenne Wells, CO 80810

COLORADO SPRINGS

Adult/Youth Counseling Service
223 North Wahsatch Avenue,
Suite 101
Colorado Springs, CO 80903

Bridge to Awareness Counseling Center, Inc.
606 South Tejon Street
Colorado Springs, CO 80903

Cate Alcohol Education Program
4740 Flintridge Drive
Suite 201-B
Colorado Springs, CO 80918

Cedar Springs BHC Services, Inc.
2135 Southgate Road
Colorado Springs, CO 80906

Chemical Dependency Center
2741 East Las Vegas Street
Colorado Springs, CO 80906

Genesis
715 South Circle Drive
Suite 105
Colorado Springs, CO 80910

Gordon S. Riegel Chemical Dependency Center
825 East Pikes Peak Avenue
Colorado Springs, CO 80903

Health Challenge Counseling Center, Inc.
3750 Astrozon Boulevard
Suite A
Colorado Springs, CO 80910

McMaster Center/El Paso County Dept. of Health and Environment
301 South Union Boulevard
Colorado Springs, CO 80910

Pathways Confidential Counseling, Inc.
1767 South 8th Street
Suite 100
Colorado Springs, CO 80905

Pike's Peak Mental Health Center
Outpatient Division
179 Parkside Drive
Colorado Springs, CO 80910

Positive Change
1120 North Circle Street
Suite 11
Colorado Springs, CO 80909

Tombs Counseling Services
2860 South Circle Drive
Suite 2129
Colorado Springs, CO 80906

COMMERCE CITY

Adams Community Mental Health Center
7191 Holly Street
Commerce City, CO 80022

Insights Counseling Services, Inc.
6025 Parkway Drive, Suite 110
Commerce City, CO 80022-5412

CORTEZ

Cortez Addiction Recovery Services, Inc.
35 North Ash Street
Cortez, CO 81321

CRAIG

Yampa Valley Psychotherapists
2045 West Victory Way
Craig, CO 81625

DELTA

Creative Counseling Place
550 Palmer Street, Suite 103
Delta, CO 81416

Midwestern Colorado Mental Health Center
Center for Mental Health
195 Stafford Lane
Delta, CO 81416

Options Counseling Center
261 Hartig Drive
Suite A North
Delta, CO 81416

DENVER

Addiction Residence Treatment Services (ARTS) Peer I Residential Treatment Facility
3712 West Princeton Circle
Denver, CO 80236

Adolescent Counseling Exchange
948 Santa Fe Drive
Denver, CO 80204

Alcohol Counseling Services of Colorado, Inc.
1300 South Lafayette Street
Denver, CO 80210

Alpar Human Development Services Alcohol Outpatient Treatment
1330 Leyden Street, Suite 103
Denver, CO 80222

Anchor Counseling, Inc.
1009 Grant Street, Suite 50
Denver, CO 80203

A Treatment Agency Inc
1745 South Federal Boulevard
Denver, CO 80219-4861

Bi-Community Correctional Services Denver Day Reporting Center
1555 Clarkson Street
Denver, CO 80203

Bridge Counseling Center
2422 South Federal Boulevard
Denver, CO 80219

Broadway Counseling Services
725 South Broadway Street
Suite 16
Denver, CO 80209

Center for Behavioral Health
2465 South Downing Street
Suite 110
Denver, CO 80210

Center for Human Development Colorado MOVES
2345 South Federal Boulevard
Suite 103
Denver, CO 80219

Choosing Life Center
1626 High Street
Denver, CO 80218

Colorado Inhalant Abuse Program
1115 Broadway Street, Suite 102
Denver, CO 80203

Columbia Health One Presbyterian/Saint Luke's Medical Center
1719 East 19th Avenue
Denver, CO 80218

Community Alcohol/Drug Rehab and Education Center (CADREC)
3315 Gilpin Street
Denver, CO 80205

Comprehensive Addiction Treatment Services
2222 East 18 Avenue
Denver, CO 80206

Denver Area Youth Services/ Days Adolescent Substance Abuse Treatment
1240 West Bayaud Avenue
Denver, CO 80223

Denver Health Community Detox Behavioral Health Services
1155 Cherokee Street
Denver, CO 80204

Denver Indian Health and Family Services
3749 South King Street
Denver, CO 80236

Dry Creek Treatment Center
222 Milwaukee Street, Suite 408-B
Denver, CO 80206-5008

Essex Growth Center
2789 West Alameda Street
Denver, CO 80219

Fresh Start, Inc.
2250 East 16th Avenue
Denver, CO 80206

Gateway Treatment Center
1250 South Parker Road
Suite 103
Denver, CO 80231

IDEA
2828 North Speer Boulevard
Suite 116
Denver, CO 80211

Inner Connections, Inc.
1556 Williams Street
Denver, CO 80218

Insights Counseling Services, Inc.
2200 East 104th Avenue
Suite 213
Denver, CO 80233

Maria Droste Services of Colorado
1355 South Colorado Boulevard
Suite C-100
Denver, CO 80222

Metropolitan Counseling Services
1601 South Federal Boulevard
Heritage Plaza Suite 115
Denver, CO 80219

Mile High Club Alcohol Abuse Halfway House
1444 Wazee Street, Suite 125
Denver, CO 80205

Multi Addictions Processing Agency (MAPA)
1650 Franklin Street, Lower Level
Denver, CO 80218

Outpatient Behavioral Health Services (OBHS)
320 West 8th Avenue, Unit 2
Denver, CO 80204

Rebound Foundation Adventures in Change
3445 West Mansfield Street
Denver, CO 80236

Servicios de la Raza Alcohol Abuse Program
4055 Tejon Street
Denver, CO 80211

Sobriety House, Inc. Stepping Stone
107 Acoma Street
Denver, CO 80223

Southwest Family Services
1800 South Sheridan Boulevard
Suite 303
Denver, CO 80232

Special Services Clinic, Inc.
301 Knox Court
Denver, CO 80219

Stout Street Foundation
1609 Gaylord Street
Denver, CO 80206-1206

1647 Gaylord Street
Denver, CO 80206

UCHSC Addiction Research Treatment Services (ARTS) Outpatient Clinic
1827 Gaylord
Denver, CO 80206

University of Colorado Health Science Center Addiction Research Treatment Service
3738 West Princeton Circle
Denver, CO 80236

Veterans' Affairs Medical Center
Substance Abuse Program
1055 Clermont Street
Denver, CO 80220

Wellspring Alcohol and Drug Abuse Services
1660 South Albion Street
Suite 600
Denver, CO 80222

Western Clinical Health Services
1038 Bannock Street
Denver, CO 80204

Youthtrack Alliance
920 Clarkson Street
Denver, CO 80128

DURANGO

La Plata Counseling South West Community Corrections
1111 Camino Del Rio Street
Durango, CO 81301

Southwest Colorado Mental Health Center Detoxification
281 Sawyer Drive
Durango, CO 81301

ELIZABETH

Centennial Mental Health Center Alcohol and Drug Outpatient Program
349 East Washington Street
Elizabeth, CO 80107

ENGLEWOOD

Mile HI Counseling, Inc.
300 East Hampden Avenue
Suite 230
Englewood, CO 80110

Valley Hope Alcohol/Drug Center
8000 East Prentice Avenue
Suite D-12
Englewood, CO 80111-2727

Alternative Pathways, Inc.
4195 South Broadway Street
Englewood, CO 80110-4632

ESTES PARK

Harmony Foundation, Inc. Alcohol/Drug Abuse Program
1600 Fish Hatchery Road
Estes Park, CO 80517

EVERGREEN

Mountain Treatment Services
6949 Highway 73
Evergreen, CO 80439

FAIRPLAY

Rocky Mountain Behavioral Health, Inc.
1271 Castello Avenue, Suite B
Fairplay, CO 80440

FLORENCE

Clear View Center
521 West 5th Street
Florence, CO 81226

FORT CARSON

U.S. Army MEDDAC Community Counseling Center
MCXE/AS/MH/AD
Specker and Ellis Street
Fort Carson, CO 80913

FORT COLLINS

Center for Life Skills Education
400 West Magnolia Street
Fort Collins, CO 80521

Hope Counseling Center
301 East Olive Street
Fort Collins, CO 80524

Larimer County Institute for Alcohol Awareness
253 Linden Street
Suite 206
Fort Collins, CO 80524

Managed Adolescent Care Center
400 Remington Street, Suite 202
Fort Collins, CO 80525

Mountain Crest Behavioral Healthcare System Addictive Disease Unit (ADU)
4601 Corbett Drive
Fort Collins, CO 80528

Seven Lakes Recovery Program
2362 East Prospect Avenue
Fort Collins, CO 80525

FORT MORGAN

Centennial Mental Health Center
910 East Railroad Street
Fort Morgan, CO 80701

FRANKTOWN

Running Creek Counseling Service
7601 Burning Tree Drive
Franktown, CO 80116

FRASER

Rangeview Counseling Center
193 County Road, Suite 804
Fraser, CO 80442

FRISCO

Bair Counseling Center
619 Main Street
Frisco, CO 80443

Columbine Recovery Center
1000 North Summit Boulevard
Suite 200
Frisco, CO 80443

GLENWOOD SPRINGS

Valley View Youth Recovery Center
1906 Blake Avenue
Glenwood Springs, CO 81601

GOLDEN

Counseling Evaluation and Treatment Program Inc
607 10th Street, Suite 103
Golden, CO 80401

Division of Youth Services Lookout Mountain School
2901 Ford Street
Golden, CO 80401

GRAND JUNCTION

Adult Adolescent Alcohol Treatment (AAAT)
726 Colorado Avenue
Grand Junction, CO 81506

Colorado West Mental Health Center
450 Ouray Street
Grand Junction, CO 81501

Counseling Works
1904 North 7th Street
Grand Junction, CO 81501

Division of Youth Services
360 28th Road
Grand Junction, CO 81501

Dos Rios Counseling Service
1008 North 5th Street
Grand Junction, CO 81501

Saint Mary's Recovery Services
436 South 7th Street
Grand Junction, CO 81501

Outpatient Site
744 Horizon Drive, Suite 210
Grand Junction, CO 81501

In Roads Counseling
1141 North 25 Street
Suite F
Grand Junction, CO 81501

Veterans' Affairs Medical Center Substance Abuse Treatment Program (SATP)
2121 North Avenue
Building 6
Grand Junction, CO 81501

GREELEY

ARC Counseling Center
1122 9th Street, Suite 102
Greeley, CO 80631-3277

Island Grove Regional Treatment Center, Inc.
1140 M Street
Greeley, CO 80631

Psychcare Family Recovery Center
928 12th Street
Greeley, CO 80631

Residential Treatment Center
1776 6 Avenue
Greeley, CO 80631

HIGHLANDS RANCH

Addiction Treatment Outpatient Services
7120 East County Line Road, Suite 101
Highlands Ranch, CO 80126

HOLYOKE

Centennial Mental Health Center Substance Abuse Services
109 North Campbell Street
Holyoke, CO 80734

IDAHO SPRINGS

Chicago Creek Roads, Inc. Hopeful Futures
984 Highway 103
Idaho Springs, CO 80452

Clear Creek Counseling
1504 Main Street
Idaho Springs, CO 80452

IGNACIO

Southern Ute Alcohol Recovery Center Peaceful Spirit
296 Mouache Road
Ignacio, CO 81137

JULESBURG

Centennial Mental Health Center Substance Abuse Services
115 Elm Street
Julesburg, CO 80737

LAFAYETTE

Lafayette Alcohol Education and Therapy
201 East Simpson Street
Suite 201-B
Lafayette, CO 80026

LA JARA

SLV Family Resources
304 Walnut Street
La Jara, CO 81140

LA JUNTA

Pathfinders
207 1/2 Colorado Avenue
La Junta, CO 81050

LAKEWOOD

Alternative Behaviors Counseling
1949 Wadsworth Street
Suite 206
Lakewood, CO 80215

Alternative Homes for Youth/ Cedars
5400 West Cedar Avenue
Lakewood, CO 80226

Attitude Development Services
12211 West Alameda Parkway, Suite 220
Lakewood, CO 80228

Bi Day Reporting
2099 Wadsworth Boulevard
Lakewood, CO 80215-3383

Cenikor Foundation, Inc. Alcohol and Drug Abuse Program
1533 Glen Ayr Drive
Lakewood, CO 80215

Community Resource for Alcohol and Family Treatment
200 South Sheridan Boulevard, Suite 240
Lakewood, CO 80226

Crossroads Counseling, Ltd.
8000 West 14 Avenue
Suite 1
Lakewood, CO 80215

Empowerment Counseling Services, Inc.
1675 Carr Street
Suite 110-B
Lakewood, CO 80215

Jefferson County Health Department Substance Abuse Counseling Program
260 South Kipling Street
Lakewood, CO 80226

DBA Family Counseling Center
7430 West 16th Avenue
Lakewood, CO 80215

Milestone Counseling Services Inc
8533 West Colfax Avenue
Lakewood, CO 80215

Serenity Education and Therapy
2255 South Wadsworth Boulevard
Suite G-3
Lakewood, CO 80226

Touchstone Counseling Center
777 South Wadsworth Boulevard
Irongate 2 Suite 205
Lakewood, CO 80226

LAMAR

New Lifestyles
105 South 5th Street
Lamar, CO 81052

Southeast Colorado for Drug Free Communities
1006 South Main Street
Lamar, CO 81052

LAS ANIMAS

Resada Alcohol and Drug Abuse Program
11000 Road, Garage 5
Las Animas, CO 81054

LEADVILLE

Mount Hope Recovery, Inc.
130 West 5th Street
Leadville, CO 80461

LIMON

Centennial Mental Health Center Substance Abuse Services
606 Main Street
Limon, CO 80828

LITTLETON

Alternative Counseling
1500 West Littleton Boulevard, Suite 201
Littleton, CO 80120

Arapahoe Mental Health Center Aquarius Center/Sami
5500 South Sycamore
Littleton, CO 80120

LONGMONT

Longmont United Hospital Addiction
1331 Linden Street
Longmont, CO 80501

LOVELAND

Hope Counseling Center
446 North Garfield Avenue
Loveland, CO 80537

Larimer County Institute for Alcohol Awareness
314 East 4th Street
Loveland, CO 80537-5604

MONTROSE

Midwestern Colorado Mental Health Center The Center for Mental Health/Substance Abuse Services
605 East Miami Road
Montrose, CO 81401

Montrose Memorial Hospital Care Center
800 South 3rd Street
Montrose, CO 81401

Touchstone Counseling
118 North Cascade Street
Montrose, CO 81401

MORRISON

Lost and Found, Inc. Substance Abuse Program
9189 South Turkey Creek Road
Morrison, CO 80465

NORWOOD

Midwestern Colorado Mental Health Center The Center for Mental Health/Norwood
1510 West Grand Avenue
Norwood, CO 81423

PAGOSA SPRINGS

Rio Blanco Counseling Center
244 Pagosa Street
Pagosa Springs, CO 81147

PARKER

First Step Counseling
10290 South Progress Way
Suite 105
Parker, CO 80134

Parker Valley Hope
22422 East Main Street
Parker, CO 80138

PETERSON AFB

Peterson Air Force Base Substance Abuse Program
21 MDOS/SGOMH 559 Vincent Street
Peterson AFB, CO 80914-7804

PUEBLO

Associates for Psychotherapy and Education, Inc.
229 West 12th Street
Pueblo, CO 81003-2810

Awareness Institute, Inc.
1245 Palmer Avenue, Suite 210
Pueblo, CO 81004

Colorado Mental Health Institute at Pueblo Circle Program
1600 West 24 Street
Building 116
Pueblo, CO 81003

Crossroads Managed Care Systems, Inc.
509 East 13th Street
Pueblo, CO 81001

1700 East Evans Street
Pueblo, CO 81004

Parkview Episcopal Medical Center Chemical Dependency Program
58 Club Manor Drive
Pueblo, CO 81008

Pueblo Youth Services Bureau Substance Abuse Services
112 West D Street
Pueblo, CO 81003

STERLING

Centennial Mental Health Sterling Office Substance Abuse Services
211 West Main Street
Sterling, CO 80751

THORNTON

Arapahoe House, Inc.
8801 Lipan Street
Thornton, CO 80221

Empowerment Counseling Services
9101 North Pearl Street, Suite 231
Thornton, CO 80229

TRINIDAD

Crossroads Managed Care Systems, Inc.
Outpatient Care
1004 Carbon Place
Trinidad, CO 81082

WALSENBURG

Crossroads Managed Care Systems, Inc.
622 South Albert Street
Walsenburg, CO 81089

WHEAT RIDGE

Adolescent and Family Institute of Colorado, Inc.
10001 West 32nd Avenue
Wheat Ridge, CO 80033

Choices in Living Counseling Center, Inc.
7100 West 44 Avenue
Suite 102
Wheat Ridge, CO 80033

Family Violence Program
4243 Harlan Street
Wheat Ridge, CO 80033-5119

West Pines Hospital at Lutheran Medical Center
3400 Lutheran Parkway
Wheat Ridge, CO 80033

WOODLAND PARK

Journeys Counseling and Education Center
320 Burdette Street
Woodland Park, CO 80863

WRAY

Prairie Land Recovery Center
340 South Birch Street
Wray, CO 80758

YUMA

Centennial Mental Health Center Alcohol and Drug Outpatient Program
215 South Ash Street
Yuma, CO 80759

CONNECTICUT

ANSONIA

Lower Naugatuck Valley Council on Alcohol/Drug Abuse Alcoholism and Drug Abuse Program
75 Liberty Street
Ansonia, CT 06401

AVON

Reid Treatment Center
Intensive Treatment
121 West Avon Road
Avon, CT 06001

BLOOMFIELD

Blue Ridge Center Administrative Unit
1095 Blue Hills Avenue
Bloomfield, CT 06002

BRANFORD

Branford Counseling Center Outpatient
342 Harbor Street
Branford, CT 06405

BRIDGEPORT

Chemical Abuse Services Agency, Inc. (CASA) Administrative Unit
690 Artic Street
Bridgeport, CT 06604

Greater Bridgeport Community Mental Health Center Acute Substance Abuse Treatment Unit
1635 Central Avenue
Bridgeport, CT 06610

Helping Hand Center
488 Stratford Avenue
Bridgeport, CT 06608

1124 Iranistan Avenue
Bridgeport, CT 06608

Horizons
Intensive Residential Drug Free Program
1635 Fairfield Avenue
Bridgeport, CT 06605

Regional Network of Programs, Inc.
Administrative Unit
Golden Hill Treatment Center/ Detox
Methadone Maintenance
Regional Adolescent Program (RAP)
171 Golden Hill Street
Bridgeport, CT 06604

Center for Human Services
1549 Fairfield Avenue
Bridgeport, CT 06605

Regional Counseling Services
480 Bond Street
Bridgeport, CT 06610

BRIDGEWATER

Midwestern Connecticut Council on Alcoholism
McDonough House/Intensive and Intermediate Residential Programs
132 Hut Hill Road
Bridgewater, CT 06752

BRISTOL

Behavioral Health Services
25 Newell Road Suite D-20
Bristol, CT 06010

Bristol Hospital Behavioral Health Services
440 C North Main Street
Bristol, CT 06010

Counseling Center of Bristol Hospital Evening Chemical Dependency Program
440 C North Main Street
Bristol, CT 06010

CANAAN

Mountainside Lodge, Inc.
187 South Canaan Road
Route 7
Canaan, CT 06018

DANBURY

Danbury Youth Services, Inc.
32 Stevens Street
Danbury, CT 06810

Midwestern Connecticut Council on Alcoholism
Outpatient Unit
Women's Program
238 White Street
Danbury, CT 06810

DANIELSON

Community Prevention/ Addiction Services Outpatient Program
37 Commerce Avenue
Danielson, CT 06239

Perception Programs, Inc.
New Perceptions 232 Broad Street
Danielson, CT 06239

DARIEN

Youth Options Darien Unit
120 Brookside Road
Darien, CT 06820

DAYVILLE

United Services, Inc. Alcohol and Drug Abuse Services
1007 North Main Street
Dayville, CT 06241

DERBY

Griffin Hospital
241 Seymour Avenue
Derby, CT 06418

EAST HARTFORD

Paces Counseling Associates Inc
991 Main Street, Suite 3-A
East Hartford, CT 06108

ENFIELD

New Directions, Inc. of North Central Connecticut
55 Main Street
Enfield, CT 06082

Evening Treatment
Intensive Outpatient
5102 Bigelow Commons
Enfield, CT 06082

FAIRFIELD

Fairfield Community Services
370 Beach Road
Fairfield, CT 06430

FARMINGTON

John Dempsey Hospital Alcohol and Drug Abuse Treatment Center
263 Farmington Avenue
Farmington, CT 06030

GLASTONBURY

Clayton House
203-205 Williams Street
Glastonbury, CT 06033

Rushford Center at Glastonbury
124 Hebron Avenue
Glastonbury, CT 06033

GREENWICH

Greenwich Hospital Recovery Program
Perryridge Road
Greenwich, CT 06830

GROTON

Connection, Inc. Women's Services of Groton
542 Long Hill Road
Groton, CT 06340

Counseling and Assistance Center
Box 27
Groton, CT 06349

HAMDEN

Wakeman Hall at the Children's Center
1400 Whitney Avenue
Hamden, CT 06517

HARTFORD

Alcohol and Drug Recovery Centers, Inc.
Coventry House/Pregnant Women's Program
46 Coventry Street
Hartford, CT 06112

Detoxification Center
500 Vine Street
Hartford, CT 06112

Ceder Crest Regional Hospital Blue Hills Substance Services
51 Coventry Street
Hartford, CT 06112

Community Health Services, Inc. Chemical Dependency Program
520 Albany Avenue
Hartford, CT 06120

Community Substance Abuse Centers
55 Fishfry Street
Hartford, CT 06120

Ambulatory Detox
Methadone Maintenance
55 Fishfry Street
Hartford, CT 06120

Greater Hartford Multiservice Center
136 Collins Street
Hartford, CT 06105

Hartford Dispensary Clinic
345 Main Street
Hartford, CT 06106

Henderson/Johnson Clinic
Methadone Maintenance Program
12 Weston Street
Hartford, CT 06120

Hispanic Alcohol and Substance Abuse Program
80 Jefferson Street
Hartford, CT 06106

Hogar Crea International of Connecticut, Inc.
33 Center Street
Hartford, CT 06120

Methadone to Abstinence Program Outpatient Methadone Maintenance
14 Weston Street
Hartford, CT 06120

Outpatient Counseling Center of ADRC Inc
16 Conventry Street
Hartford, CT 06112

Salvation Army Adult Rehab Center Alcohol Abuse Program
333 Homestead Avenue
Hartford, CT 06112

Wheeler Clinic, Inc. Hartford Outpatient
645 Farmington Avenue
Hartford, CT 06115

Youth Challenge of Greater Hartford
15–17 May Street
Hartford, CT 06105

Youth Challenge Mission for Women
32 Atwood Street
Hartford, CT 06105

LAKEVILLE

McCall Foundation, Inc.
c/o Northwest Center for Mental Health
315 Main Street
Lakeville, CT 06039

LEBANON

Southeast Council on Alcohol and Drug Dependency, Inc. (SCADD) Lebanon Pines Long-term Treatment
37 Camp Moween Road
Lebanon, CT 06249

LITCHFIELD

McAuliffe Manor
7 North Street
Litchfield, CT 06759

MANCHESTER

Community Prevention/
Addiction Services
87-B Oak Street
Manchester, CT 06040

New Hope Manor, Inc.
Residential
48 Hartford Road
Manchester, CT 06040

MANSFIELD CENTER

Natchaug Hospital, Inc.
Adult Inpatient Detox
Quinnebaug Day Treatment Center
Sachem Adult Partial
189 Storrs Road
Mansfield Center, CT 06250

MERIDEN

Midstate Medical Center
435 Lewis Avenue
Meriden, CT 06451

MIDDLEBURY

Cornerstone Continuous Care
900 Straits Turnpike
Middlebury, CT 06762

MIDDLETOWN

Connecticut Valley Hospital
Addiction Services Division
Silver Street
Middletown, CT 06457

Connection, Inc.
99 Eastern Drive
Middletown, CT 06457

Connection House
167 Liberty Street
Middletown, CT 06457

Greater Middletown Counseling
Center
196 Court Street
Middletown, CT 06457

Rushford Center, Inc.
Administrative and Prevention
Unit
Outpatient Uit
Intensive Residential Unit
Intermediate Residential Unit
MISA/Healthy Living Program
Non-Hospital Medical Unit
Partial Hospitalization Program
1250 Silver Street
Middletown, CT 06457

MILFORD

Milford Mental Health Clinic,
Inc.
Administrative Unit
Outpatient
Peer Counseling Program
949 Bridgeport Avenue
Milford, CT 06460

MONROE

Regional Network of Programs,
Inc. Monroe Builds
Communication
1014 Monroe Turnpike
Masuk High School
Monroe, CT 06468

MOOSUP

Youth Challenge Bible Training
Center
Long-term Training/Rehab
111 North Sterling Road
Moosup, CT 06354

NEW BRITAIN

Farrell Treatment Center
Outpatient Unit
Intensive Residential Unit
586 Main Street
New Britain, CT 06051

Hartford Dispensary/New
Britain Clinic
19 Rockwell Avenue
New Britain, CT 06051

New Britain General Hospital
Dept. of Behavioral Health
100 Grand Street
New Britain, CT 06050

Wheeler Clinic, Inc. Lifeline/
Pregnant Women's Program
35 Russell Street
New Britain, CT 06052

NEW HAVEN

Affiliates for Consultation and
Therapy
389 Orange Street
New Haven, CT 06511

Alcohol Services Organization
of South Central Connecticut,
Inc.
871 State Street
New Haven, CT 06511

Apt Foundation, Inc.
Central Treatment Unit/Women
with Children
1 Long Wharf Drive, Suite 10
New Haven, CT 06519

Legion Avenue Clinic/Methadone
60–62 Legion Avenue
New Haven, CT 06519

Orchard Clinic
Park Hill clinic
Women in Treatment
540 Ella T Grasso Boulevard
New Haven, CT 06519

Connecticut Mental Health
Center
Substance Abuse Treatment
Outpatient Program
1 Long Wharf Drive
New Haven, CT 06511

Dept. of Psychiatry
34 Park Street
New Haven, CT 06508

Crossroads, Inc.
54 East Ramsdell Street
New Haven, CT 06515

Amethyst House
48 Howe Street
New Haven, CT 06511

Hill Health Corporation
232 Cedar Street
New Haven, CT 06519

Hill Health Center/Northside
   Community Outpatient Services
226 Dixwell Avenue
New Haven, CT 06511

**Multicultural Ambulatory
Addiction Services**
426 East Street
New Haven, CT 06511

NEWINGTON

**Veterans Affairs Medical Center
Substance Abuse Services**
555 Willard Avenue, Suite 116-A
Newington, CT 06111

NEW LONDON

Care Center
516 Vauxhall Street
Suite 102
New London, CT 06320

Care Plus
190 Governor Winthrop
   Boulevard, Suite 101
New London, CT 06320

**Hartford Dispensary New
London Clinic**
931 Bank Street
New London, CT 06320

**Southeast Council on Alcohol
and Drug Dependency, Inc.
(SCADD)**
Altruism House/Women
1000 Bank Street
New London, CT 06320

189 Howard Street
New London, CT 06320

Outpatient Program Detox
47 Colt Street
New London, CT 06320

NEW MILFORD

New Milford Youth Agency
50 East Street
New Milford, CT 06776

NEWTOWN

Apt Foundation, Inc.
Alpha House

Daytop Intermediate and Long
   Term Program
Mile Hill Road
Newtown, CT 06470

NORTH STONINGTON

Stonington Institute
Partial Hospitalization Program
75 Swantown Hill Road
North Stonington, CT 06359

NORWALK

**Connecticut Counseling Centers,
Inc.**
Norwalk Methadone Program
Norwalk Outpatient Treatment
   Program
20 North Main Street
Norwalk, CT 06854

Connecticut Renaissance, Inc.
Administrative Unit
Norwalk Outpatient Unit
83 Wall Street
Norwalk, CT 06850

**Dept of Psychiatry and
Addictions Norwalk Hospital**
24 Stevens Street
Norwalk, CT 06856

**Family and Childrens Agency,
Inc. Project Reward**
165 Flax Hill Road
Norwalk, CT 06854

**Liberation and Meridian
Partners in Recovery**
4 Elmcrest Terrace
Norwalk, CT 06850

Pivot Ministries, Inc.
17 Quintard Avenue
Norwalk, CT 06854

Vitam Center, Inc.
Administrative Unit
Residential Drug Free Unit
57 West Rocks Road
Norwalk, CT 06852

NORWICH

**Hartford Dispensary Norwich
Clinic**
Norwich Hospital
Lippett Building
Norwich, CT 06360

**SE Council on Alcohol and
Drug Dependency, Inc.
(SCADD) Altruism House/
Male**
313 Main Street
Norwich, CT 06360

OLD SAYBROOK

**The Connection, Inc. Valley
Shore Counseling Center**
263 Main Street, Suite 108
Old Saybrook, CT 06475

ORANGE

**Family Service of Greater
Waterbury**
35 Porter Avenue
Orange, CT 06477

PLAINVILLE

Wheeler Clinic, Inc.
Adolescent Screening and
   Treatment Program
Intensive Outpatient/Day
   Treatment Program
Night Treatment Program
91 Northwest Drive
Plainville, CT 06062

PORTLAND

**Elmcrest Behavioral Health
Network**
25 Marlborough Street
Portland, CT 06480

Stonehaven
325 Main Street
Portland, CT 06480

PUTNAM

**Community Prevention and
Addictoion Services**
391 Pomfret Street
Putnam, CT 06260

ROCKY HILL

Department of Veterans Affairs Veterans Recovery Center
287 West Street
Rocky Hill, CT 06067

SHARON

Midwestern Connecticut Council on Alcoholism Trinity Glen
149 West Cornwall Road
Sharon, CT 06069

SOUTH WINDSOR

Connecticut North Treatment Center
15 Morgan Farms Drive
South Windsor, CT 06074

STAFFORD SPRINGS

Johnson Memorial Hospital
201 Chestnut Hill Road
Stafford Springs, CT 06076

Stafford Family Services
21 Hyde Park Road
Stafford Springs, CT 06076

STAMFORD

LMG, Inc.
115 Main Street
Stamford, CT 06901

Liberation Clinic
125 Main Street
Stamford, CT 06901

Viewpoint Recovery Program Intermediate Long Term
104–106 Richmond Hill Avenue
Stamford, CT 06902

STRATFORD

Family Resource Associates
3300 Main Street
Stratford, CT 06614

TORRINGTON

McCall Foundation, Inc.
Intensive Residential Program
Evening Program
Outpatient Program
58 High Street
Torrington, CT 06790

McCall House/Intermediate Residential
127 Migeon Avenue
Torrington, CT 06790

VERNON ROCKVILLE

Natchaug Hospital, Inc. River East Day Hosp Land Treatment Center
428 Hartford Turnpike Road
Vernon Rockville, CT 06066

WATERBURY

Center for Psychiatry and Clinical Neuroscience
1389 West Main Street, Suite 106
Waterbury, CT 06708

Central Naugatuck Valley Help, Inc.
Administrative Unit
Nonresidential Program
Residential Unit
900 Watertown Avenue
Waterbury, CT 06708

Connecticut Counseling Centers, Inc.
Waterbury Methadone Program
Waterbury Outpatient Program
4 Midland Road
Waterbury, CT 06708

Connecticut Renaissance, Inc. Residential Treatment Facility
31 Wolcott Street
Waterbury, CT 06702

Family Intervention Center
1875 Thomaston Avenue
Waterbury, CT 06704

Family Service of Greater Waterbury
34 Murray Street
Waterbury, CT 06710

Morris Foundation, Inc.
Administrative Unit
Center for Alcohol and Drug-Free Living
26 North Elm Street
Waterbury, CT 06702

Driving While Intoxicated Therapeutic Shelter
142 Griggs Street
Waterbury, CT 06702

Morris/Kendall House
26 North Elm Street
Waterbury, CT 06702

Woman and Children Program
79 Beacon Street
Waterbury, CT 06702

Saint Mary's Hospital Behavioral Healthcare Services
56 Franklin Street
Waterbury, CT 06706

WEST HAVEN

Veterans Affairs Medical Center Substance Abuse Treatment Program
950 Campbell Avenue
Suite 116-A3
West Haven, CT 06516

WESTPORT

Alcohol and Drug Dependency Council, Inc.
420 Post Road West
Westport, CT 06880

Hall Brooke Hospital Substance Abuse Unit
47 Long Lots Road
Westport, CT 06881

WILLIMANTIC

Community Prevention/ Addiction Services
Thomas Murphy Center
1493 West Main Street
Willimantic, CT 06226

**Hartford Dispensary
Willimantic Clinic**
54-56 Boston Post Road
Willimantic, CT 06226

Perception Program, Inc.
Perception House
134 Church Street
Willimantic, CT 06226

New Perspective Counseling
Service
Right Turn Adolescent Program
90 South Park Street
Willimantic, CT 06226

**United Services, Inc. Addiction
Recovery Services**
132 Mansfield Avenue
Willimantic, CT 06226

WINSTED

McCall Foundation, Inc.
231 North Main Street
Winsted, CT 06098

DELAWARE

CLAYMONT

Open Door, Inc.
3301 Green Street
Claymont, DE 19703

DELAWARE CITY

**Cornerstone Alcohol and Drug
Residential Program**
New Castle Avenue, Building 8
Delaware City, DE 19706

Northeast Treatment Centers
Governor Bacon Health Center
Cottage 5
Delaware City, DE 19706

Reflection House
Delaware City, DE 19706

DOVER

ABR Counseling Associates
1550 South Governor Avenue
Dover, DE 19904

**Kent County Counseling
Services**
1525 Lebanon Road
Dover, DE 19901

**Pace Alcohol and Drug
Counseling**
707 Walker Road
Dover, DE 19904

Phoenix Mental Health of Dover
567 South Governors Avenue
Dover, DE 19904

Serenity Place
327 Martin Street
Dover, DE 19901

**St. Jones Center for Behavioral
Health**
725 Horsepond Road
Dover, DE 19901

DOVER AIR FORCE BASE

**Dover Air Force Base Substance
Abuse Office**
263 Chad Street
Dover Air Force Base, DE 19902

ELLENDALE

**Kent/Sussex Detoxification
Center**
Main Street
Ellendale School House
Ellendale, DE 19941

GEORGETOWN

Children and Family First
410 South Bedford Street
Georgetown, DE 19947-1850

Corinthian House
219–221 South Race Street
Georgetown, DE 19947

Houston Hall
431 East Market Street
Georgetown, DE 19947

**Psychotherapeutic Community
Services Associates**
16 North Railroad Avenue
Georgetown, DE 19947-1242

Tau House
11 West Pine Street
Georgetown, DE 19947

**Thresholds, Inc. Sussex County
Unit**
526-D North Dupont Highway
113 Professional Building
Georgetown, DE 19947

MILFORD

**People's Place Counseling
Center**
219 South Walnut Street
Milford, DE 19963

NEWARK

**Newark Family Counseling
Center**
501 Ogletown Road
Hudson State Service Center
Newark, DE 19711

North East Treatment Center
7-D Peddlers Row Peddlers Village
Newark, DE 19702

NEW CASTLE

**Women's Correctional
Institution (WCI) Village**
660 Baylor Boulevard
New Castle, DE 19720

SEAFORD

Behavioral Health Services
801 Middleford Road Nanticoke
Memorial Hospital
Seaford, DE 19973

SELBYVILLE

**ABR Counseling Associates/
  Sussex County**
33 Keenwik Road
Selbyville, DE 19975-0000

SMYRNA

**Greentree Drug and Alcohol
  Program Delaware Correction
  Center**
Route 1
Smyrna, DE 19977

WILMINGTON

Aquila
2110 Duncan Road
Wilmington, DE 19808

Brandywine Counseling, Inc.
2713 Lancaster Avenue
Wilmington, DE 19805

Riverfront Site
350 South Madison Street
Wilmington, DE 19801

Children and Family First
2005 Baynard Boulevard
Wilmington, DE 19802

Key Program
1301 East 12 Street
Wilmington, DE 19809

Limen House
624 North Broom Street
Wilmington, DE 19805

Limen House for Men
903 Madison Street
Wilmington, DE 19801

Net Counseling Center
813 West Street
Wilmington, DE 19801

**Northeast Treatment Centers
  Kirkwood Detox**
3315 Kirkwood Highway
Wilmington, DE 19808

Pace, Inc.
5171 West Woodmill Drive
Suite 9
Wilmington, DE 19808

**Psychotherapeutic Services, Inc.
  Relapse Prevention/
  Continuous Treatment**
5207 West Woodmill Drive
Suite 34
Wilmington, DE 19808

**Sodat Counseling and
  Evaluation Center**
625 Orange Street
Wilmington, DE 19801

**Wilmington Veterans Affairs
  Med Center**
1601 Kirkwood Highway 116B
Wilmington, DE 19805

DISTRICT OF COLUMBIA

WASHINGTON

APRA/Karick Hall/PPWI
1900 Massachusetts Avenue SE
Building 17
Washington, DC 20003

**Adams Mill Alcohol Treatment
  Center**
1808 Adams Mill Road NW
Washington, DC 20009

**Addiction Prevention and
  Recovery Administration**
Detox Center
1900 Massachusetts Avenue SE
Building 12
Washington, DC 20003

Minimal Services
1300 1st Street NE
2nd Floor
Washington, DC 20002

**Andromeda Transcultural
  Hispanic Mental Health
  Center**
1400 Decatur Street NW
Washington, DC 20011

**Bureau of Rehabilitation, Inc.
  Community Care Center**
3301 16 Street NW
Washington, DC 20010

Clean and Sober Streets
425 2nd Street NW
Washington, DC 20001

**Concerned Citizens on Alcohol
  and Drug Abuse**
Pregnant/Postpartum Outpatient
  Women's Program
311 Martin Luther King
  Avenue SE
Washington, DC 20032

Consulting Counseling Center
3000 Connecticut Avenue NW
Suite 439
Washington, DC 20008-2556

**DC Employee Consultation and
  Counseling Service**
33 N Street NE, 2nd Floor
Washington, DC 20009

DC General Hospital
Dept. of Psychiatry Substance
  Abuse Program
Detox Center
1900 Massachusetts Avenue SE
DC General Hospital Unit 42
Washington, DC 20003

**DC Lifeline Addiction
  Treatment Program**
1901 East Street SE
Washington, DC 20003

**Demeter Northwest of Vanguard
  Services Unlimited**
301 I Street NW
Washington, DC 20001

**Executive Addictive Disease
  Programs, Inc.**
4335 Wisconsin Avenue NW
Washington, DC 20016

Family and Medical Counseling Services
2041 Martin Luther King Avenue SE
Suite M-2
Washington, DC 20020

Foundation for Contemporary Mental Health Next Step
2112 F Street NW
Suite 404
Washington, DC 20037

Georgetown Medical Center Alcohol and Drug Abuse Program
3800 Reservoir Road NW
Washington, DC 20007

Girard Treatment Center (GTC)
1413 Girard Street NW
Washington, DC 20009

Holy Comforter/Saint Cyprian Community Action Group/ Carriage House
901 Pennsylvania Avenue SE
Washington, DC 20003

House of Ruth Mothers/Infants Program
700 6th Street NE
Washington, DC 20003

Howard University Drug Abuse Institute
2041 Georgia Avenue NW
Suite 6B07
Washington, DC 20059

Institute for Behavioral Change
34 O Street NW
Washington, DC 20001

Karrick Hall Pregnant and Postpartum Women and Infant Program
1900 Massachusetts Avenue SE
Building 17
Washington, DC 20003

Koba Associates Diagnostic Unit
1300 First Street NE
Suite 214
Washington, DC 20003

Kolmac Clinic
1411 K Street NW
Suite 703
Washington, DC 20005

La Clinica del Pueblo Inc
1470 Irving Street NW
Washington, DC 20010-2804

Latin American Youth Center Substance Abuse Program
1419 Columbia Road NW
Washington, DC 20009

Mary E. Herring Safe House
700 Monroe Street NE
Washington, DC 20000

Metropolitan Psychiatric Group/ Mars
2021 K Street NW, Suite 206
Washington, DC 20006

Model Treatment Program
1300 First Street NE
Washington, DC 20002

Necessary Intervention for Adolescents
2146 24th Place NE
Washington, DC 20002

New Risings Women's Center
2146 24th Place NE, Suite 111
Washington, DC 20018

Oasis
910 Bladensburg Road NE
Washington, DC 20002

Partners in Drug Abuse Rehabilitation and Counseling (PIDARC)
2112 F Street NW
Suite 101
Washington, DC 20037

Pirgrim Rest Baptist Therapeutics
4606 Sheriff Road NE
Washington, DC 20019-3703

Professional Guidance Associates
1314 18th Street NW, Suite 300
Washington, DC 20036-1803

Progressive Life Center
1129 11th Street NW
Washington, DC 20001

Providence Hospital Substance Abuse Services
1053 Buchanan Street NE
Washington, DC 20017

Psychiatric Institute of Washington New Directions Recovery Center
4228 Wisconsin Avenue
Washington, DC 20016

Rap, Inc.
1949 4th St NW
Washington, DC 20002

Second Genesis Residential Therapeutic Community DC Clinic
1320 Harvard Street NW
Washington, DC 20009

Shaw Abstinence Program
602 N Street NW
Washington, DC 20002

So Others May Eat, Inc. (SOME)
60 O Street NW
Washington, DC 20001

Supervised Living Program Phase II and III
221 Orange Street SE
Washington, DC 20002

Umoja Treatment Center
5140 Nannie Helen Burroughs Avenue NE
Washington, DC 20019

Unfoldment, Inc.
2605 Wade Road SE
Barry Farms Dwellings
Washington, DC 20020

Veterans Affairs Medical Center Substance Abuse Treatment Program
50 Irving Street NW, Suite 116-A
Washington, DC 20422

Walter Reed Army Medical Center Community Counseling Ctr
6825 16th Street NW
Building 6, 2nd Floor
Washington, DC 20307

Ward and Ward Associates
7600 Georgia Avenue NW
Suite 100
Washington, DC 20012-1616

Washington Area Council on Alcoholism and Drug Abuse Inc./Comp Counseling Center
2813 12 Street NE
Washington, DC 20017

Washington Assessment/ Therapy Services
4455 Connecticut Avenue NW
Suite A-400
Washington, DC 20008

Whitman Walker Clinic, Inc. Mental Health and Addiction Treatment Services
1407 S Street NW
Washington, DC 20009

Women's Services Clinic
1900 Massachusetts Avenue SE
Building 13
Washington, DC 20003

FLORIDA

ALTAMONTE SPRINGS

Cornerstone Institute, Inc.
400 Maitland Avenue
Altamonte Springs, FL 32701

Quest Counseling Centre, Inc.
401 whooping Loop, Suite 1549
Altamonte Springs, FL 32701

Serenity Center
378 Whooping Loop, Suite 1238
Altamonte Springs, FL 32701

APOPKA

Addictions Compulsions Treatment Center/ACT Center Inc
325 West Main Street, Suite A
Apopka, FL 32712

ARCADIA

Coastal Recovery Centers, Inc. Arcadia Office
14 East Oak Street
Arcadia, FL 34266

BARTOW

Tri-County Addictions Rehab Services, Inc.
Detoxification Unit
Women's Residential
2725 Highway 60 East
Bartow, FL 33830

BAY PINES

Veterans' Affairs Medical Center Substance Abuse Treatment Program
10000 Bay Pines Boulevard
Bay Pines, FL 33744

BELLE GLADE

New Beginnings
149 Southeast Avenue, Suite D
Belle Glade

West Palm Beach County
Outpatient Substance Abuse Services
1024 NW Avenue D
Belle Glade, FL 33430

Panda/Mental Health Clinic
816 Northwest Avenue, Suite D
Belle Glade, FL 33430

BOCA RATON

Alternatives in Treatment, Inc.
7601 North Federal Highway
Suite 100
Boca Raton, FL 33487

Counseling Services Institute, Inc.
1515 North Federal Highway
Suite 216
Boca Raton, FL 33432

BOYNTON BEACH

Atlantic Counseling
200 Knuth Road
Suite 238
Boynton Beach, FL 33436

BRADENTON

Center for Rational/Emotive Therapy
4303 1st Street East 265
Bradenton, FL 34208

Inpatient Addictions Treatment Service
2020 26th Avenue East
Bradenton, FL 34208

Manatee Glens Corporation
Adolescent Recovery Center
1819 5 Street West
Bradenton, FL 34205

Outpatient Detox
2020 26th Avenue East
Bradenton, FL 34208

PAR Narcotic Addiction Treatment Center
5105 26th Street West
Bradenton, FL 34207

BRANDON

Personal Growth Counseling
113 Lithia Pinecrest Road, Suite A
Brandon, FL 33511

BRONSON

Meridian Behavioral Healthcare Inc
100 NE 90th Street
Bronson, FL 32621

BROOKSVILLE

Eckerd Family Youth Services
397 Culbreath Road
Brooksville, FL 34602

BUNNELL

Flagler City Outpatient Services
302 1/2 Moody Boulevard
Bunnell, FL 32110

CAPE CORAL

Bill Bohs MA/DBA Omega
1443 Delprado Boulevard
Cape Coral, FL 33990

CASTLEBURY

Spellman Counseling and Consulting, Inc.
274 Wilshire Boulevard, Suite 253
Castlebury, FL 32707

CITRA

Phoenix Houses of Florida
15681 North Highway 301
Citra, FL 32113

CLEARWATER

Fairwinds Treatment Center Residential
1569 South Fort Harrison Street
Clearwater, FL 34756

Family Services Centers
Clearwater Clinical Services
2188 58th Street
Clearwater, FL 33760

Focus One Inc
11681 49th Street North, Suite 8
Clearwater, FL 33762

Operation PAR, Inc.
Narcotic Addiction Treatment Center
4900 Creekside Drive
Suite 4908-B
Clearwater, FL 34620

DOC Day/Night Program
4914-B Creekside Drive
Turtle Creek Office Park
Clearwater, FL 33760

Ryan White Facility
Juvenile addiction Recovery Facility
Short-term Residential
Adult Outpatient
6150 150 Avenue North
Clearwater, FL 34620

CLERMONT

Lake Correctional Institution
19225 Route 27
Clermont, FL 34711

CLEWISTON

Hendry/Glades Mental Health Clinic, Inc.
601 West Alverdez Avenue
Clewiston, FL 33440-3504

COCOA

Alco Hall
1215 Lake Drive
Cocoa, FL 32922

Alco Rest Inc
1050 West King Street
Cocoa, FL 32922

Central Florida Treatment Center
7 North Cocoa Boulevard
Cocoa, FL 32922

Wenz Education and Counseling, Inc.
690 Friday Road
Cocoa, FL 32926

COOPER CITY

Florida Cooper Health Services, Ltd. DBA High Point
5960 SW 106th Avenue
Cooper City, FL 33328

CRAWFORDVILLE

Disc Village, Inc.
Wakula Human Services
Juvenile Outpatient
Adult Outpatient
Crawfordville, FL 32326

CROSS CITY

Kansas City Community Center, Inc. Cross City Correctional Institution
Old Radar Road
Cross City, FL 32628

DADE CITY

Harbor Behavioral Healthcare Institute East Pasco Outpatient
14527 7th Street
Dade City, FL 33525

DAYTONA BEACH

ACT Corporation Reality House
1341 Indian Lake Road
Daytona Beach, FL 32114

Adolescent Outpatient
955-G Orange Avenue
Daytona Beach, FL 32114

Counseling Associates of Port Orange
3959 South Nova Road, Suite 5
Daytona Beach, FL 32127

Daytona Methadone Treatment Center
737 Volusia Avenue
Daytona Beach, FL 32114

Miles and Associates/Daytona Beach Alcohol/Drug Intervention/Prevention Services
308 South Martin Luther King Boulevard
Daytona Beach, FL 32114

Stewart/Marchman Treatment Center, Inc.
Adult ARF
Detox Unit
1200 Red John Road
Daytona Beach, FL 32114

Adult Clinical Services
330 North Street
Daytona Beach, FL 32114

Salvation Army Residential Program
560 Ballough Road
Daytona Beach, FL 32114

Serenity House of Volusia, Inc.
547 High Street
Daytona Beach, FL 32114

DE FUNIAK SPRINGS

Cope Alcohol and Drug Program
3686 U.S. Highway 331 South
De Funiak Springs, FL 32433

DELAND

ACT Corporation De Land Outpatient Treatment
803 Woodland Boulevard
Deland, FL 32720

Community Outreach Services, Inc. De Land Residential/ Outpatient Unit 1
245 South Amelia Street
Deland, FL 32724

Memorial Hospital/West Volusia Psychiatric Services/ Substance Abuse Services
701 West Plymouth Avenue
Deland, FL 32720

Miles and Associates/De Land Alcohol/Drug Intervention/ Prevention Services
620 East New York Avenue
Suite A
Deland, FL 32720

Serenity West Farm
2775 Big John Drive
Deland, FL 32773

DELRAY BEACH

Beachcomber Family Treatment Center
4493 North Ocean Boulevard
Delray Beach, FL 33483

Drug Abuse Foundation of Palm Beach County
Linton Blvd. Unit
400 South Swinton Avenue
Delray Beach, FL 33444

Intervention Strategies, Inc.
495 NE 4th Street, Suite 2
Delray Beach, FL 33444

Pathways to Recovery, Inc. Residential and Extended Care Facility
13132 Barwick Road
Delray Beach, FL 33445

South County Mental Health Center Substance Abuse Treatment Program Unit 1
16158 South Military Trail
Delray Beach, FL 33484

Wayside House
378 NE 6th Avenue
Delray Beach, FL 33483

DELTONA

West Volusia Outpatient
1200 Deltona Boulevard Suite 20
Deltona, FL 32738

DUNEDIN

Rational Steps Main Street Psychiatric Associates
1605 Main Street
Dunedin, FL 34698

EGLIN AIR FORCE BASE

Eglin Air Force Base Substance Abuse Program
96 MDOS/SGOHA
Eglin AFB, FL 32542-6832

Substance Abuse Recovery Center
307 Boatner Road Suite 114
Eglin AFB, FL 32542

FERNANDINA BEACH

Nassau County Mental Health Alcohol and Drug Abuse Council
1890 South 14th Street
Suite 312-320
Fernandina Beach, FL
32034-4740

FERN PARK

Seminole Community Mental Health Center
237 Fernwood Boulevard
Fern Park, FL 32730

FLORIDA CITY

Miami Dade Office of Rehab Services Diversion and Treatment Program South
1600 NW 6th Court
Florida City, FL 33034

FORT LAUDERDALE

Alternative Substance Abuse Systems, Inc.
208 SE 8th Street
Fort Lauderdale, FL 33301

Broward Addiction Recovery Center (BARC)
1000 SW 2 Street
Fort Lauderdale, FL 33312

ATACC
Drug Court Treatment
601 South Andrews Street
Fort Lauderdale, FL 33301

Broward House
Chemical Dependency Treatment Program
417 Southeast 18th Street
Fort Lauderdale, FL 33316

West/Lauderdale Lakes
4487 North State Road 7
Fort Lauderdale, FL 33319

Family Institute/Fort Lauderdale
1144 SE 3 Avenue
Fort Lauderdale, FL 33316

**Fort Lauderdale Counseling
    Services**
1215 SE 2 Avenue
Fort Lauderdale, FL 33316

Lifeline of Miami
6550 Griffin Road, Suite 104
Fort Lauderdale, FL 33314

South Florida Counseling
3015 North Ocean Boulevard
Suite 109
Fort Lauderdale, FL 33308

Spectrum Programs, Inc.
5910 Northwest 9th Avenue
Fort Lauderdale, FL 33309

Adult Residential Services
2301 Wilton Drive
Fort Lauderdale, FL 33305

Broward Outpatient
2800 West Oakland Park
    Boulevard
Suite 100
Fort Lauderdale, FL 33311

**Sunrise Regional Medical
    Center**
555 SW 148th Avenue
Fort Lauderdale, FL 33325

FORT MYERS

Bill Bohs MA Omega Centre
8695 College Parkway, Suite 252
Fort Myers, FL 33919

**Charter Glade Hospital
    Chemical Dependency Unit**
3550 Colonial Boulevard
Fort Myers, FL 33906

Ruth Cooper Center
4424 Michigan Avenue
Apartment 507
Fort Myers, FL 33916

Drug Abuse Unit
2789 Ortiz Avenue SE
Fort Myers, FL 33905

Serenity Center
2709 Second Street
Fort Meyers, FL 33916

**Southwest Florida Addiction
    Services, Inc.**
Detoxification
2562 Dixie Parkway
Fort Myers, FL 33901

Residential and Outpatient
2101 McGregor Boulevard
Fort Myers, FL 33901

Residential Level 2
2450 Prince Street
Fort Myers, FL 33901

FORT PIERCE

Alpha Health Services
1025 Orange Avenue
Fort Pierce, FL 34950

**Drug Abuse Treatment
    Association, Inc. (DATA)
    Norman C. Hayslip Treatment
    Center**
4590 Selvitz Road
Fort Pierce, FL 34981

**New Horizons of the Treasure
    Coast, Inc.**
Detoxification Unit
800 Avenue H
Fort Pierce, FL 33950

Saint Lucie County Outpatient
    Branch
709 South 5th Street
Fort Pierce, FL 34950

FORT WALTON BEACH

**Bridgeway Center Addiction/
    Substance Abuse Program**
205 Shell Avenue SE
Fort Walton Beach, FL 32548

GAINESVILLE

**Bridges of America Cross Creek
    Bridge**
3361 NE 39th Avenue
Gainesville, FL 32609

Corner Drug Store, Inc.
Alachua Halfway House
3430 Northeast Avenue
Gainesville, FL 32601

Outpatient Services
1300 NW 6 Street
Gainesville, FL 32601

Diversified Human Services
2830 NW 41st Street
Thornbrook III Building M
Gainesville, FL 32606

**Meridian Behavioral
    Healthcare, Inc.**
Gainesville, FL 32608

Sid Martin Bridge Street
4400 Southwest 13th Street
Gainesville, FL 32608

**Metamorphosis Alachua County
    Drug Abuse Program**
4201 Southwest 21st Place
Gainesville, FL 32607

**North Florida Evaluation and
    Treatment Center**
1200 NE 55th Boulevard
Gainesville, FL 32641

**North Florida/South Georgia
    Veterans Health System**
1601 SW Archer Road
116A SATT
Gainesville, FL 32608

GREENVILLE

Greenville Hills Academy
SW 22nd Avenue
Greenville, FL 32331

GULF BREEZE

The Friary
4400 Hickory Shores Boulevard
Gulf Breeze, FL 32561

**Twelve Oaks Alcohol and Drug
    Recovery Center Detox**
2068 Healthcare Avenue
Route 1
Gulf Breeze, FL 32566

HIALEAH

ACF Counseling Center, Inc.
102 East 49th Street
Hialeah, FL 33013

Citrus Health Network, Inc.
4175 West 20th Avenue
Hialeah, FL 33012-5874

Dade Family Counseling Center
1490 West 49 Place
Suite 390
Hialeah, FL 33012

**Substance Abuse Control
    Center, Inc.**
Family Services/A New Life, Inc.
1095 East 4th Avenue
Hialeah, FL 33010

HILLARD

**Nassau County Mental Health,
    Alcohol, and Drug Council,
    Inc. Outpatient/Prevention**
333 Eastwood Road
Hilliard, FL 32046

HOLLY HILL

**Milestones, Inc. Center for
    Substance Abuse Intervention**
484 LPGA Boulevard
Holly Hill, FL 32117

HOLLYWOOD

**Broward Addiction Recovery
    Center (BARC) South**
6491–Taft Street
Hollywood, FL 33024

**Lock Towns CMHC Sub. Arts
    Project/Dade County Dual
    Diagnosis**
1000 SW 84 Avenue
Hollywood, FL 33025

**Memorial Regional Hospital
    Share Program**
801 SW Douglas Road
Hollywood, FL 33025

**Phoenix Group, Inc. Advanced
    Behavioral Care**
668 North Dixie Highway
Hollywood, FL 33020

Spectrum Programs, Inc.
2219 Hollywood Boulevard
Suite 102
Hollywood, FL 33020

The Starting Place, Inc.
2057 Coolidge Street
Hollywood, FL 33020

HOMESTEAD

**Associates for Psychological
    Services Homestead Alcohol
    Abuse Program**
225 NE 8 Street
Suite 3
Homestead, FL 33030

**Coalition of Florida
    Farmworkers Organization
    (COFFO)**
21 South Krome Avenue
Homestead, FL 33030

**Jewish Family Service of
    Greater Miami**
701 South Homestead Boulevard
Suite B-6
Homestead, FL 33030

**Metro Dade Office of Rehab
    Services Jack Orr Ranch**
31601 SW 197 Avenue
Homestead, FL 33030

HUDSON

Shell of Hope, Inc.
13825 U.S. Highway 19
Suite 307
Hudson, FL 34667

IMMOKALEE

**Bridges of America Hendry
    Correctional Institution**
12551 Wayne Wright Drive
Immokalee, FL 34142-9747

**David Lawrence Center The
    Pines**
425 North First Street
Immokalee, FL 33934

INDIALANTIC

Center for Nonaddictive Living
114 6th Avenue, Suite 2
Indialantic, FL 32903

INDIANTOWN

Martin Unit Treatment Center
1175 SW Allapattah Road
Indiantown, FL 34956

INTERCESSION CITY

**Center for Drug Free Living
    Adolescent Residential
    Campus**
5970 South Orange Blossom Trail
Intercession City, FL 33848

JACKSONVILLE

**Addictions Rehabilitations
    Clinic**
Naval Air Station Jax
Building 590, Keily Street
Jacksonville, FL 32212-0046

**Counseling and Assistance
    Center**
Naval Station
Jacksonville, FL 32228-0071

Davenport Center
8889 Corporate Square Court
Jacksonville, FL 32216

**Gateway Community Services,
    Inc.**
Adolescent Unit/Outpatient
Adult Intensive Residential
    Program
555 Stockton Street
Jacksonville, FL 32204

TPC Village
2671 Huffman Boulevard
Jacksonville, FL 32216

Outpatient/Edgewood
1105 West Edgewood Avenue
Jacksonville, FL 32208

Outpatient/University
1754 University Boulevard West
Jacksonville, FL 32217

Greenfield Center
1820 Barrs Street
Suite 640
Jacksonville, FL 32204

Help Center
743 West Ashley Street
Jacksonville, FL 32202

Jacksonville Metro Treatment Center
3609 Emerson Street
Jacksonville, FL 32208

Kerekes and Associates, Inc.
101 Century 21 Drive
Suite 119-F
Jacksonville, FL 32216

River Region Human Services, Inc.
330 West State Street
Jacksonville, FL 32202

Substance Abuse Program
451 Catherine Street
Jacksonville, FL 32202

Salvation Army
900 West Adams Street
Jacksonville, FL 32202

Substance Abuse Treatment Program
451 Catherine Street-CCD
Jacksonville, FL 32202

KEY WEST

Drug Court Treatment Division Project Outpatient
323 Fleming Street
Key West, FL 33041

Lower Florida Keys Health System, Inc.
1200 Kennedy Drive
Key West, FL 33040

Safe Port/Housing Authority/ Key West
301 White Street, Building 12
Key West, FL 33040

KISSIMMEE

Addictions Compulsions Treatment Center (ACT, Inc.) Kissimmee Outpatient
800 Office Plaza Boulevard
Suite 401
Kissimmee, FL 34744

Bridges of America Kissimmee CCC
2925 North Michigan Avenue
Kissimmee, FL 34744

Colonial Counseling Associates Outpatient/Kissimmee
3501 West Vine Street, Suite 290
Kissimmee, FL 34741

Osceola Counseling Center
Center for Drug Free Living
201 East Ruby Avenue
Building 9, Suite B
Kissimmee, FL 34741

Osceola Mental Health, Inc. Adult Outpatient Substance Abuse Services
230 East Monument Avenue
Kissimmee, FL 34741

LA BELLE

Hendry/Glades Mental Health Clinic, Inc. Mental Health Alcohol and Drug Abuse Treatment Program
80 Euclid Place
La Belle, FL 33935

LAKE BUTLER

Meridian Behavioral Healthcare, Inc. Union Office
395 West Main Street
Lake Butler, FL 32054

LAKE CITY

Bridges of America Lake City Community Correctional Center
1620 Lake Jeffery Street
Lake City, FL 32056

Meridian Behavioral Health Care, Inc.
3900 South First Street
Lake City, FL 32025

Turning Point Hospital
650 East Baya Avenue
Lake City, FL 32025

Veterans' Affairs Medical Center Substance Abuse Services
801 South Marion Street
Suite 116-A
Lake City, FL 32055

LAKELAND

Central Florida Human Services Centers
1325 George Jenkins Boulevard
Lakeland, FL 33802

Heart of Florida Behavioral Center
2510 North Florida Avenue
Lakeland, FL 33805

Lakeland Center
3506 Lakeland Hill Boulevard
Lakeland, FL 33805

Michiel W. Crawford LCSW
215 East Bay Street, Suite 2
Lakeland, FL 33801

Tri-County Human Services
1831 North Crystal Lake Drive
Lakeland, FL 33801

LAKE WORTH

Center for Alcohol and Drug Studies
3153 Canada Court
Lake Worth, FL 33461

Growing Together, Inc.
1000 Lake Avenue
Lake Worth, FL 33460

Quest Center
5700 Lake Worth Road, Suite 112
Lake Worth, FL 33406

LAND O LAKES

Alpha Counseling Services
6741 Land O Lakes Boulevard
Land O Lakes, FL 34639

LARGO

Boley Centers for Behavioral Healthcare, Inc.
12809 Wild Acres Road
Largo, FL 34643

Center for Behavioral Medicine
2025 Indian Rocks Road
Largo, FL 33774

Operation PAR, Inc.
13800 66th Street North
Largo, FL 34641

LECANTO

Marion/Citrus Mental Health
Center, Inc. Citrus Alcoholism
  Program
3238 South Lecanto Highway
Lecanto, FL 34461

Tri-County Rehab Center
1645 West Gulf to Lakes Highway
Lecanto, FL 32661

LIVE OAK

Meridian Behavioral
  Healthcare, Inc.
Nobles Ferry Road, Box 418
Live Oak, FL 32060

LONGWOOD

Families in Recovery
282 Short Avenue, Suite 116
Longwood, FL 32750

Human Service and Resources
  and Associates, Inc.
880 State Road 434 East
Suite 100
Longwood, FL 32750

MACCLENNY

Gateway Community Services,
  Inc.
U.S. Highway 90 West
Agricultural Building
MacClenny, FL 32063

MAITLAND

Orlando Health Care Group
2301 Lucien Way
Suite 145
Maitland, FL 32751

MARATHON

Comprehensive Psychiatric
  Center/Keys
11399 Overseas Highway
Marathon, FL 33050

Guidance Clinic of Middle Keys
3000 41st Ocean Street
Marathon, FL 33050

MARIANNA

Chemical Addictions Recovery
Effort Jackson County Outpatient
  Office
4150 Hollis Drive
Marianna, FL 32446

Community Services of North
  Florida, Inc.
4878 Blue Springs Road
Marianna, FL 32446

MAYO

Mayo Correctional Institution
Highway 27
Mayo, FL 32066

MELBOURNE

Center for Drug Free Living Inc
1204 South Hickory Street
Melbourne, FL 32901

Circles of Care, Inc. Melbourne
  Detox/Residential
400 East Sheridan Road
Melbourne, FL 32901

Family Counseling Center of
  Brevard/Melbourne
  Outpatient and Prevention
507 North Harbor City Boulevard
Melbourne, FL 32935

Harbor City Counseling Center
668 West Eau Gallie Boulevard
Melbourne, FL 32935

MIAMI

Bayview Centers, Inc.
Division of Outpatient Services
12550 Biscayne Boulevard
Miami, FL 33150

Better Way of Miami, Inc.
800 NW 28 Street
Miami, FL 33127

Catholic Charities Bureau, Inc.
  Arch Diocese of Miami/DBA
  St. Luke's Center
7707 NW 2nd Avenue
Miami, FL 33150

Comprehensive Psychiatric
  Center/North
240 NW 183rd Street
Miami, FL 33169

Comprehensive Psychiatric
  Center/South
9735 East Fern Street
Miami, FL 33157

Concept House, Inc.
Maternal Addiction Program
162 NE 49th Street
Miami, FL 33137

Outpatient Services
4850 NE 2nd Street
Miami, FL 33137

Dade Family Counseling
8352 SW 8th Street
Miami, FL 33155

DUI Resolutions
7765 South West 87th Avenue
Suite 104
Miami, FL 33173

Extended Care, Inc. DBA
  Transitions Recovery Program
1928 NE 154th Street, Suite 100
Miami, FL 33162

Family Counseling Services
South Dade
10700 Caribbean Boulevard
Suite 412
Miami FL 33183

West Dade
8900 SW 107th Avenue
Suite 200
Miami, FL 33176

Family Resource Center Family
  Enhancement Program
4770 Biscayne Boulevard
Suite 610
Miami, FL 33137

Health Crisis Network
5050 Biscayne Boulevard
Miami, FL 33137

Health and Recovery Center at
  Jackson Memorial Hospital
1611 NW 12th Avenue, Annex 4
Miami, FL 33136

Here's Help, Inc.
9016 SW 152nd Street
Miami, FL 33156

**Jewish Family Service of
    Greater Miami**
1790 SW 27th Avenue
Miami, FL 33145

18999 Biscayne Boulevard
Suite 200
Miami, FL 33180

9700 South Dixie Highway
Suite 650
Miami, FL 33156

Kedem Counseling Center, Inc.
Outpatient Substance Abuse
    Treatment
2420 SW 27th Avenue
Miami, FL 33155

**Miami Dade Office of
    Rehabilitation Services**
3140 NW 76th Street
Miami, FL 33137

Central Receiving and Treatment
Diversion and Treatment
Program/Model Cities
8500 NW 27 Avenue
Miami, FL 33147

New Opportunity House
777 NW 30 Street
Miami, FL 33127

Rehab and Aftercare Center/North
3190 NW 116 Street
Miami, FL 33167

T/G/K Correctional Facility A/C
    Program
7000 NW 41 Street
Miami, FL 33166

Miami Counseling Services
13831 SW 59th Street
Suite 101
Miami, FL 33183

New Hope Corps
17130 SW 137th Avenue
Miami, FL 33177

**Open Door Counseling Center,
    Inc.**
515 SW 12th Avenue, Suite 521
Miami, FL 33130

Regis House Prevention Services
2010 NW 7 Street
Miami, FL 33125

**South Florida Jail Ministries
    Agape Women's Center**
22790 SW 112th Avenue
Miami, FL 33170

Spectrum Programs, Inc.
Administration and Outpatient
    Service
11031 NE 6th Avenue
Miami, FL 33161

Dade Residential
140 NW 59 Street
Miami, FL 33127

Outpatient South
8353 SW 124th Street
Suite 107
Miami, FL 33127

**Substance Abuse Control
    Center, Inc. Outpatient
    Program**
6850 SW 24th Street, Suite 503
Miami, FL 33155

**Village South, Inc. Addiction
    Treatment Center**
3180 Biscayne Boulevard
Miami, FL 33137

Total Rehab Services
4011 West Flagler Street
Miami, FL 33134

**Veterans' Affairs Medical Center
    Substance Abuse Rehab
    Program**
1201 NW 16 Street
Miami, FL 33125

Outpatient Program
5220 Biscayne Boulevard
Miami, FL 33137

MIAMI BEACH

**Associates for Psychological
    Services Miami Beach
    Substance Abuse Services**
2301 Collins Avenue, Suite M-113
Miami Beach, FL 33139

**Jewish Family Service of
    Greater Miami**
300 41st Street, Suite 216
Miami Beach, FL 33141

MIDDLEBURG

**Clay County Behavioral Health
    Center**
3292 County Road, Suite 220
Middleburg, FL 32068

MONTICELLO

**Apalachee Center for Human
    Services Monticello**
U.S. 19 South
Monticello, FL 32344

NAPLES

A Kind Ear
2900 14th Street North
Unit 7
Naples, FL 34103

Alternatives Chemical
Dependency Consultant Services,
    Inc.
3065 Terrace Avenue
Naples, FL 34103

David Lawrence Center
6075 Golden Gate Parkway
Naples, FL 34103

3400 North Tamiami Trail
Suite 204
Naples, FL 34103

**Naples Research and
    Counseling Center Willough
    at Naples**
9001 Tamiami Trail East
Naples, FL 34103

NARANJA

Metatherapy Institute, Inc.
27200 Old Dixie Highway
Naranja, FL 33032

NAVARRE

Twelve Oaks Alcohol and Drug Recovery Center
Intensive Day Treatment
Outpatient Program
2068 Healthcare Avenue
Navarre, FL 32566

NEW PORT RICHEY

Anglican Family Service Inc
3110 Florida Avenue
New Port Richey, FL 34653

Shell of Hope Inc
5254 State Road 54
New Port Richey, FL 34652

The Harbor Behavioral Healthcare Institute
5390 School Road
New Port Richey, FL 34653

Adolescent Residential Center Academy
6205 Trouble Creek Road
New Port Richey, FL 34652

Detox Program
8002 King Helie Boulevard
New Port Richey, FL 34653

NEW SMYRNA BEACH

Turning Point Hospital
237 North Causeway
New Smyrna Beach, FL 32169

NOKOMIS

Doctor Lynn Bernstein and Associate
2510 Tamiami Trail North
Nokomis, FL 34275

NORTH MIAMI BEACH

Holistic Counseling Services
16103 NE 11th Court
North Miami Beach, FL 33162

OCALA

CATS, Inc.
730 SE Osceola Avenue
Ocala, FL 34471

Marion/Citrus Mental Health Center, Inc.
Adult Residential Services
Children and Family Services
Women's Day Treatment
717 SW Martin Luther King Jr. Avenue
Ocala, FL 34474

MICA
Detox Unit
5664 SW 60th Avenue
Ocala, FL 34474

Quad County Treatment Center
913 East Silver Springs Boulevard
Ocala, FL 32670

OCHOPEE

Miccosukee Human Services Program
U.S. Route 41, Tamiami Trail Mile Marker 70
Ochopee, FL 34141

OKEECHOBEE

Okeechobee Outpatient Office
1600 SE 2nd Avenue
Okeechobee, FL 34972

OPA LOCKA

Dade Family Counseling, Inc.
2734 NW 183rd Street, Suite 206
Opa Locka, FL 33056

Here's Help, Inc. Residential
15100 NW 27 Avenue
Opa Locka, FL 33054

Lock Towns CMHC, Inc.
Opa Locka Substance Abuse Outpatient
15055 NW 27th Avenue
Opa Locka, FL 33054

Daybreak North
16555 NW 25nd Avenue
Opa Locka, FL 33054

ORLANDO

Access Behavioral Care Associates
7232 Sand Lake Road, Suite 302
Orlando, FL 32819-5255

Addictions Compulsions Treatment Center, Inc.
4300 South Semoran Boulevard
Suite 207
Orlando, FL 32822

5761 South Orange Blossom Trail
Suite 2
Orlando, FL 32810

4823 Silver Star Road, Suite 140
Orlando, FL 32808

Arise Counseling Associates
120 Gatlin Avenue
Orlando, FL 32806-6908

Barbara B Fuller, LCSW PA
1910 East Hillcrest Street
Orlando, FL 32803

Bridges of America/Orlando Bridge
2100 Brengle Avenue
Orlando, FL 32808

Center for Drug Free Living, Inc.
Aftercare
New Horizons
Orlando Counseling Center
100 West Columbia Street
Orlando, FL 32806

Harbor Halfway House
1405 West Michigan Street
Orlando, FL 32805

Women's Residential Program
1780 North Mercy Drive
Orlando, FL 32808

Central Florida Substance Abuse Treatment Centers, Inc. Outpatient Methadone Maintenance
1800 West Colonial Drive
Orlando, FL 32804

Colonial Counseling Associates
9318 East Colonial Drive
Suite A-15
Orlando, FL 32817

West Office
5600 West Colonial Drive
Suite 305
Orlando, FL 32819

Outpatient/Central Office
710 East Colonial drive
Orlando, FL 32803

Department of Veterans Affairs Satellite Outpatient Clinic
5201 Raymond Street
Orlando, FL 32806

Florida Hospital
Outpatient Addictions Treatment
    Services
615 East Princeton Street
Orlando, FL 32803

Florida Psychiatric Associates Orlando Outpatient
7300 Sandlake Commons
    Boulevard
Suite 112
Orlando, FL 32819

Human Services Associates, Inc. Juvenile ARF
823 West Central Boulevard
Orlando, FL 32

Lakeside Alternatives, Inc.
434 West Kennedy Boulevard
Orlando, FL 32810

Lisa Merlin House, Inc.
3101 North Pine Hills Road
Orlando, FL 32808

Medical Services Methadone
712 West Gore Street
Orlando, FL 32806

Prucare Orlando Health Care Group
21 West Columbia Street
Orlando, FL 32806

Short Term Adult Residential Women's Residential II
5609 Claracona/Ocoee Road
Orlando, FL 32801

Specialized Treatment Education and Prevention Services, Inc.
2917 North Pine Hills Road
Orlando, FL 32808

OVIEDO

Human Service and Resources and Associates, Inc.
120 North Central Avenue
Oviedo, FL 32765

PALATKA

Putnam Behavioral Healthcare Residential Program
320 Kay Lakin Drive
Palatka, FL 32177

PALM HARBOR

Elliot and Worley Counseling
1022 Nebraska Avenue
Palm Harbor, FL 34683

PANAMA CITY

Chemical Addictions Recovery Effort
A Woman's Addiction Recovery
    Effort (AWARE)
4000 East 3rd Street
Panama City, FL 32404

Bay County Outpatient Office
Starting Over Straight
School Prevention
4000 East 3 Street
Suite 200
Panama City, FL 32404

PEMBROKE PINES

Bridges of America Broward Correctional Institution
20421 Sheridan Street
Pembroke Pines, FL 33084

PENSACOLA

Community Drug and Alcohol Commission
Women's Intervention Services and
    Education
222-A West Cervantes Street
Pensacola, FL 32501

Cordova Counseling Center
4400 Bayou Boulevard, Suite 8-D
Pensacola, FL 32503

Lakeview Center, Inc.
Adolescent Overlay
Adult Residential
Outpatient Counseling
Pathway
1221 West Lakeview Avenue
Building D
Pensacola, FL 32501

Naval Air Station Addictions Treatment Facility
499 South Avenue
Pensacola, FL 32508

Pavillion Chemical Dependency
8383 North Davis Highway
Pensacola, FL 32514

PERRY

Apalachee Center for Human Services
301 Industrial Park Drive
Perry, FL 32347

PINELLAS PARK

Bay Area Treatment Center (BATC)
6328 Park Boulevard North
Suite 4
Pinellas Park, FL 33781

Center for Rational Living Inc
Avenue North Suite 5
Pinellas Park, FL 33781

Personal Enrichment Through Mental Health Services
Crisis Stabilization Unit
11254 58 Street North
Pinellas Park, FL 33782

PLANT CITY

Drug Abuse Comp. Coord. Office (DACCO)
1308 Larrick Lane
Plant City, FL 33566

POLK CITY

Central Florida Human Services Center Polk Correctional Facility
3876 Evans Road
Polk City, FL 33868

POMPANO BEACH

Alcohol and Drug Abuse Services Division Residential Services
3275 NW 99th Way
Pompano Beach, FL 33065

Bridges of America/Turning Point
400 SW 2nd Street
Pompano Beach, FL 33060

Broward County Sheriffs Office DUI Program Unit
3900 North Powerline Road
Pompano Beach, FL 33073

Center for Positive Growth
1500 University Drive, Suite 201
Pompano Beach, FL 33071

Pompano Treatment Center, Inc. Methadone Maintenance
380 SW 12 Avenue
Pompano Beach, FL 33069

Spectrum Programs, Inc.
Outpatient Broward North
450 East Atlantic Boulevard
Pompano Beach, FL 33060

PORT CHARLOTTE

Life Transitions, Inc.
2450 Tamiami Trail
Port Charlotte, FL 33952

PORT RICHEY

Alpha Counseling Service
10730 U.S. Highway 19, Suite 4
Port Richey, FL 34668

PORT SAINT LUCIE

Recovery Associates, Inc.
8000 South U.S. 1, Suite 202
Port Saint Lucie, FL 34952

PUNTA GORDA

Charlotte Community Mental Health Services, Inc.
1700 Education Avenue
Punta Gorda, FL 33950

Coastal Recovery Centers/Kelly Hall Residential Treatment Center
2208 Castilla Avenue
Punta Gorda, FL 33950

Riverside Behavioral Center
733 East Olympic Street
Punta Gorda, FL 33950

QUINCY

Disc Village, Inc.
Gadsden Adult Outpatient
Gadsden Juvenile Outpatient
Quincy, FL 32351

RIVERVIEW

Tampa Bay Academy Youth and Family Centered Services, Inc.
12012 Boyette Road
Riverview, FL 33569

ROCKLEDGE

Family Counseling Center of Brevard, Inc.
220 Coral Sands Drive
Rockledge, FL 32955

Wuesthoff Hospital Sunrise Substance Abuse Program
110 Longwood Avenue
Rockledge, FL 32956

SAFETY HARBOR

Behavioral Sciences Center Structured Outpatient Chemical Dependency Treatment Program
727 2nd Street South
Safety Harbor, FL 34695

SAINT AUGUSTINE

Epic Community Services I
88 Riberia Street, Suite 300
Saint Augustine, FL 32084

Psychological Services of Saint Augustine Inc
28 Clark Street
Saint Augustine, FL 32095

Mental Health Resource Center, Inc. Saint John's County Community Mental Health Services
179 Marine Street
Saint Augustine, FL 32084

SAINT PETERSBURG

Behavioral Sciences Center
5100 First Avenue North
Saint Petersburg, FL 33710

Boley Behavioral Health Care
1147 16th Street North
Saint Petersburg, FL 33705

Goodwill Industries Suncoast
10596 Gandy Boulevard
Saint Petersburg, FL 33733-4456

Operation PAR, Inc.
Adolescent Residential Center
6720 54th Avenue North
Saint Petersburg, FL 33707

Children of Substance Abusers (COSA)
2000 4th Street South
Saint Petersburg, FL 33705

Juvenile Outpatient
6720 54th Avenue North
Saint Petersburg, FL 33709

SAINT PETERSBURG BEACH

Stepping Stone of Tampa, Inc.
Dolphin Village, Suite 213
Saint Petersburg Beach, FL 33706

SANFORD

Bridges of America/Sanford Bridge
500 South Holly Avenue
Sanford, FL 32771

Crossroads of Sanford
300 South Bay Avenue
Sanford, FL 32771

Grove Counseling Center, Inc.
Adolescent Outpatient Program
1550 South French Road
Sanford, FL 32771

**Specialized Treatment
   Education and Prevention
   Services**
1019 Oleander Avenue
Sanford, FL 32771

SARASOTA

Another Level of Recovery
310 South Osprey Street
Sarasota, FL 34236

Coastal Recovery Centers
3830 Bee Ridge Road
Sarasota, FL 34233

**Doctors' Hospital of Sarasota,
   Ltd. Genesis Center**
2750 Bahia Vista Street
Sarasota, FL 34239

First Step of Sarasota, Inc.
Residential Center
4613 North Washington Boulevard
Sarasota, FL 34234

Pregnant SA Women's Program
1726 18 Street
Sarasota, FL 34234

Outpatient Program
2800 Bahia Vista Street
Suite 300
Sarasota, FL 34239

SATELLITE BEACH

**Brevard Outpatient Alternative
   Treatment (BOAT)**
1127 South Patrick Drive
Suite 24
Satellite Beach, FL 32937

SEBRING

Tri-County Human Services
155 U.S. Highway 27 North
Sebring, FL 33870

SHARPES

Brevard Correctional Institution
Juvenile TASC Program
870 Camp Road
Sharpes, FL 32959

STARKE

**Bridges of America Florida
   State Prison Work Camp**
Highway 26 West
Starke, FL 32091

**Meridian Behavioral Health
   Care Bradford Guidance
   Clinic**
945 Grand Street
Starke, FL 32091

STUART

**New Horizons of the Treasure
   Coast, Inc.**
2440 SE U.S. Highway 1
Stuart, FL 34994

TALLAHASSEE

A Life Recovery Center
449 West Georgia Street
Tallahassee, FL 32304

Addiction Recovery Center
2626 Care Drive, Suite 202
Tallahassee, FL 32308

Disc Village, Inc.
Adult Outpatient
603 Martin Luther King Boulevard
Tallahassee, FL 32301

Juvenile Outpatient
3333 West Pensacola Street
Suite 140
Tallahassee, FL 32304

Salvita, Inc.
419 East Georgia Street
Tallahassee, FL 32301

Turn About, Inc.
2771 Miccosukee Road
Tallahassee, FL 32308

TAMPA

**Agency for Community
   Treatment Services, Inc.
   (ACTS)**
Outpatient Treatment Services
1815 West Sligh Avenue
Tampa, FL 33604

Transitional Housing
4403 West Martin Luther King Jr.
   Boulevard
Tampa, FL 33614

W. T. Edwards Group Home
3810 West Martin Luther King Jr.
   Boulevard
Tampa, FL 33614

DACCO Inc.
74402 North 56th Street
Building 500 and 600
Tampa, FL 33617

Chemotreatment Center
Methadone Maintenance
Detox
74402 North 56th Street
Building 600
Tampa, FL 33617

50th Street Outpatient
3630 North 50th Street
Tampa, FL 33619

Inner City Residential Program
4422 East Columbus Drive
Tampa, FL 33605

Male and Female Residential
4422 East Columbus Drive
Tampa, FL 33605

Residential Treatment Facility
3636 North 50 Street
Tampa, FL 33619

Daytop Village, Inc.
1718 West Cass Street
Tampa, FL 33606

**Healthcare Connection of
   Tampa, Inc.**
107 West 131st Avenue
Tampa, FL 33614

Hillsborough Community Correctional Center Day/Night Intensive Treatment
4102 West Hillsborough Avenue
Tampa, FL 33614

James A. Haley Veterans' Hospital Alcohol and Drug Abuse Treatment Program
13000 Bruce Downs Boulevard
Tampa, FL 33612

Larry Garvin Outpatient Program
13701 Bruce B Downs Boulevard, Suite 110
Tampa, FL 33613

Project Recovery Center for Women
305 South Hyde Park Avenue
Tampa, FL 33606

Tampa Crossroads
202 West Columbus Drive
Tampa, FL 33602

Tampa Metro Treatment Center
5202-C East Busch Boulevard
Tampa, FL 33617

Town and Country Hospital Addictions Recovery Unit
6001 Webb Road
Tampa, FL 33615

Turning Point of Tampa
5439 Beaumont Center Boulevard
Suite 1010
Tampa, FL 33634

TARPON SPRINGS

Agency for Community Treatment Services, Inc. (ACTS) Pinellas Domiciliary
3575 Old Keystone Road
Tarpon Springs, FL 34689

TAVARES

Counseling Associates and Treatment Services
102 East Alfred Street
Tavares, FL 32778

TAVERNIER

Guidance Clinic of the Upper Keys Outpatient
92140 Overseas Highway
Suite 5
Tavernier, FL 33070

TYNDALL AFB

Tyndall Air Force Base Substance Abuse Program
325 MDOS/SGOMH 340
Magnolia Circle
Tyndall AFB, FL 32403-5612

VENICE

Coastal Recovery Centers South County Clinic III
119 Corporation Way
Venice, FL 34292

First Step of Sarasota, Inc. Venice Office
2210 South Tamiami Trail
Suite 9
Venice, FL 34293

VERO BEACH

Alcohope
5925 37th Street
Vero Beach, FL 32968-4920

Center for Counseling and Addiction Recovery
1434 21st Street
Vero Beach, FL 32961

Indian River County Outpatient Branch
2300 3rd Court, Suite C
Vero Beach, FL 32960

New Life
5925 37th Street
Vero Beach, FL 32968-4920

WEST PALM BEACH

Bridges of America West Palm Beach Community Corrections
261 Fairgrounds Road
West Palm Beach, FL 33411

Center for Family Services
471 Spencer Drive
West Palm Beach, FL 33409

Comprehensive AIDS Program
2580 Metrocentre Boulevard
Suite 2
West Palm Beach, FL 33407

Drug Abuse Foundation of Palm Beach County/Sheriffs Drug Farm
673 Fairground Road
West Palm Beach, FL 33411

Drug Abuse Treatment Association, Inc. (DATA)
Outpatient
1720 East Tiffany Drive
Suite 102
West Palm Beach, FL 33407

Forest Hill Counseling Center, Inc.
3101 Forest Hill Boulevard
West Palm Beach, FL 33406

Glenbeigh Hospital of Palm Beach, Inc.
4700 Congress Avenue
West Palm Beach, FL 33407

Gratitude House
317 North Lakeside Court
West Palm Beach, FL 33407

Hanley Hazelden Center at Saint Mary's
5200 East Avenue
West Palm Beach, FL 33407

Lee Ballard, RN. CD. CAP
1408 North Killian Drive
Suite 208
West Palm Beach, FL 33403

Nina de Gerome MSW/F. Edward
McCabe Substance Abuse Services
333 Southern Boulevard
Suite 204
West Palm Beach, FL 33405

Palm Beach Treatment Center
1771 South Congress Avenue
Congress Plaza Unit 7
West Palm Beach, FL 33406

Parent and Child Team Inc
1195 North Military Trail
West Palm Beach, FL 33409

Professional Educational Consultants, Inc.
4623 Forest Hill Boulevard
Suite 110
West Palm Beach, FL 33415

Saint Marys Hospital Institute for Mental Health
901 45th Street
West Palm Beach, FL 33407

WINTER HAVEN

Tri-County Human Services
Adolescent Outpatient
Adult Outpatient
37 3rd Street SW
Winter Haven, FL 33880

WINTER PARK

Another Chance Counseling Center, Inc.
709 Executive Drive
Winter Park, FL 32789

Florida Psychiatric Associates, Inc.
1276 Minnesota Avenue
Winter Park, FL 32789

Lakeside Alternatives, Inc.
807 Morse Boulevard
Winter Park, FL 3278

Maureen R. Traynor Enterprises, Inc.
1347 Palmetto Avenue, 1st Floor
Winter Park, FL 32789

New Leaf Center, Inc.
1850 Lee Road, Suite 236
Winter Park, FL 32789-2106

Psychiatric Care Center
1600 Dodd Road
Winter Park, FL 32792

WINTER SPRINGS

Grove Counseling Center, Inc.
Adolescent
Adult Outpatient
580 Old Sanford Oviedo Road
Winter Springs, FL 32708

WOODVILLE

Disc Village, Inc.
Adolescent Treatment Program
Natural Bridge Treatment Center
2967 Natural Bridge Road
Woodville, FL 32362

ZEPHYRHILLS

Alpha Counseling Services
5040 Mission Square
Zephyrhills, FL 33541

Bridges of America Zephyrhills Corrections Institute
2739 Gall Boulevard
Zephyrhills, FL 33541

GEORGIA

ADEL

Behavioral Health Services of South Georgia
105 North Parrish Avenue
Adel, GA 31620

ALBANY

Albany Area Community Service Board/Crisis Stabilization Program and Detox
601 West 11th Avenue
Albany, GA 31701

Phoebe Putney Memorial Hospital Recovery Centers
417 3rd Avenue
Albany, GA 31703

Substance Abuse Counseling Center Family Service Center
Marine Corps Logistics Base
Code 170
Albany, GA 31704-5000

AMERICUS

Addiction Recovery Program (ARC)
696 McMath Mill Road
Americus, GA 31709

Middle Flint Behavioral Health Care Substance Abuse Detoxification Unit
425 North Lee Street
Americus, GA 31709

Sumter County Substance Abuse Outpatient Program
425 North Lee Street
Americus, GA 31709

Sumter Regional Hospital
100 Wheatley Drive
Americus, GA 31709

ASHBURN

Behavioral Health Services of South Georgia
259 East Washington Avenue
Ashburn, GA 31714

ATHENS

Athens Regional Medical Center Commencement Center
1199 Prince Avenue
Athens, GA 30613

Northeast Georgia Center Community Alcohol and Drug Abuse Prevention and Treatment
250 North Avenue
Athens, GA 30601

ATLANTA

Atlanta West Treatment Center
3201 Atlanta Industrial Parkway
NW
Building 100, Suite 101
Atlanta, GA 30331

**Charter Anchor Behavioral
Health System**
5454 Yorktowne Drive
Atlanta, GA 30349

**Charter Behavioral Health
Systems of Atlanta**
811 Juniper Street NE
Atlanta, GA 30308

2151 Peachford Road
Atlanta, GA 30338

Choices
505 Fairburn Street SW
Atlanta, GA 30312

**Columbia West Paces Medical
Center Behavioral Health Unit**
3200 Howell Mill Road
Unit 3 East
Atlanta, GA 30327

**Dekalb Community Services
Board Kirkwood Substance
Abuse Clinic**
30 Warren Street SE, Suite 5
Dekalb/Atlanta Human Services
Center
Atlanta, GA 30317

**Emory University Hospital Dept
of Psychiatry and Behavioral
Science**
1639 Pierce Drive
Atlanta, GA 30322

GPA Treatment, Inc.
4255 Chamblee-Tucker Road
Atlanta, GA 30340

**Grady Health System Drug
Dependence Unit**
60 Coca Cola Place SE
Atlanta, GA 30335

**Grady Memorial Hospital Drug
Dependence Unit**
60 Coca Cola Place SE
Atlanta, GA 30303

**Kirkwood Substance Abuse
Clinic**
66 Howard Street
Atlanta, GA 30317

Marr
2801 Clearview Place
Atlanta, GA 30340

**New Start Drug Treatment
Center**
30 Warren Street SE
Atlanta, GA 30317

**Northside Hospital Substance
Abuse Center**
1000 Johnson Ferry Road
Atlanta, GA 30342

Northside Mental Health Center
5825 Glenridge Drive, Building 4
Atlanta, GA 30342

Outreach Inc.
3030 Campbellton Road SW
Atlanta, GA 30311

649 Ashby Street NW
Atlanta, GA 30318-6644

Piedmont House Project Assist
761 Piedmont Avenue
Atlanta, GA 30309

**Plasmetics, Inc. Apollo
Addiction Recovery Center**
275 Carpenter Drive, Suite 101
Atlanta, GA 30328

Private Clinic
1447 Peachtree Street NE
Suite 900
Atlanta, GA 30309

**Renaissance Family Center for
Women**
3201 Atlanta Industrial Parkway
Building 100, Suite 101
Atlanta, GA 30305

**Saint Judes Recovery Center,
Inc.**
139 Renaissance Parkway
Atlanta, GA 30308

**Southside Healthcare Substance
Abuse Unit**
1660 Lakewood Avenue SW
Atlanta, GA 30315

Talbott Recovery Campus
5448 Yorktowne Drive
Atlanta, GA 30349

**UJIMA Continuing Care
Program**
3201 Atlanta Industrial Parkway
Building 100, Suite 101
Atlanta, GA 30331

AUGUSTA

**Augusta Metro Treatment
Center**
3171 Washington Road
Augusta, GA 30907

**Charter Augusta Behavioral
Health System**
3100 Perimeter Parkway
Augusta, GA 30909-6423

**CMHC of East Central Georgia
Alcohol and Drug Services**
3421 Mike Padgett Highway
Augusta, GA 30906

**Medical College of Georgia
Hospital and Clinics**
1120 15th Street
Augusta, GA 30912

**University Hospital Behavioral
Health Center**
1350 Walton Way
Augusta, GA 30902

**Veterans' Affairs Medical Center
Substance Abuse Treatment
Program**
Uptown Division
One Freedom Way
Augusta, GA 30904

BAINBRIDGE

**Decatur County Mental Health
Center**
200 West Broughton Street
Bainbridge, GA 31717

BARNESVILLE

**McIntosh Trail MH/MR/SA
Community Services Board**
700 Highway 341 South
Barnesville, GA 30204

BLAIRSVILLE

Georgia Mountains Community
55 Hughes Street, Suite B
Blairsville, GA 30512-3551

BLOOMINGDALE

**Tidelands CSB Adolescent
    Program**
Route 1, Box 280
Bloomingdale, GA 31302

BRUNSWICK

**Gateway Center for Human
    Development Crisis
    Stabilization Unit**
3045 Scarlet Street
Brunswick, GA 31302

**Gateway Community Service
    Board Residential Substance
    Abuse Program**
1609 Newcastle Street
Winchester Center
Brunswick, GA 31520

CARROLLTON

Carroll County Mental Health
Pathways/Carroll IDR Male
Substance Abuse Center
527 Tanner Street
Carrollton, GA 30117

Pathway Center/Sunshine House
107 Park Place Way
Carrollton, GA 30117

CHICKAMAUGA

**Lookout Mountain Community
    Services Youth Substance
    Abuse Program**
4909 West Highway 136
Chickamauga, GA 30707

CLARKSTON

**Marr, Inc. Women's Recovery
    Center**
3700-D Market Street
Clarkston, GA 30021

CLEVELAND

**White County Mental Health
    Substance Abuse Program**
1241 Helen Highway, Suite 240
Cleveland, GA 30528

CEDARTOWN

**Cosa Valley Center for MH/MR/
    SA Services Residential
    Treatment Unit**
180 Water Oak Drive
Cedartown, GA 30125

COCHRAN

**Middle Georgia Adolescent
    Residential Center**
408 Peacock Street
Cochran, GA 31014

COLQUITT

**Miller County Mental Health
    Center**
250 West Pine Street
Colquitt, GA 31737

COLUMBUS

**New Horizons MH/MR/SA
    Community Service Board
    Women's Program**
1727 Boxwood Place
Columbus, GA 31906

**New Horizons Outpatient
    Alcohol and Drug Services**
2100 Comer Avenue
Columbus, GA 31901

Saint Francis Hospital Inc.
The Bradley Center of Saint
    Francis
Columbus, GA 31904

CONYERS

GRN Community Service Board
977A Taylor Street
Conyers, GA 30012

CORDELE

**Crisp County Outpatient
    Services**
112 23rd Avenue East
Cordele, GA 31015

COVINGTON

Newton Mental Health Clinic
6119 Adams Street NE
Covington, GA 30014

CUMMING

Forsyth County Mental Health
125 North Corners Parkway
Cumming, GA 30040

DAHLONEGA

Georgia Mountains Community
266-B Mechanicsville Road
Dahlonega, GA 30533

DALTON

**Georgia Highlands Treatment
    Services**
900 Shugart Road
Dalton, GA 30720

DAWSON

**Terrell County Mental Health
    Center**
638 Forrester Drive
Dawson, GA 31742

DECATUR

Alliance Recovery Center
209-B Swanton Way
Decatur, GA 30030-3271

**Comprehensive Addiction
    Rehabilitation Programs of
    Georgia Inc (CARP)**
2145 Candler Road
Decatur, GA 30032

**Dekalb Community Service
    Board**
3110 Clifton Springs Road
Suite A
Decatur, GA 30034

Dekalb Medical Center Behavioral Health Services
2701 North Decatur Road
Decatur, GA 30033

Fox Recovery Center Alcohol and Drug Abuse Program
3100 Clifton Springs Road
Decatur, GA 30034

Our Common Welfare Inc
4289 Memorial Drive, Suite I
Decatur, GA 30032

Veterans' Affairs Medical Center Substance Abuse Treatment Program
1670 Clairmont Road
Decatur, GA 30033

DEMOREST

Habersham Mental Health Center
196 Scroggins Drive
Demorest, GA 30535-5354

DORAVILLE

Turn Around Recovery Residences
5455 Buford Highway
Suite 105-A
Doraville, GA 30340

DOUGLAS

Satilla Community Mental Health Substance Abuse Clinic
1005 Shirley Avenue
Douglas, GA 31533

DUBLIN

Mental Health/Alcohol and Drug Outpatient Services
2121-A Bellevue Avenue
Dublin, GA 31021

Twin Oaks Recovery Center
2121A Belevue Street
Dublin, GA 31021

Veterans' Affairs Medical Center
Substance Abuse Treatment Program
1826 Veterans Boulevard
Dublin, GA 31021

EASTMAN

Community Mental Health Center Eastman Annex
107 Plaza Drive
Eastman, GA 31023-2223

EISENHOWER ARMY MEDICAL CENTER

Fort Gordon Community Counseling Center
CCC Eisenhower Medical Center
12 W Bldg 300
Eisenhower Army Med Center, GA 30905

ELBERTON

Elbert County Mental Health Center
230 Tate Street
Elberton, GA 30635

FITZGERALD

Behavioral Health Services of South Georgia
124 South Grant Street
Fitzgerald, GA

FORT BENNING

U.S. Army MEDAC MCXB/AD
Building 324
Fort Benning, GA 31905-6100

FORT MCPHERSON

U.S. Army Health Clinic
Building 171
Fort McPherson, GA 30330-5000

FORT OGLETHORPE

Metro Treatment of Georgia LP Northwest Georgia Treatment Center
65 White Street
Fort Oglethorpe, GA 30742

FORT STEWART

U.S. Army MEDAC MSUB/ ADAPCP
Fort Stewart, GA 31314-5000

FORT VALLEY

Phoenix Center Behavioral Health Services
503 Camellia Boulevard
Fort Valley, GA 31030

GAINESVILLE

Georgia Mountain Community Services Lakewinds Recovery Program
472 South Enota Street
Gainesville, GA 30501

Northeast Georgia Medical Center
743 Spring Street NE
Gainesville, GA 30505

GREENSBORO

Greene County Mental Health Center
502 Martin Luther King Boulevard
Box 9
Greensboro, GA 30642

502 South Walnut Street
Suite 101
Greensboro, GA 30642

GREENVILLE

Pathways Center Meriweather County Mental Health Substance Abuse Center
756 Woodbury Highway
Greenville, GA 30222

GRIFFIN

McIntosh Trail Substance Abuse Services
Substance Abuse Outpatient Treatment
141 West Solomon Street
Griffin, GA 30223

Adolescent Substance Abuse Day
Treatment
1435 North Expressway
Griffin, GA 30223

Midway Recovery Systems, Inc.
119 South 10th Street
Griffin, GA 30223

HAHIRA

**Behavioral Health Services of
South Georgia Lowndes
Substance Acute Detox**
204 East Lawson Street
Hahira, GA 31632

HAPEVILLE

**Odyssey Family Counseling
Center**
3578 South Fulton Avenue
Hapeville, GA 30354

HARTWELL

**Hart Mental Health Substance
Abuse Clinic**
520 West Franklin Street
Hartwell, GA 30643

HINESVILLE

Fraser Recovery Center
203 Mary Lou Drive
Hinesville, GA 31313

JACKSON

Butts County Counseling Center
463 Kennedy Drive, Suite B
Jackson, GA 30233

JEFFERSON

**Jackson County Mental Health
Center**
67 Athens Street
Jefferson, GA 30549

**Potter's House Christian
Rehabilitation Center**
655 Potters House Road, Route 2
Jefferson, GA 30549

JONESBORO

**Clayton Mental Health Center
Substance Abuse Program**
853 Battle Creek Road
Jonesboro, GA 30236

KINGS BAY

**Counseling and Assistance
Center Clinical Services
Department**
881 USS James Madison Road
Kings Bay, GA 31547

LAFAYETTE

**Lookout Mountain Community
Services**
501 Mize Street
LaFayette, GA 30728

LAGRANGE

Troup County MH/SA Clinic
122 Gordon Commercial Drive
LaGrange, GA 30240

West Georgia Health System
1514 Vernon Street
LaGrange, GA 30240-4130

LAKELAND

**Behavior Health Services of
South Georgia**
Lanier County Health Department
Clinic
422 West Bostick Street
Lakeland, GA 31635

Cook Outpatient Services
422 West Bostick Street
Lakeland, GA 31635

LAWRENCEVILLE

**Gwinnett/Rockdale/Newton
Alcohol and Drug Abuse
Program**
175 Gwinnett Drive
Lawrenceville, GA 30044

Summitridge
250 Scenic Highway
Lawrenceville, GA 30045

LEESBURG

The Anchorage, Inc.
162 Hampton Lane
Leesburg, GA 31763

LITHIA SPRINGS

**Cobb/Douglas County
Community Service Board**
Parkway Medical Center, 9th Floor
Lithia Springs, GA 30122

**Columbia Parkway Medical
Center**
1000 Thornton Road
Lithia Springs, GA 30122

LOUISVILLE

**Jefferson County Mental Health
Clinic**
408 Green Street
Louisville, GA 30434

MACON

**Charter Behavioral Health
Systems**
3500 Riverside Drive
Macon, GA 31209

**Macon New Start Substance
Abuse Program**
175 Emery Highway
Macon, GA 31201

**River Edge BHC Addictive
Disease Outpatient Program**
175 Emery Highway
Macon, GA 31201

River Edge Project Connect
543 2nd Street, Lower Level
Macon, GA 31201

River Edge Recovery Center
3575 Fulton Mill Road
Macon, GA 31206

MARIETTA

**Cobb/Douglas County
Community Service Board
Adult Substance Abuse
Outpatient**
3411 Austell Road
Marietta, GA 30060

**Kennestone Hospital Mental
   Health Unit**
677 Church Street
Marietta, GA 30060

Mothers Making a Change
Marietta Parkway
Marietta, GA 30060

MCDONOUGH

**Henry County Counseling
   Center**
139 Henry Parkway
McDonough, GA 30253-6636

MIDLAND

**Alchemy Therapeutic
   Community Columbus TC**
9067 Veterans Parkway
Midland, GA 31820

MILLEDGEVILLE

Bridges Outpatient Center Inc
540 West Thomas Street, Suite E
Milledgeville, GA 31061

**Oconee Alcohol and Drug
   Program**
900 Barrows Ferry Road
Milledgeville, GA 31061

**Oconee Mental Health Center
   Day Treatment Program**
430 North Jefferson Street
Milledgeville, GA 31061

MONROE

**Walton County Mental Health
   Center**
226 Alcova Street, Suite D-11
Monroe, GA 30655

MOODY AFB

**Moody Air Force Base
   Substance Abuse Program**
347 MDOS/SGOMH
3278 Mitchell Boulevard
Moody AFB, GA 31699

MOULTRIE

**Georgia Pines Community
   Service Board Colquitt County
   Mental Health Center**
615 North Main Street
Moultrie, GA 31768

Turning Point Hospital
319 East Bypass
Moultrie, GA 31768]

NASHVILLE

**Behavioral Health Services of
   South Georgia/Berrien
   Outpatient**
201 Hazel Avenue
Nashville, GA 31639

NEWNAN

**Pathways Center Coweta
   Substance Abuse Center**
12 Savannah Street
Newnan, GA 30263-2503

OCILLA

**Behavioral Health Services of
   South Georgia Irwin
   Outpatient Program**
310 Vocational Tech Drive
Ocilla, GA 31774

RIVERDALE

**Riverwoods Southern Regional
   Psychiatric Center**
11 Upper Riverdale Road SW
Riverdale, GA 30274

ROBERTA

**Crossroads Substance Abuse
   Day Treatment**
278 Wright Avenue
Roberta, GA 31078

ROBINS AFB

**Robins Air Force Base
   Substance Abuse Program**
78 MDOS/SGOMH
655 7th Street
Robins AFB, GA 31098-2227

ROME

**Northwest Georgia Regional
   Hospital**
1305 Redmond Street
Rome, GA 30165

Star House, Inc. Halfway House
212 1/2 North 5th Avenue
Rome, GA 30161

**Three Rivers Behavioral Health
   Services**
43 Chateau Court SE
Rome, GA 30161-7238

Windwood
306 Shorter Avenue
Rome, GA 30165

ROSSVILLE

Private Clinic North
312 East Lake Avenue
Rossville, GA 30741

SAINT SIMONS ISLAND

**Charter By The Sea Behavioral
   Health System**
2927 Demere Road
Saint Simons Island, GA 31522

SANDERSVILLE

Oconee Center Adult Services
151 East Church Street
Sandersville, GA 31082

**Washington County Satellite
   Clinic**
153 East Church Street
Sandersville, GA 31082

SAVANNAH

**Tidelands Community Service
   Board**
516 Drayton Street
Savannah, GA 31401

SMYRNA

**Ridgeview Institute Adult
   Addictions Medicine**
3995 South Cobb Drive
Smyrna, GA 30080

Value Mark Browner Behavior Health Care System
3180 Atlanta Street SE
Smyrna, GA 30080

SNELLVILLE

GRN Recovery Center
3005-D Lenora Church Road
Snellville, GA 30078

SPRINGFIELD

Tidelands Community Mental Center
204 East Madison Street
Springfield, GA 31329-1086

STATESBORO

Pineland MA/MR/SA Services
508 Gentilly Road
Statesboro, GA 30458

Willingway Hospital Substance Abuse Services
311 Jones Mill Road
Statesboro, GA 30458

Women's Place
131 North College Street
Statesboro, GA 30458

SUMMERVILLE

Lookout Mountain Community Services
83 Highway 48
Summerville, GA 30747

SWAINSBORO

Ogeechee Substance Abuse Center
223 North Anderson Drive
Swainsboro, GA 30401

SYLVANIA

Ogeechee Area Mental Health Clinic
302 East Ogeechee Street
Sylvania, GA 30467

SYLVESTER

Worth County Mental Health Center Day Treatment Program
504 East Price Street
Sylvester, GA 31791

THOMASVILLE

Archbold Northside
401 Old Albany Road
Thomasville, GA 31799

Southwestern State Hospital
Gateway Dual Diagnosis
Community Residential Program
400 Pinetree Boulevard
Thomasville, GA 31792-1378

THOMSON

McDuffie County Mental Health Center
306 Greenway Street
Thomson, GA 30824

TIFTON

Behavioral Health Services of South Georgia
Tift Outpatient
334 Tifton-El Dorado Road
Tifton, GA 31794

Lakeside Addiction Recovery Center
340 Tifton-El Dorado Road
Tifton, GA 31794

TOCCOA

Stephens County MH/SA Center
1020 East Tugalo Street
Toccoa, GA 30577

TRENTON

Lookout Mountain Community Services
9622 Highway 11
Trenton, GA 30752-4621

VALDOSTA

Behavioral Health Services of South Georgia
Lowndes Project Light for Women
256 North Saint Augustine Road
Valdosta, GA 31602

Greenleaf Center, Inc. Substance Abuse Treatment Program
2209 Pineview Drive
Valdosta, GA 31602

Lowndes County Service Center
1664 East Park Avenue
Valdosta, GA 31601

Moody Air Force Base
3278 Mitchell Boulevard
347 Medical Group
Valdosta, GA 31699

WARNER ROBINS

Air Force Robins Mental Health Office
Warner Robins, GA 31098

Houston Medical Center Behavioral Science and Psychiatry
1601 Watson Boulevard
Warner Robins, GA 31093

Phoenix Center Behavioral Health Services
202 North Davis Drive
Warner Robins, GA 31093

WAYCROSS

New Visions Counseling Services
2100 Riverside Avenue
Waycross, GA 31501-7072

Saint Illa Center
3455 Harris Road
Waycross, GA 31503

WINDER

Project Adam Community Assistance Center, Inc.
112 Lanthier Street
Winder, GA 30680

HAWAII

AIEA

**YMCA Outreach Services
    School-Based Program**
Aiea High School
98-1276 Ulune Street
Aiea, HI 96701

EWA BEACH

**Kahi Mohala Chemical
    Dependency Services**
91-2301 Fort Weaver Road
Ewa Beach, HI 96706

**YMCA Outreach Services
    School-Based Program**
Campbell High School
91-980 North Road
Ewa Beach, HI 96706

HILO

**Corporate Office Outpatient
    Treatment**
1420 Kilauea Avenue
Hilo, HI 96720

**Drug Addiction Services of
    Hawaii**
305 Wailuku Drive, Suite 5
Hilo, HI 96720

HONOLULU

**Attorneys and Judges Assistance
    Program of The Supreme
    Court of Hawaii**
801 Alakea Street, Suite 202
Honolulu, HI 96813

**Drug Addiction Services of
    Hawaii, Inc. (DASH)**
Methadone Maintenance
1031 Auahi Street
Honolulu, HI 96814

**Hawaii Alcoholism Foundation
    Sand Island Treatment Center**
Residential Program
12–40 Sand Island Access Road
Honolulu, HI 96819

Hina Mauka/Teen Care
Kalani High School
4680 Kalanianaole Highway
Honolulu, HI 96821

Kalihi Palama Health Clinic
Health Care for Homeless Project
350 Sumner Street
Honolulu, HI 96817

**Kokua Kalihi Valley Family
    Services**
1846 Gulick Avenue
Honolulu, HI 96819

**Queen's Medical Center Day
    Treatment Services**
1301 Punchbowl Street
Honolulu, HI 96813

**Salvation Army Addiction
    Treatment Services**
Continuum of Care Program
Social Detox Unit
3624 Waokanaka Street
Honolulu, HI 96817

**Salvation Army Family
    Treatment Services**
Day Treatment Program
Women's Way
845 22nd Avenue
Honolulu, HI 96822

**Veterans' Affairs Substance
    Abuse Treatment Program**
300 Ala Moana Boulevard
Suite 1126
Honolulu, HI 96813

**Women's Addiction Treatment
    Services (WATCH) Saint
    Francis Medical Center**
2230 Liliha Street
Honolulu, HI 96817

**YMCA Kaimuki-Waialae Palolo
    Youth Program**
4835 Kilauea Avenue
Honolulu, HI 96816

YMCA Outreach Services
1335 Kalihi Street
Honolulu, HI 96819

**YMCA Outreach Services
    School-Based Program**
Farrington High School
1564 North King Street
Honolulu, HI 96819

Leilehua High School
Waialua Intermediate/High School
1335 Kalihi Street
Honolulu, HI 96819

Moanalua High School
2825 Ala Ilima Street
Honolulu, HI 96819

Roosevelt High School
1120 Nehoa Street
Honolulu, HI 9681

KAHUKU

Bobby Benson Center
50-660 Kamehameha Highway
Kahuku, HI 96731

Hina Mauka/Teen Care
Kahuku Intermediate and High
    School
56-490 Kamehameha Highway
Kahuku, HI 96731-2200

KAHULUI

Malama Na Makua A Keiki
388 Ano Street
Kahului, HI 96732

KAILUA

**Hawaii Counseling and
    Education Center Inc.
    Chemical Dependency
    Outpatient Treatment**
970 North Kalaheo Avenue
Suite C-214
Kailua, HI 96734

Hina Mauka/Teen Care
Kalaheo High School
730 Iliaina Street
Kailua, HI 96734

Olomana High School
42-471 Kalanianaole Highway
Kailua, HI 96734

**YMCA Outreach Services
School-Based Program**
Kailua High School
451 Ulumanu Drive
Kailua, HI 96734

KAILUA KONA

**Drug Addiction Services of
Hawaii, Inc. (DASH) Kona
Office**
74-5620-A Polani Road
Kailua Kona, HI 96740

Outpatient Treatment
74-5467 Kaiwi Street
Kailua Kona, HI 96745-2077

KANEOHE

**Alcoholic Rehab Services of
Hawaii, Inc. DBA Hina
Mauka Adult Continuum**
45-845 Pookela Street
Kaneohe, HI 96744

Habilitat Inc
45-035 Kuhonu Place
Kaneohe, HI 96744

Hina Mauka/Teen Care
Castle High School
45-386 Kaneohe Bay Drive
Kaneohe, HI 96744

KANEOHE BAY

**Substance Abuse Counseling
Center Marine Corps Base
Hawaii**
Kaneohe Bay, HI 96863

KAUNAKAKAI

Hale Hookupaa
Ala Malamalama Street
Kaunakakai, HI 96748

LAHAINA

Teen Challenge Hawaii, Inc.
Olowalu Village
Lahaina, HI 96761

LIHUE

**Child and Family Service Kauai
Office**
4375 Puaole Street, Building B
Lihue, HI 96766

Ke Ala Pono Recovery Center
4371 Puaole Street, Suite B
Lihue, HI 96766

MAKAWAO

**Aloha House Adult Residential/
Outpatient Treatment**
4593 Ike Drive
Maunaolu Campus
Makawao, HI 96768

MILILANI

Hina Mauka/Teen Care
Milliani High School
95-1200 Meheula Parkway
Mililani, HI 96789

PAHOA

**Drug Addiction Services of
Hawaii, Inc.**
Hui Hoola
15-2927 Government Main Road
Pahoa, HI 96778

PAIA

**Maui Youth and Family
Services, Inc.**
Adolescent Residential Program
1931 Baldwin Avenue
Paia, HI 96779

PEARL CITY

Hina Mauka Teen Care
Pearl City High School
2100 Hookiekie Street
Pearl City, HI 96782

PEARL HARBOR

**Naval Counseling and
Assistance Center**
Comnavbase Pearl Harbor
Pearl Harbor, HI 96860-5020

SHOFIELD BARRACKS

**Schofield Barracks Alcohol and
Drug Abuse Prevention and
Control Program**
Building T-695A
Schofield Barracks, HI
96857-5000

TRIPLER ARMY

**Tri-Service Addictions Recovery
Facility (TRISARF)**
1 Jarrett White Road
Tripler Army, HI 96859-5000

WAIANAE

New Horizons Learning Center
98-211 Poli Momi Street
Waianae, HI 96792

**Waianae Coast Community
Mental Health Center School-
Based Program**
Nanakuli and Waianae High
Schools
86-226 Farrington Highway
Waianae, HI 96792

**Waianae Coast Comprehensive
Health Center Malama
Recovery Services**
89-188 Farrington Highway
Waianae, HI 96792

WAIPAHU

**Alcohol Rehab Services of
Hawaii, Inc.**
Hina Mauka/Waipahu Site
94-216 Farrington Highway
Suite B2-306
Waipahu, HI 96797

**YMCA Outreach Services School
Based Program**
Waipahu High School
94-1211 Farrington Highway
Waipahu, HI 96797

IDAHO

BLACKFOOT

Road to Recovery, Inc.
583 West Sexton Street
Blackfoot, ID 83221

BOISE

Aerie Addictions Recovery Center, Inc.
9600 West Brookside Lane
Boise, ID 83703

Alcoholism Intervention Services
4477 Emerald Street
Boise, ID 83706

Boise Center for Recovery Outpatient Services
410 South Orchard Street, Suite 132
Boise, ID 83705

Crossroads Counseling Services
1010 North Orchard Street
Suite 2
Boise, ID 83706-2255

First Step for Women/First Step for Men
1818 West State Street
Boise, ID 83702

Healing Center, Inc.
2503 West State Street
Boise, ID 83702

Nelson Institute
1088 North Orchard Street
Suite 1
Boise, ID 83706

Port of Hope Centers, Inc.
710 North 6th Street
Boise, ID 83706

Saint Alphonsus Addiction Recovery Center
6148 Emerald Street
Boise, ID 83704

Veterans' Affairs Medical Center Substance Abuse Treatment Programs
500 West Fort Street
Boise, ID 83702

YWCA Womens Services
720 West Washington Street
Boise, ID 83702

BONNERS FERRY

Kootenai Tribe Substance Abuse Services
County Road 38-A
Bonners Ferry, ID 83805

CALDWELL

Bell Chemical Dependency Counseling, Inc.
111 East Logan Street
Caldwell, ID 83605

COEUR D'ALENE

Comprehensive Clinical Services
401 1/2 Sherman Avenue
Suite 207
Coeur d'Alene, ID 83814

Idaho Youth Ranch Anchor House
1609 Government Way
Coeur d'Alene, ID 83814

North Idaho Behavioral Health
2301 North Ironwood Place
Coeur d'Alene, ID 83814

Port of Hope Center North
218 North 23 Street
Coeur d'Alene, ID 83814

COTTONWOOD

North Idaho Correctional Institution Road to Recovery
Star Route 3
Cottonwood, ID 83522

EMMETT

Bell Chemical Dependency Counseling, Inc.
621 South Washington Street
Emmett, ID 83617

FORT HALL

Shoshone Bannock Tribal Chemical Dependency Program
Agency Road
Fort Hall, ID 83203

GOODING

Walker Center
1120A Montana Street
Gooding, ID 83330

IDAHO FALLS

Alcohol Rehabilitation Association Phoenix Center
163 East Elva Street
Idaho Falls, ID 83401

Community Alcohol and Drug Treatment Services
589 North Water Avenue
Idaho Falls, ID 83402-3712

LAPWAI

Nez Perce Tribe Alcohol and Substance Abuse
Agency Road Bia Campus
Lapwai, ID 83540

LEWISTON

Port of Hope Family Treatment Centers
828 8th Avenue
Lewiston, ID 83501

Riverside Recovery
1720 18th Avenue
Lewiston, ID 83501

Saint Joseph's Regional Medical Center, Inc.
415 6th Street
Lewiston, ID 83501

NAMPA

Port Of Hope Centers, Inc.
508 East Florida Street
Nampa, ID 83686

Mercy Medical Center for Recovery
1512 12th Avenue
Nampa, ID 83686

OROFINO

State Hospital North Chemical Dependency Unit
300Hospital Drive
Orofino, ID 83544

PAYETTE

Bell Chemical Dependency Counseling
14 South Main Street, Suite 106
Payette, ID 83661

PLUMMER

Coeur D'Alene Tribe Family Healing Center
1115 B Street
Plummer, ID 83851

POCATELLO

Road to Recovery Inc
343 East Bonneville Street
Pocatello, ID 83201-6434

600 East Oak Street
Pocatello, ID 83201

SALMON

Carroll Counseling and Consulting
1301 Main Street Suite 8
Salmon, ID 83467

TWIN FALLS

Canyon View Psychiatric and Addiction Services of Magic Valley Regional Medical Center
228 Shoup Avenue West
Twin Falls, ID 83301

Port of Hope Centers, Inc.
425 2 Avenue North
Twin Fails, ID 83301

Walker Center
263 2nd Avenue North
Twin Falls, ID 83301

WEISER

Bell Chemical Dependence Counseling, Inc.
270 East 7th Street, Suite G
Weiser, ID 83672

ILLINOIS

ADDISON

Serenity House, Inc.
891 South Route 53
Addison, IL 60101

ALBION

Southeastern/Edwards Family Counseling Center/DUI Program
254 South 5th Street
Albion, IL 62806

ALGONQUIN

Alternative Pathways
1107 South Main Street
Algonquin, IL 60102

ALSIP

Southwest YMCA
YMCA of Metropolitan Chicago
Adolescent Outpatient Treatment
3801 West 127th Street
Alsip, IL 60803

ALTON

Chestnut Health Systems, Inc. Outpatient Program
1639 Main Street
Alton, IL 62002

Community Counseling Center of Northern Madison County, Inc.
2615 Edwards Street
Alton, IL 62002

Saint Clare's Hospital Chemical Dependency Treatment Center
915 East 5 Street
Alton, IL 62002

ANNA

Fellowship House
800 North Main Street
Anna, IL 62906

ARLINGTON HEIGHTS

Arlington Center for Recovery LLC
2010 South Arlington Heights Road
Suite 210
Arlington Heights, IL 60005

Comprehensive Behavioral Services
3345-K Arlington Heights Road
Arlington Heights, IL 60004

Hakuju Counseling Center
2010 South Arlington Heights Road
Arlington Heights, IL 60005

Mercy Counseling at Arlington Heights
115 South Wilke Road
Suite 100
Arlington Heights, IL 60005

Omni Youth Services
1616 North Arlington Heights Road
Arlington Heights, IL 60004

AURORA

Association for Individual Development
400 North Highland Avenue
Aurora, IL 60506

Breaking Free, Inc. Family Support
120 Gale Street
Aurora, IL 60506

Community Counseling Center of the Fox Valley, Inc.
400 Mercy Lane
Aurora, IL 60506

El Primer Paso
325 East Galena Boulevard
Aurora, IL 60505

Comprehensive Behavioral Services, Inc.
4260 Westbrook Drive Suite 109
Aurora, IL 60504

Dreyer Medical Clinic Department of Psychiatry
1877 West Downers Place
Aurora, IL 60506

Family Guidance Centers, Inc.
751 Aurora Avenue
Aurora, IL 60505

Opportunity House
469 North Lake Street
Aurora, IL 60506

Project Safe Women's Residential
400 Mercy Lane
Aurora, IL 60505

Provena Mercy Center Alcoholism/Drug Dependency Center
1325 North Highland Avenue
Aurora, IL 60506

Reese Clinical and Consulting Services
205 North Lake Street
Suite 103
Aurora, IL 60506

BATAVIA

Sunrise Growth Center
10 East Wilson Street
Batavia, IL 60510

BEARDSTOWN

Cass County Mental Health
Center Alcoholism Treatment Program
121 East 2 Street
Beardstown, IL 62618

BELLEVILLE

Gateway Foundation, Inc. Belleville Unit
7 North High Street, 3rd Floor
Belleville, IL 62220

Mid-America Behavioral Healthcare Alcohol and Substance Abuse Programs
5 Executive Woods Court
Belleville, IL 62226

Saint Elizabeth's Hospital Addiction Services
211 South 3 Street
Belleville, IL 62222

BENSENVILLE

Bensenville Home Society Lifelink
331 South York Road
Bensenville, IL 60106

BERWYN

McNeal Hospital Behavioral Health Services
3249 South Oak Park Avenue
Berwyn, IL 60402

Youth in Crisis, Inc.
7139 West 34th Street
Berwyn, IL 60402

BLOOMINGDALE

Accurate Caring Therapy Services
201 East Army Trail Road
Bloomingdale, IL 60108

BLOOMINGTON

Alcohol-Impaired Motorists Program (AIM)
505 North Center Street
Bloomington, IL 61701

Chestnut Health Systems, Inc.
Lighthouse/Bloomington Youth
702 West Chestnut Street
Bloomington, IL 61701

Lighthouse/Adult
1003 Martin Luther King Jr. Drive
Bloomington, IL 61701

Countermeasures, Inc.
110 North Center Street
Bloomington, IL 61701

BLUE ISLAND

Guildhaus Halfway House
2413 South Canal Street
Blue Island, IL 60406

2413 West Canal Street
Blue Island, IL 60406

BOLINGBROOK

Interventions/Lifeworks
4040 west Boughton Road
Bolingbrook, IL 60440

BUFFALO GROVE

Compsych Substance Abuse Programs
1130 Lake Cook Road, Suite 280
Buffalo Grove, IL 60089

Leslie S. Berkley and Associates
1207 McHenry Road
Buffalo Grove, IL 60089-1371

Omni Youth Services Substance Abuse Treatment Program
1111 Lake Cook Road
Buffalo Grove, IL 60089

BURR RIDGE

Heritage Corridor Counseling Services, Inc.
60 Shore Drive
Burr Ridge, IL 60521

CAIRO

Community Health Emergency Services
Rural Route 1, Box 11
Cairo, IL 62914

Delta Center, Inc.
1001 Washington Street
Cairo, IL 62914

CALUMET CITY

Comprehensive Counseling and DUI Services
536 Pulaski Road
Calumet City, IL 60409

Gutierrez and Associates
613 Wentworth Avenue
Calumet City, IL 60409-4222

CAMBRIDGDE

Bridgeway Adapt Services DUI
117 South East Street
Cambridge, IL 61238

CANTON

Alcohol and Drug Professionals of Fulton County
401 West Locust Street
Canton, IL 61520

Community Mental Health Center of Fulton and McDonough Counties
229 Martin Avenue
Canton, IL 61520

CARBONDALE

Carbondale DUI and Counseling Program
2015 West Main Street, Suite B
Carbondale, IL 62901

Gateway Foundation
318 East Walnut Street
Carbondale, IL 62901

Gateway Youth Care Foundation Carbondale
1080 East Park Street
Carbondale, IL 62901

Southern Illinois Regional Social Services
604 East College Street
Carbondale, IL 62901

CARLINVILLE

Macoupin County Mental Health
Center Alcoholism Outpatient Center
100 North Side Square
Carlinville, IL 62626

CARLYLE

Community Resource Center
580 8th Street
Carlyle, IL 62231

CARMI

Egyptian Public and Mental Health Dept
200 North Main Cross Street
Carmi, IL 62821

CAROL STREAM

CSTO Counseling Centers
350 South Schmale Road
Suite 180
Carol Stream, IL 60188

CARPENTERSVILLE

Renz Addiction Counseling Center Outpatient Substance Abuse Services
211 West Main Street, Suite 218
Carpentersville, IL 60110

CARTHAGE

Hancock County Mental Health Center, Inc. Substance Abuse Program
607 Buchanan Street
Highway 136
Carthage, IL 62321

CARY

Advantage Group Foundation, Ltd.
400 Habler Road
Cary, IL 60013

CASEYVILLE

Gateway Foundation, Inc.
Caseyville Facility
600 West Lincoln Street
Caseyville, IL 62232

CENTRALIA

Community Resource Center
101 South Locust Street
Centralia, IL 62801

Psychiatric Services
838 East McCord Street
Centralia, IL 62801

Saint Mary's Hospital Alcohol and Substance Abuse Programs
400 North Pleasant Avenue
Centralia, IL 62801

CHAMPAIGN

Carle Clinic Association New Choice Adult Outpatient/ Alcohol/Drug Recovery
809 West Church Street
Champaign, IL 61820

Centerpoint Division of Mental Health Center of Champaign County
1801 Fox Drive
Champaign, IL 61824

LWS Place Alcohol/Drug Education and Outpatient Counseling
605 North Neil Street
Champaign, IL 61820

Prairie Center Health Systems
122 West Hill Street
Champaign, IL 61820

University of Illinois at Chicago Counseling Center
610 East John Street
212 Student Services Building
Champaign, IL 61820

CHARLESTON

Central East Alcohol and Drug Council
Substance Abuse Program
635 Division Street
Charleston, IL 61920

Women's Chemical Dependency Project
726 4th Street
Charleston, IL 61920

Women's Project
1501 1/2 18 Street
Charleston, IL 61920

CHESTER

Chester Memorial Hospital The Newark Center
1900 State Street
Chester, IL 62233

Human Services Center of Southern Metro East
800 Servant Street
Chester, IL 62233

CHICAGO

Academy for Counseling, Inc.
810 East 81st Street
Chicago, IL 60619

Addiction Counseling and Education Services of Catholic Charities of Chicago
721 North Lasalle Street
Chicago, IL 60610

Aftercare Inc
10459 South Kedzie Avenue
Chicago, IL 60655

Alternatives, Inc.
1126 West Granville Avenue
2nd Floor
Chicago, IL 60660

Anixter Center
2001 North Clybourn Street
Chicago, IL 60614

6610 North Clark Street
Chicago, IL 60626

Addiction Recovery for the Deaf
1706 North Kedzie Street
1st Floor
Chicago, IL 60647

Outpatient Substance Abuse Treatment
1401 South California Boulevard
3 East Room 360
Chicago, IL 60608

Association House of Chicago
116 North Kodzie Street
Chicago, IL 60622

Bobby E Wright (CMHC) Alcoholism and Substance Abuse Services
9 South Kedzie Avenue
Chicago, IL 60612

Brass Foundation, Inc.
Substance Abuse Program
1223 West Marquette Road
Chicago, IL 60636

8000 South Racine Avenue
Chicago, IL 60620

Behavioral Health Center
340 East 51st Street
Chicago, IL 60615

Cathedral Shelter of Chicago Higgins Halfway House
207 South Ashland Boulevard
Chicago, IL 60607

Adult Outpatient
1668 West Ogden Avenue
Chicago, IL 60607

Center for Addictive Problems
609 North Wells Street
Chicago, IL 60610

Catholic Health Partners Project Hope
3047 West Cermack Road
Chicago, IL 60623

Center for Alcoholism/Project Coat
9415 South Western Avenue
Chicago, IL 60619

Center for New Horizons
551 East 36th Place
Chicago, IL 60653

Chicago Department of Health Alcohol/Substance Abuse Program
140 North Ashland Avenue
Chicago, IL 60607

Chicago Lakeshore Hospital Chemical Dependence Program
4840 North Marine Drive
Chicago, IL 60640

Chicago Treatment and Counseling Center, Inc. (CTCCI)
555C West Roosevelt Road
Chicago, IL 60607

4453 North Broadway Street
Chicago, IL 60640

Columbia Grant Hospital Chemical Dependence Program
550 West Webster Street
Suite 5-SE
Chicago, IL 60614

Community Counseling Center of Chicago
5710 North Broadway
Chicago, IL 60660

Progressions
4740 North Clark Street
Chicago, IL 60640

Comprehensive Behavioral Services, Inc.
455 North Cityfront Plaza Drive
Chicago, IL 60611

Counseling Center/Lake View Substance Abuse Services
3225 North Sheffield Avenue
Chicago, IL 60657

DUI Counseling Center Bayrach Counseling Services
4059 West 47th Street
Chicago, IL 60632

2334 West Lawrence Street
Chicago, IL 60625

Dimensions of Recovery
2240 South Michigan Avenue
Chicago, IL 60616

El Rincon Community Clinic
1874 North Milwaukee Avenue
Chicago, IL 60647

Englewood Comm. Health Organization (ECHO)
845 West 69th Street
Chicago, IL 60621

Recovery Home Program
1503-05 West 68 Street
Chicago, IL 60636

Erie Family Health Center
1701 West Superior Street
Chicago, IL 60622

Family Guidance Center, Inc.
310 West Chicago Avenue
Chicago, IL 60610

Family Link, Inc.
10 West 35th Street, 2nd Floor
Chicago, IL 60616

Garfield Counseling Center
4132 West Madison Street
Chicago, IL 60624

Gateway Foundation, Inc.
2615 West 63 Street
Chicago, IL 60629

Cook County Jail/SATC
1859 South Ashland Avenue
Chicago, IL 60608

DCFS Case Coordination
4301 West Grand Avenue
Chicago, IL 60651

West Side Treatment Center
3828 West Taylor Street
Chicago, IL 60624

Genesis Family Prevention and Intervention Programs
900 North Franklin Street
Chicago, IL 60610

Great Lakes Psychological Services Substance Abuse Services
111 North Wabash Avenue
Suite 1400
Chicago, IL 60602

Gutierrez and Associates
505 North Lasalle Street Suite 400
Chicago, IL 60610

Habilitative Systems Inc
5930 West Washington Street
Chicago, IL 60644

4350 West 16th Street
Chicago, IL 60623

Haymarket Center
4910 South King Drive
Chicago, IL 60615

108 North Sangamon Street
Chicago, IL 60607

Athey Hall
932 West Washington Street
Chicago, IL 60607

The McDermott Center/Maryville
750 West Montrose Avenue
Chicago, IL 60613-3608

Hazelden/Chicago
867 North Dearborn Street
Chicago, IL 60610

Healthcare Alternative Systems, Inc.
4534 South Western Avenue
Chicago, IL 60609

1942 North California Avenue
Chicago, IL 60647

2755 West Armitage Street
Chicago, IL 60647

1949 North Humboldt Avenue
Chicago, IL 60647

Howard Brown Health Center
4025 North Sheridan Road
Chicago, IL 60613

Human Resources Development Institute
Alcohol/Substance Abuse Program
Womens Outpatient Treatment Services
33 East 114th Street
Chicago, IL 60628

11352 South State Street
Chicago, IL 60628

Englewood Counseling Services
6241 South Halstead Avenue
Chicago, IL 60621

Pre-Release Center
3026 South California Street
Building 3 and 4
Chicago, IL 60608

Women's Residential Services
2311 East 98th Street
Chicago, IL 60617

Humana Health Plan, Inc. Evergreen Center
9415 South Western Avenue
Suite 202
Chicago, IL 60620

Interventions
Central Intake
1234 South Michigan Avenue
Suite 100
Chicago, IL 60605

Crossroads
3401 West 111th Street
Chicago, IL 60655

Northside Clinic
2723 North Clark Street
1st and 2nd Floors
Chicago, IL 60614

South Wood
5701 South Wood Street
Chicago, IL 60636

Kedzie Center
1706 North Kedzie Avenue
Chicago, IL 60647

King Drive Counseling and Referral Services
6252 South Martin Luther King Drive
Chicago, IL 60637

Latino Treatment Center Chicago Outpatient
2608 West Petersen Avenue
Chicago, IL 60659

Loretto Hospital
645 South Central Avenue
Chicago, IL 60644

Lutheran Social Services of Illinois
Edgewater
1758 West Devon Street
Chicago, IL 60660

Kathy Dwyers
1764 West Devon Avenue
Chicago, IL 60660

Men's Residence
1640 West Morse Avenue
Chicago, IL 60626

Mount Greenwood
3220 West 115 Street
Chicago, IL 60655

South Residence
7843 South Essex Avenue
Chicago, IL 60649

Women's Residence
5517 North Kenmore Avenue
Chicago, IL 60640

McDermott Center
108 North Sangamon Street
Chicago, IL 60607

810 West Montrose Street
Chicago, IL 60613-3608

120 North Sangamon Street
Chicago, IL 60607

**Mercy Hospital and Medical
Center**
Alcoholism and Drug Dependency
Program
2525 South Michigan Avenue
Chicago, IL 60616

Mercy Medical at Presidential
Towers
614 West Monroe Tower 3
Chicago, IL 60606

Mercy Medical on Pulaski
5635 South Pulaski Road
Chicago, IL 60629

**Mount Sinai Hospital/Medical
Center**
California and 15 Streets
Chicago, IL 60608

**Near North Health Services
Winfield Moody Health Center**
1276 North Clybourn Street
Chicago, IL 60610

**Nearwest Professional
Counseling Residential
Services**
2207 West 18th Street
Chicago, IL 60608

New Age Services Corporation
701-709 West Roosevelt Road
Chicago, IL 60607

**New Pathways Counseling
Services, Inc.**
4419 North Kedzie Avenue, 3rd
Floor
Chicago, IL 60625

**NIA Comprehensive Center for
Developmental Disabilities**
1808 South State Street
Chicago, IL 60616

**Northwestern Memorial
Hospital Chemical
Dependence Program**
446 East Ontario Street, 8th Floor
Chicago, IL 60611

**Norwod Park Township Family
Services**
4600 North Harlem Avenue
Chicago, IL 60656

Pilsen Little Village CMHC
3113 West Cermack Road
Chicago, IL 60623

**Polish American Association
Starting Point**
3834 North Cicero Avenue
Chicago, IL 60641

**Polish American Addictions
Counseling**
6901 West Archer Avenue
Chicago, IL 60638

Reed Treatment Clinic III
4004 West Division Street
Chicago, IL 60651

**Rogers Park Substance Abuse
Center, Ltd.**
6926 North Glenwood Street
Chicago, IL 60626

**Rosemoor Assessment
Substance Abuse Program,
Inc.**
123 East 103rd Street, Suite 1
Chicago, IL 60628

**Rush/Presbyterian St. Luke's
Medical Center Alternate
Behavior Consultation**
1720 West Polk Street
Marshall Field IV Center
Chicago, IL 60612

**Saint Elizabeth's Hospital
Substance Abuse Treatment
Center**
1431 North Claremont Avenue
Chicago, IL 60622

**Saint Joseph's Hospital Partners
Recovery Program**
2900 North Lake Shore Drive
Chicago, IL 60657

**Salvation Army Harbor Light
Center**
1515 West Monroe Street
Chicago, IL 60607

**Southeast Alcohol and Drug
Abuse Center**
8640 South Chicago Avenue
Chicago, IL 60617

Substance Abuse Services, Inc.
Outpatient Unit
2101 South Indiana Avenue
Chicago, IL 60616

**Substance Abuse Services, Inc.
Outpatient**
2101 South Indiana Avenue
Chicago, IL 60616

**Tarnowski Counseling and
Clinical Services**
5642 West Diversey Street
Room 107
Chicago, IL 60639

**Thresholds Rowan Trees
Vincennes House**
500 West Englewood Street
Chicago, IL 60621

**University of Illinois at Chicago
Addiction Services**
1740 West Taylor Street, Room
C-600
Chicago, IL 60612

Urban Life Line
2149-53 East 83rd Street
Chicago, IL 60617

Veterans' Affairs Medical Center
Alcohol/Substance Abuse Program
820 South Damen Avenue
Chicago, IL 60612

West Side Holistic Family Center
4909 West Division Street
Chicago, IL 60651

Woodlawn Organization, The (TWO)
1447 East 65th Street
Chicago, IL 60637

York Behavioral Health Care
1525 East Hyde Park Boulevard
Chicago, IL 60615

Yos/Albany Park
4751 North Kedzie Avenue
Chicago, IL 60625

Yos/Austin
5912 West Division Street
Chicago, IL 60651

Youth Outreach Services, Inc.
Northwest Youth Outreach/Irving Park
6417 West Irving Park Road
Chicago, IL 60634

Youth Service Project, Inc.
3942 West North Avenue
Chicago, IL 60647

CHICAGO HEIGHTS

Aunt Marthas Youth Service Center
1526 Otto Boulevard
Chicago Heights, IL 60411

CICERO

Chicago Treatment and Counseling Center, Inc. (CTCCI)
1849 South Cicero Avenue
Cicero, IL 60804

Pro Health Advocates, Inc.
5929 West Roosevelt Road
Cicero, IL 60402

Racing Industry Charitable Foundation (RICF)
Hawthorne Racecourse
3701 South Laramie Street
Cicero, IL 60804

Youth Outreach Services
6117 West Cermak Road
Cicero, IL 60804

CLINTON

Dewitt County Human Resource
Center Substance Abuse Treatment Program
1150 Route 54 West
Clinton, IL 61727

CRYSTAL LAKE

Comprehensive Behavioral Services, Inc.
333 Commerce Drive
Crystal Lake, IL 60014

Counseling Center
735-C McArdle Drive
Crystal Lake, IL 60014

Northwest Community Counseling Services
111 South Virginia Avenue
Crystal Lake, IL 60014-5936

Professional Consultations, Inc.
Ambutal Medical Center
4900 South Route 31, Suite 117
Crystal Lake, IL 60012

DANVILLE

Prairie Center Health Systems, Inc.
3545 North Vermilion Street
Danville, IL 61832-1337

Provena United Samaritans Medical Center
Bridgeway Recover Center
600 Sager Avenue
Danville, IL 61832

Veterans' Affairs Medical Center
Alcohol/Drug Dependence Treatment Program
1900 East Main Street
Danville, IL 61832

DECATUR

Behavioral Advocate Group, Inc.
1900 East Lake Shore Drive
Suite 340
Decatur, IL 62521

Chestnut Health Systems, Inc.
2130 North 27th Street
Decatur, IL 62526

Heritage Behavioral Health Center
151 North Main Street
Decatur, IL 62523

Saint Mary's Treatment Center
1800 East Lakeshore Drive
Decatur, IL 62521

DEKALB

Ben Gordon Center Substance Abuse Services Program
12 Health Services Drive
DeKalb, IL 60115

Kishwaukee Hospital Alcohol and Chemical Dependency Treatment Center
626 Bethany Road
DeKalb, IL 60115

DES PLAINES

Family Guidance Centers Inc
1689 Elk Boulevard
Des Plaines, IL 60016

Forest Healthy System, Inc.
555 Wilson Lane
Des Plaines, IL 60016

Holy Family Medical Center Keys to Recovery
100 North River Road
Des Plaines, IL 60016

Relapse Prevention Counseling Center
1330 Webford Street
Des Plaines, IL 60016

DIXON

Adult Education Associates
748 Timbercreek Road
Dixon, IL 61021

Sinnissippi Centers, Inc.
325 Illinois Route 2
Dixon, IL 61021

DOWNERS GROVE

CAP of Downers Grove
5329 Main Street
Downers Grove, IL 60515

Rush Behavioral Health Center
2001 Butterfield Road, Suite 320
Downers Grove, IL 60515

DUNDEE

Professional Consultations
302 West Main Street
Dundee, IL 60118

DUQUOIN

Impact Incarceration Program
Rural Route 1
DuQuoin, IL 62832

EAST HAZELCREST

South Suburban Council on Alcoholism and Substance Abuse
1909 Cheker Square
East Hazelcrest, IL 60429

EAST PEORIA

Ripper and Associates, Ltd.
204 Pinecrest Drive
East Peoria, IL 61611

EAST SAINT LOUIS

Comp. Mental Health Center of Saint Clair County, Inc.
913 Martin Luther King Drive
East Saint Louis, IL 62201

402 North 9th Street
East Saint Louis, IL 62201

129 North 9th Street
East Saint Louis, IL 62201

EDWARDSVILLE

Intensive Outpatient Care
315 North Main Street
Edwardsville, IL 62025

EFFINGHAM

Foil Counseling and DUI Services, Inc.
1901 South 4th Street, Suite 28
Effingham, IL 62401

Heartland Human Services
Guidance and Counseling Center
1108 South Willow Street
Effingham, IL 62401

ELDORADO

Egyptian Public and Mental
Health Dept. Alcohol Outpatient
1412 Highway 45 North
Eldorado, IL 62930

ELGIN

Abacus Program
555 Tollgate Street, Suite A
Elgin, IL 60120

CSTO Counseling Centers, Inc.
115 South Grove Street, Suite 201
Elgin, IL 60120

Latino Treatment Center
54 Fountain Square Plaza
Elgin, IL 60120

Lutheran Social Services of Illinois
675 Varsity Drive
Elgin, IL 60120

Renz Addiction Counseling Center
Substance Abuse Services
76/80 South Grove Avenue
Elgin, IL 60120

Saint Joseph Hospital Cornerstone Program
77 North Airlite Street
Elgin, IL 60120

ELK GROVE VILLAGE

ABLC Behavioral Health Resources
901 Biesterfield Road, Suite 400
Elk Grove Village, IL 60007

Alexian Brothers Medical Center
800 Biesterfield Road
Elk Grove Village, IL 60007

ELMHURST

Elmhurst Memorial Hospital Behavioral Health Services
200 Berteau Avenue
Elmhurst, IL 60126

Kevin and Associates, Inc.
110 Cottage Hill Street, Suite 305
Elmhurst, IL 60126

EVANSTON

Behavioral Health Center
500 Davis Street
Evanston, IL 60201

Evanston Hospital Chapman Center
2650 North Ridge Avenue
Evanston, IL 60201

Peer Services, Inc.
906 Davis Street
Evanston, IL 60201

Saint Francis Hospital Outpatient Addiction Services
355 Ridge Avenue
Evanston, IL 60202

EVERGREEN PARK

Little Company of Mary Hospital Behavioral Health Services
2800 West 95th Street
Evergreen Park, IL 60805

FAIRFIELD

Southeastern/Wayne Family Counseling Center
407 North Basin Drive
Fairfield, IL 62837

FLORA

Clay County Counseling Center
118 West North Avenue
Flora, IL 62839

Southeastern/Clay Family Counseling Center
901 West 3rd Street
Flora, IL 62839

FLOSSMOOR

Family Link, Inc. Counseling and Assessment Center
3608 West Vollmer Road
Flossmoor, IL 60422

FOREST PARK

Riveredge Hospital/One South
8311 West Roosevelt Road One South
Forest Park, IL 60130

FOX LAKE

Western Lake County Alcohol and Drug Dependency Treatment Program
17 West Grand Avenue
Fox Lake, IL 60020

FRANKLIN PARK

Leyden Family Services
Mental Health Center Alcoholism Services
10001 West Grand Avenue
Franklin Park, IL 60131

Leyden Youth Outreach Services
10013-15 West Grand Avenue
Franklin Park, IL 60131

FREEPORT

Alpine Park Center
773 West Lincoln Boulevard
Suite 101
Freeport, IL 61302

Sojourn House, Inc.
565 North Turner Avenue
Freeport, IL 61032

GALENA

Sojourn House, Inc. DUI Program
706 South West Street
Galena, IL 61036

GALESBURG

Bridgeway, Inc. Adapt Services
2323 Windish Drive
Galesburg, IL 61401

Galesburg Cottage Hospital
695 North Kellogg Street
Galesburg, IL 61401

GENESEO

Good Shepherd Foundation
4166 South Oakwood Avenue
Geneseo, IL 61254

GENEVA

Attitude Behavior Modification Systems, Inc.
324 West State Street
Geneva, IL 60134

Comprehensive Behavioral Services, Inc.
825 West State Street, Suite 109
Geneva, IL 60134

GOLCONDA

Family Counseling Center, Inc.
Market and Washington Streets
Golconda, IL 62938

GRANITE CITY

Alcoholic Rehab Community Home Arch House
1313 21st Street
Granite City, IL 62040

Chestnut Health Systems, Inc.
50 Norhtgate Industrial Drive
Granite City, IL 62040-6805

Saint Elizabeth Medical Center/ BHS
2100 Madison Avenue
Granite City, IL 62040

GREAT LAKES

Naval Hospital Alcohol Rehabilitation Department
2705 Sheridan Road
Great Lakes, IL 60088-5234

GREENVILLE

Bond County Health Department Prairie Counseling Center
503 South Prairie Street
Greenville, IL 62246

GURNEE

Michael L Klestinski and Associates
68 Ambrogio Drive
Gurnee, IL 60031

HANOVER PARK

Renz Addiction Counseling Center
7431 Astor Street
Hanover Park, IL 60103

HARVARD

Lutheran Social Services
Division Street, Unit 3
Harvard, IL 60033

HARVEY

Foundation I Center for Human Development Methadone Treatment Unit
15400 South Page Avenue
Harvey, IL 60426

Ingalls Memorial Hospital Health Management Center
1 Ingalls Drive
Wyman Gordon Pavillion, Room 207
Harvey, IL 60426

HAZEL CREST

Mercy Counseling at Hazel Crest
17577 South Kedzie Street
Hazel Crest, IL 60429

Recovery Concepts
17065 Dixie Highway
Hazel Crest, IL 60429

Highland Park Hospital Chemical Dependency Services
718 Glenview Avenue
Highland Park, IL 60035

HILLSBORO

Gateway Foundation, Inc.
Graham Correctional Center Substance Abuse Treatment Center
I55 and Highway 185
Hillsboro, IL 62049

Montgomery County Prevention and Treatment Program
Route 185
Hillsboro, IL 62049

HINSDALE

Interventions Du Page
11 South 250 Route 83
Hinsdale, IL 60521

New Day Center of Hinsdale Hospital
120 North Oak Street
Hinsdale, IL 60521

HOFFMAN ESTATES

Leyden Family Service MH Center Share Program
1776 Moon Lake Road
Hoffman Estates, IL 60194

HOPEDALE

Hopedale Hall Chemical Dependency Program for Older Adults
Railroad and Tremont Streets
Hopedale Medical Complex
Hopedale, IL 61747

INA

Jefferson County Comp Services, Inc. Vantage Program
BMRCC
Ina, IL 62846

JACKSONVILLE

Park Place Center
201 East Morgan Street
Jacksonville, IL 62651

Wells Center
1300 Lincoln Avenue
Jacksonville, IL 62650

Wells Center Department of Corrections
Jacksonville, IL 62650

JERSEYVILLE

Tri-County Counseling Center
220 East County Road
Jerseyville, IL 62052

JOLIET

Healy and Associates
2317 West Jefferson Street
Suite 204
Joliet, IL 60455

Interventions/Lifeworks
214 North Ottawa Street
Joliet, IL 60431

Joliet Counseling Center
54 North Ottawa Street, Suite 120
Joliet, IL 60432

Paramos Counseling Center
815 North Larkin Avenue, Suite 204
Joliet, IL 60435

Saint Joseph Medical Center Substance Abuse Program
333 North Madison Street
Joliet, IL 60435

Silver Cross Hospital Chemical Dependency Unit
1200 Maple Road
Joliet, IL 60432

Stepping Stones, Inc.
1621 Theodore Street
Joliet, IL 60435

Will County Health Department Addiction Services
407 West Jefferson Street
Joliet, IL 60433

William Reid Group
68 North Chicago Street
Joliet, IL 60432

JUSTICE

Mercy Medical In Justice
81 Street and Kean Avenue
Justice, IL 60458

KANKAKEE

Aunt Martha's Youth Service Center, Inc.
335 NorthSchuyler Street
Suite 420
Kankakee, IL 60901

Duane Dean Prevention and Treatment Center
700 East Court Street
Kankakee, IL 60901

New Hope Counseling Center
150 North Schulyer Avenue
Suite 1002
Kankakee, IL 60901

Saint Mary's Hospital of Kankakee
500 West Court Street
Kankakee, IL 60901

LAGRANGE

Elder and Associates Inc
475 West 55th Street
LaGrange, IL 60525

LAKE FOREST

Rush Behavioral Health Center at Lake Forest Hospital
Westmoreland Road
Lake Forest, IL 60045

LAKE VILLA

Gateway Foundation, Inc.
25480 West Cedarcrest Lane
Lake Villa, IL 60046

Lake County Health Dept. Mental
Health Division Outpatient
  Substance Abuse NW Satellite
121 East Grand Avenue
Lake Villa, IL 60046

Victory Outpatient Chemical Dependency Programs
2031 Grand Avenue, Suite 200
Lake Villa, IL 60046

LAKE ZURICH

Omni Youth Services Ela Township Office
157 East Main Street
Lake Zurich, IL 60047

LA SALLE

North Central Behavioral Health System
2960 Chartres Street
LaSalle, IL 61301

LAWRENCEVILLE

Southeastern Illinois Counseling Centers, Inc.
1501 Olive Street
Lawrenceville, IL 62439

LIBERTYVILLE

Addictions Associates, Inc.
322 Peterson Road
Libertyville, IL 60048

Alliance Institute for the Treatment of Chemical Dependency
501 West Peterson Road
Libertyville, IL 60048

Condell Medical Center Living
Free/Outpatient Addiction
  Recovery Program
345 North Milwaukee Avenue
Libertyville, IL 60048

LINCOLN

Alcohol and Related Counseling
1411 North Kickapoo Street
Lincoln, IL 62656

Mental Health Centers of Central Illinois
304 8th Street
Lincoln, IL 62656

LOMBARD

Alexian Brothers/Lake Cook Behavioral Health
2 East 22nd Street, Suite 301
Lombard, IL 60148

Elmhurst Memorial Hospital Guidance Center
470 East Roosevelt Road
Lombard, IL 60148

Catholic Charities Diocese of Joliet
26 West Saint Charles Road
Lombard, IL 60148

MACHESNEY PARK

Alpine Park Center
7507 North 2nd Street
Machesney Park, IL 61115-2815

MACOMB

CMHC of Fulton/McDonough
Counties Substance Abuse Services
301 East Jefferson Street
Macomb, IL 61455

McDonough District Hospital Recovery Center
525 East Grant Street
Macomb, IL 61455

MANTENO

Kankakee Minimum Security Unit
37040 South Illinois Street
Route 102
Manteno, IL 60950

Riverside Resolve Center
411 Division Street
Manteno, IL 60950

Substance Abuse Services, Inc. Branden House
800 Bramble Street
Manteno, IL 60950

MARSHALL

Human Resources Center of Edgar and Clark Counties
1006 South 6th Street
Marshall, IL 62441

MARYVILLE

Chestnut Health Systems, Inc.
21487 Vadalabene Road
Maryville, IL 62062

MATTOON

Central East Alcohol and Drug Council
Adolescent Outpatient Services
513 North 13 Street
Mattoon, IL 61938

Outpatient Services
416 North 19 Street
Mattoon, IL 61938

MAYWOOD

Substance Abuse Operations
308 South 5 Avenue
Maywood, IL 60153

The Way Back Inn, Inc.
104 Oak Street
Maywood, IL 60153

201 South 2 Avenue
Maywood, IL 60153

MCHENRY

Family Service and CMHC For McHenry County
5320 West Elm Street
McHenry, IL 60050

Michael L Klestinski and Associates
5400 West Elm Street, Suite 200
McHenry, IL 60050

MELROSE PARK

Procare Recovery Center
1414 West Main Street
Melrose Park, IL 60160

**Westlake Community Hospital
Substance Abuse Center**
1225 Lake Street
Melrose Park, IL 60160

Yos/North Avenue
2140 West North Avenue
Melrose Park, IL 60160

MENDOTA

**Mendota Community Hospital
DUI/Outpatient Services**
1315 Memorial Drive
Mendora, IL 61342

METROPOLIS

MASSAC County Mental Health
206 West 5th Street
Metropolis, IL 62960

MONMOUTH

Bridgeway Adapt Services
219 Euclid Street
Monmouth, IL 61462

MONTICELLO

**Piatt County Mental Health
Center**
1921 North Market Street
Monticello, IL 61856

MORRIS

**Grundy County Health
Department**
1320 Union Street
Morris, IL 60450-2426

**Institute for Personal
Development**
1401 Lakewood Drive, Suite A
Morris, IL 60450

MOUNT CARMEL

Southeastern Counseling Center
Wabash Family
311 West 5th Street
Mount Carmel, IL 62863

MOUNT CARROLL

Sinnissippi Centers, Inc.
1122 Healthcare Drive
Mount Carroll, IL 61053

MOUNT STERLING

**Brown County Mental Health
Center Alcoholism Services**
111 West Washington Street
Mount Sterling, IL 62353

MOUNT VERNON

**Jefferson County Comp.
Services, Inc. Vantage Point**
Route 37 North
Mount Vernon, IL 62864

MUNDELEIN

**Omni Youth Services Mundelein
Libertyville**
505 East Hawley Street
Mundelein, IL 60060

NAPERVILLE

Alpha Counseling Center Inc
25 West 550 Royce Road
Naperville, IL 60565

Linden Oaks Hospital
852 West Street
Naperville, IL 60540

NASHVILLE

**Washington County Vocational
Workshop**
781 East Holzhauer Drive
Nashville, IL 62263

NEWTON

**Jasper County Counseling
Services**
106 East Edwards Street
Newton, IL 62448

**Southeastern Illinois Counseling
Centers, Inc.**
902 West Jourdan Street
Newton, IL 62448

NORTH CHICAGO

**Lake County Health Department
Behavioral Health Alcoholism
Treatment Center**
3001 Green Bay Road
Building 126
North Chicago, IL 60064

**Northern Illinois Council on
Alcohol and Substance
Abuse(NICASA) Women's and
Children's Program**
2031 Dugdale Road
North Chicago, IL 60064

**Veterans' Affairs Medical Center
Substance Abuse Program**
3001 Greenbay Road
Building B-11
North Chicago, IL 60064

NORTHFIELD

**Adolescent Substance Abuse
Program**
405 Central Avenue
Northfield, IL 60093

OAK BROOK

Patricia Ely and Associates
2625 Butterfield Road
Oak Brook, IL 60523

OAK BROOK TERRACE

**Alexander Zubenko and
Associates**
17 West 620 14th Street
Suite 202
Oak Brook Terrace, IL 60181

OAK FOREST

Bremen Youth Services
15350 Oak Park Avenue
Oak Forest, IL 60452

OAK LAWN

**Associates in Alcohol and Drug
Counseling**
8938 South Ridgeland Avenue
Suite 100
Oak Lawn, IL 60453

Christ Hospital and Medical Center Substance Abuse Services
4440 West 95th Street 5 West
Oak Lawn, IL 60453

Crossmont and Associates, Inc.
10522 South Cicero Avenue
Suite 4-A
Oak Lawn, IL 60453

OAK PARK

Education and Intervention, Inc.
1515 North Harlem Avenue, Suite 202
Oak Park, IL 60302-1205

Family Services Center and Mental Health Center of Oak Park and River Forest
120 South Marion Street
Oak Park, IL 60302

Grateful Hand Foundation, Inc. Grateful House
412 South Wesley Avenue
Oak Park, IL 60302

Procare Recovery Center
723 South Boulevard, 1st Floor
Oak Park, IL 60302

York Behavioral Health
1 Erie Court, 4th Floor
Oak Park, IL 60302

Yos/Oak Park
723 South Boulevard
Oak Park, IL 60302

OLNEY

Southeastern Illinois Counseling
Centers, Inc. Alcohol Outpatient Services
4 Micah Drive
Olney, IL 62450

OLYMPIA FIELDS

Intercept Programs, Inc.
20200 Governors Drive
Suite 104-5
Olympia Fields, IL 60461

Olympia Fields
2400 West Lincoln Highway
Suite 107
Olympia Fields, IL 60461

ONARGA

Nexus-Adolescent Chemical Health
212 East Seminary Road
Onarga, IL 60955-0003

ORLAND PARK

William Reid Group
62 Orland Square Drive, Suite 605
Orland Park, IL 60462

OTTAWA

Choices at Community Hospital of Ottawa
1100 East Norris Drive
Ottawa, IL 61350

DUI Assessments and Services
417 West Madison Street
Suite 205
Ottawa, IL 61350

James R. Gage and Associates
1784 Dhessie Lane
Ottawa, IL 61350

PALATINE

Lutheran Social Services
4811 Emerson Avenue
Suite 112
Palatine, IL 60067

The Bridge Youth and Family
Services Comprehensive Prevention
721 South Quintin Road
Palatine, IL 60067

PALOS HEIGHTS

7270 College Drive, Suite 101
Palos Heights, IL 60463

PALOS HILLS

Baxter and Sheehan, Inc.
Palos Hills, IL 60465

PARIS

Human Resources Center of Edgar and Clark Counties
118 East Court Street
Paris, IL 61944

PARK RIDGE

Lutheran General Hospital Addiction Treatment Program
1700 Luther Lane, 2 North Unit
Park Ridge, IL 60068

Maine Township for Addiction
1400 North Northwest Highway
Suite 100
Park Ridge, IL 60068

PAWNEE

Pawnee Counseling Center
528 Douglas Street
Pawnee, IL 62558

PEKIN

Behavioral Medicine at Pekin Hospital Lifeway ACDU
600 South 13th Street
Pekin, IL 61554

Tazwood Center for Human Services
3223 Griffin Avenue
Pekin, IL 61554

PEORIA

Alcohol and Related Counseling
416 Main Street, Suite 619
Peoria, IL 61602

Human Service Center
218 NE Jefferson Avenue
Peoria, IL 61603

New Leaf Retreat
3500 West New Leaf Lane
Peoria, IL 61614

White Oaks Center
3400 New Leaf Lane
Peoria, IL 61615

White Oaks Knolls
2101 West Willow Knolls Drive
Peoria, IL 61615

Proctor Hospital
5409 North Knoxville Street
Peoria, IL 61614

Professional Consultants
411 Hamilton Boulevard
Suite 1000
Peoria, IL 61602

T. W. Mathews and Associates
7501 North University Street
Suite 215
Peoria, IL 61614

PITTSFIELD

Counseling Center of Pike County
121 South Madison Street
Pittsfield, IL 62363

PONTIAC

Institute for Human Resources
310 Torrance Avenue
Pontiac, IL 61764

PRAIRIE VIEW

NICASA
2900 North Main Street
Prairie View, IL 60069

PRINCETON

North Central Behavioral Health Systems
530 Park Avenue East
Princeton, IL 61356

QUINCY

Family Therapy Associates
200 North 8 Street
Suite 111
Quincy, IL 62301

Great River Recovery Resource
428 South 36 Street
Quincy, IL 62301

Newman Clinic
Broadway at 14th Street
Quincy, IL 62305-7005

Park Place Center
301 Oak Street
Quincy, IL 62301

RED BUD

Human Service Center of Southern Illinois
East Substance Abuse Services
10257 State Route 3
Red Bud, IL 62278

RIDGEWAY

Egyptian Public and Mental Health Dept.
711 Main Street
Ridgeway, IL 62979

ROBINSON

Southeastern Counseling Center Crawford Family Counseling Center
204 West Highland Street
Robinson, IL 62454

ROCHELLE

Sinnissippi Centers, Inc.
417 North 6th Street
Rochelle, IL 61068

ROCK FALLS

KSB Hospital Recovery Center
1503 First Avenue
Suite A
Rock Falls, IL 61071

ROCKFORD

Al Tech, Inc. Drug and Alcohol Outpatient
3415 North Main Street
Rockford, IL 61103

Alpine Park Center
5411 East State Street
Suite 212
Rockford, IL 61108

Comprehensive Behavioral Services, Inc.
6016 Fincham Street
Rockford, IL 61108

Family Addiction Instruction Recovery Treatment Center
5301 East State Street
Suite 101
Rockford, IL 61108

PHASE, Inc.
319 South Church Street
Rockford, IL 61101-1316

Rockford Memorial Hospital Addiction Treatment and Education Program
950 South Mulford Road
Rockford, IL 61108

Rosecrance Center
1505 North Alpine Road
Rockford, IL 61107

3815 Harrison Avenue
Rockford, IL 61108

420 East State Street
Rockford, IL 61104-1015

Youth Outpatient Program
1021-23 West Jefferson Street
Rockford, IL 61101

ROCK ISLAND

Alcohol and Drug Education Services
1705 2nd Avenue, Suite 100
Rock Island, IL 61201-8718

Center for Alcohol and Drug
Services Freedom House Clinic I
4230 11th Street
Rock Island, IL 61201

Paul A. Hauck, PhD., Ltd. Substance Abuse Services
1800 3 Avenue
Suite 302
Rock Island, IL 61201

Robert Young Center for Community Mental Health
2701 17 Street
Rock Island, IL 61201

ROLLING MEADOWS

Rolling Meadows Counseling Services
1645 Hicks Road
Rolling Meadows, IL 60008

ROUND LAKE

Northern Illinois Council on
Alcoholism and Substance Abuse
31979 North Fish Lake Road
Round Lake, IL 60073

RUSHVILLE

Schuyler Counseling and Health
   Services
127 South Liberty Street
Rushville, IL 62681

SAINT CHARLES

Human Resources Development
   Institute Illinois Youth
   Center/Valley View
34 W 826 Villa Maria Road
Saint Charles, IL 60174

Renz Counseling Center
230 West River Drive
Saint Charles, IL 60174

SALEM

Community Resource Center
1325-C West Whitaker Street
Salem, IL 62881

SCHAUMBURG

Haymarket Center
1990 East Algonquin Road
Schaumburg, IL 60173

Professional Consultations, Inc.
1650 Moon Lake Boulevard
Schaumburg, IL 60194

Wendy Stebbins and Associates
1701 East Woodfield Road
Suite 415
Schaumburg, IL 60173

SCOTT AFB

375th Medical Group SGOHS
   Substance Abuse Control
   Program
310 West Losey Street
Scott AFB, IL 62225-5252

SHELBYVILLE

Central East Alcohol and Drug
   Council
155 South Morgan Street
Shelbyville, IL 62565

SHERIDAN

Gateway Foundation, Inc.
Sheridan Correctional Facility
   Substance Abuse Treatment
   Center
4017 East 2603 Road
Sheridan, IL 60551

SKOKIE

Alon Treatment Center
9150 North Crawford Avenue
Skokie, IL 60076

SPARTA

Human Service Center of
   Southern Illinois
104 Northtown Road
Sparta, IL 62286

SPRINGFIELD

Alcohol and Addictions
   Outpatient Center
550 North Street
Springfield, IL 62704

Gateway Foundation, Inc.
   Springfield Facility
2200 Lake Victoria Drive
Springfield, IL 62703

Midwest Psychological Systems
   DUI and Substance Abuse
   Services
987 Clock Tower Drive
Springfield, IL 62704

Personal Consultants
1945 South Spring Street
Springfield, IL 62704

1430 South 8th Street
Springfield, IL 62703

Saint John's Hospital Libertas
   Program
800 East Carpenter Street
Springfield, IL 62769

Stillmeadow Counseling Center
706 South Grand Avenue West
Springfield, IL 62704

Triangle Center
120 North 11 Street
Springfield, IL 62703

SPRING VALLEY

Spring Valley Outpatient
   Services
213 East Saint Paul Street
Spring Valley, IL 61362

STERLING

Community Employee
   Assistance Agency
2804 West Lefevre Road
Sterling, IL 61081

Lutheran Social Services
   Sterling
1901 First Avenue
Sterling, IL 61081

Sinnissippi Centers, Inc.
2611 Woodlawn Road
Sterling, IL 61081

STREAMWOOD

Streamwood Behavioral Health
   Center
1400 East Irving Park Road
Streamwood, IL 60107

STREATOR

North Central Behavioral Health
   Systems
104 6 Street
Streator, IL 61364

Saint Mary's Hospital
   Behavioral Health Service
111 East Spring Street
Streator, IL 61364

SULLIVAN

Moultrie County Counseling
   Center Moultrie County DUI
   Referral
2 West Adams Street
Sullivan, IL 61951

SUMMIT

Des Plaines Valley Community Center Family Outpatient Addiction
7355 West Archer Avenue
Summit, IL 60501

SYCAMORE

Attitude/Behavioral Modification Systems, Inc.
134 West State Street
Sycamore, IL 60178

TAYLORVILLE

Gateway Foundation, Inc. Taylorville Correctional Center
Route 29 South, Box 1000
Taylorville, IL 62568

Triangle Center
320 North Western Avenue
Taylorville, IL 62568

TINLEY PARK

Medical Control Centers
7060 Centennial Drive, Suite 104
Tinley Park, IL 60477

TUSCOLA

Douglas County Drug Alcohol Evaluation and Remedial Education Program
114 West Houghton Street
Tuscola, IL 61953

URBANA

Creative Consultations
302 West Elm Street
Urbana, IL 61801

Prairie Center Health Systems, Inc. Killarney Street Unit
718 Killarney Drive
Urbana, IL 61801

VANDALIA

Community Resource Center
421 West Main Street
Vandalia, IL 62471

Helm DUI Services
716 School Street
Vandalia, IL 62471

Wells Center Vandalia Correctional Center
Vandalia, IL 62471

VERNON HILLS

Lake County Health Department Behavioral Health Women's Residential Services
24647 North Milwaukee Avenue
Vernon Hills, IL 60061

VIENNA

Family Counseling Center, Inc.
408 East Vine Street
Vienna, IL 62995

VILLA PARK

Life Awareness Center, Inc. Adult Outpatient Treatment
335 South Ardmore Street
Villa Park, IL 60181

WATERLOO

Human Support Services of Monroe County Substance Abuse Alternatives
988 North Illinois Route 3
Waterloo, IL 62298

WATSEKA

Iroquois Mental Health Center
Outpatient Alcoholism Program
908 East Cherry Street
Watseka, IL 60970

WAUCONDA

Interventions Contact
26991 Anderson Road
Wauconda, IL 60084

WAUKEGAN

Lake County Health Dept. Behavioral Health Division
MISA Case Management
3012 Grand Avenue
Waukegan, IL 60085

Northern Illinois Council on Alcoholism and Substance Abuse
1113 Greenwood Avenue
Waukegan, IL 60087

Bridge House
3016 Grand Avenue
Waukegan, IL 60085

Victory Memorial Hospital Chemical Dependency Programs
1324 North Sheridan Road
Waukegan, IL 60085

WESTCHESTER

Procare Recovery Center
9855 Roosevelt Road
Westchester, IL 60154

WEST FRANKFORT

Franklin/Williamson Human Services, Inc.
902 West Main Street
West Frankfort, IL 62896

WHEATON

DuPage County Health Department
111 North County Farm Road
Wheaton, IL 60187

Du Page County Psychological Services
421 North County Farm Road
Wheaton, IL 60187

Pape and Associates
618 South West Street
Wheaton, IL 60187

William Reid Group
2100 Manchester Road
Building A, Suite 303
Wheaton, IL 60187

WHEELING

Omni Youth Services
222 East Dundee Road
Wheeling, IL 60090

Scott Bayrach, Ltd.
925 North Milwaukee Avenue
Suite 1016
Wheeling, IL 60090

WINFIELD

Behavioral Health Services of Central Du Page Hospital
27 West 350 High Luke Road
Winfield, IL 60190

WOODRIDGE

Interventions/Woodridge
2221 West 64 Street
Woodridge, IL 6051

New Visions Counseling Services, Inc.
8263 Janes Avenue, Suite I
Woodridge, IL 60517

WOOD RIVER

Wood River Township Hospital Flex Care Program
101 East Edwardsville Road
Wood River, IL 62095

WOODSTOCK

McHenry County Youth Service
Bureau Outpatient Substance Abuse Treatment
101 South Jefferson Street
Woodstock, IL 60098

Centegra/Memorial Medical Center Chemical Dependency Services
527 West South Street
Woodstock, IL 60098

YORKVILLE

Kendall County Health and Human Servs
500-A Countryside Center
Yorkville, IL 60560

ZION

Zion Township Crew
2800 Sheridan Road
Zion, IL 60099

INDIANA

ALBION

Addiction Recovery Centers of Indiana
100 West Main Street
Albion, IN 46701

ANDERSON

Center for Mental Health, Inc.
2020 Brown Street
Anderson, IN 46015

1808 Main Street
Anderson, IN 46015

Community Hospital of Anderson and Madison County
1515 North Madison Avenue
Anderson, IN 46011

Crestview Center
2201 Hillcrest Drive
Anderson, IN 46012

House of Hope of Madison County, Inc.
902 High Street
Anderson, IN 46012

ANGOLA

Cameron Memorial Community Hospital Substance Abuse Services
416 East Maumee Avenue
Angola, IN 46703

Northeastern Center Steuben County Satellite
200 Hoosier Drive
Angola, IN 46703

ATTICA

Wabash Valley Hospital Outpatient Services
101 Suzie Lane
Attica, IN 47918

AUBURN

Northeastern Center Dekalb County Satellite
1800 Wesley Road
Auburn, IN 46706

BATESVILLE

Community Mental Health Center, Inc.
215 East George Street
Batesville, IN 47006

BEDFORD

Center for Behavioral Health, Inc.
Lawrence County Services
1315 Hillcrest Road
Bedford, IN 47421

BEECH GROVE

Saint Francis Hospital and Health Centers Behavioral Health Services
1600 Albany Street
Beech Grove, IN 46107

BLOOMINGTON

BHC Meadows Hospital
3800 North Prow Road
Bloomington, IN 47404

Bloomington Hospital Chemical Dependency Unit
601 West 2nd Street
Bloomington, IN 47402

Partners in Recovery DBA Sunrise Counseling Centers
924 West 17th Street
Bloomington, IN 47404

**South Central Community
Mental Health Center DBA
Center for Behavioral Health**
645 South Rogers Street
Bloomington, IN 47403

BLUFFTON

CAP, Inc.
122 Lamar Street
Bluffton, IN 46714

**Park Center, Inc. Bluffton
Counseling Services**
1115 South Main Street
Bluffton, IN 46714

BOONVILLE

**Southwest Indiana Mental
Health Center, Inc.**
315 South 3rd Street
Boonville, IN 47601

BROOKVILLE

**Community Mental Health
Center, Inc.**
Highway 101 and Cooley Road
Brookville, IN 47012

BROWNSBURG

Hill and Associates
23 Boulevard Motif
Brownsburg, IN 46112

CARMEL

**Behavior Corporation Substance
Abuse Outpatient Services**
697 Pro Med Lane
Carmel, IN 46032

CEDAR LAKE

Awakenings
10800 West 133rd Avenue
Suite 2
Cedar Lake, IN 46303

CHURUBUSCO

Wise Choices, Inc.
209 South Main Street
Churubusco, IN 46723

CLINTON

**Hamilton Center at Vermillion
County Center**
825 South Main Street
Suite 207
Clinton, IN 47842

COLUMBIA CITY

**Otis R Bowen Center for Human
Services, Inc.**
201 North Line Street
Columbia City, IN 46725

COLUMBUS

Brumbaugh and Associates
2209 Central Avenue
Columbus, IN 47201

Quinco Consulting Center
806 Jackson Avenue
Columbus, IN 47201

**SOAR LLC/Steps of Addiction
Recovery**
1601 Orinoco Avenue
Columbus, IN 47201

Tara Treatment Center, Inc.
3985 Williamsburg Street
Columbus, IN 47203

CONNORSVILLE

**Fayette Memorial Hospital DBA
Whitewater Valley Care
Pavilion**
450 Erie Street
Connersville, IN 47331

CORYDON

**Lifespring Mental Health
Services Harrison County
Office**
Corydon/New Middletown Road
Corydon, IN 47112

Recovery Care Center, Inc.
109 North Elm Street
Corydon, IN 47112

CRAWFORDSVILLE

**Wabash Valley Hospital, Inc.
Outpatient Services**
1480 Darlington Avenue
Crawfordsville, IN 47933

DANVILLE

**Cummins Mental Health Center,
Inc. Addictions Program**
6655 East U.S. 36
Danville, IN 46122

**Hendricks Community Hospital
Mental Health Inpatient
Services**
1000 East Main Street
Danville, IN 46122

**Lebanon Hospital LLC DBA
BHC Lebanon Hospital**
5250 East U.S. 36
Danville, IN 46122

DECATUR

**Park Center, Inc. Decatur
Counseling Services**
809 South High Street
Decatur, IN 46733

**Adams County Memorial
Hospital Stress Center**
805 High Street
Decatur, IN 46733

DELPHI

**Wabash Valley Hospital
Outpatient Services**
108 North Washington Street
Delphi, IN 46923

DYER

**Saint Margaret Mercy
Healthcare Centers**
24 Joliet Street
Dyer, IN 46311

EAST CHICAGO

Tri-City Comprehensive Mental Health Center, Inc. Substance Abuse Services
3903 Indianapolis Boulevard
East Chicago, IN 46312

4522 Indianapolis Boulevard
East Chicago, IN 46312

ELKHART

Center for Problem Resolution
211 South 5th Street
Elkhart, IN 46516

Renewal Center
401 West Lexington Street
Elkhart, IN 46516

ENGLISH

Southern Hills Counseling Center, Inc. Crawford County Services
523 North Main Street
English, IN 47118-0400

EVANSVILLE

Charter Behavioral Health System
7200 East Indiana Street
Evansville, IN 47715

Chrysalis Addiction Services, Inc.
Outpatient Program
Women's Program
501 John Street, Suite 7
Evansville, IN 47713

Chrysalis Women's Addiction Services
35 East Chandler Streetm Suite 7
Evansville, IN 47713

Evansville State Hospital Addiction Service Unit
3400 Lincoln Avenue
Evansville, IN 47714

Saint Mary Medical Center Behavioral Science Services
3700 Washington Avenue
Evansville, IN 47750

Southwest Indiana Mental Health Center Inc.
Eiseman Annex
12 East Chandler Avenue
Evansville, IN 47713

Moulton Center
1 North Barker Street
Evansville, IN 47712

Robert M Spear Building
415 Mulberry Street
Evansville, IN 47713

Stepping Stone
30 South Stockwell Road
Evansville, IN 47714

Stockwell Center
60 South Stockwell Road
Evansville, IN 47714

Welborn Memorial Baptist Hospital Parkside Addiction Services
500 4th Street
Evansville, IN 47713

FORT WAYNE

Addictive Behaviors Counseling Center, Inc.
6070-B East State Boulevard
Fort Wayne, IN 46815

Allen County Community Corrections Day Reporting Center
109 East Superior Street
Fort Wayne, IN 46802

Alternatives Counseling and Learning Center
3024 Fairfield Avenue, M-404A
Fort Wayne, IN 46807

Alternatives Outreach
2030 Inwood Drive
Fort Wayne, IN 46815

Brown and Associates Consulting, Inc.
2324 Lake Avenue
Fort Wayne, IN 46805-5404

CAP, Inc. Counseling Service
1417 North Anthony Boulevard
Fort Wayne, IN 46805

6001 South Anthony Street
Suite 100
Fort Wayne, IN 46806

Charter Beacon Behavioral Health Systems
1720 Beacon Street
Fort Wayne, IN 46805

Family and Children's Services, Inc.
2712 South Calhoun Street
Fort Wayne, IN 46807

Fort Wayne Women's Bureau, Inc.
Transitions
2435 Oliver Street
Fort Wayne, IN 46802

2440 Bowser Street
Fort Wayne, IN 46803

Hope House
1115 Garden Street
Fort Wayne, IN 46802

1129 Garden Street
Fort Wayne, IN 46802

Lutheran Hospital of Indiana, Inc. Chemical Dependency Services
3024 Fairfield Avenue
Fort Wayne, IN 46804

Park Center, Inc.
909 East State Boulevard
Fort Wayne, IN 46805

Parkview Behavioral Health
1909 Carew Street
Fort Wayne, IN 46805

7230 Engle Road, Suite 240
Fort Wayne, IN 46804

Phoenix Chemical Dependency Program
2200 Lake Avenue, Suite 260
Fort Wayne, IN 46805

Ray of Light Counseling Centers, Inc.
1315 West Main Street
Fort Wayne, IN 46808

Transitions Program
303 East Washington Boulevard
Fort Wayne, IN 46802

Washington House, Inc.
2720 Culbertson Street
Fort Wayne, IN 46802

Wise Choices, Inc.
916 West Coliseum Street
Fort Wayne, IN 46808

FRANKFORT

**Howard Community Hospital
Community Counseling Center**
250 Alhambra Avenue
Frankfort, IN 46041

FRANKLIN

Brumbaugh and Associates
200 East Jefferson Street
Franklin, IN 46131-4450

Tara Treatment Center, Inc.
Alcohol and Drug Treatment
Center
6231 South U.S. Highway 31
Franklin, IN 46131

GARRETT

**DSM Group/DBA Dekalb
Professional Counseling**
1202 West Quincy Street
Garrett, IN 46738

GARY

Choices Counseling Service
475 Broadway Street, Suite 404
Gary, IN 46402

Discovery House, Inc.
4195 South Cleveland Street
Gary, IN 46408

**Edgewater System for Balanced
Living Inc**
1100 West 6th Avenue
Gary, IN 46402

**Holliday Health Care
Professional Corporation**
8410 Maple Avenue
Gary, IN 46403

Serenity House of Gary, Inc.
5157 Harrison Street
Gary, IN 46408

GASTON

**Interventions, Inc. Muncie
Program**
6951 North Creek 700 West
Gaston, IN 47342

GOSHEN

**Addiction Recovery Centers of
Indiana Goshen Addictions
Program**
114 North Main Street
Goshen, IN 46526

**Center for Problem Resolution,
Inc.**
117 West Washington Street
Goshen, IN 46526

Oaklawn
330 Lakeview Drive
Goshen, IN 46527

GRANGER

**Charter Behavioral Health
System**
6407 North Main Street
Granger, IN 46530

GREENCASTLE

**Cummins Mental Health Center,
Inc. Greencastle Clinic**
308 Medic Way
Greencastle, IN 46135

Discover Recovery LLC
110 South Indiana Street
Greencastle, IN 46135

GREENFIELD

**Community Hospitals of
Indiana, Inc.**
145 Green Meadows Drive, Suite 1
Greenfield, IN 46140

GREENSBURG

**Community Mental Health
Center, Inc.**
1033-B East Freeland Road
Greensburg, IN 47240

GREENWOOD

BHC Valle Vista Health System
898 East Main Street
Greenwood, IN 46013

CPC Valle Vista Health System
896 East Main Street
Professional Building
Greenwood, IN 46142

Indy Interventions
500 Polk Street
Greenwood, IN 46143

**Tara Treatment Center, Inc.
United Way Center for
Human Services**
500 South Polk Street Suite 18
Greenwood, IN 46142

HAMMOND

Burgos Counseling Services Inc
6431 Kennedy Avenue
Hammond, IN 46323

HIGHLAND

**Relapse Prevention and
Recovery Center**
2331 45th Street
Highland, IN 46322

HOBART

**Charter Behavioral Health
System**
101 West 61 Avenue and SR 51
Hobart, IN 46342

**Southlake Center for Mental
Health, Inc.**
Southlake Center Associates
1348 South Lake Park Avenue
Hobart, IN 46342

HUNTINGTON

**Otis R Bowen Center for Human
Services, Inc.**
1340 Etna Avenue
Huntington, IN 46750

Parkview Behavioral Health
1215 Etna Avenue
Huntington, IN 46750

INDIANAPOLIS

Adult and Child Mental Health
Center Substance Abuse Services
8320 Madison Avenue
Indianapolis, IN 46227

Alpha Resources
4822 West 34th Street
Indianapolis, IN 46224

Behavior Corporation
Outpatient Services
6100 North Keystone Avenue
Suite 360
Indianapolis, IN 46220

2506 Willowbrook Parkway
Indianapolis, IN 46220

Broad Ripple Counseling Center
6208 North College Street
Indianapolis, IN 46220

1115 Prospect Street
Indianapolis, IN 46203

**Charter Behavioral Health
    System**
5602 Caito Drive
Indianapolis, IN 46226

7212 North Shadeland Avenue
Indianapolis, IN 46256

**Community Addiction Services
    of Indiana, Inc.**
Mirage Center
4615 North Michigan Road
Indianapolis, IN 46208

Prevention, Intervention and
    Treatment Services
1040 East New York Street
Indianapolis, IN 46202

5110 Madison Avenue
Indianapolis, IN 46227

**Community Hospitals of
    Indiana, Inc.**
6919 East 10th Street, Building C
Indianapolis, IN 46219

Fairbanks Hospital
8102 Clearvista Parkway
Indianapolis, IN 46256

Fallcreek Counseling Service
2511 East 46 Street
Building P
Indianapolis, IN 46205

3500 Lafayette Street
Suite 305
Indianapolis, IN 46222

**Family Service Assoc. of
    Indianapolis Substance Abuse
    Services**
615 North Alabama Street
Room 220
Indianapolis, IN 46204

Life Effectiveness Training
147 East Maryland Street
Indianapolis, IN 46204

520 East 12th Street
Indianapolis, IN 46202

Magellan Behavioral Health
5420 Southern Avenue, Room 401
Indianapolis, IN 46241

**Methodist Hospital Substance
    Abuse Services**
1701 NorthSenate Street
Indianapolis, IN 46206

**Midtown Community Mental
    Health Center**
832 North Meridian Street
Indianapolis, IN 46204

Project Home
850 North Meridian Street
Indianapolis, IN 46202

Riverside Residential Center
1415 North Pennsylvania Street
Indianapolis, IN 46202

**Saint Vincent Hospital and
    Health Care Center, Inc.**
Assisted Living Program
1661 Handball Lane
Indianapolis, IN 46260

**Salvation Army Harbor Light
    Center**
927 North Pennsylvania Street
Indianapolis, IN 46204

Volunteers of America, Inc.
611 North Capitol Avenue
Indianapolis, IN 46204

**Winona Memorial Hospital
    Behavioral Health Services**
3232 North Meridian Street
Indianapolis, IN 46208

JASPER

**Southern Hills Counseling
    Center**
480 Eversman Drive
Jasper, IN 47546

JEFFERSONVILLE

**Charter Behavioral Health
    System**
2700 River City Park Road
Jeffersonville, IN 47130

**Lifespring Mental Health
    Services**
207 West 13 Street
Jeffersonville, IN 47130

Dual Diagnosis
1401 Mitchell Avenue
Jeffersonville, IN 47130

KENDALLVILLE

**Northeastern Center Substance
    Abuse Services**
220 South Main Street
Kendallville, IN 46755

Wise Choice, Inc.
671-B Dowling Street
Kendallville, IN 46755

KNOX

Porter Starke Services, Inc.
1003 Edgewood Drive
Knox, IN 46534

KOKOMO

Howard Community Hospital
Mental Health Center
3500 South LaFountain Street
Kokomo, IN 46902

Psychiatric Services
3548 South LaFountain Street
Kokomo, IN 46902

New Choices
2705 South Berkley Street
Suite 1B
Kokomo, IN 46901

Saint Joseph Hospital Trinity House
1907 West Sycamore Street
Kokomo, IN 46901

LAFAYETTE

Charter Behavioral Health System
3700 Rome Drive
Lafayette, IN 47905

Home With Hope, Inc. Transitional Halfway House
1001 Ferry Street
Lafayette, IN 47901

New Directions, Inc.
360 North 775 East Street
Lafayette, IN 47905

Wabash Valley Hospital, Inc. Outpatient Service
610 Main Street
Lafayette, IN 47901

LAGRANGE

Addiction Recovery Centers of Indiana Cornerstone of Recovery
400 Union Street
LaGrange, IN

Northeastern Center
2155 North Street
LaGrange, IN 46761

LAWRENCEBURG

Community Mental Health Center
427 Eads Parkway
Lawrenceburg, IN 47025

Substance Abuse Services
285 Bielby Road
Lawrenceburg, IN 47025

LEBANON

Behavior Corp Boon County Offices Outpatient Services
602 Ransdell Road
Lebanon, IN 46052

LIGONIER

Northeastern Center
Lincolnway South
Ligonier, IN 46767

LINTON

Hamilton Center, Inc.
1815 North Meridian Street
Linton, IN 47441

Greene County Center
Lonetree Road
Linton, IN 47441

LOGANSPORT

Affiliated Service Providers of Indiana, Inc.
1015 Michigan Avenue
Logansport, IN 46947

Four County Counseling Center
1015 Michigan Avenue
Logansport, IN 46947

LOOGOOTEE

Knox County Hospital Martin County Office
200 John F Kennedy Avenue
Loogootee, IN 47553

MADISON

Lifespring Mental Health Services
319 West 2nd Street
Madison, IN 47250

Madison State Hospital Lou Scalo Center for Adult Addiction
711 Green Road
Madison, IN 47250

MARION

Grant/Blackford Mental Health, Inc.
Branson Place
925 South Branson Street
Marion, IN 46953

Cornerstone
505 Wabash Avenue
Marion, IN 46952

Community Support Program
206 West 8th Street
Marion, IN 46953

Milestone Counseling Services
701 Wabash Avenue
Marion, IN 46952

Trinity House/Saint Joseph Hospital and Health Center
417 South Branson Street
Marion, IN 46953

MARTINSVILLE

Center for Behavioral Health, Inc.
2222 Burton Lane
Martinsville, IN 46151-9405

MERRILLVILLE

Anglican Social Services of Northern Indiana
8555 Grand Boulevard
Merrillville, IN 46401

B Gutierrez and Associates, Inc.
200 East 80th Street, Suite 200
Merrillville, IN 46410

Methodist Hospitals of Gary, Inc. Inpatient Addiction Treatment
8701 Broadway Street
Merrillville, IN 46410

Southlake Center for Mental Health, Inc.
290 A East 90th Drive
Merrillville, IN 46410

8555 Taft Street
Merrillville, IN 46410

MICHIGAN CITY

Saint Anthony Memorial Health Center
301 West Homer Street
Michigan City, IN 46360-3370

Swanson Center Satellite Outpatient
450 St. John Road, Suite 501
Michigan City, IN 46360

MISHAWAKA

Charter Behavioral Health System
2410 Grape Road
Mishawaka, IN 46545

Children's Campus, Inc.
1411 Lincolnway West
Mishawaka, IN 46544

MONTICELLO

Wabash Valley Hospital, Inc. Outpatient Services
207 North Bluff Street
Monticello, IN 47960

MOUNT VERNON

Southwest Indiana Mental Health Center, Inc. Posey Regional Services
100 Vista Drive
Mount Vernon, IN 47620

MUNCIE

AMH, Inc. DBA Associates in Mental Health
3111 West Jackson Street
Muncie, IN 47304

Ball Memorial Hospital
Middletown Center for Chemical Dependency
2401 University Avenue
Muncie, IN 47303

Comprehensive Mental Health Services
240 North Tillotson Avenue
Muncie, IN 47304

MUNSTER

Saint Margaret Mercy Healthcare Centers, Inc. Behavioral Medical Outpatient
312 Ridge Road
Munster, IN 46321

NASHVILLE

Quinco Consulting Center Brown County Consulting Associates
Jefferson and Mound Streets
Nashville, IN 47448

NEW ALBANY

Hedden House
801 Vincennes Street
New Albany, IN 47150

Lifespring Mental Health Services
904 East Spring Street
New Albany, IN 47150

NEW CASTLE

Christian Counseling and Addiction Services, Inc.
New Castle Church of Christ
11th Street
New Castle, IN 47362

502 South Main Street
New Castle, IN 47362

Comprehensive Mental Health Services, Inc.
930 North 14th Street
New Castle, IN 47362

NINEVEH

Tara Treatment Center, Inc.
Ninevah Square
7919 South 100 East
Nineveh, IN 46164

NOBLESVILLE

Behavior Corporation
Noblesville Outpatient Services
54 North 9th Street, Suite 205
Noblesville, IN 46060

Community Addiction Services of Indiana, Inc.
942 North 10th Street
Noblesville, IN 46060

NORTH VERNON

Quinco Consulting of North Vernon
1260 East Buckeye Street
North Vernon, IN 47265

OSGOOD

Community Mental Health Center, Inc.
240 West Craven Street
Osgood, IN 47037

PAOLI

Southern Hills Counseling Center, Inc. Orange County Services
488 West Hospital Road
Paoli, IN 47454

PERU

Four County Counseling Center Miami County Satellite
16 South Broadway Street
Peru, IN 46970

PETERSBURG

Knox County Hospital Pike County Office
400 Main Street
Petersburg, IN 47567

PLYMOUTH

Northern Indiana Hospital LLC DBA BHC of Northern Indiana
1800 North Oak Road
Plymouth, IN 46563

Otis R Bowen Center for Human Services, Inc.
990 Illinois Street
Plymouth, IN 46563

PORTAGE

Porter Starke Services, Inc. Substance Abuse Program
3220 Lancer Street
Portage, IN 46368

PORTLAND

Comprehensive Mental Health Services, Inc.
931 West Water Street
Portland, IN 47371

PRINCETON

Southwest Indiana Mental Health Center, Inc. Gibson Regional Services
310 South 5th Avenue
Princeton, IN 47670

RENSSELAER

Wabash Valley Hospital, Inc. Outpatient Services
1207 East Grace Street
Rensselaer, IN 47978

RICHMOND

Dunn Mental Health Center, Inc.
809 Dillon Drive
Richmond, IN 47375

Addiction Services
831 Dillon Drive
Richmond, IN 47374

Behavioral Health Care Associates
600 Promenade Street
Richmond, IN 47375

Reid Hospital Health Care Services
1401 Chester Boulevard
Richmond, IN 47374

Richmond State Hospital Adult Chemical Dependency
498 NW 18th Street
Richmond, IN 47374

RISING SUN

Community Mental Health Center, Inc.
315 Industrial Access Road
Rising Sun, IN 47040

ROCHESTER

Four County Counseling Center
321 East 8th Street
Rochester, IN 46975

Wayfarer Addictions Counseling
816 1/2 Main Street
Rochester, IN 46975

ROCKPORT

Southern Hills Counseling Center, Inc.
107 North 2nd Street
Rockport, IN 47635

ROCKVILLE

Hamilton Center, Inc. Parke County Center
205 North Jefferson Street
Rockville, IN 47872

RUSHVILLE

Dunn Mental Health Center, Inc.
119 East 3rd Street
Rushville, IN 46173

Rush County Substance Abuse Services
246 North Main Street
Rushville, IN 46173

SALEM

Lifespring Mental Health Services
Highway 60 East
Salem, IN 47167

SCHERERVILLE

Southlake Center for Mental Health, Inc.
2001-A South U.S. Highway 41
Schererville, IN 46375

SCOTTSBURG

Lifespring Mental Health Services
40 East Cherry Street
Scottsburg, IN 47170

SEYMOUR

Quinco Consulting Center Preferred Counseling Associates
321 West Bruce Street, Suite C
Seymour, IN 47274

SHELBYVILLE

Community Hospitals of Indiana, Inc. Gallahue Mental Health Center
7 East Hendricks Street
Shelbyville, IN 46176

SOUTH BEND

Addiction Recovery Centers of Indiana Michiana Addictions Recovery Center
127 West Wayne Street
South Bend, IN 46601

Life Treatment Centers, Inc.
1402 South Michigan Street
South Bend, IN 46613-2214

Madison Center, Inc.
813 South Michigan Street
South Bend, IN 46613

Madison Center for Children
701 North Niles Avenue
South Bend, IN 46617

Madison Hospital
403 East Madison Street
South Bend, IN 46617

Quietcare Building
712 North Niles Avenue
South Bend, IN 46617

Mother Earths Counseling Center for Addictions
1211 Vasaar Avenue
South Bend, IN 46624-0688

Options Institute, Inc.
116 South Taylor Street
South Bend, IN 46601-1522

Pathways Center for Behavioral Health
615 North Michigan Street
South Bend, IN 46601

Victory Clinic Services II
4218 Western Avenue
South Bend, IN 46619

YWCA of Saint Joseph County Mother and Child Program
802 Lafayette Boulevard
South Bend, IN 46601

SPENCER

Center for Behavioral Health, Inc.
751 East Franklin Street
Spencer, IN 47460-1829

Hamilton Center, Inc.
51 South Main Street
Spencer, IN 47460

SULLIVAN

Hamilton Center, Inc. Sullivan County Center
201 West Graysville Street
Sullivan, IN 47882

TELL CITY

Lake Cumberland Regional Hospital 3Southern Hills Counseling Center, Inc.
1443 9th Street
Tell City, IN 47586

TERRE HAUTE

A P and C Clinic PC DBA Associated Psychologists, Inc.
1801 North 6th Street, Suite 600
Terre Haute, IN 47804

Discover Recovery LLC
1509-B Wabash Avenue
Terre Haute, IN 47807

Hamilton Center, Inc.
500 8th Avenue
Terre Haute, IN 47804

Recovery Associates, Inc. Fellowship House
2940 Jefferson Street
Terre Haute, IN 47802

Terre Haute Regional Hospital Lamb Center
3901 South 7 Street
Terre Haute, IN 47802

VALPARAISO

Christian Service Center, Inc.
791 Juniper Street
Valparaiso, IN 46385

Joseph Corporation DBA Care Counseling Services
793-2 Juniper Road
Valparaiso, IN 46385

Porter Memorial Hospital Mother and Child Detox
814 Laporte Avenue
Valparaiso, IN 46383

Porter/Starke Services, Inc.
601 Wall Street
Valparaiso, IN 46383

600 North Vale Park Road
Valparaiso, IN 46383

VERNON

Jennings County Alcohol and Drug Program
28 Perry Street
Vernon, IN 47282

VEVAY

Community Mental Health Center, Inc.
205 West Main Street
Vevay, IN 47043

VINCENNES

Knox County Hospital DBA Samaritan Center
515 Bayou Steet
Vincennes, IN 47591

400 North 1st Street
Vincennes, IN 47591

WABASH

Otis R. Bowen Center for Human Services, Inc.
710 North East Street
Wabash County Hospital Lower Level
Wabash, IN 46992

Parkview Behavioral Health
216 Manchester Avenue
Wabash, IN 46992

WARSAW

Kosciusko Community Hospital Med Park Center
2101 East Center Street
Warsaw, IN 46580

Otis R. Bowen Center for Human Services, Inc.
850 North Harrison Street
Warsaw, IN 46580

WASHINGTON

Knox County Hospital
2007 State Street
Washington, IN 47501

WEST LAFAYETTE

Wabash Valley Hospital, Inc. Riverside
2900 North River Road
West Lafayette, IN 47906

WINAMAC

Four County Counseling Center Pulaski County Satellite
616 West 11th Street
Winamac, IN 46996

WINCHESTER

Dunn Mental Health Center, Inc.
132 North Main Street
Winchester, IN 47394

IOWA

AMES

Center for Addictions Recovery, Inc.
511 Duff Avenue
Ames, IA 50010

Seven 12 House Youth Recovery House
712 Burnett Street
Ames, IA 50010

ANAMOSA

Anamosa State Penitentiary Substance Abuse Program
North High Street
Anamosa, IA 52205

ATLANTIC

Alcohol and Drug Assistance Agency, Inc.
320 Walnut Street
Atlantic, IA 50022

AUDUBON

New View Substance Abuse Center
212 Market Street
Audubon, IA 50025-1136

BURLINGTON

Alcohol and Drug Dependency Services of Southeast Iowa
1340 Mount Pleasant Street
Lincoln Center
Burlington, IA 52601

Burlington Medical Center Riverview Rehabilitation Center
602 North 3 Street
Burlington, IA 52601

Woodlands Treatment Center
4715 Sullivan Slough Road
Burlington, IA 52601

CARROLL

New Vision Substance Abuse Treatment and Prevention Center
322 West 3 Street
Carroll, IA 51401

CEDAR FALLS

Daniel J Murphy, MD
310 West 4th Street
Cedar Falls, IA 50613

CEDAR RAPIDS

Area Substance Abuse Council, Inc.
3601 16 Avenue SW
Cedar Rapids, IA 52404

Mercy Medical Center Sedlacek Treatment Center
701 10 Street SE
Cedar Rapids, IA 52403

Saint Lukes Methodist Hospital Chemical Dependency Services
1030 5th Avenue SE
Cedar Rapids, IA 52403

CHARITON

Southern IA Economic Development Association
115 South Main Street
City Hall
Chariton, IA 50049

Lucas County Health Center
1200 North 7th Street
Chariton, IA 50049

CHEROKEE

Behavioral Health Management Services Synergy Center
1231 West Cedar Loop, Suite 210
Cherokee, IA 51012

CLARINDA

Clarinda Correctional Facility The Other Way Substance Abuse Treatment Program
2000 North 16 Street
Clarinda Treatment Complex
Clarinda, IA 51632

CLINTON

New Directions, Inc. Center for Alcohol and Other Chemical Dependency
217 6th Avenue South
Clinton, IA 52732

2219 Garfield Street
Clinton, IA 52732

Samaritan Health Systems The Bridge
638 South Bluff Boulevard
Clinton, IA 52732

CORYDON

Southern IA Economic Development Association
Courthouse Room 302
Corydon, IA 50060

COUNCIL BLUFFS

Jennie Edmundson Memorial Hospital Addictions Treatment Program
933 East Pierce Street
Council Bluffs, IA 51501

Alegent Health/Mercy Hospital Chemical Dependency Services
800 Mercy Drive
Council Bluffs, IA 51503

DAVENPORT

Center for Alcohol and Drug Services
1523 South Fairmount Street
Davenport, IA 52802

Prevention and Adolescent Services
1601 Harrison Street and Forest
    Grove Street
Davenport, IA 52802

Country Oaks
12160 Utah Avenue
Davenport, IA 52804

**Family Resources, Inc.
Wittenmyer Youth Center**
2800 Eastern Avenue
Davenport, IA 52803

**Genesis Medical Center West
Campus Addictions Recovery
Programs**
West Central Park at Marquette
Davenport, IA 52804

DECORAH

Northeast Iowa Mental Health
Center Alcohol and Related
    Problems Service Center
905 Montgomery Street
Decorah, IA 52101

DES MOINES

**Bernie Lorenz Recovery House,
Inc.**
4014 Kingman Boulevard
Des Moines, IA 50311

**Des Moines General Hospital
Gateway Centers**
603 East 12th Street
Des Moines, IA 50309

**First Step Mercy Recovery
Center**
1818 48th Street
Des Moines, IA 50310

House of Mercy
1409 Clark Street
Des Moines, IA 50314-1964

**Iowa Methodist Medical Center
Powell Chemical Dependency
Center**
700 East University Street
Des Moines, IA 50309

United Community Services
1301 19th Street
Des Moines, IA 50314

**VA Central Iowa Health Care
System**
3600 30th Street
Des Moines, IA 50310-5774

DUBUQUE

**Mercy Turning Point Treatment
Center**
Professional Arts Plaza, Suite 206
Dubuque, IA 52001

**Substance Abuse Services
Center, Inc.**
Nesler Centre
Town Clock Plaza, Suite 270
Dubuque, IA 52001 [ELDORA]

**Addiction Management Systems,
Inc.**
West Edgington Avenue State
    Training School
Eldora, IA 50627

EMMETSBURG

**Marian Behavioral Care
Chemical Dependency
Services**
2508 West Main Street
Emmetsburg, IA 50536

FORT DODGE

**Community and Family
Resources, Inc.**
726 South 17 Street
Fort Dodge, IA 50501

New Life Associates, Inc.
809 Central Avenue, Suite 315
Fort Dodge, IA 50501-4732

Trinity Regional Hospital
802 Kenyon Road
Fort Dodge, IA 50501

FORT MADISON

**Iowa State Penitentiary
Substance Abuse Program**
31 Avenue G
Fort Madison, IA 52627

**River Center for Community
Mental Health**
815 Avenue, Suite H
Fort Madison, IA 52627

HUMBOLDT

**Community and Family
Resources**
19 6th Street South
Humboldt, IA 50548

IDA GROVE

Gordon Recovery
106 Main Street
Ida Grove, IA 51445

INDEPENDENCE

**Pathways Behavioral Services,
Inc.**
209 2 Avenue NE
Independence, IA 50644

IOWA CITY

**Mid Eastern Council on
Chemical Abuse (MECCA)**
430 Southgate Avenue
Iowa City, IA 52240

**University of Iowa Hospitals
and Clinics Chemical
Dependency Center**
200 Hawkins Drive
Iowa City, IA 52242

**Veterans' Affairs Medical Center
Substance Abuse Treatment
Program**
Highway 6 West, 116A
Iowa City, IA 52246

IOWA FALLS

Freedom House
210 Iowa Street
Iowa Falls, IA 50126

KEOKUK

**Alcohol and Drug Dependency
Services**
5 North 13th Street
Keokuk, IA 52632

**River Center for Community
Mental Health**
208 Bank Street
Keokuk, IA 52632

KEOSAUQUA

Sieda Drug and Alcohol Services
Courthouse/Magistrates Office
115 South Main Street
Keosauqua, IA 52565

LE MARS

Gordon Recovery Center, Inc.
22 First Street NE
Le Mars, IA 51031

MARSHALLTOWN

Substance Abuse Treatment Unit of Central Iowa
9 North 4th Avenue
Marshalltown, IA 50158

MASON CITY

Prairie Ridge
320 North Eisenhower Avenue
Mason City, IA 50401

MITCHELLVILLE

Iowa Correctional Institution for Women
300 Elm Street SW
Mitchellville, IA 50169

MOUNT PLEASANT

Alcohol and Drug Dependency Services
207 South Harrison Street, Suite 4
Mount Pleasant, IA 52641

Mental Health Institute Iowa Residential Treatment Center
1200 East Washington Street
Mount Pleasant, IA 52641

Mount Pleasant Correctional Facility Therapeutic Community Program
1200 East Washington Street
Mount Pleasant, IA 52641

MUSCATINE

Community Health Resources New Horizons Outpatient Substance Abuse Program
1616 Cedar Street
Muscatine, IA 52761

NEW HAMPTON

Pathways Behavioral Services, Inc.
951 North Linn Avenue, Suite 3
New Hampton, IA 50659

NEWTON

Capstone Center, Inc. Substance Abuse Division
306 North 3rd Avenue East
Newton, IA 50208

Newton Correctional Facility Substance Abuse Treatment Program
1203 South 60th Avenue West
Newton, IA 50208

ONAWA

Gordon Recovery Center, Inc.
22 First Street NE
Le Mars, IA 51031

ORIENT

Zion Brown Treatment Center
Rural Route 1, Box 287
Orient, IA 50858-9609

OTTUMWA

Ottumwa Regional Health Center Family Recovery Center
312 East Alta Vista Avenue
Ottumwa, IA 52501

Southern Iowa Economic
Development Assoc. Drug and Alcohol Services
226 West Main Street
Ottumwa, IA 52501

PELLA

Capstone Center, Inc.
712 Union Street
Pella, IA 50219-1768

POCAHONTAS

Community and Family Resources, Inc.
218 1/2 North Main Street
Pocahontas, IA 50574-1624

ROCKWELL CITY

Community and Family Resources
515 Court Street Courthouse Annex
Rockwell City, IA 50579

Tree Substance Abuse Program Trinity Recovery Center Affiliate
North Central Correctional Facility
313 Lanedale Street
Rockwell City, IA 50579

SAC CITY

New View Substance Abuse Center
100 South State Street
Sac City, IA 50583

SIOUX CITY

Gordon Recovery Center, Inc.
Adult Residential
2309 Jackson Street
Sioux City, IA 51104

Outpatient
800 5th Street, Suite 200
Sioux City, IA 51101

Women and Children's Center
2720 Stone Park Boulevard
Sioux City, IA 51104

Mercy Behavioral Care Chemical Dependency Services
4301 Sergeant Road
Sioux City, IA 51106

SPENCER

Northwest Iowa Alcoholism and Drug Treatment Unit, Inc.
1900 Grand Avenue North
Suite E-8
Spencer, IA 51301

STORM LAKE

Vista Addiction and Recovery Center North Campus of Buena Vista County Hospital
1305 West Milwaukee Street
Storm Lake, IA 50588

TAMA

Meskwaki Alcohol/Drug Abuse Center
Tama, IA 52339

WAPELLO

Alcohol Drug Dependency Services
214 Prairie Street
Wapello, IA 52653

WATERLOO

Allen Memorial Hospital Counseling Center
1825 Logan Avenue
Waterloo, IA 50703

Pathways Behavioral Services, Inc.
2222 Falls Avenue
Waterloo, IA 50701

1221 Franklin Street
Waterloo, IA 50703

WAVERLY

Pathways Behavioral Services, Inc.
123 2nd Street NE
Waverly, IA 50677-1763

WEBSTER CITY

Community and Family Resources
914 Willson Street
Webster City, IA 50595

WINTERSET

Madison County Memorial Hospital The Bridge Counseling Center
300 Hutchings Street
Winterset, IA 50273

KANSAS

ABILENE

Dickinson County Council on Alcohol and Other Drugs, Inc.
400 NW 3 Street
Abilene, KS 67410

ARKANSAS CITY

Cowley County Mental Health and Counseling Center
115 East Radio Lane
Arkansas City, KS 67005

Curo Populus Alcohol and Drug Treatment Program
325 North First Street
Arkansas City, KS 67005-1012

ATCHISON

Atchison Valley Hope Alcoholism Treatment Center
1816 North 2 Street
Atchison, KS 66002

New Freedom, Inc. Counseling Services
1600 Skyway Street
Atchison, KS 66002

Northeast Kansas Mental Health Center
1301 North 2nd Street
Atchison, KS 66002

AUGUSTA

Valley Hope at Augusta Medical Complex
2101 Dearborn Street
Augusta, KS 67010

BELOIT

Beloit Juvenile Correctional Facility
1720 North Hersey Street
Beloit, KS 67420

BONNER SPRINGS

Mainstream Inc of Kansas City
12215 State Avenue
Bonner Springs, KS 66012

COLBY

Citizens Medical Center Substance Abuse Services
100 East College Drive
Colby, KS 67701

Thomas County Council on Alcohol/Drug Abuse, Inc.
775 East College Drive
Colby, KS 67701

COLUMBUS

Elm Acres Youth Home for Girls
501 Central Avenue
Columbus, KS 66725

Family Life Center Alcohol and Drug Abuse Program
201 West Walnut Street
Columbus, KS 66725

CONCORDIA

Kerrs Counseling
135 East 6th Street
Concordia, KS 66901

DODGE CITY

New Chance, Inc.
500 East Wyatt Earp Boulevard
Dodge City, KS 67801

**Unlimited Recovery
Opportunities of Kansas**
1111 6th Avenue
Dodge City, KS 67801

EL DORADO

**South Central Mental Health,
Inc. Counseling Center**
2365 West Central Street
El Dorado, KS 67042

ELLSWORTH

Ellsworth Correction Facility
1607 State Street
Ellsworth, KS 67439

EMPORIA

Corner House, Inc.
418 Market Street
Emporia, KS 66801

**Counseling and Psychological
Services**
1512 West 6th Avenue
Emporia, KS 66801

**Henderson/Simmons Counseling
Services**
517 Merchant Street, Suite 200
Emporia, KS 66801

Mental Health Center of East
Central Kansas Alcohol and Drug
Services
1000 Lincoln Street
Emporia, KS 66801

**Newman Memorial County
Hospital Recovery Road**
1320 C of E Drive, Suite 5
Emporia, KS 66801

EUREKA

**Eureka Substance Abuse
Program**
612 East 3rd Street
Eureka, KS 67045

FORT LEAVENWORTH

US Army MEDDAC ADAPCP
550 Pope Avenue
Fort Leavenworth, KS
66027-2332

GARDEN CITY

**Area Mental Health Center
Substance Abuse Services**
1111 East Spruce Street
Garden City, KS 67846

**Western Kansas Foundation for
Alcohol and Chemical
Dependency Inc.**
811 North Main Street
Garden City, KS 67846

GARNETT

**Southeast Kansas Mental Health
Center Alcohol and Drug
Abuse Services**
318 East 6th Street
Garnett, KS 66032

GOODLAND

**Northwest Kansas Medical
Center Substance Abuse Unit**
First and Sherman Streets
Goodland, KS 67735

GREAT BEND

**Central Kansas Psychological
Services Eldean Kohrs**
925 Patton Street
Great Bend, KS 67530

GREENSBURG

**Iroquois Center for Human
Development**
103 South Grove Street
Greensburg, KS 67054

HAYS

Dream, Inc.
765 East 41st Street
Hays, KS 67601

**Hays Medical Center Hays
Behavioral Health Center**
201 East 7th Street
Hays, KS 67601

**High Plains Mental Health
Center Alcohol and Drug
Abuse Services**
208 East 7 Street
Hays, KS 67601

**Smoky Hill Foundation for
Chemical Dependency, Inc.**
1106 East 27th Street, Suite 10
Hays, KS 67601

**Kelly Center/Fort Hays State
University**
600 Park Street
Hays, KS 67601

Peters and Associates
1503 Vine Street, Suite B
Hays, KS 67601

HOISINGTON

Women's Recovery Center
1410 North Vine Street
Hoisington, KS 67544

HORTON

**Kickapoo Substance Abuse
Program**
Four Winds Halfway House
Route 1
Horton, KS 66439

HUMBOLDT

**Southeast Kansas Mental Health
Center**
1106 South 9th Street
Humboldt, KS 66748

HUCHINSON

**Charter Hutchinson Counseling
Center**
400 West 2nd Street, Suite C
Hutchinson, KS 67501

**Horizons Mental Health Center,
Inc. Substance Abuse Services**
1715 East 23rd Avenue
Hutchinson, KS 67502-1188

Mirror, Inc.
2100 West Jackson Street
Hutchinson, KS 67501

Reno Alcohol and Drug Services
112 North Poplar Street
Hutchinson, KS 67501

Reno County Community Corrections
400 West 2nd Street, Suite B
Hutchinson, KS 67501

INDEPENDENCE

Four County Mental Health
Center Alcohol and Drug Program
3701 West Main Street
Independence, KS 67301

JUNCTION CITY

Geary Community Hospital Substance Abuse Services
1102 Saint Mary's Road
Junction City, KS 66441

KANSAS CITY

Addiction Stress Center
1330 North 78 Street
Kansas City, KS 66112

Associated Youth Services, Inc.
16205 37th Street
Kansas City, KS 66106

Heart of America Family Services, Inc.
5424 State Avenue
Kansas City, KS 66102

Kansas City Treatment Center
1404 Minnesota Avenue
Kansas City, KS 66102

Kansas City Metro Methadone Program
3901 Rainbow Boulevard
Kansas City, KS 66160

Kansas Multicultural Alcohol and Drug Treatment Center
2940 North 17 Street
Kansas City, KS 66104

Project Turn Around
739 Minnesota Avenue
Kansas City, KS 66101

Salvation Army Shield of Service
1203 Minnesota Avenue
Kansas City, KS 66101

Substance Abuse Center of Eastern Kansas, Inc.
3505 Rainbow Boulevard
Kansas City, KS 66103

Wyandotte Mental Health Center, Inc. Alcohol and Drug Abuse Services
3615 Eaton Street
Kansas City, KS 66103

LANSING

Gateway Foundation Lansing Correctional Facility
Kansas Avenue and Highway 7
Lansing, KS 66043

LARNED

Larned Correctional Mental
Health Facility Substance Abuse
Treatment Program
Mental Health Consortium
Route 3
Larned, KS 67550

Larned State Hospital CDRP/ SSH Jung Building
Route 3
Larned, KS 67550

Sunrise, Inc.
523 North Main Street
Larned, KS 67550

LAWRENCE

Alpha Recovery
5020 West 15th Street Suite B
Lawrence, KS 66049

Bert Nash Community Mental Health Center Substance Abuse Services
336 Missouri Street Suite 202
Lawrence, KS 66044

Cedar Branch Recovery Systems PA
14 Westwood Road
Lawrence, KS 66044

DCCCA, Inc. First Step House
345 Florida Street
Lawrence, KS 66044

Haskell Health Center
2415 Massachusetts Street
Lawrence, KS 66049

LEAVENWORTH

Addiction Recovery Services
520 South 4th Street
Leavenworth, KS 66048

Northeast Kansas Mental Health
and Guidance Center Recovery
Services of Northeast Kansas
818 North 7 Street
Leavenworth, KS 66048

VA Medical Center Dwight D Eisenhower Substance Abuse Treatment Program
4101 South 4th Street, Suite A-6
Leavenworth, KS 66048

LENEXA

First Things First
9230 Pflumm Road
Lenexa, KS 66215

LIBERAL

Alcohol and Drugs Counseling Services
504 North Kansas Street, Suite B
Liberal, KS 67901

Family Alcohol and Drug Services, Inc.
316 West 7 Street
Liberal, KS 67905

Fernandez/Martin Addiction Counselors
317 North 7th Street, Suite B-5
Liberal, KS 67901

Southwest Kansas Alcoholism and Drug Addiction Services
529 North New York Street
Liberal, KS 67901-0797

MANHATTAN

Edelman Associates
404 Humboldt Street Suite C
Manhattan, KS 66502

**Pawnee Mental Health Center
    Substance Abuse Services**
2001 Claflin Street
Manhattan, KS 66502

Peak, Larry M.
1133 College Avenue
Building B Upper Level
Manhattan, KS 66502

**Potter, Greg, Ph.D. Alcohol and
    Drug Abuse Services**
714 Poyntz Street, Suite A
Manhattan, KS 66502

MCCONNELL AFB

**McConnell Air Force Base
    Substance Abuse Program**
22 MDOS/SGOMH 57950
Leavenworth Street Suite 6E-4
McConnell AFB, KS 67221-3506

MCDONALD

Cheyenne County AB/AO
502 Decatur Avenue
McDonald, KS 67745

MISSION

Mission Valley Hope
5410 West 58th Terrace
Mission, KS 66205

NEWTON

Mirror, Inc.
130 East 5 Street
Newton, KS 67114

**Prairie View Mental Health
    Center Chemical Dependency
    Treatment**
1901 East First Street
Newton KS 67114

OLATHE

Choices
540 East Santa Fe Street
Olathe, KS 66061

**Community Outreach Services,
    Inc.**
226 South Kansas Avenue
Olathe, KS 66061

Cypress Recovery, Inc.
230 South Kansas Street
Olathe, KS 66061

**Johnson County Adolescent
    Center for Treatment (ACT)**
301 North Monroe Street
Olathe, KS 66061

Total Wellness Center
14161 South Mur Len Street
Olathe, KS 66062

OSKALOOSA

**Northeast Kansas Mental Health
    Center**
1102 Walnut Street
Oskaloosa, KS 66066

OTTAWA

Franklin County Mental Health
Clinic, Inc. Substance Abuse
    Program
204 East 15 Street
Ottawa, KS 66067

OVERLAND PARK

Bridge Way Recovery, Inc.
6800 College Boulevard, Suite 520
Overland Park, KS 66211

Cindy Parkans LSCSW
8100 Marty Street, Suite 102
Overland Park, KS 66204

Interchange
5350 College Boulevard Suite 205
Overland Park, KS 66211

PARSONS

**Labette Center for Mental
    Health Service, Inc. Alcohol
    and Drug Abuse Program**
1730 Belmont Street
Parsons, KS 67357

PITTSBURG

**Bartholomew and Dillon
    Counseling Service**
204 North Smith Street
Pittsburg, KS 66762

**Crawford County Mental Health
    Center**
Alcohol and Drug Program
3101 Michigan Street
Pittsburg, KS 66762

Elm Acres Youth Home, Inc.
1002 East Madison Street
Pittsburg, KS 66762

Pesciluna Center
401 West Euclid Street
Pittsburg, KS 66762

PRATT

**South Central Kansas
    Foundation on Chemical
    Dependency, Inc.**
501 South Ninnescah Street
Pratt, KS 67124

SAINT JOHN

New Day, Inc.
308 North Gray Street
Saint John, KS 67576

SALINA

Central Kansas Foundation
1805 South Ohio Street
Salina, KS 67401

**Dunn Counseling and
    Consulting, Inc.**
1407 South Santa Fe Street
Salina, KS 67401

Saint Francis at Salina
5907 West Cloud Street
Salina, KS 67401

SHAWNEE

Menninger SUCS at Mill Creek
6301 Pflumm Street, Suite 140
Shawnee, KS 66216

Mirror, Inc.
6221 Richards Road
Shawnee, KS 66216

Total Concept EAP
6301 Pflumm Road, Suite 140
Shawnee, KS 66216

SHAWNEE MISSION

Catholic Community Services
10200 West 75th Street
Building B-274
Shawnee Mission, KS 66204

**Charles Stebbins Counseling
    Services**
8000 West 127th Street
Shawnee Mission, KS 66213

Clinical Associates PA
7315 Frontage Road, Suite 110
Shawnee Mission, KS 66204

Columbia Health Systems,Inc.
10114 West 105th Street
Suite 100
Shawnee Mission, KS 66212

**Shawnee Mission Medical
    Center Addiction Recovery
    Unit**
9100 West 74th Street
Shawnee Mission, KS 66201

SYRACUSE

**Syracuse Chemical Addiction
    Treatment of Kansas, Inc.
    (SCAT)**
504 North Johnson Street
Syracuse, KS 67878

TOPEKA

ADAPT/TCF
815 SE Rice Road
Topeka, KS 66607

**Carole Dorsch Counseling
    Services**
2914 Plass Court, Suite A
Topeka, KS 66611

**Relapse Prevention Counseling,
    Inc.**
1913 SW 29th Terrace
Topeka, KS 66611

**Saint Francis Hospital Medical
    Center**
1700 SW 7 Street, 3rd Floor
Topeka, KS 66606

**Shawnee Community Mental
    Health Center Substance
    Abuse Recovery Program**
330 SW Oakley Street
Topeka, KS 66606

**Shawnee Regional Prevention
    Center**
2209 Southwest 29th Street
Topeka, KS 66603

**Sims/Kemper Clinical
    Counseling**
1709 SW Medford Avenue
Topeka, KS 66604

**Veterans' Affairs Medical Center
    Alcohol/Drug Treatment Unit**
2200 Gage Boulevard
Building 15-1C
Topeka, KS 66622

Women's Recovery Center
1324 SW Western Street
Topeka, KS 66604

WAMEGO

**L and L Assessment and
    Counseling Center**
5245 North Highway 99
Wamego, KS 66547

WELLINGTON

**Sumner County Mental Health
    Center**
Wellington, KS 67152

**Sumner Mental Health Drug
    Addiction Services**
1601 West 16th Street
Wellington, KS 67152

WICHITA

**Addiction Specialist of Kansas,
    Inc.**
650 Carriage Parkway, Suite 135
Wichita, KS 67208

**Adolescent/Adult/Family
    Recovery Program**
3540 West Douglas Street
Wichita, KS 67203

**Alcoholism Family Counseling
    Center**
714 South Hillside Street
Wichita, KS 67211

**Associated Word of Life
    Counselors Addiction
    Treatment**
3811 North Meridian Street
Wichita, KS 67204

Bharati, Ralph, MD PA
7701 East Kellogg Street
Suite 610
Wichita, KS 67207

Behavior Consultants
1604 North Market Street
Wichita, KS 67220

Center for Human Development
2601 East Central Street
Wichita, KS 67214

Family Psychological Center
804 South Oliver Street
Wichita, KS 67218

**Great Meeting is on for Your
    Success**
1015 East 9th Street
Wichita, KS 67214

Hunter Health Clinic, Inc.
2318 East Central Street
Wichita, KS 67214

**Indian Alcoholism Treatment
    Services**
313 North Seneca Street
Suite 109
Wichita, KS 67203

**Individual and Family Systems
    Recovery**
2400 North Woodlawn Street
Suite 210
Wichita, KS 67220

Knox Center, Inc.
2400 North Woodlawn Street
Suite 210
Wichita, KS 67220

Life Challenges Consulting
566-A South Oliver Street
Wichita, KS 67218

Lighthouse of Wichita Inc
204 South Osage Street
Wichita, KS 67213

Miracles, Inc.
1250 North Market Street
Wichita, KS 67214

Mirror, Inc.
210 North Saint Francis Street
Wichita, KS 67214

New Attitudes, Inc.
9319 East Harry Street, Suite 110
Wichita, KS 67207

New Beginning
2423 East 13th Street
Wichita, KS 67214

Outpatient Drug Alcohol
Treatment and Assessment
8911 East Orme Street, Suite B
Wichita, KS 67207

Parallax Program, Inc.
3401 East Funston Street
Wichita, KS 67218

PMA Addiction Medicine
1725 East Douglas Street
Wichita, KS 67211

Recovery Unlimited
3312 West Douglas Street
Wichita, KS 67203

Relapse Prevention Counseling
1333 North Broadway, Suite D
Wichita, KS 67214

Saint Mark United Methodist
Church Counseling and
Outreach
1525 North Lorraine Street
Wichita, KS 67214

Sedgwick County Dept of
Corrections Adult Facility
209 North Emporia Street
Wichita, KS 67203

Sward, Jon M., Ph.D.
1999 North Amidon Street
Suite 211
Wichita, KS 67203

Therapeutic Alliance
1333 North Broadway, Suite D
Wichita, KS 67214

Tiyospaye, Inc.
1856 Woodland Street
Wichita, KS 67203-2742

Wichita Treatment Center
1044 North Waco Street
Wichita, KS 67202

KENTUCKY

ALBANY

Adanta Behavioral Health
Services Albany Clinic
Highway 127 South
Albany, KY 42602

ASHLAND

Our Lady of Bellefonte Hospital
Chemical Dependency
Careunit
Saint Christopher Drive
Ashland, KY 41101

Pathways, Inc.
Withdrawal Unit
201 22nd Street
Ashland, KY 41101

Boyd County Outpatient Unit
Withdrawal Unit
201 22 Street
Ashland, KY 41101

BARBOURVILLE

Cumberland River
Comprehensive Care Center
317 Cumberland Avenue
Barbourville, KY 40906

Decisions, Inc.
Knox County Court House
Fiscal Court Conference Room
Barbourville, KY 40906

BARDSTOWN

Caritas Peace Counseling Center
300 North 2nd Street
Bardstown, KY 40004

Communicare Clinic
331 South 3 Street
Bardstown, KY 40004

Family Institute Project Calm
116 East Flaget Avenue
Bardstown, KY 40004

BARDWELL

Western Kentucky MH/MR
Board Carlisle County
Services
Highway 51 South
Bardwell, KY 42023

BARLOW

Western Kentucky MH/MR
Board Ballard County
Services
Highway 60
Barlow, KY 42024

BEATTYVILLE

Kentucky River Community
Care, Inc.
Beattyville By Pass
Beattyville, KY 41311

BENHAM

**Cumberland River
  Comprehensive Care Center**
Tri-Cities Center
Main Street
Benham, KY 40807

BENTON

**Western Kentucky MH/MR
  Board Benton/Marshall
  County Services**
1304 Main Street
Benton, KY 42025

**Kentucky River Community
  Care, Inc.**
North Court Square
Booneville, KY 41314

BOWLING GREEN

**Bowling Green Professional
  Associates**
959 Lovers Lane
Bowling Green, KY 42103

Leap, Inc.
1733 Campus Plaza Court
Suite 15
Bowling Green, KY 42101-7901

Lifeskills, Inc.
Bowling Green Center
Park Place
822 Woodway
Bowling Green, KY 42102

Prevention Counseling Services
1045 Elm Street
Bowling Green, KY 42101

BRANDENBURG

East Hill Associates
2025 Bypass Road, Suite 1
Brandenburg, KY 40108

BROOKSVILLE

Comprehend, Inc.
Bracken County Community Care
  Outpatient Drug Services
134 Grandview Drive
Brooksville, KY 41004

BROWNSVILLE

Lifeskills, Inc.
1120 South Main Street
Brownsville, KY 42210

BURKESVILLE

**Adanta Behavioral Health
  Services Burkesville Clinic**
390 Keen Street
Burkesville, KY 42717

CAMPBELLSVILLE

**Adanta Behavioral Health
  Services Campbellsville Clinic**
3020 Lebanon Road
Campbellsville, KY 42718

CAMPTON

**Kentucky River Community
  Care,**
Inc. Wolfe County Health
  Department
605 Highway 15 South
Suites 1 and 2
Campton, KY 41301

CARLISLE

Bluegrass West Comprehensive
Care Center Nicholas County
  Comprehensive Care
Post Office Building, Room 4
Carlisle, KY 40311

CARROLLTON

**Comprehensive Care Centers of
  Northern Kentucky**
Carroll County Center
1714 Highland Avenue
Carrollton, KY 41008

CLINTON

**Western Kentucky MH/MR
  Board Clinton/Hickman
  County Services**
South Washington Street
Clinton, KY 42031

COLUMBIA

**Adanta Behavioral Health
  Services Columbia Clinic**
808 C Jamestown Street
Columbia KY 42728

Westlake Regional Hospital
100 Westlake Drive
Columbia, KY 42728

CORBIN

**Baptist Regional Medical Center
  Adult Chemical Dependency
  Unit**
1 Trillium Way
Corbin, KY 40701

Corbin Professional Associates
1707 Cumberland Falls Road
Falls Road Plaza LL-4
Corbin, KY 40701

Cumberland River
Comprehensive Care Center
American Greetings Road
Corbin, KY 40701

Independence House
3110 Cumberland Falls Highway
Corbin, KY 40701

Decisions, Inc.
801 Master Street, Suite 4
Corbin, KY 40701

COVINGTON

**DUI Defendant Referral
  Systems, Inc.**
808 Scott Street
Covington, KY 41011

Lindemann, David
722 Scott Street
Covington, KY 41012

Transitions, Inc.
Women's Residential Addiction
  Program (WRAP)
1629 Madison Avenue
Covington, KY 41011

CYNTHIANA

Bluegrass West Comprehensive Care
Harrison County Comprehensive Care
122 East Pleasant Street
Cynthiana, KY 41031

DANVILLE

Bluegrass South Comprehensive Care
Court Referral Services
1000 Lexington Road, Suite 1
Danville, KY 40422

Recovery Center
650 High Street
Danville, KY 40422

DAYTON

Transitions, Inc. Droege House
925 5th Avenue
Dayton, KY 41074

DIXON

Community Methodist Hospital DUI Program
Ambulatory Care Center
1355 U.S. Highway 41 A South
Dixon, KY 42409

EDDYVILLE

Western Kentucky Drug and Alcohol Intervention Services, Inc.
1216 Fairview Avenue
Eddyville, KY 42038

EDGEWOOD

Saint Elizabeth Medical Center Chemical Dependency Units
200 Medical Village Drive
Edgewood, KY 41017

EDMONTON

Prevention Counseling Services
1608 West Stockton Road
Edmonton, KY 42129

ELIZABETHTOWN

Caritas Peace Counseling Center
790 North Dixie Highway Suite 800
Elizabethtown, KY 42701

Communicare Recovery Center
1311 North Dixie Avenue
Elizabethtown, KY 42701

Heartland Counseling Services PSC
29 Public Square
Elizabethtown, KY 42701

Hub City Education Services
30 Public Square
Elizabethtown, KY 42701

FAIRDALE

Shelton Counseling
10601 West Manslick Road
Fairdale, KY 40118

FALMOUTH

Comprehensive Care Centers of Northern Kentucky
Pendelton County Center
318 Mountjoy Street
Falmouth, KY 41040

Saint Luke Hospital Alcohol Drug Treatment Center
512 South Maple Avenue
Falmouth, KY 41040

FLEMINGSBURG

Comprehend, Inc. Fleming
County CMHC Outpatient Alcohol and Drug Offices
610 Elizaville Road
Flemingsburg, KY 41041

FLORENCE

Commonwealth Substance Abuse Specialists
7415 Burlington Pike, Suite A
Florence, KY 41042

Comprehensive Care Centers of Northern Kentucky
Boone County Comprehensive Care Center
7459 Burlington Park
Florence, KY 41042

Modlin and Associates Alcohol and Drug Treatment Center and Education Center
2 Dortha Avenue
Florence, KY 41042

FORT CAMPBELL

Community Counseling Services
21st Street and Indiana Avenue
MCXD/CLC Building 2437
Fort Campbell, KY 42223

FORT MITCHELL

Cincinnati Counseling Services, Inc.
100 Chrysler Avenue
FAA Building/Buttermilk Pike
Fort Mitchell, KY 41017

FRANKFORT

Bluegrass Education and Treatment for Addiction
925 Wash Road
Frankfort, KY 40601

Bluegrass West Comprehensive Care Center
Frankfort Office
191 Doctors Drive
Frankfort, KY 40601

Halfway House
943 Wash Road
Frankfort, KY 40601

Counseling Center, Inc.
309 West Main Street
Frankfort, KY 40601

Decisions, Inc.
101 Saint Clair Street
Frankfort, KY 40601

FRANKLIN

Counseling Services RAP
215-B Bluegrass Road
Franklin, KY 42135

Lifeskills, Inc.
112 South High Street
Franklin, KY 42134

FRENCHBURG

Pathways, Inc. Menifee County Outpatient Unit
HCR 69 US 460 west
Frenchburg, KY 40322

FULTON

Fulton County Mental Health Service
350 Browder Street
Fulton, KY 42041

GEORGETOWN

Bluegrass West Comprehensive Care
Scott County Clinic
1226 Paris Pike
Georgetown, KY 40324

Counseling Center, Inc.
137 East Main Street
Georgetown, KY 40324

GLASGOW

Lifeskills, Inc. Barren County Office
608 Happy Valley Road
Glasgow, KY 42142

Prevention Counseling Services
130 North Race Street
Glasgow, KY 42141

GRAYSON

Pathways, Inc. Carter County Outpatient Unit
515 West Main Street
Grayson, KY 41143

GREENSBURG

Adanta Behavioral Health Services Greensburg Clinic
429 Hodgensville Road
Greensburg, KY 42743

Jane Crawford Hospital Behavioral Center
202 Milby Street
Greensburg, KY 42743-1136

GREENUP

Pathways, Inc. Greenup County Outpatient Unit
1018 Walnut Street
Greenup, KY 41144

GREENVILLE

DUI Defendant Referral Systems, Inc.
117 South Main Street
Harbin Library
Greenville, KY 42345

Pennyroyal Mental Health Services Muhlenberg County MH/MR Center
506 Hopkinsville Street
Greenville, KY 42345

HARLAN

Cumberland River Comprehensive Care Center
134 Comp Drive
Harlan, KY 40831

Decisions, Inc.
Harlan County Courthouse
Fiscal Conference Room
1st and Central Street
Harlan, KY 40831

HARRODSBURG

Bluegrass South Comprehensive Care
Crisis Stabilization Unit
710 Perryville Road
Harrodsburg, KY 40330

Ransdell Community Mental Health Center
352 Mr Kwik Shopping Plaza
Harrodsburg, KY 40330

HAZARD

Kentucky River Community Care, Inc.
115 Rockwood Lane
Daniel Boone Parkway
Hazard, KY 41701

HENDERSON

DUI Defendant Referral Systems, Inc.
128 2nd Street, Suite C
Henderson, KY 42420

Employee Assistance DUI Services, Inc.
Citi Center Building
230 Second Street, Suite 308
Henderson, KY 42420

New Choice Center
435 South Y Street
Henderson, KY 42420

Pathways Counseling Services
323 3rd Street
Henderson, KY 42420

Regional Addiction Resources (RAR)
6347 Highway 60 East
Henderson, KY 42420

HINDMAN

Kentucky River Community Care, Inc.
Highway 80
Hindman, KY 41822

HOPKINSVILLE

Alliance Counseling
110 West 2nd Street
Hopkinsville, KY 42240

FHC Cumberland Hall
210 West 17th Street
Hopkinsville, KY 42240-1912

Pennyroyal Center
Adult Clinic
Children's Services
735 North Drive
Hopkinsville, KY 42240

Adolescent Chemical Dependency
Program
676 North Drive
Hopkinsville, KY 42240

**Volta Program Substance Abuse
Treatment Center**
Russellville Road Highway 68
Johnson Building
Hopkinsville, KY 42240

**Western Kentucky Drug and
Alcohol Intervention Services,
Inc.**
600 South Main Street
Hopkinsville, KY 42240

HYDEN

**Kentucky River Community
Care, Inc.**
Hurts Creek Shopping Center
Post Office Building
Hyden, KY 41749

INEZ

**Gateway Counseling Services,
Inc.**
Main Street
Inez, KY 41224

**Mountain Comprehensive Care
Center Martin County Clinic**
Rockcastle Street, Route 3
Inez, KY 41224

IRVINE

**Bluegrass South Comprehensive
Care**
Irvine Comprehensive Care Center
Handy Brothers Shopping Center
Irvine, KY 40336

ISOM

**Kentucky River Community
Care, Inc.**
Route 7 and Highway 15
Isom, KY 41824

JACKSON

**Kentucky River Community
Care, Inc.**
Outpatient/Next Step
3775 Highway 15 South
Jackson, KY 41339

Sewell Family Children's Center
3875 Highway 15 South
Jackson, KY 41339

JAMESTOWN

**Adanta Behavioral Health
Services**
Jamestown Clinic
Russell School Program
Highway 127 South
Jamestown, KY 42629

Windows of Discovery
Russell County Courthouse
Jamestown, KY 42629

LANCASTER

**Garrard Community Mental
Health**
67 Public Square
Lancaster, KY 40444

LAWRENCEBURG

Bluegrass West Comprehensive
Care Center Lawrenceburg
Comprehensive Care Center
1060 Glensboro Road
Lawrenceburg, KY 40342

LEBANON

Communicare
Route 4/Springfield Road
Lebanon, KY 40033

LEITCHFIELD

Communicare
300 South Clinton Street
Health Department Annex
Leitchfield, KY 42754

LEXINGTON

**Alcohol Related Offenders
Program**
1388 Alexandria Drive
Lexington, KY 40504

Anchor Counseling
106 Dennis Drive
Lexington, KY 40503

Baker Programs
174 North Martin Luther King
Boulevard
Lexington, KY 40507

Bluegrass Driver School, Inc.
169 East Reynolds Road
Suite 202-A
Lexington, KY 40517

**Bluegrass East Comprehensive
Care**
Aftercare Program
Narcotics Addiction Program
201 Mechanic Street
Lexington, KY 40507

Drug and Alcohol Program
Teen Primary Outpatient Program
200 West 2 Street
Lexington, KY 40507

Forensic Services
177 North Upper Street
Lexington, KY 40507

Growth Resources
1517 Nicholasville Road
Lexington, KY 40503

Pride Program
1101 South Limestone Avenue
Lexington, KY 40508

**Charles I Schwartz Chemical
Dependency Treatment Center**
627 West 4th Street
Lexington, KY 40508

**Charter Ridge Behavioral
Health System**
3050 Rio Dosa Drive
Lexington, KY 40509

Chrysalis House, Inc.
251 East Maxwell Street
Lexington, KY 40508

Chrysalis Family Program
120 Chrysalis Court
Lexington, KY 40508

Clark and Clark
480 West 2nd Street
Lexington, KY 40507

Counseling Center, Inc.
248 East Short Street
Lexington, KY 40507

DUI Defendant Referral Systems
431 South Broadway
Suite 331
Lexington, KY 40508

Family Preservation
570 East Main Street
Lexington, KY 40502

Hope Center
360 West Loudon Street
Lexington, KY 40508

Kentucky Alcohol Offenders
174 North Martin Luther King
    Boulevard
Lexington, KY 40507

Leap, Inc.
174 North Martin Luther King
    Boulevard
Lexington, KY 40507

**Lexington Professional
    Associates**
1718 Alexandria Drive, Suite 204
Lexington, KY 40504

**Modlin and Rulli Alcohol and
    Drug Treatment and
    Education Center**
174 North Martin Luther King
    Boulevard
Lexington, KY 40507

Morton Center, Inc.
535 West 2nd Street
Lexington, KY 40508

**Patti Hard Marriage and Family
    Therapy**
1517 Nicholasville Road
Lexington, KY 40503

Saint Joseph Hospital
One Saint Joseph Drive
Lexington, KY 40504

Samaritan Hospital
310 South Limestone Street
Lexington, KY 40508

Shepherds House, Inc.
154 Bonnie Brae Drive
Lexington, KY 40508

University Hospital
800 Rose Street
Lexington, KY 40536-0226

Van Hoose and Associates
501 Darby Creek Road, Suite 3
Lexington, KY 40509

**Veterans' Affairs Medical Center
    Substance Abuse Treatment
    Program**
2250 Leestown Road
Lexington, KY 40511

LIBERTY

**Adanta Behavioral Health
    Services Liberty Clinic**
112 Liberty Square
Liberty, KY 42539

LONDON

Decisions, Inc.
c/o Best Western
Highway East 80
London, KY 40741

Windows of Discovery
105 South Broad Street
London, KY 40741-1800

LOUISA

**Gateway Counseling Services,
    Inc.**
Jefferson Lawrence County
    Library
102 West Main Street
Louisa, KY 41230

**Pathways, Inc. Lawrence
    County Outpatient Unit**
314 East Madison
Louisa, KY 41230

LOUISVILLE

Alcohol Awareness Counseling
4400 Breckenridge Lane
Breckenridge Business Center
Suite 307
Louisville, KY 40201

Baptist Hospital East Chemical
Dependency Program Center for
    Behavioral Health
4000 Kresge Way
Louisville, KY 40207

**Bluegrass Pleasant Grove
    Counseling Center**
5330 South 3rd Street, Suite 114
Louisville, KY 40214

4801 Sherburn Lane, Suite 203
Louisville, KY 40207

Bumpas, Thomas J.
6000 Brownsboro Park Boulevard
Suite G
Louisville, KY 40207

Caritas Peace Counseling Center
2120 Newburg Road, Suite 200
Louisville, KY 40205

**Charter Louisville Behavioral
    Health System**
1405 Browns Lane
Louisville, KY 40207

**Chemical Dependency
    Counseling**
4342 Taylor Boulevard
Louisville, KY 40215

Counseling Center, Inc.
2210 Goldsmith Lane, Suite 126
Louisville, KY 40205

David Harmon and Associates
4010 Dupont Circle, Suite 226
Louisville, KY 40207

Eastern Star Baptist Church
824 South 24th Street
Louisville, KY 40211

**Dismas Charities Drug and
    Alcohol Treatment Program**
1501 Lytle Street
Louisville, KY 40203

Dr. Donald T. Stokes and Associates, Inc.
1941 Bishop Lane
Watterson City West Building
Suite 505
Louisville, KY 40218

Dual Diagnosis Unit Central State Hospital
10510 Lagrange Road
Louisville, KY 40223

Healing Place for Women
1607 West Broadway
Louisville, KY 40203

Interlink Counseling Services, Inc.
8311 A and B Preston Highway
Louisville, KY 40219

Jefferson County Drug Court
2516 West Madison Street
Louisville, KY 40211

John P. Sohan Counseling Services
1169 Eastern Parkway
Medical Arts Building, Suite 3358
Louisville, KY 40217

Kentucky Correctional Institute for Women Alcohol and Drug Abuse Program
600 South Preston Street
Louisville, KY 40202

Leap, Inc.
5201 Dixie Highway
Louisville, KY 40216

310 West Liberty Street
Louisville, KY 40202

Lighthouse Adolescent Recovery Center
1935 Bluegrass Avenue
Louisville, KY 40215

Methadone/Opiate Rehabilitation and Education Center
1448 South 15th Street
Louisville, KY 40210

Morton Center, Inc.
982 Eastern Parkway
Kosair Charities Center
Louisville, KY 40217

Norton Psychiatric Clinic
200 East Chestnut Street
Louisville, KY 40232

Rehabilitation and Recovery, Inc.
1169 Eastern Parkway, Suite 1138
Louisville, KY 40217

Seven Counties Services/ Jefferson Alcohol and Drug Abuse Center
600 South Preston Street
Louisville, KY 40202

Tabler/Dawson and Associates
2520 Bardstown Road
Louisville, KY 40201

Talbot House
520 West Saint Catherine Street
Louisville, KY 40203

Ten Broeck Hospital Substance Abuse Services
8521 La Grange Road
Louisville, KY 40242

Triad Recovery Center
214 South 8th Street
Louisville, KY 40202

Volunteers of America
Freedom House
1432 South Shelby Street
Louisville, KY 40217

Third Step Program
1436 South Shelby Street
Louisville, KY 40217

Wellness Institute
332 West Broadway
Suite 1707
Louisville, KY 40202

Whelan, Patrick
1238 East Broadway
Louisville, KY 40204

MADISONVILLE

DUI Defendant Referral System, Inc.
333 1/2 Union Street
Madisonville, KY 42431

Madisonville Regional Medical Center Addiction Recovery Center (ARC)
Hospital Drive
Madisonville, KY 42431

Pennyroyal Mental Health Services
1303 West Noel Street
Madisonville, KY 42431

MANCHESTER

Cumberland River Comprehensive Care Center
Route 9, Box 940
Manchester, KY 40962

DUI Defendant Referral Systems, Inc.
224 White Street
Manchester, KY 40962

MARION

Community Methodist Hospital
212 West Depot Street
Marion, KY 42064

MAYFIELD

Western Kentucky Drug and Alcohol Intervention Services, Inc.
1301 Princeton Drive
Mayfield, KY 42066

William H. Fuller Memorial Substance Abuse Center
1525 Cuba Road
Mayfield, KY 42066

MAYSVILLE

Comprehend, Inc. Mason County CMHC
611 Forest Avenue
Maysville, KY 41056

MCKEE

Cumberland River Comprehensive Care Center
McKee, KY 40447

MIDDLESBORO

Cumberland River Comprehensive Care Center
324 1/2 North 19th Street
Middlesboro, KY 40965

Decisions, Inc.
Days Inn Conference Room B
1252 North 12th Street
Middlesboro, KY 40965

MONTICELLO

Adanta Behavioral Health Services Wayne County Clinic
1994 North Main Street
Monticello, KY 42633

Windows of Discovery
Wayne County Courthouse
Monticello, KY 42633

MOREHEAD

Pathways, Inc. Rowan County Outpatient Unit
321 East Main Street
Morehead, KY 40351

MORGANTOWN

Lifeskills, Inc.
211 East Logan Street
Morgantown, KY 42261

MOUNT STERLING

Pathways, Inc.
Hillcrest Hall
2479 Grassy Lick Road
Mount Sterling, KY 40353

Montgomery County Outpatient Unit
300 Foxglove Drive
Mount Sterling, KY 40353

MOUNT VERNON

Cumberland River Comprehensive Care Center
Mount Vernon, KY 40456

Decisions, Inc.
Rock Castle County Courthouse
Circuit Court Room
Main Street
Mount Vernon, KY 40456

MUNFORDVILLE

Lifeskills, Inc. Hart County Office
118 West 3 Street
Munfordville, KY 42765

MURRAY

Behavioral Medicine, Inc.
100 North 6th Street
Murray, KY 42071-2000

Western Kentucky MH/MR Board
Murray/Calloway County MH/ MR Services
903 Sycamore Street
Murray, KY 42071

NEWPORT

Comprehensive Care Centers of Northern Kentucky
Campbell County Center
10th and Monmouth Streets
Newport, KY 41071

Modlin and Associates
1699 Monmouth Street
Newport, KY 41071

Transitions, Inc.
York Street House
601 York Street
Newport, KY 41071

NICHOLASVILLE

Bluegrass East Comprehensive Care
Jessamine County Center
324 Southview Drive
Nicholasville, KY 40356

OWENSBORO

Employee Assistance DUI Services, Inc.
5000 Backsquare Drive
Building C
Owensboro, KY 42301

Owensboro Area Shelter and Information Services (OASIS)
Owensboro, KY 42302

Saradon Center
920 Frederica Street
Midtown Office Complex
Suite 410
Owensboro, KY 42301

OWENTON

Comprehensive Care Centers of Northern Kentucky
114 West Brown Street
Owenton, KY 40359

OWINGSVILLE

Pathways, Inc.
Bath County Outpatient
Route 36
Owingsville, KY 40360

PADUCAH

Behavioral Medicine, Inc.
102 South 31 Street
Paducah, KY 42001

Charter Hospital of Paducah Substance Abuse Program
435 Berger Road
Paducah, KY 42001

Western Kentucky Drug and Alcohol Intervention Services, Inc.
6th Street
Irvin Cobb Hotel
Paducah, KY 42001

Joseph L. Friedman Substance Abuse Center
1405 South 3 Street
Paducah, KY 42003

PAINTSVILLE

Gateway Counseling Services, Inc.
U.S. 23 North
Wiley Complex
Paintsville, KY 41240

Mountain Comprehensive Care Center Johnson County Clinic
1024 Broadway
Paintsville, KY 41240

PARIS

Bluegrass West Comprehensive Care Center Bourbon County
269 East Main Street
Paris, KY 40361

Stoner Creek Psychiatric Center Burbon Community Hospital
9 Linville Drive
Paris, KY 40361

PIKEVILLE

DUI Defendant Referral Systems, Inc.
419 3rd Street
Pikeville, KY 41501

Gateway Counseling Services, Inc.
89 Division Street
Pikeville, KY 41501

Mountain Comprehensive Care Center Pike County Outpatient Clinic
804 Hambley Boulevard, Suite 4
Pikeville, KY 41501

PINEVILLE

Cumberland River Comprehensive Care Center
110 Kentucky Avenue
Pineville, KY 40977

PRESTONSBURG

Gateway Counseling Services, Inc.
Highway 1428 South
Prestonsburg, KY 41653

Mountain Comprehensive Care Center
Layne House
965 South Lake Drive
Prestonsburg, KY 41653

Outpatient Services
18 South Front Avenue
Prestonsburg, KY 41653

PRINCETON

Pennyroyal Mental Health
Services Caldwell County Mental Health Center
115 McGoodwin Street
Princeton, KY 42445

Western Kentucky Drug and Alcohol Intervention Services, Inc.
108 West Main Street
Princeton, KY 42445

RADCLIFF

Lincoln Trail Hospital United Health Care
3909 South Wilson Road
Radcliff, KY 40160

RICHMOND

Comprehensive Care Center
415 Gibson Lane
Richmond, KY 40475

RUSSELLVILLE

Lifeskills, Inc.
237 East 6 Street
Russellville, KY 42276

SALYERSVILLE

Lifestyle Counseling
Old Fire Station Jockey Lot
Salyersville, KY 41465

Mountain Comprehensive Care Center Magoffin County Clinic
145 Allen Drive
Highway 114
Salyersville, KY 41465

SANDY HOOK

Pathways, Inc. Elliott County Outpatient Unit
Route 17 and Route 132
Sandy Hook, KY 41171

SCOTTSVILLE

Lifeskills, Inc. Scottsville Counseling Center
512 Bowling Green Road
Scottsville, KY 42164

SHELBYVILLE

Creative Spirits
615 Washington Street
Shelbyville, KY 40065-1131

Family Institute Project Calm
702 Washington Street
Shelbyville, KY 40065

Insight Outfitters
935 Trout Lane
Shelbyville, KY 40065

SHEPHERDSVILLE

Trummell and Associates Counseling Center
1729-A Highway 44 East
Shepherdsville, KY 40165

SMITHLAND

Livingston County MH/MR Services
Highway 60
McKinney Building
Smithland, KY 42081

SOMERSET

Adanta Behavioral Health Services
Somerset Clinic
101 Hardin Lane
Somerset, KY 42501

Lake Cumberland Regional Hospital
305 Langdon Street
Somerset, KY 42501

Pulaski Child and Adolescent Services
104 Hardin Lane
Somerset, KY 42501

Windows of Discovery
107 West Mount Vernon Street
Somerset, KY 42501

SOUTHGATE

Commonwealth Substance Abuse Specialists
525 Alexandria Pike
South Hills Medical Center
Suite 100
Southgate, KY 41071

SOUTH WILLIAMSON

Mountain Comprehensive Care Center
2000 Central Avenue
South Williamson, KY 41503

SPRINGFIELD

Springfield Counseling Services
208-C West Main Street
Springfield, KY 40069

STANFORD

Bluegrass South Comprehensive Care Court Referral
410 Anderson Heights
Stanford, KY 40484

Fort Logan Comprehensive Care Center
110 Somerset Street
Stanford, KY 40484

STANTON

Bluegrass East Comprehensive Care Center Stanton Unit
354 West College Street
Stanton, KY 40380

TOMPKINSVILLE

Lifeskills, Inc.
200 East 4 Street
Tompkinsville, KY 42167

VANCEBURG

Comprehend, Inc. Lewis County CMHC Outpatient Alcohol and Drug Office
502 2nd Avenue
Vanceburg, KY 41179

VERSAILLES

Bluegrass West Comprehensive Care
Woodford County Center
125b Big Sink Pike
Versailles, KY 40383

WARSAW

Commonwealth Substance Abuse Specialists
100 West High Street
Warsaw, KY 41095

Comprehensive Care Centers of Northern Kentucky
Gallatin City Center
203 West Martin Street
Warsaw, KY 41095

WEST LIBERTY

Pathways, Inc.
Morgan County Outpatient Unit
280 Prestonsburg Street
Morgan County Office Building
West Liberty, KY 41472

WHITESBURG

Whitesburg DUI Service Agency
117 Hayes Street, Suite 203
Whitesburg, KY 41858

WHITLEY CITY

Adanta Behavioral Health Services
Whitley City Clinic
South Fork Centera
Highway 27
Whitley City, KY 42653

WILLIAMSBURG

Cumberland River Comprehensive Care Center
Cemetary Road
Williamsburg, KY 40769

WILLIAMSTOWN

Comprehensive Care Centers of Northern Kentucky
Grant County Center
308 Barnes Road
Williamstown, KY 41097

Modlin and Rulli Alcohol and Drug Treatment and Education Center
214-C South Main Street
Williamstown, KY 41097

WINCHESTER

Bluegrass East Comprehensive Care
26 North Highland Street
Winchester, KY 40391

Counseling Center, Inc.
52 North Maple Street
Winchester, KY 40391

LOUISIANA

ALEXANDRIA

Crossroads Regional Hospital Substance Abuse Services
110 John Eskew Drive
Alexandria, LA 71315

Louisiana Black Alcoholism Council, Inc.
2403 Harris Street
Alexandria, LA 71307

Veterans' Affairs Medical Center
Chemical Dependency Clinic
Building 6, 116E
Alexandria, LA 71301

BASTROP

Bastrop Alcohol and Drug Abuse Clinic
218 North Franklin Street
Bastrop, LA 71220

BATON ROUGE

Alcohol and Drug Abuse Council of Greater Baton Rouge
1801 Florida Boulevard
Baton Rouge, LA 70802

BHC Meadow Wood Hospital Center for Addictive Disorders
9032 Perkins Road
Baton Rouge, LA 70810

Baton Rouge Area Alcohol and Drug Center, Inc.
1819 Florida Boulevard
Baton Rouge, LA 70802

Baton Rouge Substance Abuse Clinic
4615 Government Street
Building A
Baton Rouge, LA 70806

Behavioral Health Center
3601 North Boulevard
Baton Rouge, LA 70806

Community Counseling
2356 Drusilla Lane
Baton Rouge, LA 70809

Louisiana Health and Rehabilitation Options
2744 Florida Boulevard
Baton Rouge, LA 70802

O'Brien House
1231 Laurel Street
Baton Rouge, LA 70802

Our Lady of the Lake Hospital Tau Chemical Dependency Center
8080 Margaret Ann Drive
Baton Rouge, LA 70809

Salvation Army
7361 Airline Highway
Baton Rouge, LA 70805

Serenity House, Inc.
3370 Victoria Drive
Baton Rouge, LA 70805

BELLE CHASSE

Plaquemines Alcohol and Drug Abuse Clinic
3708 Main Street
Belle Chasse, LA 70037

BOGALUSA

Washington Parish Alcohol and Drug Abuse Clinic
2601 Avenue F
Bogalusa, LA 70427

CHALMETTE

Saint Bernard Alcohol and Drug Abuse Clinic
2712 Palmisano Boulevard
Building A
Chalmette, LA 70043

CHARENTON

Chitimacha Human Services Department
3287 Chitimacha Trail
Charenton, LA 70523

CROWLEY

Crowley and Ville Platte Alcohol and Drug Abuse Clinic
703 East 8 Street
Crowley, LA 70526

ELTON

Coushatta Health Department
2003 CC Bel Road
Elton, LA 70532

FRANKLINTON

Seven Acres Substance Abuse Center
23046 Yacc Road
Franklinton, LA 70438

GONZALES

Parish of Ascension Substance Abuse Center
1112 SE Ascension Complex Avenue
Gonzales, LA 70737

Power House Services, Inc.
715 West Worthey Road
Gonzales, LA 70737

GREENSBURG

Saint Helena Alcohol and Drug Abuse Clinic
102 North 2nd Street
Greensburg, LA 70441

HAMMOND

Hammond Alcohol and Drug Abuse Clinic
202 East Robert Street
Hammond, LA 70401

HARVEY

Family House/Louisiana
1125-B Inca Court
Harvey, LA 70058

HOUMA

Terrebonne Alcohol and Drug Abuse Clinic
521 Legion Avenue
Houma, LA 70364

Detox Center
1116 Church Street
Houma, LA 70364

JENNINGS

Jefferson Davis Chemical Health, Inc.
203 North Cutting Street
Jennings, LA 70546

KENNER

Kenner Substance Abuse Clinic
1919 Veterans Boulevard
Kenner, LA 70062

KINDER

Allen Parish Hospital
108 6th Avenue
Kinder, LA 70648

LAFAYETTE

Charter Cypress Behavioral Health Service
302 Dulles Drive
Lafayette, LA 70506

Gatehouse Foundation
206 South Magnolia Street
Lafayette, LA 70501

Lafayette Alcohol and Drug Abuse Clinic
400 Saint Julien Street
Suite 1
Lafayette, LA 70506

Saint Francis Foundation
1610 West University Street
Lafayette, LA 70506

Vermilion Hospital for Psychiatric and Addictive Medicine
2520 North University Avenue
Lafayette, LA 70507

LAKE CHARLES

Joseph R. Briscoe Alcohol and Drug Abuse Center
4012 Avenue H
Lake Charles, LA 70601

Lake Charles Substance Abuse Clinic, Inc.
711 North Prater Street
Lake Charles, LA 70601

Lake Charles Memorial Hospital Recovery Center
1701 Oak Park Boulevard
Lake Charles, LA 70601

LA PLACE

River Parishes Alcohol and Drug Abuse Clinic
421 West Airline Highway
Suite L
La Place, LA 70068

LEESVILLE

Vernon Alcohol and Drug Abuse
300 South 1st Street
Leesville, LA 71446

LULING

Saint Charles Parish Hospital Psychiatric Unit
1057 Paul Maillard Road
Luling, LA 70070

MAMOU

Savoy Medical Center New Horizons
120 Country Club Lane
Mamou, LA 70554

MANDEVILLE

Alcohol and Drug Treatment Unit
SE Hospital
Highway 190
Mandeville, LA 70470

Fontainebleau Treatment Center
Highway 190 West
Mandeville, LA 70448

Northlake Alcohol and Drug Abuse Clinic
101 Brookside Drive
Mandeville, LA 70448

MARKSVILLE

Hamilton House
103 South Main Street
Marksville, LA 71351

Tunica/Biloxi Indians of Louisiana Substance Abuse Prevention Program
Highway 1
Marksville, LA 71351

Washington Street Hope Center
106 South Washington Street
Marksville, LA 71351

MARRERO

West Bank Alcohol and Drug Abuse Clinic
5001 Westbank Expressway
Marrero, LA 70072

METAIRIE

Jefferson Substance Abuse Clinic
3101 West Napoleon Avenue
Suite 2000
Metairie, LA 70001

New Freedom, Inc.
401 Veteran's Memorial Boulevard
Suite 102
Metairie, LA 70005

MINDEN

Minden Mental Health and Substance Abuse Clinic
421 Meadowview Drive
Minden, LA 71055

MONROE

Four Runners Community Action Program Serenity House
2502 Georgia Street
Monroe, LA 71211

Monroe Alcohol and Drug Abuse Clinic
3208 Concordia Street
Monroe, LA 71201

Southern Oaks Addiction Recovery Center
4781 South Grand Street
Monroe, LA 71202

MORGAN CITY

Fairview Treatment Center
1101 Southeast Boulevard
Morgan City, LA 70380

Saint Mary Addictive Disorders Clinic
521 Roderick Street
Morgan City, LA 70380

NATCHITOCHES

Natchitoches Alcohol and Drug Abuse Clinic
212 Medical Drive
Natchitoches, LA 71457

NEW IBERIA

New Iberia Alcohol and Drug Abuse Clinic
611 West Admiral Doyle Drive
New Iberia, LA 70560

NEW ORLEANS

Basic of Louisiana, Inc.
1452 Broad Street
New Orleans, LA 70119

BHC East Lake Hospital
3600 Chestnut Street
New Orleans, LA 70115

Bridge House, Inc.
1160 Camp Street
New Orleans, LA 70130

CCYAD Foundation Youth Against Drugs
1528 Louisa Street
New Orleans, LA 70117

Covenant House New Orleans
611 North Rampart Street
New Orleans, LA 70112

Desire Narcotic Rehab Center, Inc.
3307 Desire Parkway
New Orleans, LA 70126

4116 Old Gentilly Road
New Orleans, LA 70126

Division of Addictive Disorders
LSU Medical School
1542 Tulane Avenue
New Orleans, LA 70112

Oscar Carter Rehabilitation Center
5500 North Johnson Street
New Orleans, LA 70117

DRD New Orleans Medical Clinic
530 South Galvez Street
New Orleans, LA 70119

Family Service of Greater New Orleans Community Care
2515 Canal Street
Suite 201
New Orleans, LA 70119

Foundation House/New Orleans
3942 Laurel Street
New Orleans, LA 70115

Grace House of New Orleans, Inc.
1401 Delachaise Street
New Orleans, LA 70115

Guillaume Center, Inc.
210 State Street
New Orleans, LA 70118

Methodist Psychiatric Pavilion
5610 Read Boulevard
New Orleans, LA 70127

Metropolitan Treatment Center, Inc.
3604 Tulane Avenue
New Orleans, LA 70119

New Orleans Substance Abuse Clinic
2025 Canal Street
Suite 300
New Orleans, LA 70112

Ochsner Addictive Behavior
1516 Jefferson Highway, Floor 4
New Orleans, LA 70121

Odyssey House Louisiana, Inc.
1125 North Tonti Street
New Orleans, LA 70119

Velocity Foundation, Inc.
4730 Washington Avenue
New Orleans, LA 70113

Veterans Administration Hospital
1601 Perdido Street
Unit 116A
New Orleans, LA 70146

NEW ROADS

Bonne Sante Chemical Health and Wellness Center
282-A Hospital Road
New Roads, LA 70760

OPELOUSAS

New Beginnings of Opelousas
1692 Linwood Loop
Opelousas, LA 70570

Opelousas Alcohol/Drug Abuse Clinic
532 North Court Street
Opelousas, LA 70570

PINEVILLE

Alexandria/Pineville Alcohol and Drug Abuse Clinic
401 Rainbow Drive
Pineville, LA 71361

Cenla Chemical Dependency Council
Bridge House/Phase II
401 Rainbow Drive
Pineville, LA 71361

Gateway Adolescent Unit
Pineville, LA 71360

Rainbow House Detox
Rainbow Drive
Pineville, LA 71361

Red River Treatment Center Central Louisiana State Hospital
Unit 6-D
Pineville, LA 71360

PORT ALLEN

People Rehabilitation and Recovery Services Corporation
710 Louisiana Avenue
Port Allen, LA 70767

RAYNE

American Legion Hospital Pauline Faulk Center
301 South Chevis Street
Rayne, LA 70578

RAYVILLE

Palmetto Addiction Recovery Center
86 Palmetto Road
Rayville, LA 71269

RUSTON

Louisiana Tech University Teen Institute
Ruston, LA 71272

Professional Counseling Services of Ruston
101 Reynolds Drive
Ruston, LA 71270

Ruston Alcohol and Drug Abuse Clinic
206 Reynolds Drive
Suite B-3
Ruston, LA 71270

SCHRIEVER

Assisi Bridge House
600 Bull Run Road
Schriever, LA 70395

SCOTT

Opportunities, Inc.
808 Pitt Road
Scott, LA 70583

SHREVEPORT

Buckhalter Recovery Center
527 Crockett Street
Shreveport, LA 71101

Caddo and Bossier Center
6220 Greenwood Road
Shreveport, LA 71119

Center for Families, Inc. Center for Addictive Disorders
864 Olive Street
Shreveport, LA 71104

Council on Alcohol/Drug Abuse of NW Louisiana
2000 Fairfield Avenue
Shreveport, LA 71104

The Adolescent Center
431 Jordan Street
Shreveport, LA 71101

CPC Brentwood Hospital Chemical Dependency Unit
1800 Irving Place
Shreveport, LA 71101

DDTP
510 East Stoner Avenue
Shreveport, LA 71101-4295

Doctors Hospital Addictive Disease Unit
1130 Louisiana Avenue
Shreveport, LA 71101

First Step Services, Inc.
2004 Creswell Street
Shreveport, LA 71104

Northwest Regional Alcohol and Drug Abuse Clinic
6244 Greenwood Road
Shreveport, LA 71119

Pines Treatment Center
6240 Greenwood Road
Shreveport, LA 71119

Sharing Through Examples of Personal Sobriety (STEPS)
525 Crockett Street
Shreveport, LA 71101

Volunteers of America Madre Program
345 Jordan Street
Shreveport, LA 71101

SLIDELL

Slidell Alcohol and Drug Abuse Clinic
2335 Carey Street
Slidell, LA 70458

TALLULAH

Delta Community Action Association Delta Recovery Center
404 East Craig Street
Tallulah, LA 71282

THIBODAUX

South Louisiana Rehabilitation Center Power House
614 Jackson Street
Thibodaux, LA 70301

Thibodaux Alcohol and Drug Abuse Clinic
303 Hickory Street
Thibodaux, LA 70301

WINNFIELD

Winnfield Alcoholism and Drug Abuse Clinic
308 Main Street, Suite 208-B
Winnfield, LA 71483

WINNSBORO

Northeast Louisiana Substance Abuse, Inc.
210 Main Street
Winnsboro, LA 71295

MAINE

ALBION

Health Reach Network
New Directions/Albion
School Street
Albion, ME 04910-1568

ALFRED

York County Shelters Inc
Shaker Hill Road
Alfred, ME 04002

ASHLAND

Aroostook Mental Health Center
  Outpatient Services
Walker Street
Ashland, ME 04732

AUBURN

Catholic Charities Maine Saint
  Francis House
88 3rd Street
Auburn, ME 04210

Community Concepts, Inc.
2 Court Street
Auburn, ME 04210

Family Intervention Services
233 Main Street
Auburn, ME 04210

Hayden, William, LSAC
81 Main Street, Box 3
Auburn, ME 04210

AUGUSTA

Bachand, Robert P.
33 Water Street
Augusta, ME 04330

Crisis and Counseling Center
99 Western Avenue
Augusta, ME 04330

Health Reach Network
Hearthside
Belgrade Road
Route 27
Augusta, ME 04330

New Directions
1 Weston Court
Augusta, ME 04330

Kassal, Jeannette, LCPC, LADC
74 Winthrop Street
Augusta, ME 04330

Maine General Medical Center
  Spruce Street Residence
9 Spruce Street
Augusta, ME 04330

Veterans' Affairs Medical Center
  Chemical Dependence
  Recovery Program
Route 17 East, 116-A2
Augusta, ME 04330

Wellness Health Association,
  Inc.
283 Water Street
Augusta, ME 04330

BANGOR

ABBAK Counseling Services
Bangor, ME 04402

Acadia Healthcare, Inc.
268 Stillwater Avenue
Bangor, ME 04401

Alternative Counseling Services
27 State Street
Suite 20-24
Bangor, ME 04401

BMHI/Acadia Recovery
  Community Substance Abuse
  Services
Bangor, ME 04401

Columbia Psychology Associate
82 Columbia Street
Bangor, ME 04401-6357

Community Health and
  Counseling Services
  Substance Abuse Services
900 Hammond Street, Suite 915
Bangor, ME 04401

Dunning, Frances
13-A North High Street
Bangor, ME 04401

Levenson, Laura
73 Pine Street
Bangor, ME 04401

Northeast Care Foundation
268 Center Street
Bangor, ME 04401

Outpatient Chemical
  Dependency Agency
185 Harlow Street
Bangor, ME 04401

Project Atrium, Inc. Janus
  House
51 Forth Street
Bangor, ME 04401

Sign of Hope Counseling
  Association
115 Franklin Street, Suite GA
Bangor, ME 04401

Tingley, Charles
248 Center Street
Bangor, ME 04401

Veterans Administration Bangor
  Clinic
304 Hancock Street, Suite 3-B
Bangor, ME 04401

Wabanaki Mental Health
  Association
277 State Street, Suite 3-B
Bangor, ME 04401

Wellspring, Inc.
Men's Program
98 Cumberland Street
Bangor, ME 04401

Outpatient Services
136 Union Street
Bangor, ME 04401

Women's Program
319 State Street
Bangor, ME 04401

BAR MILLS

Drug Rehabilitation, Inc. Day
  One Residence
James C Harrod Center
Bar Mills, ME 04004

BATH

**Midcoast Hospital Addiction
   Resource Center**
1356 Washington Street
Bath, ME 04530

BELFAST

Kelley, Karen, LSAC
143 High Street
Belfast, ME 04915

**Waldo County General Hospital
   Counseling Service**
118 Northpoint Avenue
Belfast, ME 04915

**Westbay Counseling Services,
   Inc.**
22 Spring Street
Belfast, ME 04915

BINGHAM

Health Reach Network
New Directions/Bingham
Upper Main Street
Bingham, ME 04920

BOOTHBAY HARBOR

Helmstadter, John
54 Oak Street
Boothbay Harbor, ME 04538

BRIDGTON

Danley, Colleen
Route 302
Roosevelt Trail Professional
   Building
Bridgton, ME 04009

Lake Region Counseling Center
Chase Street
Bridgton, ME 04009

**Tri-County Mental Health
   Services Substance Abuse
   Services**
41 North High Street
Bridgton, ME 04009

BRUNSWICK

Bellville Counseling Association
8 Stanwood Street
Brunswick, ME 04011

Connor, Pat
153-B Park Row
Brunswick, ME 04011-2005

**Counseling and Assistance
   Center Naval Air Station**
Building 12
Brunswick, ME 04011

BUCKSPORT

Lawrence, Suzanne, BS LSAC
505 Main Street
Bucksport, ME 04416

CALAIS

**Calais Regional Hospital
   Substance Abuse Treatment
   Facility**
50 Franklin Street
Calais, ME 04619

CAMDEN

**Midcoast Substance Abuse
   Council**
89 Elm Street
Camden, ME 04843

New Dawn Associates
88 Elm Street
Camden, ME 04843

CARIBOU

**Aroostook Mental Health Center
   Outpatient Substance Abuse
   Services**
Downtown Mall
Saint Peter Building
Caribou, ME 04736

COOPERS MILLS

Health Reach Network
New Directions/Coopers Mill
Main Street
Coopers Mills, ME 04341

DAMARISCOTTA

**Addiction Resource Center of
   Lincoln County**
Rural Route 2, Box 3-A
Damariscotta, ME 04543

DANFORTH

**Aroostook Mental Health Center
   East Grand Rural Health
   Center**
Houlton Road
Danforth, ME 04424

DOVER FOXCROFT

**Mayo Regional Hospital
   Substance Abuse Services**
75 West Main Street
Dover Foxcroft, ME 04426

EAST MILLINOCKET

Denney, Elizabeth
103 Main Street
East Millinocket, ME 04430

ELLSWORTH

Open Door Recovery Center
10 High Street
Ellsworth, ME 04605

**Substance Abuse Services of
   Ellsworth**
53 Church Street
Ellsworth, ME 04605

FARMINGTON

**Evergreen Behavioral Services
   Mount Blue Health Center**
Rural Route 4
Farmington, ME 04938

Health Reach Network
New Directions/Farmington
Farmington, ME 04938-1568

Tri-County SACS
28 High Street
Farmington, ME 04938

FORT KENT

Aroostook Mental Health Center Outpatient Substance Abuse Services
96 Market Street
Fort Kent, ME 04743

FREEPORT

Thacher, Sarah A.
102 South Freeport Road
Freeport, ME 04032

GORHAM

Southwestern Maine Associates PA
510 Main Street
Gorham, ME 04038

HALLOWELL

True, Robert A., LCSW
402 Water Street
Hallowell, ME 04347

Your Choice, Inc.
24 Wilder Street
Hallowell, ME 04347

HARTLAND

Health Reach Network
New Directions/Scott Webb Health Center
1 Great Moose Drive
Hartland, ME 04943

HINCKLEY

George Walter Associates
Route 201
Hinckley, ME 04944

HOULTON

Aroostook Mental Health Center Outpatient Substance Abuse Services
11 Riverside Street
Houlton, ME 04730

Paul, William
4 Charles Street
Houlton, ME 04730

KENNEBUNK

Ristine, Susannah
7 Blue Wave Professional Center
Kennebunk, ME 04043

KEZAR FALLS

Counseling Services, Inc. Sacopee Valley Unit
Kezar Falls, ME 04047

KINGFIELD

Health Reach Network
New Directions/Kingfield
2 Stanley Avenue
Kingfield, ME 04947

LEEDS

Health Reach Network
New Directions/Leeds
Church Hill Road
Leeds, ME 04263

LEWISTON

Catholic Charities Maine Fellowship House
95 Blake Street
Lewiston, ME 04240

Central Maine Counseling Services, Inc.
55 Lisbon Street
Lewiston, ME 04240

Iannotti, Dominick J., Addiction and Behavior Counseling
145 Lisbon Street Suite 208
Lewiston, ME 04240

Facing Change PA
4 Park Street Suite 1
Lewiston, ME 04240

Saint Mary's Regional Medical Center Chemical Dependency Service
100 Campus Avenue
Lewiston, ME 04243

Transitions Counseling, Inc.
105 Middle Street
Lewiston, ME 04240

Tri-County Substance Abuse Counseling Services
1155 Lisbon Street
Lewiston, ME 04240

LIMESTONE

Aroostook Mental Health Center Residential Treatment Facility
Route 1A
Limestone, ME 04750

LINCOLN

Riverside Community Center
43 Fleming Street
Lincoln, ME 04457

LISBON FALLS

Right Direction
679 Lisbon Road
Lisbon Falls, ME 04252

LIVERMORE FALLS

Evergreen Behavioral Services Mount Blue Health Center
80 Main Street
Livermore Falls, ME 04254

Health Reach Network
New Directions/Livermore Falls
80 Main Street
Livermore Falls, ME 04254

LUBEC

Regional Medical Center
Eastport Health Care
Substance Abuse Services
South Lubec Road
Lubec, ME 04652

MACHIAS

Cornerstone
2 Lower Main Street
Machias, ME 04654

MADAWASKA

Aroostook Mental Health Center Outpatient Substance Abuse Services
66 Fox Street
Madawaska, ME 04756

MADISON

Health Reach Network
New Directions/Madison
South Main Street
Madison, ME 04950

MEXICO

**New England Counseling
Services, Inc.**
3 Brown Street
Mexico, ME 04257

Saint Mary's Counseling Center
6 Porters Bridge Road
Mexico, ME 04257

NEWPORT

**Northeast Occupational
Exchange**
18 Main Street
Newport, ME 04953

OLD ORCHARD BEACH

Milestone Extended Care
28 Portland Avenue
Old Orchard Beach, ME 04064

PERRY

**Pleasant Point Health Center
Substance Abuse Program**
Pleasant Point Indian Health
Center
Perry, ME 04667

PITTSFIELD

**Acadia Recovery Community
Sebasticook Valley Hospital**
169 South Street
Pittsfield, ME 04967

PORTLAND

Access Team
82 Elm Street
Portland, ME 04101

Catholic Charities of Maine
Counseling Services
562 Congress Street
Portland, ME 04101

Evodia House
79 Allen Avenue
Portland, ME 04103

**Chemical Dependency Recovery
Program (CDRP)**
980 Forest Avenue, Suite 204
Portland, ME 04103

Coose, Chris
Top of the Hill Counseling
87 Saint Lawrence Street
Portland, ME 04101

Crossroads for Women
66 Pearl Street
Portland, ME 04101

Day One Outpatient Office
23 Ocean Avenue
Portland, ME 04103

Family Institute of Maine
38 Deering Street
Portland, ME 04101

**Food Addiction and Chemical
Dependency Consultant**
219 Vaughn Street, Apartment 5
Portland, ME 04102

Hood, Betsy, PA
95 High Street
Portland, ME 04101

Ingraham, Inc.
Bridge Program
54 Maple Street
Portland, ME 04101

Mainstay Program
165 Cumberland Avenue
Portland, ME 04101

Randall Place
12 Randall Street
Portland, ME 04103

McKenney Counseling Service
175 Lancaster Street
Suite 714-F
Portland, ME 04101

Milestone Foundation
65 India Street
Portland, ME 04101

Portland Public Health
389 Congress Street
Portland, ME 04101

**Recovery Center at Mercy
Hospital**
144 State Street
Portland, ME 04101

Serenity House
30 Mellen Street
Portland, ME 04101

**Transitions Counseling
Associates**
222 Saint Johns Street
Portland, ME 04102

491 Stevens Avenue
Portland, ME 04103

158 Danforth Street
Portland, ME 04101

Wellness Health Association Inc
650 Brighton Avenue
Portland, ME 04102

PRESQUE ISLE

**Aroostook Mental Health Center
Outpatient Substance Abuse
Services**
1 Edgemont Drive
Presque Isle, ME 04769

PRINCETON

**Indian Township Health Center
Human Services Division**
Passamaquoddy Tribe
Peter Dana Point
Indian Township
Princeton, ME 04668

RICHMOND

Health Reach Network
New Directions/Richmond
24 Gardiner Street
Richmond, ME 04357

ROCKLAND

Alternate Choices
81 Park Street
Rockland, ME 04841

Barnett, Amy
336 Main Street
Rockland, ME 04841

Midcoast Mental Health Center
12 Union Street
Rockland, ME 04841

Penobscot Bay Medical Center
Choice Skyward
22 White Street
Rockland, ME 04841-2931

ROCKPORT

Pyschiatric and Addiction
Recovery Center
Pen Bay Medical Center
6 Glen Cove Drive
Rockport, ME 04856-4240

RUMFORD

Rumford Community Hospital
Substance Abuse Services
420 Franklin Street
Rumford, ME 04276

SACO

Counseling Services, Inc.
333 Lincoln Street
Saco, ME 04072

Dayowl Counseling
23 Water Street
Saco, ME 04072

Transitions Counseling
Associates
5 Horton Avenue
Saco, ME 04005

SANFORD

Counseling Services, Inc.
1 High Street
Sanford, ME 04073

SCARBOROUGH

Jackson Brook Institute (JBI)
600 Roundwood Drive Box 10
Scarborough, ME 04074

SEARSPORT

Searsport Counseling Associates
7 Knox Brothers Avenue
Searsport, ME 04974

SKOWHEGAN

Corson, Donna Dearborn
Oxbow Road
Skowhegan, ME 04976

Health Reach Network
New Directions/Skowhegan
251 North Avenue
Skowhegan, ME 04976

Youth and Family Services, Inc.
Substance Abuse Program
Route 201
Skowhegan, ME 04976

SOUTH PARIS

Community Concepts, Inc.
Supported Journey
Oxford Hills High School
250 Main Street
South Paris, ME 04281

Tri-County Mental Health
Services
Oxford Hills Unit
28 East Main Street
South Paris, ME 04281

SOUTH PORTLAND

Day One
Maine Youth Center
675 West Brook Street
South Portland, ME 04106

Discovery House
400 Western Avenue
South Portland, ME 04106

Rice, Ted, Counseling and
Consultation Services
182 Highland Avenue
South Portland, ME 04106

SOUTHWEST HARBOR

Acadia Family Center
Clark Point Road
Southwest Harbor, ME 04679

STRONG

Health Reach Network
New Directions/Strong
Strong, ME 04983

THORNDIKE

Steppingstone
Rural Route 1
Thorndike, ME 04986

VAN BUREN

Aroostook Mental Health Center
Outpatient Alcoholism
Services
2 Main Street
Van Buren, ME 04785

WALDOBORO

Alternate Choices Counseling
Services
32 Friendship Street
Waldoboro, ME 04572

WATERFORD

Kimball, Elaine
Brownhill Road
Waterford, ME 04088

WATERVILLE

Health Reach Network
New Directions
8 Highwood Street
Waterville, ME 04901

WINDHAM

Crossroads for Women
114 Main Street
Windham, ME 04062

WINSLOW

Discovery House of Central
Maine
13 Bay Street
Winslow, ME 04901

YARMOUTH

World Tree Psychotherapy
261 Main Street
Yarmouth, ME 04096

YORK

Family Resource Services
15 Hospital Drive
York, ME 03909

MARYLAND

ABERDEEN

Ashley, Inc. Outpatient Program
10 Howard Street
Aberdeen, MD 21001

Abingdon

Emmorton Psych
3105 Emmorton Road
Abingdon, MD 21009

ANNAPOLIS

Addictions Services Methadone Program
2200 Somerville Road
Annapolis, MD 21401

Alcohol and Drug Programs Management, Inc.
107 Ridgely Avenue
Suite 13B
Annapolis, MD 21401

Cornerstone Care
2525 Riva Road Suite C
Annapolis, MD 21401

Pathfinder Health Services
2448 Holly Avenue Suite 200
Annapolis, MD 21401

Pathways
2620 Riva Road
Annapolis, MD 21401

Samaritan House
2610 Greenbrier Lane
Annapolis, MD 21401

Sheppard Pratt at Annapolis
147 Old Solomon Island Road
Suite 206
Annapolis, MD 21401

BALTIMORE

Adapt Cares/Primary
3101 Towanda Avenue
Baltimore, MD 21215

Addict Referral and Counseling Center, Inc. (ARCC)
21 West 25 Street
Baltimore, MD 21218

Alcohol and Drug Abuse Program
630 West Fayette Street
Room 1-106
Baltimore, MD 21202

All Addictions Treatment Center
3655-A Old Court Road, Suite 12
Baltimore, MD 21208

Alliance, Inc. SPMI/SA Day Program
9201 Philadelphia Road
Baltimore, MD 21237

Alternatives to Dependencies
518 Eastern Boulevard
Baltimore, MD 21212

40 West Chesapeake Avenue
Suite 205
Baltimore, MD 21204

Atlantic Coast Evaluation and Recovery Services
98 North Broadway Street
Suite 205
Baltimore, MD 21231

Aware
6229 North Charles Street
Building A
Baltimore, MD 21212

Awele Treatment and Rehab Clinic
2300 North Calvert Street
Suite 102
Baltimore, MD 21218

Baltimore American Indian Center, Inc. Substance Abuse and Prevention Program
113 South Broadway
Baltimore, MD 21231

Baltimore Behavioral Health, Inc.
200 South Arlington Avenue
Baltimore, MD 21223

Baltimore City Health Department
Daybreak Rehabilitation Program
Gateway Adolescent Program
2490 Giles Road
Baltimore, MD 21225

Baltimore County Office of Substance Abuse
Comprehensive Treatment
Program
401 Washington Avenue
Suite 300
Baltimore, MD 21204

Baltimore County Outpatient Cocaine Abuse Treatment Program
208 Washington Avenue
Baltimore, MD 21204

Baltimore Health System/Next Passage Drug Free Substance Abuse Counseling Services
2901 Druid Park Drive
Suite A-103
Baltimore, MD 21215

Baltimore Recovery Center Continuing Care/Aftercare
100 South Arlington Street
Baltimore, MD 21201

Baltimore Rescue Mission, Inc.
4 North Central Avenue
Baltimore, MD 21202

Bay Life Counseling Services Franklin Square at White Marsh
8114 Sandpiper Circle, Suite 116
Baltimore, MD 21236

Bright Hope House, Inc.
1611 Baker Street
Baltimore, MD 21217

Charles H Hickey Jr School Adolescent Drug Treatment Unit
2400 Cub Hill Road
Baltimore, MD 21234

Chesapeake Counseling
825 Eastern Boulevard
Baltimore, MD 21221

Comprehensive Psycho/Social Services
1401 Reisterstown Road
Suite L1
Baltimore, MD 21208

Counseling Resource Associates
6423 Frederick Avenue, Suite 3
Baltimore, MD 21228

Crossroads Centers
2 West Madison Street
Baltimore, MD 21201

Damascus House
4203 Ritchie Highway
Baltimore, MD 21225

Deaf Substance Abuse Treatment Services Family Services Foundation, Inc.
2310 North Charles Street
Baltimore, MD 21218

Dependency Recovery
26 West Pennsylvania Avenue
Baltimore, MD 21204

Echo House Multi Service Center Seekers After a New Direction (SAND)
1705 West Fayette Street
Baltimore, MD 21223

EPOCH Counseling Center
Dundalk
1107 North Point Boulevard
East Point Office Park, Suite 205
Baltimore, MD 21224

Counseling Center/East
621 East Stemmers Run Road
Baltimore, MD 21221

Counseling Center
3902 Annapolis Road
Baltimore, MD 21228

Evelyn Jordan Drug Treatment Program Walter P Carter Center
630 West Fayette Street
Room 1-135
Baltimore, MD 21201

Family Service Foundation, Inc. Substance Abuse Program
4806 Seton Drive, Suite 204
Baltimore, MD 21215

Fayette House
1319 South Fulton
Baltimore, MD 21223

First Step Inc.
8303 Liberty Road
Baltimore, MD 21244

Glass Counseling Center Intensive Outpatient Program
405 Frederick Road
Catonsville Professional Building
Baltimore, MD 21228

Glass Substance Abuse Program, Inc.
Methadone Program
821 North Eutaw Street
Suite 101
Baltimore, MD 21201

Glenwood Life Drug Abuse Treatment Program
516 Glenwood Avenue
Baltimore, MD 21212

Greater Baltimore Medical Center
Weinberg Community Health Center
1200 East Fayette Street
Baltimore, MD 21204

Harbel Prevention and Recovery Center
5807 Harford Road
Baltimore, MD 21214

Harbor Clinical Services
1055 Taylor Avenue, Suite 300
Baltimore, MD 21214

Harbour Center
924 East Baltimore Street
Baltimore, MD 21202-4739

Health Care for the Homeless, Inc.
111 Park Avenue
Baltimore, MD 21201

Help and Recovery Today, Inc. (HART, Inc.)
8200 Harford Road
Suite 200
Baltimore, MD 21234

Helping Up Mission
1029 East Baltimore Street
Baltimore, MD 21202

Institutes for Behavior Resources, Inc. (IBR) Mobile Health Services/Primary
2457 Maryland Avenue
Baltimore, MD 21224

JAI Medical Center
5010 York Road
Baltimore, MD 21212

Jewish Addiction Services Drug Abuse Services
1515 Reisterstown Road
Suite 300
Baltimore, MD 21208

Johns Hopkins Bayview Medical Center
Behavioral Pharmaceutical Research Unit
5510 Nathan Shock Drive
Baltimore, MD 21224

Center for Addiction and
    Pregnancy
Community Psychiatry Program
4940 Eastern Avenue
M F Lord Building, Suite D-2 East
Baltimore, MD 21224

Johns Hopkins Hospital
Comprehensive Women's Center
Outpatient Program
Program for Alcohol and Other
    Drug Dependency
Stop Program
911 North Broadway
Baltimore, MD 21205

**Judith P. Ritchey Youth
    Services Center**
8840 Belair Road
Baltimore, MD 21236

**Liberty Medical Center
    Substance Abuse Program
    Overcome**
3101 Towanda Avenue
Baltimore, MD 21215

**Loyola College Alcohol and
    Drug Education and
    Treatment Program**
4501 North Charles Street
Charleston 02-B
Baltimore, MD 21210

Man Alive Research, Inc.
2100 North Charles Street
Baltimore, MD 21218

**Methadone for Business
    Achievers**
821 North Eutaw Street Suite 201
Baltimore, MD 21201

**Mountain Manor Treatment
    Center**
Outpatient/Residential
3800 Frederick Avenue
Baltimore, MD 21229

New Outlook
821 North Eutaw Street
Suite 201
Baltimore, MD 21201

Nilsson House
5665 Purdue Avenue
Baltimore, MD 21239

Operation Recovery
301 Saint Paul Place Suite 812
Baltimore, MD 21202

**Peoples Community Health
    Center**
Addiction Program
3028 Greenmount Avenue
Baltimore, MD 21218

Powell Recovery Center
14 South Broadway
Baltimore, MD 21231

Quarterway Outpatient Clinic
730 Ashburton Street
Baltimore, MD 21216

Raphael, Ralph D., Ph.D., PA
21 West Road Suite 150
Baltimore, MD 21204

Re-Entry Aftercare Center
319 West Monument Street
Baltimore, MD 21201

2100 Guilford Avenue
Baltimore, MD 21218

428 East Preston Street
Baltimore, MD 21202

Reflective Treatment Center
301 North Gay Street
Baltimore, MD 21202

707 Constitution Street
Baltimore, MD 21202

**Residential Substance Abuse
    Treatment for Women**
301 North Calverton Road
Baltimore, MD 21223

**Resource Group Counseling and
    Education Center**
7801 York Road, Suite 215
Baltimore, MD 21204

S and S Counseling Service
429 Eastern Boulevard
Baltimore, MD 21221

Safe House
7 West Randall Street
Baltimore, MD 21230

**Saint Agnes Hospital Mental
    Health Clinic**
900 South Caton Avenue
Baltimore, MD

**Sinai Hospital Addiction
    Recovery Program**
2401 West Belvedere Avenue
Baltimore, MD 21215

**South Baltimore Family Health
    Center, Inc.**
631 Cherry Hill Road
Baltimore, MD 21225

**Total Health Care, Inc.
    Substance Abuse Services**
1800 North Charles Street
8th Floor
Baltimore, MD 21217

Towson Addiction Center
22 West Pennsylvania Avenue
Suite 402
Baltimore, MD 21204

**Treatment Resources for Youth
    (TRY)**
2517 North Charles Street
Baltimore, MD 21218

**Tuerk House Alcohol and Drug
    Program**
730 Ashburton Street
Baltimore, MD 21216

Turning Corners, Inc.
5200 Moravia Road
Baltimore, MD 21206

**Universal Counseling Services,
    Inc.**
101 West Read Street
Suite 422
Baltimore, MD 21201

University of Maryland
Federal Aftercare Clinic
Methadone Treatment Program
Needle Exchange Program
630 West Fayette Street
First Floor
Baltimore, MD 21201

Harambee Treatment Center
3939 Reistertown Road
Baltimore, MD 21215

Valley House
28 South Broadway
Baltimore, MD 21231

Veterans' Affairs Medical Center Substance Abuse Treatment Unit
10 North Green Street
Baltimore, MD 21201

Weisman/Kaplan Houses
2521–2523 Maryland Avenue
Baltimore, MD 21218

William Donald Schaefer House
907 Druid Lake Drive
Baltimore, MD 21217

BARSTOW

Calvert Substance Abuse Services
315 Stafford Road
Barstow, MD 20610

DWI Services, Inc. Calvert County Treatment Facility
315 Stafford Road
Barstow, MD 20610-0730

BEL AIR

Harford County Adolescent Substance Abuse Program
715 Shamrock Road
Bel Air-Lee Professional Center
Bel Air, MD 21014

Mann House, Inc.
14 Williams Street
Bel Air, MD 21014

TRW Associates
728 Bel Air Road
Suite 137
Bel Air, MD 21014

BEL ALTON

Jude House, Inc.
9505 Crain Highway South
Bel Alton, MD 20611

BOWIE

Counseling Services, Inc.
2905 Mitchellville Road
Bowie, MD 20716

BURTONSVILLE

New Horizon Health Services
4140 Sandy Spring Road
Burtonsville, MD 20866

CALIFORNIA

Walden Counseling Center
Saint Andrew's Church Road
California, MD 20619

CAMBRIDGE

Dorchester County Health Department
Addictions Program
310 Gay Street
Cambridge, MD 21613

CAPITOL HEIGHTS

Renaissance Treatment Center
601 60th Place
Capitol Heights, MD 20743

CATONSVILLE

EPOCH Counseling Center/West
800 Ingleside Avenue
Catonsville, MD 21228

CENTREVILLE

Queen Anne's County Health Department Alcohol and Drug Services
205 North Liberty Street
Centreville, MD 21617

CHELTENHAM

Cheltenham Young Women's Residential Treatment Program
11001 Frank Tippett Road
Cheltenham, MD 20623

CHESAPEAKE BEACH

Calvert County Substance Abuse Program
3819 Harbor Road
Chesapeake Beach, MD 20732

CHESTERTOWN

A. F. Whitsitt Center/ Quarterway
Sheeler Road
Chestertown, MD 21620

Publick House
114 A South Lynchburg Street
Chestertown, MD 21620

CHEVERLY

Prince George's County Health Deptartment Addictions/ Northern Region
3003 Hospital Drive
Cheverly, MD 20785

CLINTON

Counseling Services Alternatives, Inc.
7900 Old Branch Avenue
Suite 202
Clinton, MD 20735

Prince George's County Health Dept. Addictions/Southern Region
9314 Piscataway Road
Clinton, MD 20735

COCKEYSVILLE

Community Counseling and Resource Center Alcohol and Drug Treatment
10400 Ridgland Road
Cockeysville, MD 21030

COLLEGE PARK

Ethos Foundation
7309 Baltimore Avenue
Suite 217
College Park, MD 20740

Insight, Inc.
4907 Niagra Road
College Park, MD 20740

Recovery Network
6201 Greenbelt Road, Suite U-18
College Park, MD 20740

University of Maryland Health Center Alcohol and Drug Treatment
University Health Center
Suite 2106
College Park, MD 20742

COLUMBIA

Columbia Addiction Center
10774 Hickory Ridge Road
Hawthorne Industrial Park
Columbia, MD 21044

Howard County Addictions Services Center
7101 Riverwood Drive
Columbia, MD 21046

Pathfinder Health Services Substance Abuse Services
10840 Little Patuxent Parkway
Suite 203
Columbia, MD 21044

CROFTON

DWI Assessment and Counseling
1520 Birdwood Court
Crofton, MD 21114

New Way Clinic
2135 Espey Court, Suite 2
Crofton, MD 21114

CROWNSVILLE

Chrysalis House
1570 Crownsville Road
Crownsville, MD 21032

Hope House
26 Marbury Drive
Crownsville, MD 21032

Second Genesis, Inc.
107 Circle Drive
Phillips Building
Crownsville, MD 21032

CUMBERLAND

Allegany County Addictions Services
Alcohol and Drug Outpatient
12500 Willowbrook Road SE
Cumberland MD 21502

Joseph S. Massie Unit
Country Club Road
Thomas B. Finan Center Cottage Four
Cumberland, MD 21502

Lois E. Jackson Unit
10102 SE Country Club Road
Thomas B. Finan Center Cottage Three
Cumberland, MD 21502

Family Therapy Services
621 Crest Drive
Cumberland, MD 21502

DELMAR

Delmarva Counseling Center
28 East State Street
Delmar, MD 21875

DENTON

Caroline County Health Department Caroline Counseling Center
104 Franklin Street
Denton, MD 21629

DERWOOD

Metro Alcohol and Drug Abuse Services, Inc.
15719 Crabbs Branch Way
Derwood, MD 20855

DUNDALK

EPOCH Counseling Center/ Southeast
7701 Dunman Way
Dundalk, MD 21222

EAST NEW MARKET

Charter Behavioral Health Systems
3680 Warwick Road
East New Market, MD 21631

EASTON

Shore Behavioral Health Services
29515 Canvas Back Drive, Suite A
Easton, MD 21601

Talbot County Addictions Program
100 South Hanson Street
Easton, MD 21601

ELDERSBURG

Metwork Health Service, Inc.
2120-A Liberty Road
Eldersburg, MD 21784

ELKTON

Cecil County Health Department Alcohol and Drug Center
401 Bow Street
Elkton, MD 21921

Haven House, Inc.
Outpatient Unit
111 East Main Street, Suite A
Elkton, MD 21921

1195 Augustine Herman Highway
Elkton, MD 21921

ELLICOTT CITY

Charter Behavioral Health System Warwick Manor at Columbia
4785 Dorsey Hall Road, Suite 118
Ellicott City, MD 21042

Counseling Resources
8388 Court Avenue Wall Building
Ellicott City, MD 21043

Jael Health Services
10176 Baltimore National Pike
Suite 115
Ellicott City, MD 21042

Montgomery General Hospital Outpatient Addiction Treatment Services
2850 North Ridge Road, Suite 207
Ellicott City, MD 21043

Taylor Manor Hospital Dual Diagnosis Program
4100 College Avenue
Ellicott City, MD 21041

EMMITSBURG

Mountain Manor Safe Harbor Project Potomac Health Services for Pregnant Clients
Route 15 and Keysville Road
Emmitsburg, MD 21727

Mountain Manor Treatment Center Emmitsburg Rehabilitation/Outpatient
Route 15
Emmitsburg, MD 21727

FORESTVILLE

Children and Parent Programs
5408 Silver Hill Road, 5th Floor
Forestville, MD 20747

Comprehensive Alcohol/Drug Counseling Service, Inc.
2810 Walters Lane
Room 10
Forestville, MD 20747

Prince Georges County Health Department Addictions/ Central Region
5408 Silver Hill Road, First Floor
Forestville, MD 20747

FORT GEORGE G. MEADE

Kimbroush Ambulatory Care Center Substance Abuse Rehab Clinic
85th Medical Battalion Avenue
Fort George G Meade, MD 20755

FORT HOWARD

Veterans' Affairs Maryland Health Care System
9600 North Point Road
Building 51
Fort Howard, MD 21052

FREDERICK

Allied Counseling Group Drug and Alcohol Treatment
306 West Patrick Street
Frederick, MD 21701

Catoctin Counseling Center
250 West Patrick Street
Frederick, MD 21701

Crossroad Center
176 Thomas Johnson Drive
Suite 104
Frederick, MD 21702

Frederick County Substance Abuse Services
300 B Scholls Lane
Frederick, MD 21702

Gale House, Inc.
Gale House
336 North Market Street
Frederick, MD 21701

Olson House
608 East Patrick Street
Frederick, MD 21701

Guidelines Counseling Program, Inc.
309 West Patrick Street
Frederick, MD 21701

Mountain Manor Treatment Center Outpatient Services
137 North Market Street
Suite 2A
Frederick, MD 21701

FROSTBURG

Frostburg State University
Substance Abuse Facts and
Education Program (SAFE)
Compton 017
Frostburg, MD 21532

GAITHERSBURG

Circle Treatment Center
424 North Frederick Avenue
Suite 8A
Gaithersburg, MD 20877

Ethos Foundation
19638 Clubhouse Road
Suite 215
Gaithersburg, MD 20878

Guide Program, Inc.
Adolescent Treatment Program
1 West Deer Park Drive
Room 101
Gaithersburg, MD 20877

Adult Program
1 West Deer Park Drive
Room 401
Gaithersburg, MD 20877

GERMANTOWN

Alcohol/Drug Education Counseling Center
20120 Timber Oak Lane
Germantown, MD 20874

GLEN BURNIE

Alcohol and Drug Programs Management, Inc.
7495 Baltimore-Annapolis
Boulevard
Glen Burnie, MD 21061

Anne Arundel County Health Department
Addictions Services/Adolescent and Family
407 South Crain Highway
2nd Floor
Glen Burnie, MD 21060

Addictions Services/Drug Intervention
7495 Baltimore Annapolis
Boulevard
Suite 200
Glen Burnie, MD 21060

Ejal Health Services, Inc.
550 Crain Highway Unit 8
Glen Burnie, MD 21061

Recovery Resources Group, Inc.
2-B Crain Highway SW
Glen Burnie, MD 21061

Transformation
407 South Crain Highway
Suite 101
Glen Burnie, MD 21061

We Care Arundel Health Service, Inc.
13 Aquahart Road, Suite A
Glen Burnie, MD 21061

GRANTSVILLE

Meadow Mountain Drug Treatment Program
234 Recovery Road
Grantsville, MD 21536

HAGERSTOWN

Behavioral Health Services of Washington County Health Systems
1198 Kenly Avenue Suite 101
Hagerstown, MD 21740

Catoctin Counseling Center
162 West Washington Street
Hagerstown, MD 21740

Functional Social Work, Inc. Drug and Alcohol Treatment Unit
10401 Sharpsburg Pike
Hagerstown, MD 21740

Jail Substance Abuse Program (JSAP) Aftercare
13126 Pennsylvania Avenue
Hagerstown, MD 21742

W House, Inc.
37 East Antietam Street
Hagerstown, MD 21740

Washington County Health Department
Comprehensive Addiction Program
1302 Pennsylvania Avenue
Hagerstown, MD 21742

Jail Substance Abuse Program
500 Western Maryland Parkway
Hagerstown, MD 21740

Intensive Substance Abuse Program
13126 Pennsylvania Avenue
Hagerstown, MD 21742

Wells House Residential Facility
324 North Locust Street
Hagerstown, MD 21740

HAVRE DE GRACE

Ashley, Inc. Quarterway Unit
800 Tydings Lane
Havre de Grace, MD 21078

SAFE Associates Inc
420 South Stokes Street
Havre De Grace, MD 21078

HUNTINGTOWN

Courage to Change Counseling Program
4020 Hidden Hill Drive
Huntingtown, MD 20639

HYATTSVILLE

Prince George's County Health Department Center for Addiction and Pregnancy
3003 Hospital Drive
Hyattsville, MD 20781

JESSUP

Clifton T. Perkins Hospital Center Alcohol and Drug Abuse Services
8450 Dorsey Run Road
Jessup, MD 20794

Regimented Offender Treatment Center for Men
Jessup, MD 20794

JOPPA

Joppa Health Services, Inc.
623-A Pulaski Highway
Joppa, MD 21085

LANHAM

Kolmac Clinic
7726 Finns Lane, Suite 101
Lanham, MD 20706

LAUREL

Act II Counseling Services, Inc.
379 Main Street, Suite 4
Laurel, MD 20707

Counseling Services, Inc.
150 Washington Boulevard
Suite 200
Laurel, MD 20707

Flynn/Lang Counseling Center
13 C Street, Suite H
Laurel, MD 20707

Mental Health and Addiction Services Laurel Regional Hospital
7300 Van Dusen Road
Laurel, MD 20707

Reality, Inc.
Aftercare
Quarterway House
419 Main Street
Laurel, MD 20707

Continuing Care Facility
429 Main Street
Laurel, MD 20707

We Care Health Services Inc
8730-1 Cherry Lane
Laurel, MD 20707

LEONARDTOWN

Marcey Halfway House
Leonardtown, MD 20650

LUSBY

Calvert County Substance Abuse Program South Maryland Community Center
20 Appeal Lane
Lusby, MD 20657

LUTHERVILLE TIMONIUM

Awakenings Counseling Program
2 West Aylesbury Road
Lutherville Timonium, MD 21093

MILLERSVILLE

Comprehensive Treatment Center of Maryland
1110 Benfield Boulevard I-97
Business Park, Suite H Front
Millersville, MD 21108

MOUNT RAINIER

C. A. Mayo and Associates, Inc.
3403 Perry Street
Mount Rainier, MD 20712

NEW CARROLTON

Awele Social Health Clinic, Inc.
7515 Annapolis Road, Suite 406
New Carrollton, MD 20784

OAKLAND

Garrett County Health Department Addictions Service
221 South 3 Street
Oakland, MD 21550

ODENTON

Ferry Point, Inc. Treatment Center
8379 Piney Orchard Parkway
Odenton, MD 21113

OWINGS MILLS

Phoenix Counseling and Consulting Services, Inc.
10806 Reisterstown Road
Suite 1-B
Owings Mills, MD 21117

Right Turn of Maryland, LLC
10225 Jensen Lane
Owings Mills, MD 21117

PASADENA

New Life Addiction Counseling Services
2528 Mountain Road
Pasadena, MD 21122

PATUXENT RIVER

Counseling and Assistance Center
47096 Liljencrantz Road
Building 438
Patuxent River, MD 20670

PERRY POINT

VA Medical Center Substance Abuse Treatment Program
Building 22
Perry Point, MD 21902

PRINCE FREDERICK

Calvert Substance Abuse Services New Leaf Counseling Center
Route 4 and Stokely Road
Prince Frederick, MD 20678

RANDALLSTOWN

First Step Inc/Northwest Area Program Family Resource Center
3525 Resource Drive
Randallstown, MD 21133

ROCKVILLE

Avery House Halfway House for Women and Children
14705 Avery Road
Rockville, MD 20853

Avery Road Treatment Center
Detoxification Program
Intermediate Care Facility
14703 Avery Road
Rockville, MD 20853

Charter Behavioral Health System at Potomac Ridge
14901 Broschart Road
Rockville, MD 20850

Jail Addictions Services
1307 Seven Locks Road
Rockville, MD 20850

Montgomery County Department of Health and Human Services
The Other Way Day Treatment Program
401 Fleet Street
Rockville, MD 20850

Outpatient Addiction Services
751 Twinbrook Parkway
Rockville, MD 20851

Lawrence Court Halfway House
1 Lawrence Court
Rockville, MD 20850

Montgomery Recovery Services, Inc.
14636 Rothgeb Drive
Rockville, MD 20850

OACES Corporation
330A Hungerford Drive
Rockville, MD 20850

Second Genesis, Inc. Montgomery County
14701 Avery Road
Rockville, MD 20853

Suburban Hospital Addiction Treatment Center
6001 Montrose Road, Suite 205
Rockville, MD 20850

White Flint Recovery, Inc.
1335 Rockville Pike
Suite 106
Rockville, MD 20852

SABILLASVILLE

Catoctin Summit Adolescent Program
5980 Cullen Drive
Sabillasville, MD 21780

SALISBURY

Hudson Health Services, Inc.
Willis Hudson Alcohol and Drug Treatment Center
1506 Harting Drive
Salisbury, MD 21802

Peninsula Addiction Services
104 West Market Street
Salisbury, MD 21801

Peninsula Regional Medical Center
100 East Carroll Street
Salisbury, MD 21801-5493

Second Wind, Inc.
309 Newton Street
Salisbury, MD 21801

Wicomico Behavioral Health
108 East Main Street
Salisbury, MD 21801

SEVERNA PARK

Stress and Health Management Center Inc.
540 Ritchie Highway
Suite 101
Severna Park, MD 21146

SILVER SPRING

Another Way, Inc.
11308 Grandview Avenue
2nd Floor
Silver Spring, MD 20902-4634

Bilingual Counseling Center
2419 Reedie Drive Suite 201
Silver Spring, MD 20902

D. A. Wynne and Associates Inc.
1709 Elton Road
Silver Spring, MD 23903

**Guide Program, Inc. Adult
    Treatment Services**
11141 Georgia Avenue, Suite 420
Silver Spring, MD 20902

Kolmac Clinic
1003 Spring Street
Silver Spring, MD 20910

Saint Luke Institute
8901 New Hampshire Avenue
Silver Spring, MD 20903

**Second Genesis, Inc. Outpatient
    Adolescent Family Services**
1721 Elton Road
Silver Spring, MD 20901

**Thomas Comp. Counseling
    Services, Inc.**
800 Pershing Drive
Suite 105A
Silver Spring, MD 20910

SNOW HILL

**Worcester County Center for a
    Clean Start**
Snow Hill, MD 21863

**Worcester County Health
    Department Alcohol and
    Other Drug Services**
6040 Public Landing Road
Snow Hill, MD 21863

SUITLAND

**Prince Georges County Health
    Department Addictions/
    Northern Region**
5408 Silver Hill Road, Room 213
Suitland, MD 20747

SYKESVILLE

Adapt Counseling Incorporated
1643 Liberty Road Suite 204
Sykesville, MD 21784

**Clinical Services Program
    Residential Substance Abuse
    Treatment**
Central Laundry Facility
Sykesville, MD 21784

Shoemaker Center
6655 Buttercup Road
Sykesville, MD 21784

Women's Project
6655 Buttercup Road
Sykesville, MD 21784

TAKOMA PARK

Washington Adventist Hospital
7600 Carroll Avenue
Takoma Park, MD 20912

THURMONT

Catoctin Counseling Center
18 North Church Street
Thurmont, MD 21788

TOWSON

Pathfinder Health Services
300 East Joppa Road, Suite 303
Towson, MD 21286

Towson University
8000 York Road
Towson, MD 21252-0001

UPPER MARLBORO

**Another Spring Counseling
    Services**
5302 Water Street, Suite 204
Upper Marlboro, MD 20772

**Drinking Driver Monitor
    Program**
14735 Main Street
PG County Courthouse
Room 068-B
Upper Marlboro, MD 20772

**Institute of Life and Health
    Alcohol andDrug Assessment
    and Therapy Program**
5311 Water Street, Suite D
Upper Marlboro, MD 20772

Second Genesis, Inc.
Mellwood House
4620 Mellwood Road
Upper Marlboro, MD 20772

VALLEY LEE

**Seafarers Addiction
    Rehabilitation Center**
45705 Locust Grove Drive
Valley Lee, MD 20692

WALDORF

**Charles County Health
    Department Substance Abuse
    Program**
2670 Crain Highway, Site 300
Waldorf, MD 20604

**Mid Atlantic Mental Health
    Center, Inc. QUIT Program**
2 Industrial Park Drive, Suite B
Waldorf, MD 20602

Open Arms, Inc.
2590 Business Park Court
Waldorf, MD 20601-2904

WESTMINSTER

**Carroll County Health
    Department**
Bureau of Addiction Outpatient
    Treatment Services
290 South Center Street
Westminster, MD 21157

**Junction, Inc. Drug and Alcohol
    Abuse Treatment Program**
98 North Court Street
Westminster, MD 21157

**Mountain Manor Treatment
    Center**
Carroll Plaza, Suite 2
Westminster, MD 21158

Reentry Mental Health Services Addiction Services
40 South Church Street
Suite 105
Westminster, MD 21157

Westminster Rescue Mission
685 Lucabaugh Mill Road
Westminster, MD 21157

WESTOVER

Somerset County Health Department Behavioral Health Services
7920 Crisfield Highway
Westover, MD 21871

WHEATON

Counseling Plus, Inc.
11141 Georgia Avenue, Suite A-24
Wheaton, MD 20902

MASSACHUSETTS

ALLSTON

Granada House, Inc
70 Adamson Street
Allston, MA 02134

ATTLEBORO

The Road Back
7 Forest Street
Attleboro, MA 02703

BEDFORD

Veterans' Affairs Addiction Treatment Center
200 Springs Road
Room 116 A
Bedford, MA 01730

BELMONT

McLean Hospital Alcohol and Drug Abuse Treatment Center
115 Mill Street
Appleton Building
Belmont, MA 02178

BEVERLY

Leland Unit Beverly Hospital
85 Herrick Street
Beverly, MA 01915

BOSTON

Bay Cove Human Services
66 Canal Street
Boston, MA 02111

Boston Alcohol and Substance Abuse Program
30 Winter Street
Boston, MA 02108

Boston Childrens Services Alcohol/Drug Use Assessment and Treatment Program
271 Huntington Avenue
Boston, MA 02116

Boston Public Health Commission
Acupuncture Clinic
Addiction Services
Outpatient Counseling
723 Massachusetts Avenue
Boston, MA 02118

Bridge Over Troubled Waters, Inc.
Youth Intervention Program
47 West Street
Boston, MA 02111

Entre Familia
1010 Massachusetts Avenue
Boston, MA 02118

Fenway Community Health Center
Acupuncture Detoxification Clinic
Outpatient Substance Abuse Services
7 Haviland Street
Boston, MA 02115

Harvard Vanguard Medical Associates
23 Miner Street
Boston, MA 02215

Justice Resource Institute Health Division
130 Boylston Street
Boston, MA 02116

Latino Health Institute Substance Abuse Clinic
95 Berkeley Street
Boston, MA 02116

Marathon Acute Treatment Services
Administration Building, 2nd Floor
Long Island Health Campus
Boston, MA 02122

Massachusetts General Hospital Addiction Services/Outpatient
15 Blossom Street
Boston, MA 02114

Span, Inc.
110 Arlington Street
Boston, MA 02116

Spaulding Rehabilitation Hospital
125 Nashua Street
Boston, MA 02114

Veterans' Affairs Medical Center Substance Abuse Treatment Program
251 Causeway Street
Boston, MA 02130

BRAINTREE

Family Counseling and Guidance Center
40 Independence Avenue
Braintree, MA 02184

BRIGHTON

Addiction Treatment Center of New England, Inc. Methadone Services
77 Warren Street
Brighton, MA 02135

Saint Elizabeth's Hospital Comprehensive Alcohol and Addiction Program
736 Cambridge Street
Cardinal Cushing Building
Brighton, MA 02135

BROCKTON

Brockton Hospital Substance Abuse Services
680 Center Street
Brockton, MA 02302

Catholic Charities
Edwina Martin Recovery House
678 North Main Street
Brockton, MA 02401

Alcohol Detox
Outpatient Services
Substance Abuse Services
Resurrection House
686 North Main Street
Brockton, MA 02401

MSPCC Family Counseling Center Outpatient Substance Abuse Services
231 Main Street
Brockton, MA 02401

Old Colony Services Corporation Mental Health Clinic
15-A Bolton Place
Brockton, MA 02401

South Bay Mental Health Center
37 Belmont Street
Brockton, MA 02401

Veterans' Affairs Medical Center Alcohol and Drug Dependence Program
940 Belmont Street
Brockton, MA 02401

BROOKLINE

Bournewood Health Systems
300 South Street
Brookline, MA 02467-3694

CAMBRIDGE

Caspar, Inc.
Outpatient Program
126 Prospect Street
Cambridge, MA 02139

Womanplace Halfway House for Women
11 Russell Street
Cambridge, MA 02140

CHARLESTOWN

John F. Kennedy Family Service Center, Inc. Outpatient Substance Abuse Services
27 Winthrop Street
Boston (Charlestown), MA 02129

CHELSEA

Bay Cove Human Services
Chelsea Substance Abuse Clinic
100 Everett Avenue
Unit 4
Chelsea, MA 02150

CHICOPEE

Community Health Care, Inc. Community Substance Abuse Centers
628 Center Street
Chicopee, MA 01013

CLINTON

Clinton Hospital
201 Highland Street
Clinton, MA 01510

CONCORD

Assabet Human Services, Inc. Outpatient Substance Abuse Services
Damonmill Square
Suite 2A
Concord, MA 01742

Emerson Hospital Aftercare Addiction Services/Outpatient
133 Old Road to Nine Acre Corner
Concord, MA 01742

DANVERS

Cab Health and Recovery Services, Inc.
Inpatient Detox Unit
Opiate Addiction Treatment Services
Residential Intermediate Care Facility
111 Middleton Road
Danvers, MA 01923

DORCHESTER

Boston Hamilton House, Inc. Hamilton Recovery Home
25 Mount Ida Road
Dorchester, MA 02122

Carney Hospital Drug and Alcohol Program/Outpatient Psychiatry
2100 Dorchester Avenue
Dorchester, MA 02124

Codman Square Health Center Outpatient Substance Abuse Services
637 Washington Street
Dorchester, MA 02124

Dorchester House
1353 Dorchester Avenue
Dorchester, MA 02122

Federal Dorchester Neighborhood Houses
Little House/Outpatient
Youth Assistance
275 East Cottage Street
Dorchester, MA 02125

First Hispanic Academy
632 Blue Hill Avenue
Dorchester, MA 02121-3213

First, Inc.
First Step
Outpatient Services
321 Blue Hill Avenue
Dorchester, MA 02121

Interim House, Inc. Recovery Home
62 Waldeck Street
Dorchester, MA 02124

Victory Programs, Inc.
New Victories/Recovery Home
9 Virginia Street
Dorchester, MA 02125

Shepherd House
22 and 24 Windermere Road
Dorchester, MA 02125

Womens Hope
10 Chamblet Street
Dorchester, MA 02125

EAST BOSTON

North Suffolk Mental Health
408 Meridian Street
East Boston, MA 02128

Rehabilitation and Health, Inc. Recovery Home
52 White Street
East Boston, MA 02128

EVERETT

Tri City Mental Health and Retardation Center, Inc.
173 Chelsea Street
Everett, MA 02149

FALL RIVER

Family Service Assoc. of Greater Fall River Outpatient Substance Abuse Services
151 Rock Street
Fall River, MA 02720

Portuguese Youth Cultural Organization
Outpatient Substance Abuse Services
186 South Main Street
Fall River, MA 02721

Stanley Street Treatment and Resources
Alcoholism/Drug Detox Program
Chemical Dependency Services/ Outpatient
Women's Rehab Program
386 Stanley Street
Fall River, MA 02720

Steppingstone, Inc.
Halfway House
466 North Main Street
Fall River, MA 02720

Outpatient Substance Abuse Services
101 Rock Street
Fall River, MA 02720

Therapeutic Community
522 North Main Street
Fall River, MA 02720

FALMOUTH

CCAIRU Gosnold Counseling Center
Outpatient Substance Abuse Services
196 Ter Heun Drive
Falmouth, MA 02540

Cape Cod Detoxification Center
200 Ter Heun Drive
Falmouth, MA 02540

Stephen Miller House Recovery Home
165 Woods Hole Road
Falmouth, MA 02540

FITCHBURG

Luk Crisis Center, Inc. Youth Assistance Program
99 Day Street
Fitchburg, MA 01420

FLORENCE

Cooley Dickinson Hospital Outpatient Behavioral Health Services
10 Main Street
Florence, MA 01062

FRAMINGHAM

Farmingham Detox Program
3 Merchant Road
Framingham, MA 01704-0606

Genesis Counseling Services, Inc.
24 Union Avenue, Suite 11
Framingham, MA 01702

New England Aftercare Ministries, Inc. The Bridge House/Halfway House
18–20 Summit Street
Framingham, MA 01701

South Middlesex Opportunity Council Behavioral Health Services
1100 Wooster Road, 4th Floor
Framingham, MA 01701

Victory Programs, Inc. Women's Hope Center
Loring Avenue
Framingham, MA 01701

Wayside Metrowest Counseling Center
88 Lincoln Street
Framingham, MA 01701

GARDNER

Gardner Athol Area Mental Health Association, Inc. Pathway House
34 Catherine Street
Gardner, MA 01440

North Central Human Services
31 Lake Street
Gardner, MA 01440

GEORGETOWN

Baldpate Hospital Outpatient Services
Baldpate Road
Georgetown, MA 01833

GLOUCESTER

Health and Education Services
298 Washington Street
Gloucester, MA 01930

GREENFIELD

Franklin Medical Center
Beacon Clinic
60 Wells Street
Greenfield, MA 01301

Beacon Recovery Center
164 High Street
Greenfield, MA 01301

Beacon House for Men/Recovery
House
57 Beacon Street
Greenfield, MA 01301

Beacon House for Women/
Recovery House
153 High Street
Greenfield, MA 01301

HANSCOM AFB

**Hanscom Air Force Base
Substance Abuse Program**
66 MDOS/SGOFH 90 Vandenberg
Drive
Hanscom AFB, MA 01731

HAVERHILL

Team Coordinating Agency, Inc.
Community Outreach
Outpatient Substance Abuse
Services
66-76 Winter Street
Haverhill, MA 01831

Phoenix East
20 Newcomb Street
Haverhill, MA 01831

Youth Assistance Program
350 Main Street
Haverhill, MA 01831

HINGHAM

Project Turnabout
224 Beal Street
Hingham, MA 02043

HOLYOKE

**Holyoke Hospital Partial
Hospitalization IOUTPT
Program**
575 Beech Street
Holyoke, MA 01040

**MSPCC Family Counseling
Center Outpatient Substance
Abuse Services**
113 Hampden Street
Holyoke, MA 01040

Providence Hospital
1233 Main Street
Holyoke, MA 01040

Substance Abuse Outpatient
Programs
317 Maple Street
Holyoke, MA 01040

Honor House
40 Brightside Drive
Holyoke, MA 01040

HOPKINTON

**SMOC Behavioral Health
Services Serenity House**
44 Wilson Street
Hopkinton, MA 01748

HYANNIS

Cape Cod Human Services
Outpatient Substance Abuse
Services
460 West Main Street
Hyannis, MA 02601

**CCAIRU, Inc. Transitional Care
Facility**
71 Pleasant Street
Hyannis, MA 02601

JAMAICA PLAIN

**Arbour Substance Abuse
Program**
49 Robinwood Avenue
Jamaica Plain, MA 02130

**Boston Alcohol Detox Project,
Inc.**
170 Morton Street
Jamaica Plain, MA 02130

Brigham and Women's Hospital
Brookside Community Health
Center
3297 Washington Street
Jamaica Plain, MA 02130

South Jamaica Plain Health Center
FACTS Program
687 Centre Street
Jamaica Plain, MA 02130

**Faulkner Hospital Addiction
Recovery Program**
1153 Centre Street
Jamaica Plain, MA 02130

Sullivan House
65 Glenn Road
Jamaica Plain, MA 02130

**Veterans Affairs Medical Center
Substance Abuse Treatment
Program**
150 South Huntington Avenue
Jamaica Plain, MA 02130-1831

**Volunteers of America
Outpatient Clinic**
441 Centre Street
Jamaica Plain, MA 02130

LAWRENCE

Arbour Counseling Services
599 Canal Street
1 East
Lawrence, MA 01840

**Centro Panamericano, Inc.
Substance Abuse Outpatient
Services**
101 Amesbury Road
Suite 402
Lawrence, MA 01841

Family Services, Inc.
430 North Canal Street
Lawrence, MA 01840

**Greater Lawrence Mental
Health Center, Inc.**
30 General Street
Lawrence, MA 01841-0007

Habit Management Institute
599 Canal Street
Lawrence, MA 01840

Psychological Center
1 South Union Street
Lawrence, MA 01840

Pegasus Youth Residence
482 Lowell Street
Lawrence, MA 01840

Women's View
582–584 Haverhill Street
Lawrence, MA 01841

LEOMINSTER

Community Health and Prevention Services
Detoxification Center
17 Orchard Street
Leominster, MA 01453

Outpatient Counseling
71 Pleasant Street
Leominster, MA 01453

LOWELL

Center for Family Development
45 Merrimack Street
Lowell, MA 01850

Family Service of Greater Lowell
97 Central Street
Suite 400
Lowell, MA 01852

Habit Management Institute
650 Suffolk Street
Lowell, MA 01854

Lowell Community Health Center, Inc. Community Health Initiatives/Outpatient
685 Lawrence Street
Lowell, MA 01852

Lowell House, Inc.
Outpatient Substance Abuse Services
555 Merrimack Street
Lowell, MA 01854

Residential Services
102 Appleton Street
Lowell, MA 01852

LYNN

Center for Addictive Behaviors, Inc.
Ryan Rehabilitation Center
100 Green Street
Lynn, MA 01902

Lynn Community Health Center
269 Union Street
Lynn, MA 01901

Project Cope
Outpatient Substance Abuse Services
117 North Common Street
Lynn, MA 01902

Willow Street Medical Center
100 Willow Street
Lynn, MA 01901

MALDEN

Adult/Adolescent Counseling, Inc.
389 Main Street
Malden, MA 02148

Eastern Middlesex Alcoholism Services
Recovery House
12 Cedar Street
Malden, MA 02148

HRI Counseling Centers, Inc.
DBA Arbour Counseling Services
Recovery Network
6 Pleasant Street
Malden, MA 02148

MARBLEHEAD

Marblehead Counseling Center, Inc. Outpatient Substance Abuse Program
66 Clifton Avenue
Marblehead, MA 01945

MARLBOROUGH

UMASS Memorial Healthcare
Psychiatric and Addictions Services
57 Union Street
Marlborough, MA 01752

Advocates, Inc. Community Counseling
133 East Main Street
Marlborough, MA 01752

MARSHFIELD

North River Counseling, Inc.
769 Plain Street, Suite 1
Marshfield, MA 02050

MATTAPAN

Marathon, Inc.
River Street Detoxification Center
Stair Program
249 River Street
Mattapan, MA 02126

MIDDLEBORO

Community Care Services
94 South Main Street
Middleboro, MA 02346

MILFORD

Wayside Community Counseling Center
Substance Abuse Program
10 Asylum Street
Milford, MA 01757

NANTUCKET

Family and Children's Service/ Nantucket Outpatient Substance Abuse Services
Off Vesper Lane
Nantucket, MA 02554

NATICK

Metro West Medical Center
67 Union Street
Natick, MA 01760

NEW BEDFORD

Center for Health and Human Services
Outpatient Alcohol and Drug Program
800 Purchase Street
Suite 350
New Bedford, MA 02740

Methadone Services
88–90 Gifford Street
New Bedford, MA 02741

Marcotic Treatment Program
86 Gifford Street
New Bedford, MA 02741

Harmony House
234 Earle Street
New Bedford, MA 02746

**New Bedford Child and Family
Services**
1061 Pleasant Street
New Bedford, MA 02740

**Professional Counseling Center
Outpatient Substance Abuse
Services**
466 County Street
New Bedford, MA 02740

NEWBURYPORT

John Ashford Link House
37 Washington Street
Newburyport, MA 01950

**Turning Point, Inc. Outpatient
Substance Abuse Counseling**
5 Perry Way
Newburyport, MA 01950

NEWTON

Newton Outpatient Center
64 Eldredge Street
Newton, MA 02456

NORFOLK

**Caritas Southwood Hospital
Outpatient Substance Abuse
Services**
111 Dedham Street, Route 1-A
Norfolk, MA 02056

NORTH ADAMS

**North Adams Regional Hospital
Substance Abuse Services**
Hospital Avenue
North Adams, MA 01247

NORTHAMPTON

**Community Health Care, Inc.
Substance Abuse Center**
297 Pleasant Street
Northampton, MA 01060

**Veterans' Affairs Medical Center
Substance Abuse Treatment
Program**
421 North Main Street
Northampton, MA 01060

NORTHBOROUGH

**Northborough Family and
Youth Services Outpatient
Substance Abuse Services**
63 Main Street
Northborough, MA 01532

NORTH DARTMOUTH

**Saint Lukes Hospital
Psychiatric Outpatient
Services**
74 Faunce Corner
North Dartmouth, MA 02747

NORTON

**North Cottage Program, Inc.
Halfway House**
69 East Main Street
Norton, MA 02766

OAK BLUFFS

**Martha's Vineyard Community
Services Island Counseling
Center/Outpatient**
Off Edgartown/Vineyard Haven
Road
Oak Bluffs, MA 02557

PITTSFIELD

**Berkshire Medical Center
Hillcrest Hospital Thomas W.
McGee Unit**
165 Tor Court
Pittsfield, MA 01201

**Mental Health and Substance
Abuse Services of the
Berkshires**
131 Bradford Street
Pittsfield, MA 01202

Keenan House Recovery Home
206 Francis Avenue
Pittsfield, MA 01201

PLYMOUTH

**Center for Health and Human
Services/AFR**
71 Christa McAuliffe Boulevard
Plymouth, MA 02360

High Point Treatment Center
Detox, Outpatient, STIT Programs
1233 State Road
Plymouth, MA 02360

QUINCY

**Bay State Community Services,
Inc.**
Outpatient Substance Abuse
Service
15 Cottage Avenue
Quincy, MA 02169

**Quincy Detoxification Center,
Inc. DBA Faxon Recovery
Service**
120 Whitwell Street
Quincy, MA 02169

South Shore Halfway House
10 Dysart Street
Quincy, MA 02169

**South Shore Mental Health
Center Outpatient Substance
Abuse Program**
6 Fort Street
Quincy, MA 02169

**Spectrum Health Systems, Inc.
Right Turn**
1458 Hancock Street
Quincy, MA 02169

ROXBURY

Boston Public Health Commission Narcotic Addiction Clinic/Methadone Services
300 Frontage Road
Roxbury, MA 02118

Casa Esperanza, Inc.
291 Eustis Street
Roxbury, MA 02119

Dimock Community Health Center
Alcohol and Drug Detox Program
John Flowers Recovery Home
Substance Abuse Services
55 Dimock Street
Roxbury, MA 02119

Habit Management, Inc. Boston Methadone Services
99 Topeka Street
Roxbury, MA 02119

Hope House, Inc. Recovery Home
42 Upton Street and 24 Hanson Street
Roxbury, MA 02118

La Alianza Hispana, Inc. Outpatient Services
409 Dudley Street
Roxbury, MA 02119

Roxbury Comprehensive Community Health Center, Inc. Methadone Services
435 Warren Street
Roxbury, MA 02119

Salvation Army Harbor Light Center
407 Shawmut Avenue
Roxbury, MA 02118

Tecumseh House Drop In Center
107 Fisher Avenue
Roxbury, MA 02120

Victory Programs, Inc.
Victory House/Recovery Home
566 Massachusetts Avenue
Roxbury, MA 02118

Volunteers of America Hello House
686 Massachusetts Avenue
Roxbury, MA 02118

SALEM

Cab Health and Recovery Systems
27 Congress Street
Salem, MA 01970

Health and Education Services Outpatient Substance Abuse Program
162 Federal Street
Salem, MA 01970

North Shore Medical Center Addictive Disease Unit
81 Highland Avenue
Salem, MA 01970

Salem Hospital Addictive Disease Program/Outpatient
172 Lafayette Street
Salem Hospital/Professional Services Building
Salem, MA 01970

SOMERVILLE

Cambridge Health Alliance
26 Central Street
Somerville, MA 02143

Caspar, Inc.
Alcohol and Drug Education
Youth Assistance
226 Highland Avenue
Somerville, MA 02143

Intervention/Detox
245 Beacon Street
Somerville, MA 02143

Men's Recovery Home
16 Highland Avenue
Somerville, MA 02143

9 Kidder Avenue
Somerville, MA 02144

New Day
242 Highland Avenue
Somerville, MA 02143

Central Street Health Center
26 Central Street
Somerville, MA 02143

Mass Alliance of Portuguese Speakers
Acupuncture Services
Outpatient Substance Abuse Services
92 Union Square
Somerville, MA 02143

North Charles Institute
Outpatient Substance Abuse Services
260 Beacon Street
Somerville, MA 02143

Somerville Mental Health Assoc, Inc.
5 Hall Avenue
Somerville, MA 02144

SOUTH BOSTON

Arch Foundation, Inc.
675 East 4 Street
South Boston, MA 02127

Middlesex Human Services Agency
5 G Street
South Boston, MA 02127

SOUTHBRIDGE

Harrington Memorial Hospital
Wells Human Services Center
29 Pine Street
Southbridge, MA 01550

Youth Opportunities Upheld, Inc. Family Services/Youth Program
52 Charlton Street
Southbridge, MA 01550

SOUTH YARMOUTH

Habit Management Institute/ Yarmouth Methadone Services
20 Forsyth Street
South Yarmouth, MA 02664

SPRINGFIELD

Bay State Medical Center
Carlson Recovery Center
Sloan Clinic
471 Chestnut Street
Springfield, MA 01199

Opportunity House
59–61 Saint James Avenue
Springfield, MA 01109

Women's Division/My Sisters
House
89 Belmont Avenue
Springfield, MA 01108

Child and Family Service, Inc.
367 Pine Street
Springfield, MA 01105

Gandara Center
Addiction Recovery Program
29-33 Arch Street
Springfield, MA 01107

Mental Health and Substance
Abuse
2155 Main Street
Springfield, MA 01104

Habit Management Institute
2257 Main Street
Springfield, MA 01107

Marathon, Inc.
5 Madison Avenue
Springfield, MA 01105

Northern Educational Services, Inc.
Ethos I/Recovery Home
56 Temple Street
Springfield, MA 01105

Ethos III Outpatient Services
756 State Street
Springfield, MA 01109

Providence Hospital
Insights Program
209 Carew Street
Springfield, MA 01104

Methadone Program
227 Mill Street
Springfield, MA 01105

STONEHAM

**Boston Regional Medical Center
Addictions Treatment
Services/Outpatient**
5 Woodland Road
Stoneham, MA 02180

TAUNTON

**Community Counseling of
Bristol County Outpatient
Substance Abuse Services**
68 Church Green Street, Suite 2
Taunton, MA 02780

**Greater Taunton Council on
Alcoholism**
71 Main Street
Taunton, MA 02780

TEWKSBURY

HART House
365 East Street
Tewksbury, MA 01876

**Lowell Community Health
Center, Inc. Community
Health Initiatives/Detox**
Tewksbury Hospital
365 East Street, Unit 1
Tewksbury, MA 01876

**Middlesex Human Service
Agency, Inc. DUI Program**
Tewksbury Hospital
365 East Street, Hall III
Tewksbury, MA 01876

UPTON

**Riverside Community Care
Blackstone Valley Outpatient
Care**
206 Milford Street
Upton, MA 01568

WAKEFIELD

**Eastern Middlesex Human
Services Outpatient**
338 Main Street, Suite 304
Wakefield, MA 01880

WALTHAM

Hurley House Recovery Home
12–14 Lowell Street
Waltham, MA 02154

**Middlesex Regional Addiction
Treatment Center**
775 Trapelo Road
Waltham, MA 02154

Outpatient Services
50 Prospect Street
Suite 201
Waltham, MA 02154

WELLESLEY

**Charles River Hospital Dual
Diagnosis Program**
203 Grove Street
Wellesley, MA 02181

WESTBOROUGH

**Spectrum Addiction Services,
Inc.**
Primary Care
Spectrum Residential Program
155 Oak Street
Westborough, MA 01581

WEST FALMOUTH

CCAIRU Emerson House
554 West Falmouth Highway
West Falmouth, MA 02574

WESTFIELD

**Community Health Care Inc.
Substance Abuse Center**
125 North Elm Street
Westfield, MA 01085

**Providence Hospital Westfield
Counseling Center**
41 Church Street
Westfield, MA 01085

WESTWOOD

Westwood Lodge Hospital
45 Clapboardtree Street
Westwood, MA 02090

WOBURN

Arbour/Choate Counseling Services
500 West Cummings Park
Suite 3900
Woburn, MA 01801

WORCESTER

Adcare Hospital Substance Abuse Treatment Program
107 Lincoln Street
Worcester, MA 01605

Catholic Charities/Worcester Crozier House
10 HammondStreet
Worcester, MA 01610

Community Healthlink
Detoxification Program
Outpatient Substance Abuse Services
12 Queen Street
Worcester, MA 01610

DUI Program
72 Jaques Avenue
Worcester, MA 01610

Recovery Home
142 Burncoat Street
Worcester, MA 01606

Family Health Center of Worcester
26 Queen Street
Worcester, MA 01610

Henry Lee Willis Community Center
Channing House Recovery Home
21 Catherine Street
Worcester, MA 01605

Linda F. Griffin House
15 Northampton Street
Worcester, MA 01605

Outpatient Substance Abuse Services
44 Front Street, Suite 210
Worcester, MA 01609

Lincoln Group, The
79 June Street
Worcester, MA 01602

Saint Vincent's Hospital Deptartment of Alcohol and Drug Services/Outpatients
25 Winthrop Street
Worcester, MA 01604

Spectrum Addiction Services, Inc.
Outpatient Services
105 Merrick Street
Worcester, MA 01609

585 Lincoln Street
Worcester, MA 01605

Youth Opportunities Upheld, Inc. Structured Outpatient Services
81 Plantation Street
Worcester, MA 01604

MICHIGAN

ADRIAN

Emma L. Bixby Medical Center Sage Center for Substance Abuse Treatment
818 Riverside Avenue
Adrian, MI 49221

Family Service and Children's Aid
405 Mill Street
Adrian, MI 49221

McCullough Vargas and Associates
127 South Winter Street
Adrian, MI 49221

ALBION

Psychological Consultants of BC Chemical Dependency Resources
300-B Drive North
Albion, MI 49224

ALGONAC

Downriver Community Services, Inc. Substance Abuse Services
555 Saint Clair River Drive
Algonac, MI 48001

ALLEGAN

Allegan County Community Mental Health Services
3285 122nd Avenue
Allegan, MI 49010

CSAS, Inc. Family Recovery Center of Allegan County
138 B Hubbard Street
Allegan, MI 49010

ALLEN PARK

Pro Med Management Evergreen Counseling Centers
15101 Southfield Road
Allen Park, MI 48101

Josephine Sheehy Program
7445 Allen Road
Suite 190
Allen Park, MI 48107

ALMA

Human Aid, Inc.
1750 Wright Avenue
Alma, MI 48801

Pine River Recovery Center
300 Warwick Drive
Alma, MI 48801

ALPENA

Birchwood Center for Chemical Dependency
1501 West Chisholm Street
Alpena Hospital
Alpena, MI 49707

Catholic Human Services, Inc.
154 South Ripley Boulevard
Alpena, MI 49707

Sunrise Centre
630 Walnut Street
Alpena, MI 40707

ANN ARBOR

**Ann Arbor Veterans
    Administration Medical
    Center**
2215 Fuller Road
Ann Arbor, MI 48105

**Catholic Social Services
    Substance Abuse Services**
4952 Packard Road
Ann Arbor, MI 48104

**Center for Behavior and
    Medicine**
2004 Hogback Road, Suite 16
Ann Arbor, MI 48105

Chelsea Community Hospital
Older Adult Recovery Program
955 West Eisenhower Circle
Suite E
Ann Arbor, MI 48103

Chelsea Arbor Treatment Center
900 Victors Way Suite 310
Ann Arbor, MI 48108

**Child and Family Service of
    Washtenaw Chemical
    Dependency Program**
3879 Packard Road
Ann Arbor, MI 48104

Dawn, Inc.
Dawn Re-Entry
502 West Huron Street
Ann Arbor, MI 48104

Dawn Farm Detox
544 North Division Street
Ann Arbor, MI 48104

Home of New Vision
2500 Packard Street, Suite 201-A
Ann Arbor, MI 48104

**Huron Valley Consultation
    Center**
Carpenter Outpatient
2750 Carpenter Road
Ann Arbor, MI 48108

Eisenhower Outpatient
955 West Eisenhower Circle
Suite B
Ann Arbor, MI 48103

**Institute for Psychology and
    Medicine**
2010 Hogback Road
Suite 6
Ann Arbor, MI 48105

Jackson Counseling Agency
1900 West Stadium Boulevard
Suite 5
Ann Arbor, MI 48103

**Mercy Health Service McAuley
    Chemical Dependency Center**
2006 Hogback Road
Ann Arbor, MI 48105

Spectrum
2301 Platt Road
Ann Arbor, MI 48107

AUBURN HILLS

**Havenwyck Hospital Substance
    Abuse Services**
1525 University Drive
Auburn Hills, MI 48326

BAD AXE

Huron Counseling Services
1108 South Van Dyke Road
Bad Axe, MI 48413

List Psychological Services
65 Patrick Street, Suite 5
Bad Axe, MI 48413

BALDWIN

**Family Health Care Counseling
    Center**
1101 Washington Avenue
Baldwin, MI 49304

BARAGA

**KBTCAP Outpatient Counseling
    Services**
427 North Superior Avenue
Baraga, MI 49908

BARK RIVER

**Hannaville Three Fires Halfway
    House Substance Abuse
    Program**
3017 D Road
Bark River, MI 49807

BATTLE CREEK

Battle Creek Health System
165 North Washington Avenue
Battle Creek, MI 49016

**Chemical Dependency
    Resources**
151 North Avenue
Battle Creek, MI 49017

Oakridge Counseling Center
497 East Columbia Avenue
Suite 16
Battle Creek, MI 49015-4463

SPGB Services Inc
34 West Jackson Street
Suite 2, Lower Level
Battle Creek, MI 49224

**Veterans' Affairs Medical Center
    Substance Abuse Treatment
    Unit**
550 Armstrong Road
Battle Creek, MI 49015

BAY CITY

BASIS, Inc.
New Friendship House of Bay
    County
Residential Treatment Services
Riverside Outpatient
700 North Van Buren Street
Bay City, MI 48708

Riverside Center
904 6th Street
Bay City, MI 48708

Catholic Family Services
915 Columbus Avenue
Bay City, MI 48708

List Psychological Services
3741 East Wilder Road
Bay City, MI 48706

BELLAIRE

Antrim Kalkaska Community MH
205 East Cayuga Street
Bellaire, MI 49615-0220

CHIP Counseling Center
7053 M-88 Highway South
Bellaire, MI 49615

BELLEVILLE

Community Care Services Substance Abuse Service
25 Owen Street
Belleville, MI 48111

Eastwood Clinics
418 Main Street
Belleville, MI 48111

BENTON HARBOR

Berrien County Health Department Alcohol/Drug Abuse Program
769 Pipestone Street
Benton Harbor, MI 49022

Empowered Living Human Services
105 East Main Street, Suite 404
Benton Harbor, MI 49022

KADAC Holding Company Gateway Services at Benton Harbor
1610 Mall Drive
Benton Harbor, MI 49022

BENZONIA

Benzie Counseling Center
850 Michigan Avenue
Benzonia, MI 49616

Grand Traverse Band of Ottawa/Chippewa Indians Substance Abuse Services
7283 Hoadley Road
Benzonia, MI 49616

BERKLEY

Oakland Family Services Berkley Substance Abuse Services
2351 West 12 Mile Road
Berkley, MI 48072

Recovery Consultants, Inc.
2710 West Twelve Mile Road
Berkley, MI 48072-1630

Respite Counseling Center
3622 West Eleven Mile Road
Berkley, MI 48072

Smith Counseling Services Substance Abuse Services
2790 Coolidge Highway
Berkley, MI 48072

BIG RAPIDS

Nova Counseling Associates, Inc.
1724 North State Street
Big Rapids, MI 49307

BIRMINGHAM

Frazho, Joyce K., MSW
111 South Old Woodward Avenue
Suite 256
Birmingham, MI 48009

HFHS Behavior Services Chemical Dependency Program
350 North Old Woodward Street
Suite 3
Birmingham, MI 48009

Smith, Lewis, Ph.D., PC
600 North Woodward Avenue
Suite 303
Birmingham, MI 48009

BLOOMFIELD HILLS

Auro Medical Center Substance Abuse Services
111 South Woodward Avenue
Suite 120
Bloomfield Hills, MI 48304

Center for Contemporary Psychology PC Outpatient Substance Abuse
35980 Woodward Avenue, Suite 1
Bloomfield Hills, MI 48304

Family Center for Psychological Services
36700 Woodward Avenue
Suite 40, Lower Level
Bloomfield Hills, MI 48304-0928

Oakland Psychological Clinic PC Substance Abuse Services
2050 Woodward Avenue
Suite 110
Bloomfield Hills, MI 48304

Pro Med Management Evergreen Counseling Centers
1760 South Telegraph Road
Bloomfield Hills, MI 48302

Recovery Consultants, Inc.
1591 Opdyke Road
Bloomfield Hills, MI 48304

BRIGHTON

Advanced Counseling Services
7600 Grand River Street
Suite 295
Brighton, MI 48116

Brighton Hospital Alcoholism Treatment Services
12851 East Grand River Street
Brighton, MI 48116

Center for Behavior and Medicine
10299 East Grand River Street
Suite I
Brighton, MI 48116

SOS Livingston
325 South Grand River
Brighton, MI 48116

CADILLAC

Catholic Human Services
140 West River Street
Suite 7
Cadillac, MI 49601

CALUMET

Phoenix House, Inc.
422 Pine Street
Calumet, MI 49913

Up Contract Services, Inc.
1175 Calumet Avenue, Suite C
Calumet, MI 49913

CANTON

Center for Behavior and Medicine
2200 Canton Center Road
Suite 200-B
Canton, MI 48187

Downriver Mental Health Clinic Advanced Counseling Services PC
6223 Canton Road, Suite 210
Canton, MI 48187

Family Service
8564 North Canton Center Road
Canton, MI 48187-5065

Hegira Programs, Inc. Oakdale Recovery Center
43825 Michigan Avenue
Canton, MI 48188

CARO

List Psychological Services
443 North State Street
Caro, MI 48723

Thumb Area Behavioral Services Center
1309 Cleaver Road
Caro, MI 48723

CENTER LINE

New Alternatives
25501 Van Dyke Street
Center Line, MI 48015

Options Counseling Services, Inc.
25529 Van Dyke Street
Center Line, MI 48015

CENTREVILLE

Centreville Psychological Services
227 West Main Street
Centreville, MI 49032

CHARLEVOIX

Bay Area Substance Education Services, Inc.
6123 Old U.S. 31 South
Charlevoix, MI 49720

CHIP Counseling Center
6777 U.S. 31 South
Charlevoix, MI 49720

Grand Traverse Band of Ottawa/Chippewa Indians Substance Abuse Services
6429 M-66
Charlevoix, MI 49720

Northern Michigan CMH Dual Diagnosis Program
218 Garfield Street
Charlevoix, MI 49720

CHARLOTTE

Eaton Substance Abuse Program, Inc.
551 Courthouse Drive
Charlotte, MI 48813

CHEBOYGAN

CHIP Counseling Center
520 North Main Street
Suite 106
Cheboygan, MI 49721

Sue Patrick Substance Abuse Services
520 North Main Street
Suite 200
Cheboygan, MI 49721

CHELSEA

Chelsea Arbor Treatment Center
Chelsea Community Hospital
775 South Main Street
Chelsea, MI 48118

CLARE

Human Aid, Inc.
1426 North McEwan Street
Clare, MI 48617

CLARKSTON

Insight Recovery Center/ Clarkston
9075 Big Lake Road
Clarkston, MI 48347

North Oakland Counseling Associates
6401 Citation Drive, Suite C
Clarkston, MI 48346

Saint Joseph Mercy Hospital Mercy Behavioral Center
6770 Dixie Highway, Suite 308
Clarkston, MI 48346

Triad Associates PC
8062 Ortonville Road
Clarkston, MI 48348-4456

CLAWSON

Chambers and Associates Company
12 Church Avenue
Clawson, MI 48017-1110

CLINTON TOWNSHIP

Action Counseling Clinic, Inc. Substance Abuse Services
23823 15 Mile Road
Clinton Township, MI 48035-3111

Catholic Social Services of MaComb Substance Abuse Services
15980 19 Mile Street
Clinton Township, MI 48038

Chambers and Associates Company
42110 Garfield Street, Suite 200
Clinton Township, MI 48038

Eastwood Community Clinics
35455 Garfield Road
Suite C
Clinton Township, MI 48035

**Metro Family Support
Counseling PC**
16950 19 Mile Road, Suite 2
Clinton Township, MI 48038

**Options Counseling Services,
Inc.**
22900 East Remick Street
Clinton Township, MI 48035

**Saint Joseph Mercy Center for
Behavioral Medicine**
43411 Garfield Street, Suite A
Clinton Township, MI 48038

**Salvation Army Harbor Light
Center MaComb County
Satellite**
42590 Stepnitz Drive
Clinton Township, MI 48036

COLDWATER

**Community Health Center of
Branch County Substance
Treatment and Referral
Service**
316 East Chicago Street
Coldwater, MI 49036

DAVISBURG

**Makenzie Counseling Group,
Inc.**
586 Broadway Street
Davisburg, MI 48350

**New Oakland Child/Adolescent
Family Center**
12731 Andersonville Road
Davisburg, MI 48350

DEARBORN

**Arab Community Center for
Economic and Social Services
(ACCESS)**
2601 Saulino Court
Dearborn, MI 48120

Eastwood Clinics
19855 West Outer Drive
Suite 204W
Dearborn, MI 48124

Family Services, Inc.
19855 West Outer Drive
Suite 104
Dearborn, MI 48124

Henry Ford Health Systems
5111 Auto Club Drive
Dearborn, MI 48126

Insight
23400 Michigan Avenue
Suite 405
Dearborn, MI 48124

Oakwood Healthcare Systems
18101 Oakwood Boulevard
Dearborn, MI 48123

**Personal Dynamics Center
Substance Abuse Program**
23810 Michigan Avenue
Dearborn, MI 48124

Serenity Manor, Inc.
1637 Ferney Street
Dearborn, MI 48120

DEARBORN HEIGHTS

**Catholic Social Services of
Wayne County Substance
Abuse Services**
20382 Van Born Road
Dearborn Heights, MI 48125

Parkview Counseling Center
25639 Ford Road
Dearborn Heights, MI 48127

**Westside Mental Health
Services**
24548 West Warren Avenue
Dearborn Heights, MI 48127

DETROIT

**Adult Psychiatric Clinic North
Central**
4321 East McNicholse Road
Detroit, MI 48212

**American Indian Health and
Family Services of Southeast
Michigan**
4880 Lawndale Street
Detroit, MI 48210

**BAPCO Substance Abuse
Treatment and Prevention
Program**
17357 Klinger Street
First Community Baptist Church
Detroit, MI 48212

Boniface Fort Street Clinic
5882 Fort Street
Detroit, MI 48209

Boniface Human Services
Outpatient Program
5884 West Fort
Detroit, MI 48209

Boniface Youth Services
1025 East Forest Street
Room 315
Detroit, MI 48201

**Catholic Social Services of
Wayne County**
9851 Hamilton Avenue
Detroit, MI 48202

**Center of Behavioral Therapy
PC**
24453 Grand River Avenue
Detroit, MI 48219

**Childrens Center of Wayne
County**
79 West Alexandrine Street
Detroit, MI 48201

**Community Treatment Center
Monica House**
15380 Monica Street
Detroit, MI 48238

Comprehensive Services, Inc.
4630 Oakman Boulevard
Detroit, MI 48204

Deaf Options, Inc.
220 Bagley Street, Suite 1020
Detroit, MI 48226

**Department of Human Services
Gratiot Clinic**
3506 Gratiot Avenue
Detroit, MI 48207

**Detroit Central City Community
Mental Health, Inc.**
10 Peterboro Street
Detroit, MI 48201

Detroit East, Inc. Community Mental Health
1970 East Larned Street
Detroit, MI 48207

Detroit Light House Program
3750 Woodward Avenue
Suite C-40
Detroit, MI 48201

Detroit Rescue Mission
3535 3 Street
Detroit, MI 48201

Genesis III
11017 Mack Avenue
Detroit, MI 48214

Eastwood Clinics
15085 East 7 Mile Road
Detroit, MI 48205

11542 Conner Street
Detroit, MI 48205

Outpatient
15125 Gratiot Avenue
Detroit, MI 48205

Eleonore Hutzel Recovery Center
301 East Hancock Street
Detroit, MI 48201

13301 Mound Road
Detroit, MI 48213

Emmanuel House Recovery Program
18570 Fitzpatrick Court
Detroit, MI 48228

Family Services of Detroit/ Wayne County
Downtown Detroit Office
220 Bagley Street
Michigan Building Suite 700
Detroit, MI 48226

18585 Mack Street
Detroit, MI 48236

Harper Hospital
50 East Cnafield Street
Detroit, MI 48201

Harper House/Change Alternative Living/Outpatient
2940 East 8 Mile Road
Detroit, MI 48234

Heartline Inc
8201 Sylvester Street
Detroit, MI 48214

Insight Recovery Center
7430 2nd Avenue
Detroit, MI 48202

Islamic Health and Human Services, Inc.
1249 Washington Boulevard
Book Tower Building
Suite 2040-41
Detroit, MI 48226

Jefferson House
8311 East Jefferson Avenue
Detroit, MI 48214

Latino Family Services, Inc.
3815 West Fort Street
Detroit, MI 48216

Mariners Inn
445 Ledyard Street
Detroit, MI 48201

Mercy Hospital Chemical Dependency Services
5555 Conner Avenue
Detroit, MI 48213

12535 Harper Street
Detroit, MI 48213

Metro Arts Therapy Services
1274 Library Street, Suite 301
Detroit, MI 48226

11000 West McNichols Road
Detroit, MI 48221

Metro East Substance Abuse Treatment Corporation
8047 East Harper Avenue
2nd Floor
Detroit, MI 48213

13627 Gratiot Avenue
Detroit, MI 48205

13929 Harper Avenue
Detroit, MI 48213

Metro Matrix Human Services
Peter Claver Career
450 Elliott Street
Detroit, MI 48201

Project Transition
16260 Dexter Avenue
Detroit, MI 48221

Nardin Park Recovery Center
9605 West Grand River Avenue
Detroit, MI 48204

Neighborhood Service Organization (NSO)
24 Hour Walk-In Center
3430 3rd Street
Detroit, MI 48201

Calvin Wells Treatment Center
8600 Woodward Street
Detroit, MI 48202

Gratiot Services Center
3506 Gratiot Avenue
Detroit, MI 48207

Neighborhood Services Department
Detroit Department of Human Services
8809 John C. Lodge
Herman Keifer Hospital
Building 5
Detroit, MI 48202

New Center Community Mental Health Services
2051 West Grand Boulevard
Grand Dex Plaza
Detroit, MI 48208

North Park
1001 Puritan Street
Detroit, MI 48202

Metro Youth and Family Services Program
1249 Washington Boulevard
Book Tower, Suite 1537
Detroit, MI 48226

New Life Home for Recovering Women
17131 Gitre Street
Detroit, MI 48205

New Life Recovery, Inc.
6690 Michigan Avenue
Detroit, MI 48210

New Light Recovery Center, Inc.
300 West McNichols Street
Detroit, MI 48203

Northeast Guidance Center
Specialty Services Program
2070 Chalmers Street
Detroit, MI 48215

Northeast Health Services, Inc.
3800 Woodward Avenue
Suite 1002
Detroit, MI 48201-2030

Parkview Counseling Center
18609 West 7 Mile Road
Detroit, MI 48219

Positive Images
694 East Grand Boulevard
Detroit, MI 48207

Quality Behavioral Health, Inc.
3455 Woodward Avenue
Suite 101
Detroit, MI 48201

Renaissance Education and Training Center
18420 West McNichols Road
Detroit, MI 48219

Renaissance West Community Mental Health Chemical Dependency Service
13940 Tireman Street
Detroit, MI 48228

Sacred Heart Rehabilitation Center, Inc. Alcohol and Drug Treatment Services
220 Bagley Street
Michigan Building, Suite 1022
Detroit, MI 48201

Salvation Army Evangeline Center for Women/Children
130 West Grand Boulevard
Detroit, MI 48216

Salvation Army Harbor Light Substance Abuse Center
2643 Park Avenue
Detroit, MI 48201

Self-Help Addiction Rehab (SHAR)
1852 West Grand Boulevard
Detroit, MI 48208

Aftercare
5675 Maybury Grand Avenue
Detroit, MI 48208

Clark Center
174 South Clark Street
Detroit, MI 48209

Day Treatment
14301 Longview Street
Detroit, MI 48213

East Center
4216 McDougall Street
Detroit, MI 48207

Sobriety House, Inc.
2081 West Grand Boulevard
Detroit, MI 48208

Southwest Detroit Community Mental Health Services, Inc. Substance Abuse Services
1700 Waterman Street
Detroit, MI 48209

Star Center, Inc.
13575 Lesure Street
Detroit, MI 48227

UPC Jefferson Research Clinic
2761 East Jefferson Avenue
Detroit, MI 48207

Veterans Affairs Medical Center Chemical Dependence Treatment Services
4646 John Road
Detroit, MI 48201

Wayne County Juvenile Detention Chemical Dependency Program
1333 East Forest Street
Detroit, MI 48207

Wendie D. Lee Institute of Life Management, Inc.
11000 West McNichols Street
Suite 212
Detroit, MI 48221

DOWAGIAC

Pokagon Band of Potawatomi Indian Tribe Keepers of The Fire Substance Abuse Program
714 North Front Street
Dowagiac, MI 49047

SACSJC Myrtle Treatment Center
420 West High Street
Dowagiac, MI 49047

EAST LANSING

Gateway Community Services First Step
910 Abbott Road
Suite 100
East Lansing, MI 48823

Lansing Psychological Associates
234 Michigan Avenue
East Lansing, MI 48823

Meridian Professional Psychological Consultants
5031 Park Lake Road
East Lansing, MI 48823

Psychological Associates in Rehab
780 West Lake Lansing Road, Suite 300
East Lansing, MI 48823

Total Health Care of Michigan
2900 Hannah Boulevard Suite 200
East Lansing, MI 48823

EASTPOINTE

Eastwood Clinics
20811 Kelly Road, Suite 103
Eastpointe, MI 48021-3139

ESCANABA

Delta Menominee DHD and other Drug Services
2920 College Avenue
Delta County Service Center
Escanaba, MI 49829

Marquette Medical Center
2500 7th Avenue
South Doctors Park, Suite 102
Escanaba, MI 49829

FARMINGTON

Eastwood Center at Botsford General Hospital
28050 Grand River Avenue
Farmington, MI 48336

FARMINGTON HILLS

Broe Rehabilitation Services, Inc.
33634 West Eight Mile Road
Farmington Hills, MI 48335

Catholic Social Services of Oakland County
29475 Inkster Road
Farmington Hills, MI 48334

Chambers and Associates
32330 West Twelve Mile Road
Suite 12
Farmington Hills, MI 48334

Davis Counseling Center
37923 West 12 Mile Road
Entry A
Farmington Hills, MI 48331

Gerger Spivack and Associates
37923 West 12 Mile Road
Farmington Hills, MI 48331

Key Psychological Services
30630 12 Mile Road, Suite D
Farmington Hills, MI 48334

Oakland Family Services
23332 Orchard Lake Road
Farmington Hills, MI 48336

23450 Middlebelt Road
Farmington Hills, MI 48336

Pioneer Counseling Centers
28511 Orchard Lake Road
Suite A
Farmington Hills, MI 48334-2951

FERNDALE

Community Services of Oakland
345 East 9 Mile Road
Ferndale, MI 48220

HFHS Second Step Program
Kingswood Hospital
10300 West 8 Mile Road
Ferndale, MI 48220

FLINT

Auburn Counseling Associates
400 North Saginaw Street
Suite 300
Flint, MI 48502

Catholic Social Services
901 Chippewa Street
Flint, MI 48503

Community Recovery Services
711 North Saginaw Street
Suite 323
Flint, MI 48503

CRS at Flint Corrections Center
411 East 3 Street
Flint, MI 48503

CRS at Flint New Paths
765 East Hamilton Avenue
Flint, MI 48505

Daniels, Dan, ACSW
4511-G Miller Road
Flint, MI 48507

Dot Caring Centers, Inc.
3500-G Flushing Road, Suite 100
Flint, MI 48504

Flint Odyssey House, Inc.
1225 Martin Luther King Avenue
Flint, MI 48503

1013 Garland Street
Flint, MI 48503-1445

Genesis Regional Medical Center Addiction Treatment
2811 East Court Street
Flint, MI 48506

Hurley Mental Health Associates
1125 South Linden Road
Flint, MI 48502

Insight Recovery Center
1110 Eldon Baker Drive
Flint, MI 48507

4413-G Corunna Road
Flint, MI 48532

McLaren Behavioral Health Center
5057-G West Bristol Road
Flint, MI 48532

National Council on Alcoholism and Addictions/Greater Flint Area
202 East Boulevard Drive
Suite 310
Flint, MI 48503

Taylor Psychological Clinic
1172 Robert T Longway Street
Flint, MI 48503

Transition House, Inc.
931 Martin Luther King Boulevard
Flint, MI 48503

Woodward Counseling, Inc.
1207 North Ballenger Highway,
Suite G
Flint, MI 48504

FORT GRATIOT

Blue Water Mental Health Clinic
1501 Krafft Road
Fort Gratiot, MI 48059

FRANKLIN

Beacon Hill Clinic
31000 Lahser Road, Suite 1
Franklin, MI 48025

FRASER

Oakland Psychological Clinic Substance Abuse Services
16664 15 Mile Road
Fraser, MI 48026

GARDEN CITY

Garden City Hospital
Brookfield Clinic
6245 North Inkster Road
Garden City, MI 48135

GAYLORD

Catholic Human Services, Inc. Alcohol and Drug Services
111 South Michigan Avenue
Gaylord, MI 49735

Counseling and Health Substance Abuse Services
651 North Otsego Avenue
Gaylord, MI 49735

Northern Michigan Community Mental Health Dual Diagnosis Program
800 Livingston Boulevard
Suite 2-A
Gaylord, MI 49735

GLADWIN

Human Aid, Inc. Substance Abuse Services
137 Commerce Court
Gladwin, MI 48624

GRAND BLANC

Oakland Psychological Clinic PC
8341 Office Park Drive
Grand Blanc, MI 48439

GRAND HAVEN

Child/Family Services of Western Michigan, Inc.
321 South Beechtree Street
Grand Haven, MI 49417

Ottagan Addictions Rehab, Inc.
57 Robbins Road
Grand Haven, MI 49417

GRAND RAPIDS

ACAC Inc
3949 Sparks Street SE, Suite 103
Grand Rapids, MI 49546

Advanced Therapeutics Corporation Solutions
738 Lafayette Street NE
Grand Rapids, MI 49503

Anderson Substance Abuse Treatment Center
3501 Lake Eastbrook Boulevard
Suite 120
Grand Rapids, MI 49546

Beauchamp Consulting and Associates
6159 28th Street SE, Suite 16
Grand Rapids, MI 49546-6911

Bethany Christian Services Substance Abuse Counseling Program
901 Eastern Avenue NE
Grand Rapids, MI 49503

Center for Family Recovery
4477 Cascade Road SE
Grand Rapids, MI 49546

Community Alternatives Program Project Rehab
801 College Street SE
Grand Rapids, MI 49507

Eastern Clinic
1555 Eastern Street SE
Grand Rapids, MI 49507

Family Outreach Center Outpatient Substance Abuse Counseling
1939 South Division Avenue
Grand Rapids, MI 49507

Forest View Psychiatric Hospital Dual Diagnosis Program
1055 Medical Park Drive SE
Grand Rapids, MI 49546

Fountain Hill Center for Counseling Consultation
534 Fountain Street NE
Grand Rapids, MI 49503

Grand Rapids Center for Psychotherapy
3350 Eagle Park Drive
Suite 102-B
Grand Rapids, MI 49505

Kooistra, Jansma, Teitsma, DiNallo, and Van Hoek
3330 Claystone Street SE
Grand Rapids, MI 49546

Life Guidance Services
3351 Claystone Street SE
Suite 112
Grand Rapids, MI 49546

1400 Leonard Street NE
Grand Rapids, MI 49505

Longford Care Unit of Kent Community Hospital
750 Fuller Avenue NE
Grand Rapids, MI 49503

Mel Trotter Ministries
225 Commerce Street SW
Grand Rapids, MI 49503

Montiegel and Miller Company
161 Ottawa Avenue NW
Suite 200-F
Grand Rapids, MI 49503

North Kent Guidance Services
5270 Northland Drive, Suite A
Grand Rapids, MI 49525-1040

Our Hope Association
324 Lyon Street NE
Grand Rapids, MI 49503

Pathfinder Resources, Inc.
Demey Center
245 State Street SE
Grand Rapids, MI 49503

Jellema House
523 Lyon Street NE
Grand Rapids, MI 49503

Pine Rest Christian Mental Health Services
300 68 Street SE
Grand Rapids, MI 49501

Project Rehabilitation
Adult Residential Services
200 Eastern Avenue SE
Grand Rapids, MI 49503

Community Services
Hispanic Residential Program
822 Cherry Street SE
Grand Rapids, MI 49503

Shiloh and Dakota
130 68th Street
Grand Rapids, MI 49548

Psychology Associates
1000 Parchment Street
Grand Rapids, MI 49546-3663

Reality Counseling Services
2420 Burton Street, Suite 201
Grand Rapids, MI 49546

Salvation Army Turning Point
1931 Boston Street SE
Grand Rapids, MI 49506

Wedgewood Christian Youth and Family Services, Inc.
3300 36th Street SE
Grand Rapids, MI 49512

Cutlerville Recovery
300 68th Street SE
Grand Rapids, MI 49548

West Michigan Addiction Consultants PC Professional Recovery System
3001 Fuller Ave NE
Grand Rapids, MI 49505

GRAYLING

Grace Center/Saint Francis Human Resource Center
6459 West Street, Suite M-72
Grayling, MI 49738

GREENVILLE

North Kent Guidance Services
106 South Greenville West Drive
Greenville, MI 48838

GROSSE POINTE

Eastwood Clinics Grosse Point Woods
19251 Mack Avenue
Mack Office Building Suite 300
Grosse Pointe, MI 48236

GROSSE POINTE FARMS

Vonschwarz Associates Community Resource Services
456 Touraine Street
Grosse Pointe Farms, MI 48236

GROSSE POINTE PARK

Catholic Social Services of Wayne County Substance Abuse Services
15200 East Jefferson Street
Suite 105
Grosse Pointe Park, MI 48230

HANCOCK

Christian Counseling
100 Quincy Street
Hancock, MI 49930

Marquette Medical Clinic
1045 Quincy Street
Hancock, MI 49930

Western UP District Health Department Substance Abuse Services
540 Depot Street
Hancock, MI 49930

HARRISON TOWNSHIP

Saint John Hospital/MaComb Center Chemical Dependency Unit
26755 Ballard Road
Harrison Township, MI 48045

HART

New Life Recovery and Prevention Services, Inc.
220 Washington Street
Hart, MI 49420

HARTFORD

Van Buren County Health Department Substance Abuse Services
57418 County Road 681
Hartford, MI 49057

HASTINGS

Barry County Substance Abuse Services
220 West Court Street
Hastings, MI 49058

HIGHLAND PARK

Black Family Development, Inc. Family Abstinence Commitment to Empower (FACE)
211 Glendale Street, Room 206
Riverview Medical Center
Highland Park, MI 48203

Christian Guidance Center
13220 Woodward Avenue
Highland Park, MI 48203

New Center Community Mental Health Services
211 Glendale Road, 4th Floor
Highland Park, MI 48203

New Era Alternative Treatment Center
211 Glendale Street, Suite SB
Highland Park, MI 48203

HILLSDALE

Bridgeway Center of Foote Hospital
1360 South Hillsdale Road
Hillsdale, MI 49242

Hillsdale Community Health Center
170 South Howell Street
Hillsdale, MI 49242

HOLLAND

Child/Family Services of Western Michigan, Inc. Substance Abuse Services
412 Century Lane
Holland, MI 49423

Holland Community Hospital
602 Michigan Avenue
Holland, MI 49423

Behavioral Health Services
854 South Washington Avenue
Suite 330
Holland, MI 49423-7132

Mercy Glen Family Recovery Center Substance Abuse Services
603 East 16 Street
Holland, MI 49423

Ottagan Addictions Rehab, Inc.
483 Century Lane
Holland, MI 49423

Chester A. Ray Center
231 Washington Boulevard
Holland, MI 49423

Harbor House for Women
377 Lincoln Street
Holland, MI 49423

Pine Rest Christian Mental Health Services
926 South Washington Street
Holland, MI 49423

HOLLY

Highland Waterford Center, Inc. Holly Gardens
4501 Grange Hall Road
Holly, MI 48442

North Oakland Center for Human Potential
521 East Street
Holly, MI 48442

HOLT

Child and Family Services of Michigan, Inc. Capitol Area Substance Abuse Services
4801 Willoughby Street
Suite 2
Holt, MI 48842

HOUGHTON LAKE

Human Aid, Inc. Substance Abuse Services
202 Health Parkway
Houghton Lake, MI 48617

HOWELL

Brighton Hospital Livingston Counseling and Assessment Services, Inc.
3744 East Grand River Avenue
Howell, MI 48843

McAuley/McPherson Behavioral Services
620 Byron Road, 3rd Floor
Howell, MI 48843

IONIA

Arbor Circle Corporation DBA
848 East Lincoln Avenue
Ionia, MI 48846

Inner Access Therapy Center
227 West Main Street, Suite 206
Ionia, MI 48846

IRON MOUNTAIN

Dickinson/Iron Substance Abuse Services, Inc. Outpatient
427 South Stephenson Avenue
Iron Mountain, MI 49801

Veterans' Affairs Medical Center Substance Abuse Treatment Program
325 East H Street
Iron Mountain, MI 49801

IRON RIVER

Dickinson/Iron Substance Abuse Services, Inc.
117 West Genesee Street
Iron River, MI 49935

IRONWOOD

Lutheran Social Services of Wisconsin and Upper Michigan, Inc.
Villa Manor
126 West Arch Street
Ironwood, MI 49938

JACKSON

Bridgeway Center of Foote Hospital
900 E Michigan Avenue
Jackson, MI 49201

Family Service and Children's Aid
330 West Michigan Street
Jackson, MI 49201

Michigan Therapeutic Consultants PC
605 West Michigan Avenue
Jackson, MI 49201

National Council on Alcoholism
950 West Monroe Street
Suite G-400
Jackson, MI 49202

Washington Way Recovery Center
2424 West Washington Street
Jackson, MI 49203

KALAMAZOO

Child and Family Psychological Services
5380 Holiday Terrace
Kalamazoo, MI 49009

Gateway New Beginnings KADAC Holding Company
1625 Gull Road
Kalamazoo, MI 49001

Gateway Northside Outreach Services
118 Roberson Street
Kalamazoo, MI 49007

Gateway Outpatient Services
5360 Holiday Terrace
Kalamazoo, MI 49006

Gateway Villa
1910 Shaffer Road
Kalamazoo, MI 49001

Guidance Clinic
2615 Stadium Drive
Kalamazoo, MI 49008

Kalamazoo Psychology PC
122 West South Street
Suite 207
Kalamazoo, MI 49007

New Way Counseling Center
1128 South Westnedge
Kalamazoo, MI 49008

Sandra Fields/Neal and Associates, Inc.
535 South Burdick Street
Suite 165
Kalamazoo, MI 49007-5261

Senior Services, Inc. Older Adult Recovery Program
918 Jasper Street
Kalamazoo, MI 49001

University Substance Abuse Clinic SPADA
1000 Oakland Drive
Kalamazoo, MI 49008

Victory Clinical Services
1020 South Westnedge Street
Kalamazoo, MI 49008

Western Michigan University
Substance Abuse Services
Sindecuse Health Center
Room 3235
Kalamazoo, MI 49008

Womancare, Inc.
2836 West Main Street
Kalamazoo, MI 49006

KALKASKA

**Antrim Kalkaska Community
   Mental Health Center**
509 North Birch Street
Kalkaska, MI 49646-0267

**Interventions Counseling
   Service**
556 South Cedar Street
Kalkaska, MI 49646

KENTWOOD

**Pathfinders Resources, Inc.
   Women and Children's Center**
3333 36th Street NE
Kentwood, MI 49512

KINGSFORD

**Community Substance Abuse
   Services, Inc.**
373 Woodward Avenue
Kingsford, MI 49801

LAKE ORION

Guest House
1840 West Scripps Road
Lake Orion, MI 48361

**Oakland Psychological Clinic
   PC Substance Abuse Services**
2633 South Lapeer Road
Lake Orion, MI 48360

L'ANSE

**Keweenaw Bay Tribal Alcohol
   Program**
Brewry Road, Route 2
L'Anse, MI 49946

LANSING

**Comprehensive Substance
   Abuse Treatment**
House of Commons
517 North Walnut Street
Lansing, MI 48933

Older Adult Prevention and
   Treatment Program
808 Southland Street, Suite A
Lansing, MI 48910

Southland Counseling Center
808 Southland Street, Suite C
Lansing, MI 48910

**Cristo Rey Counseling Services
   Substance Abuse Program**
1717 North High Street
Lansing, MI 48906

Dimensions of Life
510 West Willow Street
Lansing, MI 48906

Glass House
419 North Martin Luther King
   Boulevard
Lansing, MI 48915

Holden House
3300 South Pennsylvania Avenue
Lansing, MI 48910

Insight Recovery Center
2929 Covington Court
Lansing, MI 48912

Marina Levine Rehab Services
1808 South Pennsylvania Avenue,
   Suite C
Lansing, MI 48910

**National Council on Alcoholism
   Lansing Regional Area**
3400 South Cedar Street
Suite 200
Lansing, MI 48910

Reality Counseling Services
610 East Grand River
Lansing, MI 48906

Total Health Education, Inc.
2627 North East Street
Lansing, MI 48906

Treatment Works, Inc.
3401 East Saginaw Street
Lansing, MI 48912

LAPEER

**Alcohol Information and
   Counseling Center**
1575 Suncrest Drive
Lapeer County Health Department
Lapeer, MI 48446

**Christian Family Services of
   Lapeer County**
441 Clay Street
Lapeer, MI 48446

**Completion House, Inc. DBA
   Turning Point**
24 East Park Street
Lapeer, MI 48446

**Lapeer County Community
   Mental Health**
1570 Suncrest Drive
Lapeer, MI 48446

**Lapeer Regional Hospital Vail
   Center**
1375 North Main Street
Lapeer, MI 48446

List Psychological Services
350 North Court Street
Lapeer, MI 48446

LINCOLN PARK

Boniface Human Services
25050 West Outer Drive
Suite 201
Lincoln Park, MI 48146

Community Care Services
Counseling and Resource Center
26184 West Outer Drive
Lincoln Park, MI 48146

LIVONIA

Arbor Hills Medical Center
27550 Joy Road
Livonia, MI 48150

**Butterfly Center The Recovery
   Corporation**
27485 5 Mile Road
Livonia, MI 48154

**Catholic Social Service of
Wayne County**
17316 Farmington Road
Livonia, MI 48152

Eastwood Clinics
17250 Farmington Road
Livonia, MI 48154

**Employee Assistance Associates,
Inc.**
38705 7 Mile Road
Suite 130
Livonia, MI 48152

Family Services, Inc.
16755 Middlebelt Road
Livonia, MI 48154

**Hegira Programs, Inc. Livonia
Counseling Center**
13325 Farmington Road
Livonia, MI 48150

**New Directions Center for
Christian Counseling**
37625 Ann Arbor RoadSuite 107
Livonia, MI 48150

**Oakland Psychological Clinic
Substance Abuse Services**
29865 6 Mile Road, Suite 112
Livonia, MI 48152

Pioneer Counseling Centers
37650 Professional Center Drive
Suite 145-A
Livonia, MI 48154

**Saint Mary Hospital Chemical
Dependency Services**
36475 5 Mile Road
Livonia, MI 48154

**University Psychiatric Center
Livonia Substance Abuse
Program**
16832 Newburgh Road
Livonia, MI 48154

LUDINGTON

**New Life Recovery and
Prevention Services**
1105 South Washington Street
Ludington, MI 49431

MADISON HEIGHTS

Gateway Counseling Center
27301 Dequindre Road
Madison Heights, MI 48071

Medical Resource Center, Inc.
1400 East 12 Mile Road
Madison Heights, MI 48071

MANISTEE

**Manistee/Benzie Community
Mental Health Counseling
Center**
395 3rd Street
Manistee, MI 49660

MANISTIQUE

**Hiawatha Behavioral Health
Authority**
125 North Lake Street
Manistique, MI 49854

LMAS Addiction Services
300 Walnut Street
Manistique, MI 49854

MARLETTE

**Family Resource Counseling
and Learning Center, Inc.**
6444 Morris Street
Marlette, MI 48453

MARQUETTE

Bell Behavioral Services
425 Corning Street, Suite B
Marquette, MI 49855

**Great Lakes Recovery Center,
Inc.**
241 Wright Street
Marquette, MI 49855

228 West Washington Street
Suite 3
Marquette, MI 49855

**Lutheran Social Services of
Wisconsin and Upper
Michigan**
1009 West Ridge Street
Marquette, MI 49855

**Marquette General Hospital
Addiction Services**
420 West Magnetic Street
Marquette, MI 49855

MARYSVILLE

**Eastern Michigan Counseling
Associates**
1600 Gratiot Boulevard
Building A, Suite 3
Marysville, MI 48040

MASON

**Correctional Assessment and
Treatment Services Comp.
Substance Abuse Treatment
Program**
630 North Cedar Street
Ingham County Jail
Mason, MI 48854

MEMPHIS

**Sacred Heart Rehabilitation
Center, Inc.**
400 Stoddard Road
Memphis, MI 48041

MENOMINEE

**Beacon/Bay Area Program for
Behavioral Medicine**
1110 10th Avenue
Menominee, MI 49858

**Delta Menominee District
Health Department**
2608 10th Street
Menominee, MI 49858

MIDLAND

**Family and Children's Services
of Midland**
1714 Eastman Avenue
Midland, MI 48641

**Focus Substance Abuse
Counseling and Information
Service**
4604 North Saginaw Road
Suite C
Midland, MI 48640

H. G. Swift Counseling Services
5100 Eastman Avenue, Suite 2
Midland, MI 48640

Ten Sixteen Treatment Center
1016 Eastman Avenue
Midland, MI 48640

MILFORD

Oakland Psychological Clinic PC Substance Abuse Services
1203 North Milford Road
Suite A
Milford, MI 48381

MIO

Ausable Valley Community Mental Health Substance Abuse Services
325 North Mount Tom Road
Mio, MI 48647

MONROE

Catholic Social Services of Monroe County
16 East 5th Street
Monroe, MI 48161

Substance Abuse Services
123 West First Street
Gateway Building
Monroe, MI 48161

Eastwood Clinics
708 South Monroe Street
Monroe, MI 48161-2126

Mercy Memorial Hospital
Family Center
700 Stewart Road
Monroe, MI 48162

Substance Abuse Services
718 North Macomb Street
Monroe, MI 48162

Monroe County Jail Substance Abuse Education and Counseling Program
100 East 2 Street
Monroe, MI 48163

Salvation Army Harbor Light
Monroe County Alcohol Center
3580 South Custer Road
Monroe, MI 48161

Monroe County Center
25 South Monroe Street
Monroe, MI 48161

Vets Incorporated
14 South Monroe Street
Monroe, MI 48161

MOUNT CLEMENS

Clinton Counseling Center
Comprehensive Youth Services
2 Crocker Boulevard
Suite 101
Mount Clemens, MI 48043

43565 Elizabeth Road
Mount Clemens, MI 48043

Macomb Family Services Inc I
2 Crocker Boulevard
Suite 202
Mount Clemens, MI 48043

New Beginnings Counseling
39 B Crocker Boulevard
Mount Clemens, MI 48043

MOUNT PLEASANT

Choices of Mount Pleasant, Inc.
1234 East Broomfield Road
Building A, Suite 5
Mount Pleasant, MI 48858

Mount Pleasant Counseling Services
3480 South Isabella Road
Mount Pleasant, MI 48858

OJIBWE Substance Abuse Program
2250 Enterprise Drive
Mount Pleasant, MI 48855

Omega Counseling Centers
105 South Franklin Street
Suite 221
Mount Pleasant, MI 48858

MUSKEGON

Child and Family Services
1352 Terrace Street
Muskegon, MI 49442

Mercy Counseling and Recovery Center
1771 Wells Street
Muskegon, MI 49442

West Michigan Therapy, Inc.
130 East Apple Avenue
Muskegon, MI 49442

MUSKEGON HEIGHTS

East Side Substance Abuse Clinic
445 East Sherman Boulevard
Muskegon Heights, MI 49444

NEW BALTIMORE

Harbor Oak Hospital/Pioneer Health Care
35031 23 Mile Road
New Baltimore, MI 48047

Personal Home Care Services, Inc. Center for Counseling
32743 23 Mile Road
New Baltimore, MI 48047-1985

Self and Others
33497 23 Mile Road, Suite 130
New Baltimore, MI 48047

NEWBERRY

LMAS Addiction Services
County Road 428
Hamilton Lake Road
Newberry, MI 49868

NEW HAVEN

Community Human Services, Inc.
57737 Gratiot Avenue
New Haven, MI 48048

NILES

Addiction Recovery Centers, Inc.
306 East Main Street
Niles, MI 49120

Lakeland KADAC Holding Co.
1209 South 11th Street, Unit 14
Niles, MI 49120

NORTHVILLE

**Hegira Programs, Inc.
Northville Counseling Center**
115 North Center Street
Suite 202
Northville, MI 48167

Northville Psychiatric Hospital
41001 West Seven Mile Road
Northville, MI 48167

NORTON SHORES

**Alcohol and Chemical Abuse
Consultants, Inc.**
427 Seminole Street
Norton Shores, MI 49441

NOVI

Insight Recovery Center
24230 Karim Boulevard
Suite 303
Novi, MI 48375

**Orchard Hills Psychiatric
Center Substance Abuse
Services**
40000 Grand River, Suite 306
Novi, MI 48375

Saint Joseph Mercy Hospital
39575 West Ten Mile Road
Suite 202
Novi, MI 48375

OAK PARK

**Lutheran Child and Family
Services of Michigan
Substance Abuse Services**
15160 West Eight Mile Road
Oak Park, MI 48237

**Metropolitan Rehabilitation
Clinics**
21700 Greenfield Street
Suite 130
Oak Park, MI 48237

OSCODA

**Birchwood Center for Chemical
Dependency**
5671 Skeel Avenue
Oscoda, MI 48750

OTTER LAKE

**Turning Point Recovery Center
Otter Lake Residential Unit**
6727 Sherman Drive
Otter Lake, MI 48464

OWOSSO

Catholic Social Services
120 West Exchange Street
Suite 204
Owosso, MI 48867

**Memorial Healthcare Plus
Positive Alts Counseling/
Education**
1488 North M-52
Owosso, MI 48867

PAW PAW

Gateway
181 West Michigan Street
Paw Paw, MI 49079

**New Journey Substance Abuse
Program**
410 East Michigan Street
Paw Paw, MI 49079

PETOSKEY

CHIP Counseling Center
2503 Charlevoix Avenue
Petoskey, MI 49770

Harbor Hall
704 Emmet Street
Petoskey, MI 49770

**Little Traverse Bay Bands of
Odawa Indians Substance
Abuse Programs**
1345 U.S. 31 North
Petoskey, MI 49770

**Northern Michigan Community
Mental Health Dual Diagnosis
Program**
1 MacDonald Drive, Suite B
Petoskey, MI 49770

**Northern Michigan Hospitals
Harbor Hall Outpatient
Substance Abuse Program**
820 Arlington Street
Petoskey, MI 49770

**Women's Resource Center of
Northern Michigan, Inc.**
423 Porter Street
Petoskey, MI 49770

PLAINWELL

**Pathways Psychological
Associates**
112 East Chart Street
Plainwell, MI 49080

PLYMOUTH

**Growth Works Counseling and
Intervention Services**
271 South Main Street
Plymouth, MI 48170

**Orchard Hills Psychiatric
Center**
199 North Main Street, Suite 202
Plymouth, MI 48170

**Personalized Nursing Light
House, Inc.**
575 Main Street, Suite 6
Plymouth, MI 48170

PONTIAC

**Catholic Social Services of
Oakland County**
53 Franklin Boulevard
Pontiac, MI 48341

El Centro La Familia
35 West Huron Street, Suite 200
Pontiac, MI 48342

Mercy Network Central
35 West Huron Street
Pontiac, MI 48342

**Oakland Family Services
Substance Abuse Services**
114 Orchard Lake Road
Pontiac, MI 48341

**Parkview Company Counseling
Center**
989 University Drive, Suite 2
Pontiac, MI 48342

**Pontiac General Hospital and
Medical Center North
Oakland Medical Center**
461 West Huron Street
Pontiac, MI 48341-1651

**Procare at Pontiac Osteopathic
Hospital**
24 East Huron Street
Pontiac, MI 48342

Chemical Dependency Unit
50 North Perry Street
Pontiac, MI 48058

Residential Unit
16 1/2 East Huron Street
Pontiac, MI 48342

Saint Joseph Mercy Hospital
900 Woodward Avenue
Pontiac, MI 48341

Sequoia Recovery Services
363 West Huron Street
Pontiac, MI 48341

Turning Point Recovery Center
Completion House
54 Seneca Street
Pontiac, MI 48342-2349

University Unit/Outpatient
Counseling
131 University Drive
Pontiac, MI 48342

Woodward Counseling, Inc.
35 South Johnson Street
Suite 3D
Pontiac, MI 48341

PORTAGE

**Mid-America Psychological
Services**
8036 Moorsbridge Road
Portage, MI 49024

PORT HURON

**Blue Lake Residential Care
Facilities Clearview
Substance Abuse Services**
1406 8th Street
Port Huron, MI 48060

**Catholic Social Services of Saint
Clair County/Substance Abuse
Services**
2601 13th Street
Port Huron, MI 48060

**Center for Human Resources
Military Street**
1001 Military Street
Port Huron, MI 48060

Cornell Center
1025 Court Street
Port Huron, MI 48060

**Professional Counseling Center
PC**
520 Superior Street
Port Huron, MI 48060

REDFORD

**Botsford Family Service Center
Substance Abuse Services**
26905 Grand River Avenue
Redford, MI 48240

Redford Counseling Center
25945 West 7 Mile Road
Redford, MI 48240

REED CITY

**Human Aid, Inc. Substance
Abuse Services**
834 South Chestnut Street
Reed City, MI 49677

RICHMOND

MaComb Family Services, Inc.
67515 Main Street, Suite C
Richmond, MI 48062

ROCHESTER HILLS

Eastwood Clinics
725 Barclay Circle Drive
Suite 215
Rochester Hills, MI 48307-4512

Oakland Family Services
1460 Walton Boulevard, Suite 220
Rochester Hills, MI 48309

ROMEO

**Community Human Services,
Inc.**
332 South Main Street
Romeo, MI 48065

ROMULUS

**Hegira Programs, Inc. Romulus
Help Center**
9340 Wayne Road
Suite A
Romulus, MI 48174

Transitions of Michigan
9844 Harrison Road
Romulus, MI 48174

ROSEVILLE

Parkview Counseling Center
27115 Gratiot Street
Roseville, MI 48066

ROYAL OAK

**Catholic Social Services of
Oakland County/Talbott
Center**
1424 East 11 Mile Road
Royal Oak, MI 48067

Eastwood Community Clinics
30701 North Woodward Avenue
Suite 200
Royal Oak, MI 48073

Residential Substance Abuse
Treatment Program
1515 North Stephenson Highway
Royal Oak, MI 48067

SAGINAW

**Aleda E. Lutz VA Medical
Center**
1500 Weiss Street
Saginaw, MI 48602

**American Comprehensive
Treatment Services, Inc.**
1527 South Washington Street
Saginaw, MI 48601

**Arete Community Treatment
Centers**
709 Lapeer Street
Saginaw, MI 48607

**Boysville of Michigan, Inc.
Holland House**
614 East Holland Avenue
Saginaw, MI 48601

**Catholic Family Service Family
Counseling Services**
710 North Michigan Avenue
Saginaw, MI 48602

Dot Caring Centers, Inc.
Halfway House/Residential
Center
1915 Fordney Street
Saginaw, MI 48601

Saginaw Valley Center
3190 Hallmark Court
Saginaw, MI 48603

**Health Source Saginaw Pathway
Chemical Dependency
Services**
3340 Hospital Road
Saginaw, MI 48603

Insight Recovery Center
3216 Christy Way
Saginaw, MI 48602

**Intervention and Rehab
Associates, Inc.**
1616 Court Street
Saginaw, MI 48602

**Restoration Community
Outreach**
1205 Norman Street
Saginaw, MI 48601

Saginaw Odyssey House
128 North Warren Street
Saginaw, MI 48607

**Saginaw Psychological Services,
Inc.**
2100 Hemmeter Street
Saginaw, MI 48603

**Samaritan Counseling Center of
Saginaw Valley**
2405 Bay Street
Faith Lutheran Church
Saginaw, MI 48602

**STM Clinic Mental Health and
Substance Abuse Services**
1 Tuscola Street, Suite 302
Saginaw, MI 48607

SAINT CLAIR SHORES

Cube
22811 Greater Mack Avenue
Hampton Square Building
Suite 107
Saint Clair Shores, MI 48080

**Down River Mental Health
Clinic Advanced Counseling
Services**
19501 East Eight Mile Road
Saint Clair Shores, MI 48080

**Henry Ford Health Systems
Behavioral Services**
21603 Eleven Mile Road, Suite 1
Saint Clair Shores, MI 48081

**Pro Med Management Evergreen
Counseling Centers**
19900 10 Mile Road
Saint Clair Shores, MI 48081

SAINT IGNACE

**American Indian Substance
Abuse Program**
225 Waseh Drive
Saint Ignace, MI 49781

**LMAS Health Department
Substance Abuse Program/
Mackinac County**
749 Hombach Street
Saint Ignace, MI 49781

SAINT JOHNS

**Clinton County Counseling
Center**
1000 East Sturgis Street
Saint Johns, MI 48879

SAINT JOSEPH

Kadac Hold Gateway Services
1234 Napier Avenue
Saint Joseph, MI 49085

SAINT LOUIS

Recovery Unlimited
215 West Saginaw Street
Saint Louis, MI 48880

SANDUSKY

**Sanilac County Health
Department Alcohol and Drug
Program**
171 Dawson Street
Sandusky, MI 48471

SAULT SAINTE MARIE

**American Indian Substance
Abuse Program**
2154 Shunk Road
Sault Sainte Marie, MI 49783

**Great Lakes Recovery Center,
Inc.**
New Hope House/Men
301 East Spruce Street
Sault Sainte Marie, MI 49783

New Hope House/Women
1111 Minneapolis Street
Sault Sainte Marie, MI 49783

**Upper Michigan Behavioral
Health Services**
500 Osborne Boulevard
Sault Sainte Marie, MI 49783

SHELBY TOWNSHIP

Devon Center
52188 Van Dyke Street, Suite 320
Shelby Township, MI 48316-1863

MaComb Family Services
45445 Mound Road Suite 109
Shelby Township, MI 48316

**Pro Med Management Evergreen
Counseling Centers**
53950 Van Dyke Street
Shelby Township, MI 48087

SOUTHFIELD

**Burdette and Doss Associates
Psychological Services**
17352 West 12 Mile Road
Suite 100
Southfield, MI 48076

Central Therapeutic Services, Inc.
17600 West 8 Mile Road
Suite 7
Southfield, MI 48075

Clark and Associates Psychological Services
16250 Northland Drive
Suite 245
Southfield, MI 48075

Counseling Associates
26699 West 12 Mile Road
Suite 100
Southfield, MI 48034

Family Service of Detroit and Wayne Counties
15565 Northland Street
Suite 505 West
Southfield, MI 48075

Oakland Psychological Clinic PC Substance Abuse Services
21700 Northwestern Highway
Suite 750
Southfield, MI 48075

Pathway Family Center
22190 Providence Road Suite 300
Southfield, MI 48075

Providence Hospital and Medical Center
16001 West 9 Mile Road
Southfield, MI 48037

Wedgewood Christian Counseling Center
17117 West 9 Mile Road
Suite 1325
Southfield, MI 48075

SOUTHGATE

Downriver Guidance Clinic
131010 Allen Road
Southgate, MI 48195

Family Services, Inc
13331 Reeck Road
Southgate, MI 48195

SOUTH HAVEN

Black River Counseling Group
352 Blue Star Highway
South Haven, MI 49090

New Journey Substance Abuse Program
300 Kalamazoo Street
South Haven, MI 49090

STANTON

Omega Counseling Centers
111 East Main Street, Suite B
Stanton, MI 48888

STERLING

Sterling Area Health Center
725 East State Street
Sterling, MI 48659

STERLING HEIGHTS

Crossroads Counseling Center
38850 Van Dyke Street, Suite 102
Sterling Heights, MI 48312

Pro Med Management Evergreen Counseling Centers
33200 Dequindre Road
Suite 200
Sterling Heights, MI 48310

Pioneer Counseling Center
36250 Dequindre Road
Suite 310
Sterling Heights, MI 48310

Professional Counseling Associates
36250 Dequindre Road, Suite 320
Sterling Heights, MI 48310

STURGIS

Michiana Addiction and Prevention Services
300 West Chicago Street
Suite 1212
Sturgis, MI 49091

SUTTONS BAY

Grand Traverse Band of Ottawa Chippewa Indians Substance Abuse Services
2300 North Stallman Road
Suttons Bay, MI 49682

TAWAS CITY

Ausable Valley Community Mental Health Substance Abuse Services
1199 West Harris Avenue
Tawas City, MI 48763

TAYLOR

Community Care Services Substance Abuse Service
26650 Eureka Road
Taylor, MI 48180

Downriver Mental Health/ Advanced Psychiatric Services Chemical Dependency Program
20600 Eureka Road, Suite 819
Taylor, MI 48180

TECUMSEH

Sage Center for Substance Abuse Treatment at Bixby Medical Center
415 East Kilbuck Street
Tecumseh, MI 49286

TEMPERANCE

Catholic Social Services of Monroe County
8330 Lewis Street
Temperance, MI 48182

THREE RIVERS

Michiana Addiction and Prevention Services
222 South Main Street
Three Rivers, MI 49093

TRAVERSE CITY

Addiction Treatment Services Inc
940 East 8th Street
Traverse City, MI 49686

Bay Area Counseling
2226 South Airport Road West
Suite C
Traverse City, MI 49684

Catholic Human Services
1000 Hastings Street
Traverse City, MI 49686

Charles Bethea Associates
2046B South Airport Road
Traverse City, MI 49684

Grand Traverse Band of Ottawa/Chippewa Indians Substance Abuse Services
940 East 8th Street
Traverse City, MI 49684

Great Lakes Community Health
701 South Elmwood Street
Suite 19
Traverse City, MI 49684

Rubritius, Jeffrey W., MSW
13685 Southwest Bay Shore Drive
Suite 106-W
Traverse City, MI 49684

Munson Medical Center Alcohol and Drug Treatment Center
1105 6 Street
Traverse City, MI 49684

Northern Michigan Alcoholism and Addiction Treatment Services, Inc.
116 East 8 Street
Traverse City, MI 49684

Phoenix Hall
445 East State Street
Traverse City, MI 49684

Wedgewood Christian Counseling Center
3301 Veterans Drive
Suite 125
Traverse City, MI 49684

TRENTON

Oakwood Healthcare Systems
5450 Fort Street
Trenton, MI 48183

TROY

Insight
631 East Big Beaver Road
Suite 111
Troy, MI 48083

Perspectives of Troy PC
2690 Crooks Road
Suite 300
Troy, MI 48084

Rivers Bend PC
33975 Dequindre Street, Suite 5
Troy, MI 48083

WAKEFIELD

Gogebic Community Mental Health
103 West U.S. 2
Wakefield, MI 49968

WALKER

Northwest Counseling Center
3755 Remembrance Road NW
Walker, MI 49504

WALLED LAKE

Oakland Family Services
2045 West Maple Road
Suite D 405
Walled Lake, MI 48088

WARREN

Catholic Social Services of Macomb Substance Abuse Program
12434 East 12 Mile Road
Suite 201
Warren, MI 48093

Harper/Warren Chemical Dependency Program
4050 East 12 Mile Road
Warren, MI 48092

Horizon Health System Community Hospital
26091 Sherwood Street, Suite 4-A
Warren, MI 48091-1296

Medical Resource Center, Inc. Michigan Counseling Services
23700 Van Dyke Avenue
Warren, MI 48089

Michigan Psychological Center, Inc.
26451 Ryan Road
Warren, MI 48091

Sacred Heart Rehabilitation Center, Inc.
28573 Schoenherr Street
Warren, MI 48093

WATERFORD

Catholic Social Services of Oakland County/Waterford
6637 Highland Road
Waterford, MI 48327

Community Programs, Inc.
1435 North Oakland Boulevard
Waterford, MI 48327

Perfect Solutions, Inc.
2710 Dixie Highway, Suite C
Waterford, MI 48328-1711

WATERSMEET

Lac Vieux Desert Substance Abuse Program
Choate Road
Watersmeet, MI 49969

WEST BLOOMFIELD

Affordable Counseling
5745 West Maple Road
Suite 207
West Bloomfield, MI 48322

Henry Ford Maplegrove Center Behavioral Services
6773 West Maple Road
Maplegrove Center
West Bloomfield, MI 48322

New Oakland Child and Adolescent Family Center
5600 West Maple Road
Suite D-402
West Bloomfield, MI 48322

New Start, Inc.
5839 West Maple Road
Suite 112
West Bloomfield, MI 48322

WEST BRANCH

Ausable Valley Comm. Mental Health Center
Substance Abuse Program
511 Griffin Street
West Branch, MI 48661

Substance Acute Detox
403 East Houghton Avenue
West Branch, MI 48661

WESTLAND

Hegira Programs, Inc. Westland Counseling Center
8623 North Wayne Street
Suite 310
Westland, MI 48185

Oakwood Healthcare Systems
2001 South Merriman Road, Suite 500
Westland, MI 48186

Pro Med Management Evergreen Counseling Centers
8623 North Wayne Road
Suite 200
Westland, MI 48185

WETMORE

LMAS Addiction Services Alger County
9526 Prospect Avenue
Wetmore, MI 49895

WILSON

Hannahville Health Center
14925-N Hannahville Road
Suite B-1
Wilson, MI 49896

WYANDOTTE

Henry Ford Wyandotte Hospital
2333 Biddle Avenue
Wyandotte, MI 48192

Wyandotte Health Center Substance Abuse Services
1622 Eureka Street
Wyandotte, MI 48192

YPSILANTI

Beyer Hospital Chemical Dependency Services
135 South Prospect Street
Ypsilanti, MI 48198

Christine Morgan and Therry Ministering Center
948 Watling Boulevard
Ypsilanti, MI 48197

Dawn, Inc. Dawn Farm
6633 Stony Creek Road
Ypsilanti, MI 48197

MINNESOTA

AH-GWAH-CHING

Lakeside Center Chemical Dependency Services
723 Ah-Gwah-Ching Road
Ah-Gwah-Ching, MN 56430

AITKEN

Northland Counseling Center
936 2nd Street NW
Aitkin, MN 56431-1104

ALBERT LEA

Fountain Lake Treatment Center
408 Fountain Street
Albert Lea, MN 56007

ALEXANDRIA

Douglas County Hospital Chemical Dependency Unit
700 Cedar Street
Marian Building, Suite 154
Alexandria, MN 56308

ANOKA

Anoka/Metro Regional Treatment Center
3300 4 Avenue North
Anoka, MN 55303

Riverplace Counseling Center
1814 South Ferry Street
Anoka, MN 55303

Transformation House
1410 South Ferry Street
Anoka, MN 55303

Transformation House II
2532 North Ferry Street
Anoka, MN 55303

AUSTIN

Agape Halfway House, Inc.
200 5 Street SW
Austin, MN 55912

Austin Med Center Behavioral Health Center Chemical Dependency Services
101 14th Street NW, Suite 4
Austin, MN 55912

BARNESVILLE

Red River Serenity Manor, Inc.
123 2 Street NE
Barnesville, MN 56514

BEMIDJI

Counseling Associates of Bemidji
3217 Bemidji Avenue North
Bemidji, MN 56601

Lakes Region Chemical Dependency
1411 Bemidji Avenue
Bemidji, MN 56601

Upper MS Mental Health Center Program for Addictions Recovery
722 15 Street
Bemidji, MN 56601

BRAINERD

Adapt of Minnesota
510 Bluff Avenue
Brainerd, MN 56401

Brainerd Regional Human Services Center Aurora Chemical Dependency Program
1777 Highway 18 East
Brainerd, MN 56401

Break Free Adolescent Outpatient
2801 Andrew Street
Brainerd, MN 56401

Saint Joseph's Medical Center Focus Unit
523 North 3 Street
Brainerd, MN 56401

BRECKENRIDGE

Saint Francis Medical Center Hope Unit
401 Oak Street
Breckenridge, MN 56520

BROOKLYN CENTER

Allina Behavioral Health Services Brooklyn Center Program
6200 Shingle Creek Parkway
Brookdale Corporate Center
Suite 480
Brooklyn Center, MN 55430

BUFFALO

Central Minnesota Mental Health Center
105 2nd Avenue NE
Buffalo, MN 55313

Professional Counseling Center of Buffalo
Wright One Plaza
Highway 55 West
Buffalo, MN 55313

BURNSVILLE

Fairview Ridges Hospital
Adult Chemical Program
156 Cobblestone Lane
Burnsville, MN 55337

River Ridge Nonresidential Treatment Center
1515 East Highway 13
Burnsville, MN 55337

Riverside Medical Center
1510 East 122nd Street
Burnsville, MN 55337

CAMBRIDGE

Cambridge Memorial Hospital Dellwood Recovery Center
701 South Dellwood Avenue
Cambridge, MN 55008

CASS LAKE

Ahnji-Be-Mah-Diz Center Leech Lake Halfway House
421 3rd Street NE
Cass Lake, MN 56633

CENTER CITY

Hazelden Foundation
15245 Pleasant Valley Road
Center City, MN 55012

CHASKA

Stafford CD Treatment Center, Inc.
212 Walnut Street
Chaska, MN 55318

CLOQUET

Liberalis Womens Program
512 Skyline Boulevard
Cloquet, MN 55720

COTTAGE GROVE

Anthony Lewis Center
7064 West Point Douglas Road
Suite 102
Cottage Grove, MN 55016

CROOKSTON

Glenmore Recovery Center
323 South Minnesota Street
Crookston, MN 56716

DELANO

Professional Counseling Center of Delano
500 Highway 12
Delano, MN 55328

DETROIT LAKES

Glenmore Clinic Outpatient Program
714 Lake Avenue
Detroit Lakes, MN 56501

Lakes Counseling Center
211 West Holmes Street
Detroit Lakes, MN 56501

DULUTH

Equay-Say-Way Treatment Center
205 West 2nd Street, Suite 150
Duluth, MN 55802

Marty Mann Halfway House
714 North 11 Avenue East
Duluth, MN 55805

Messabi Work Release Program
23 Mesaba Avenue
Duluth, MN 55806

Miller Dawn Medical Center, Inc. Chemical Dependency
502 East 2nd Street
Duluth, MN 55805

Port Rehabilitation Center
23 Mesaba Avenue
Duluth, MN 55806

**Pride Institute Outpatient
Program**
205 West 2nd Street, Suite 448
Duluth, MN 55801

**Thunderbird and Wren Halfway
House**
229 North 4 Avenue West
Duluth, MN 55806

EAGAN

**Twin Town Treatment Center
Eagan Outpatient**
2121 Cliff Drive, Suite 101
Eagan, MN 55122

EAST GRAND FORKS

Northwest Recovery Center, Inc.
910 Central Avenue
East Grand Forks, MN 56721

EDEN PRAIRIE

Pride Institute
14400 Martin Drive
Eden Prairie, MN 55344

**Regents Hospital/New
Connections Programs Eden
Prairie Outpatient Treatment**
6446 City West Parkway
Suite 205
Eden Prairie, MN 55344

EDINA

**Allina Behavioral Health
Services**
3400 West 66th Street
Southdale Place, Suite 385
Edina, MN 55435

Fairview Recovery Services
Chemical Dependency Treatment
Program
3101 West 69 Street
Edina, MN 55435

Outpatient
Services
7600 France Avenue
Edina, MN 55435

ELY

Arrowhead Center, Inc.
118 South 4 Avenue East
Ely, MN 55731

FAIRMONT

**Chain of Lakes Behavioral
Health Services Inc**
Rural Route 1
Fairmont, MN 56031

Sunrise Recovery Center
Rural Route 1
Fairmont, MN 56031

FARIBAULT

Faribault Family Focus
303 NE 1st Ave
Suite 110
Faribault, MN 55021

New Dimensions Program
1101 Linden Lane
Faribault, MN 55021-6400

FARMINGTON

Journey Counseling Services
209 Oak Street
Farmington, MN 55024

FERGUS FALLS

**Fergus Falls Regional
Treatment Center Chemical
Dependency Services**
1400 North Union Avenue
Fergus Falls, MN 56537

**Lakeland Mental Health Center,
Inc. Chemical Dependency
Outpatient Program**
126 East Alcott Avenue
Fergus Falls, MN 56537

Lakes Region Halfway House
217 North Union Avenue
Fergus Falls, MN 56537

FOREST LAKE

Fairview Recovery Services
Adolescent Residential Treatment
Program
246 11th Avenue SE
Forest Lake, MN 55025

Outpatient Program
1120 SE 4th Street
Forest Lake, MN 55025

FRIDLEY

Transformation House I
351-7 4th Avenue NE
Fridley, MN 55432

GRAND MARAIS

**Cook County Social Services
North Shore Chemical
Dependency Outpatient
Program**
Arrowhead Professional Building
Grand Marais, MN 55604

GRAND PORTAGE

**Grand Portage Chemical
Dependency Services**
Grand Portage, MN 55605

GRAND RAPIDS

Hope House of Itasca County
604 South Pokegama Avenue
Grand Rapids, MN 55744

**North Homes, Inc. Adolescent
Outpatient Program**
924 County Home Road
Grand Rapids, MN 55744

**Northland Recovery Center
Substance Abuse Services**
1215 7 Avenue SE
Grand Rapids, MN 55744

**Rapids Counseling Services,
Inc.**
717 NE 4th Street
Grand Rapids, MN 55744

GRANITE FALLS

Project Turnabout
660 18 Street
Granite Falls, MN 56241

HASTINGS

Cochran Programs
1200 East 18th Street, Building 4
Hastings, MN 55033

Dakota County Receiving Center
1200 East 18 Street, Building 1
Hastings, MN 55033

Twin Town Dakota County Jail Program Dakota County Workhouse
1580 West Highway 55
Hastings, MN 55033

HIBBING

University Medical Center Mesabi Outpatient
750 34th Street East
Hibbing, MN 55746

HOPKINS

Omegon Inc
2000 Hopkins Crossroads
Hopkins, MN 55305

HUTCHINSON

Hutchinson Community Hospital
Outpatient Chemical Dependency Program
Hutchinson Receiving Center
1095 Highway 15 South
Hutchinson, MN 55350

INTERNATIONAL FALLS

Northland Counseling Center
1404 Highway 71
International Falls, MN 56649

Rational Alternatives, Inc.
206 14 Street East
International Falls, MN 56649

JACKSON

Ashley House, Inc. DBA Road to Recovery
308 West Ashley Street
Jackson, MN 56143

LA CRESCENT

Counseling Clinic of La Crescent
33 South Walnut Street
La Crescent, MN 55947

LITCHFIELD

Charter Behavioral Health Systems of Litchfield
114 North Holcombe Street
Litchfield, MN 55355

LITTLE FALLS

Effective Living Center, Inc.
72 East Broadway
Little Falls, MN 56345

Saint Gabriel's Hospital Chemical Dependency Unit
815 SE 2 Street
Little Falls, MN 56345

LITTLEFORK

Pineview Recovery Center
912 Main Street
Littlefork, MN 56653

LORETTO

Vinland National Center
Lake Independence
Loretto, MN 55357

LUVERNE

Southwestern Mental Health Center
2 Round Wind Road
Luverne, MN 56156

MAHNOMEN

Mahnomen County Human Services Outpatient Treatment
311 North Main Street
Mahnomen, MN 56557

MANKATO

Addictions Recovery Technologies
12 Civic Center Plaza
Suite 2116
Mankato, MN 56001

House of Hope
119 Fulton Street
Mankato, MN 56001

Immanuel/Saint Joseph's Hospital Family Recovery Program
1025 Marsh Street
5th Floor
Mankato, MN 56001

MAPLE LAKE

Maple Lake Recovery Center
207 Division Street
Maple Lake, MN 55358

MARSHALL

Project Turnabout
1220 Birch Street
Marshall, MN 56258

MINNEAPOLIS

African American Family Services
2616 Nicollet Avenue South
Minneapolis, MN 55408

Allina Behavioral Health Services
825 Nicollet Avenue, Suite 1020
Minneapolis, MN 55402-2614

American Indian Services, Inc.
2200 Park Avenue South
Minneapolis, MN 55404

Anthony Louis Center
1000 Paul Parkway
Minneapolis, MN 55434

Bridgeway Treatment Center
22 27 Avenue SE
Minneapolis, MN 55414

Changing Lifestyle Counseling of Saint Louis Park
7515 Wayzata Boulevard
Suite 202
Minneapolis, MN 55426

Chemical Health Advisory Services, Inc. DBA Basics
2415 Emerson Avenue South
Minneapolis, MN 55405

Chicanos Latinos Unidos En Servicio
2110 Nicollet Avenue
Minneapolis, MN 55404-2528

Chrysalis Center for Women
2650 Nicollet Avenue South
Minneapolis, MN 55408

Community Health and Human Services
4149 Lyndale Avenue North
Minneapolis, MN 55412

Community University Health Care Center Southeast Asian Outpatient Program
2001 Bloomington Avenue South
Minneapolis, MN 55404

Create, Inc.
1911 Pleasant Avenue
Minneapolis, MN 55403

Telesis
1345 Shenandoah Lane
Hennepin County Adult
    Workhouse
Minneapolis, MN 55447

Eden Programs, Inc.
Eden Day Mens Program
1025 Portland Avenue South
Minneapolis, MN 55404

Eden Renew Outpatient Program
Eden Women's Program
2649 Park Avenue South
Minneapolis, MN 55407

Fairview Recovery Services
Adolescent Program
Adult Inpatient Program
Hearing Impaired Chemical
Dependency Program
2450 Riverside Avenue
Minneapolis, MN 55454

Adolescent Outpatient
2960 Winnetka Avenue North
Suite 101
Minneapolis, MN 55427

Hazelden Center for Youth and Families
11505 36th Avenue North
Minneapolis, MN 55441

Health Recovery Center, Inc.
3255 Hennepin Avenue South
Minneapolis, MN 55408

HFA Addiction Medicine
914 South 8th Street, Suite D-131
Minneapolis, MN 55404

Intervention Institute
349 13th Avenue NE
Minneapolis, MN 55413

Lifestyle Counseling of Richfield/Bloomington
9607 Girard Avenue South
Minneapolis, MN 55431

Living Word Recovery Services
7308 Aspen Lane, Suite 153-A
Minneapolis, MN 55428

Minnesota Indian Women's Resource Center
2300 15 Avenue South
Minneapolis, MN 55404

Minneapolis Psychiatric Institute Abbott/Northwestern Hospital Campus
800 East 28th Street
Wasie Center, 4th Floor
Minneapolis, MN 55407-3799

Mission Care Detox Center
3409 East Medicine Lake
    Boulevard
Minneapolis, MN 55441

My Home/Excelsior Project Inc Outpatient Program
2344 Nicollet Avenue South
Suite 20
Minneapolis, MN 55401

New Connection Programs Blaine Outpatient Treatment
10267 University Avenue NE
Minneapolis, MN 55434

Nuway House II
2518 First Avenue South
Minneapolis, MN 55404

On Belay House
115 Forestview Lane North
Minneapolis, MN 55441-5910

Park Avenue Center
2525 Park Avenue
Minneapolis, MN 55404

Pathways Psychological Services Outpatient Program
7575 Golden Valley Road
Suite 119
Minneapolis, MN 55427

Pride Institute Outpatient Program
1406 West Lake Street, Suite 204
Minneapolis, MN 55408

Prodigal House
5103 Minnehaha Avenue South
Minnesota Veterans Home Bldg 1
Minneapolis, MN 55417

Progress Valley I
3033 Garfield Avenue South
Minneapolis, MN 55408

Progress Valley II
308 East 78th Street
Minneapolis, MN 55423

Recovery Resource Center
1900 Chicago Avenue
Minneapolis, MN 55404

River Ridge Treatment Center
700 South 3rd Street, Suite 101
Minneapolis, MN 55415

Salvation Army Harbor Light
Beacon Program
1010 Currie Avenue North
Minneapolis, MN 55405

3 RS Counseling Center
2220 Central Avenue NE
Minneapolis, MN 55413

Turning Point, Inc.
1500 Golden Valley Road
Minneapolis, MN 55405

1105 16 Avenue North
Minneapolis, MN 55411

Unity Hospital Substance Abuse Services
550 Osborne Road 2 East
Minneapolis, MN 55432

Veterans' Affairs Medical Center Addictive Disorders Section
1 Veterans Drive
Highway 55 and County 62
Minneapolis, MN 55417

Wayside House, Inc.
3705 Park Center Boulevard
Minneapolis, MN 55416

West Metro Recovery Services
5810 North 42nd Avenue
Minneapolis, MN 55331

MINNETONKA

New Connection Programs
Adolescent Outpatient Program
Hennepin County Home School
14300 County Road 62
Minnetonka, MN 55345

Regents Hospital Home School Program
14300 County Road, Suite 62
Minnetonka, MN 55345

River Ridge Nonresidential Treatment Center
15612 West Highway 7
Highwood Office Center Suite 150
Minnetonka, MN 55345

MONTICELLO

Big Lake Community Hospital Counseling Center
407 Washington Street
Monticello, MN 55362

MOORHEAD

Clay County Receiving Center
715 North 11 Street
Moorhead, MN 56560

Wellness Center of Fargo/ Moorhead
403 Center Avenue
Suite 409
Moorhead, MN 56560

MORRIS

Stevens Community Memorial Hospital New Beginning Center
400 East First Street
Morris, MN 56267

MORTON

Lower Sioux Alcoholism Program
Route 1
Morton, MN 56270

NAVARRE

Lifestyle Counseling of Mound
2389 Blaine Avenue
Navarre, MN 55392

NETT LAKE

Anishinaabe Miikana Gidamaajitaamin Bois Forte
13090 Westley Drive
Nett Lake, MN 55772

NEVIS

Pine Manor, Inc. Chemical Dependency Services
Route 2
Nevis, MN 56467

NEW BRIGHTON

Amethyst Counseling Services Outpatient Chemical Dependency Treatment Services
1405 Silver Lake Road
New Brighton, MN
55112

NEW ULM

Brown County Detox and Evaluation Center
510 North Front Street
New Ulm, MN 56073

New Ulm Medical Center
1324 North 5 Street
New Ulm, MN 56073

NORTHFIELD

Northfield Family Focus
220 Division Street
Northfield, MN 55057

OAKDALE

We Care Counseling Center
6060 50 Street North, Suite 1
Oakdale, MN 55128

OWATONNA

Owatonna Family Focus
215 Sout Oak Avenue
Owatonna, MN 55060

West Hills Lodge, Inc.
545 Florence Avenue
Owatonna, MN 55060

PINE CITY

Meadow Creek
Route 4
Pine City, MN 55063

Pine Shores Chemical Dependency Services
Route 2
Pine City, MN 55063

PIPESTONE

Southwest Mental Health Center
1016 8th Avenue SW
Pipestone, MN 56164

PLYMOUTH

Ark Counseling of Plymouth
1884 Berkshire Street
Plymouth, MN 55447

PRESTON

Visions
124 Main Street
Preston, MN 55965

PRIOR LAKE

Lifestyle Counseling Services
16511 Anna Trail SE
Suite C
Prior Lake, MN 55372

REDBY

**Northern Winds Treatment
    Center Oosh Kii Mii Kah Nah**
Redby, MN 56670

**Red Lake Group Home
    Adolescent Inpatient Program**
Redby, MN 56670

**Red Lake Tribal Substance
    Abuse Prevention Programs**
Redby, MN 56670

REDWOOD FALLS

**Project Turnabout/Redwood
    Falls Outpatient Program**
334 South Jefferson Street
Redwood Falls, MN 56283

RICHFIELD

Progress Valley II
308 East 78 Street
Richfield, MN 55423

ROCHESTER

**Aiimsonion Clinic Chemical
    Dependency Program**
300 3 Avenue SE
Ironwood Square Suite 206
Rochester, MN 55904

**Charter Behavioral Health
    Systems of Rochester**
333 16th Avenue NW
Rochester, MN 55901

Dunatos Outpatient Program
Rochester, MN 55903

Fountain Center
4104 18 Street NW
Cedarwood Mall
Rochester, MN 55901

**Franciscan Skemp Health Care
    Center**
1623 4th Street NW
Rochester, MN 55901-1827

Gables, The
604 5 Street SW
Rochester, MN 55902

Guest House
4800 48 Street NE
Rochester, MN 55903

**Mayo Adult Chemical
    Dependency Treatment Center**
1216 2nd Street SW
Generose Building, First Floor East
Rochester, MN 55902

**Mayo Foundations Outpatient
    Addictions Service**
121 2nd Street SW
Generose Building
Rochester, MN 55905

Pathway House
613 2nd Street SW
Rochester, MN 55902

Pathway to Parenthood
103 6 Avenue SW
Rochester, MN 55902

**Zumbro Valley Mental Health
    Center, Inc.**
Crisis Receiving Unit
2116 SE Campus Drive
Suite 105
Rochester, MN 55904

Recovery Basics
1932 Viking Drive NW
Rochester, MN 55906

Right to Recovery Program
917 North Broadway Street
Rochester, MN 55906

ROSEAU

**Glenmore Recovery Center
    Outpatient Clinic**
101 South Main Street
Roseau, MN 56751

SAINT CLOUD

**Central Minnesota Mental
    Health Center Alcohol and
    Drug Abuse Services**
1321 13th Street North
Saint Cloud, MN 56303

Effective Living Center, Inc.
114 1st Avenue West
Saint Cloud, MN 56301

Focus 12 Halfway House
3220 North 8 Street
Saint Cloud, MN 56303

Journey Home
210 5 Avenue NE
Saint Cloud, MN 56304

Passage Home
1003 South 8 Avenue
Saint Cloud, MN 56301

**Saint Cloud Hospital Recovery
    Plus**
1406 North 6 Avenue
Saint Cloud, MN 56301

**Veterans' Affairs Medical Center
    Alcohol/Drug Dependence
    Treatment Program**
4801 North 8 Street
Unit 116C
Saint Cloud, MN 56303

SAINT PAUL

**African American Family
    Services**
1041 Selby Avenue
Saint Paul, MN 55104

Ahrens Residence
1609 Jackson Street
Saint Paul, MN 55117

**Charter Behavioral Health
    Systems of West Saint Paul**
1555 Livingston Avenue
Suite 101
Saint Paul, MN 55118

Conceptual Counseling, Inc.
245 East 6 Street
Suite 435
Saint Paul, MN 55101

Hazelden/Fellowship Club
680 Stewart Avenue
Saint Paul, MN 55102

**Juel Fairbanks Chemical
    Dependency Services, Inc.**
806 North Albert Street
Saint Paul, MN 55104

Kelly Institute
2700 University Avenue West
Suite 20
Saint Paul, MN 55114

Model Cities Family Development Center
839 University Avenue
Saint Paul, MN 55104

Pride Institute Outpatient Program
405 Sibley Street, Suite 125
Saint Paul, MN 55101

Ramsey County Receiving Center
155 East 2nd Street
Saint Paul, MN 55101-1424

Regions Hospital
445 Etna Street, Suite 55
Saint Paul, MN 55106

Saint Joseph Hospital/Health East
Adolescent Behavioral Health Services
Chemical Dependency Program
69 West Exchange Street
Saint Paul, MN 55102

Senior Chemical Dependency Program
1380 Frost Avenue
Saint Paul, MN 55109

Twin Town Treatment Center
1706 University Avenue
Saint Paul, MN 55104

United Hospital Chemical Dependency Services
333 North Smith Avenue
Suite 4900
Saint Paul, MN 55102

SAINT PETER

Charter Behavioral Health System of Saint Peter Outpatient Program
116 South 3rd Street
Saint Peter, MN 56082

Johnson Chemical Dependency Center
100 Freeman Drive
Johnson Hall
Saint Peter, MN 56082

SAWYER

Mash Ka Wisen Treatment Center
Sawyer, MN 55780

SHAKOPEE

Stafford CD Treatment Center, Inc.
1100 East 4 Avenue
Suite 60
Shakopee, MN 55379

STILLWATER

Cedar Ridge, Inc. Extended Care Program
11400 Julianne Avenue North
Stillwater, MN 55082

Stillwater Outpatient
6381 Osgood Avenue
Stillwater, MN 55082

Washington County Jail Program Human Services, Inc.
14900 61st Street North
Stillwater, MN 55082

THIEF RIVER FALLS

Glenmore Recovery Center Outpatient Clinic
621 North Labree Avenue
Thief River Falls, MN 56701

Northwest Recovery Center, Inc.
115 6th Street West
Thief River Falls, MN 56701

TWO HARBORS

Lake View Memorial Hospital Outpatient Chemical Dependency Unit
325 11 Avenue
Two Harbors, MN 55616

VIRGINIA

Arrowhead Center, Inc.
505 12 Avenue West
Virginia, MN 55792

Halfway House
450 Pine Mill Court
Virginia, MN 55792

Range Mental Health Center, Inc. Detoxification Service
901 9 Avenue
Virginia, MN 55792

Twelfth Step House, Inc.
512 2 Street North
Virginia, MN 55792

WABASHA

Hiawatha Valley Mental Health Center
611 Broadway Avenue, Suite 100
Wabasha, MN 55981

WACONIA

Counseling Center of Waconia
24 South Olive Street
Waconia, MN 55387

Cornerstone Recovery Center
301 Industrial Boulevard
Waconia, MN 55387

WADENA

Bell Hill Recovery Center
Wadena, MN 56482

Neighborhood Counseling Center
11 2nd Street SW
Wadena, MN 56482

WASECA

Waseca Family Focus
203 South State Street
Waseca, MN 56093

WAVERLY

Charter Behavioral Health Services
109 North Shore Drive
Waverly, MN 55390

WAYZATA

Way 12 Halfway House
645 East Wayzata Boulevard
Wayzata, MN 55391

WHITE EARTH

Chi-Ska-Wes-Eh Halfway Home
White Earth, MN 56591

**White Earth Chemical
Dependency Program**
Richwood Road
White Earth, MN 56591

WILLMAR

Bradley Center
1550 Highway 71 NE
Willmar Regional Treatment
Center
Willmar, MN 56201

**Cardinal Recovery Center/
Willmar Regional Treatment
Center**
316 Becker Avenue SW
Cardinal Square Suite 323
Willmar, MN 56201

**Cardinals Prairie Youth
Program**
1550 Highway 71 NE
Willmar, MN 56201

Woodland Centers
Apple Tree Square
Highway 12
Willmar, MN 56201

WINNEBAGO

**Adolescent Treatment Center of
Winnebago**
550 Cleveland Avenue West
Winnebago, MN 56098

WINONA

**Franciscan Skemp Behavioral
Health**
Amethyst House
428 West Broadway
Winona, MN 55987

1600 Gilmore Avenue
Suite 110-A
Winona, MN 55987

**Winona Counseling Clinic
Chemical Dependency
Services**
111 Market Street
Winona, MN 55987

WINSTED

Counseling Center of Winsted
551 4 Street North
Winsted, MN 55395

WOODSTOCK

**New Life Treatment Center
County Road**
120 East Dakota
Woodstock, MN 56186

WORTHINGTON

**Addiction Recovery
Technologies of Worthington**
424 10th Street
Worthington, MN 56187

**Southwest Mental Health Center
Challenges**
701 11th Street
Worthington, MN 56187

MISSISSIPPI

BILOXI

Veterans Affairs Medical Center
400 Veterans Avenue
Biloxi, MS 39531

BRANDON

**Region 8 Community Mental
Health Center New Roads
Alcohol and Drug Services**
105 Office Park, Box 88
Brandon, MS 39043

CLARKSDALE

Region I Mental Health Center
Alcohol and Drug Services
1742 Cheryl Street
Health Services Building
Clarksdale, MS 38614

CLINTON

Victory Manor Recovery Center
100 West Northside Drive
Clinton, MS 39056

COLUMBUS

**Baptist Memorial Hospital
Chemical Dependency Unit**
525 Willowbrook Road
Columbus, MS 39703

Recovery House, Inc.
770 Golding Road
Columbus, MS 39704

COLUMBUS AFB

**Columbus Air Force Base
Substance Abuse Program**
14 MDOS/SGOMH
201 Independence Drive
Suite 101
Columbus AFB, MS 39701-5300

CORINTH

**Magnolia Regional Health
Center Crossroads Psychiatric
Unit**
611 Alcorn Drive
Corinth, MS 38834

**Timber Hills Mental Health
Services**
601 Foote Street
Corinth, MS 38834

GREENVILLE

Delta Community Mental Health Services Substance Abuse Services
1654 East Union Street
Greenville, MS 38701

GREENWOOD

Region 6 Community Mental Health Center
Old Browning Road, Box 1505
Greenwood, MS 38935-1505

GRENADA

Grenada Lake Medical Center
960 Avent Drive
Grenada, MS 38901

GULFPORT

BHC Hill Hospital
11150 Highway 49 North
Gulfport, MS 39503

Branch Medical Clinic Addiction Treatment Facility
5501 Marvin Shield Boulevard
Code 100
Gulfport, MS 39501

HATTIESBURG

Pine Belt Mental Healthcare Resources
Programs for Chemical
Dependency
820 South 28 Avenue
Hattiesburg, MS 39401

Pine Grove Recovery Center
2255 Broadway Drive
Hattiesburg, MS 39401

JACKSON

Alcohol Services Center, Inc. Drug Treatment Unit
950 North West Street
Jackson, MS 39202

Baptist Behavioral Health Services
1225 North State Street
Jackson, MS 39201

Center for Independent Learning, Inc.
Special Women's Program
Transitional Services
4550 Manhattan Road
Jackson, MS 39286

Friends of Alcoholics
1422 Foa Road
Jackson, MS 39209

Harbor Houses of Jackson, Inc.
Men's Division Alcoholism
Treatment
1019 West Capitol Street
Jackson, MS 39203

Women's Division
3588 Flowood Drive
Jackson, MS 39208

Metro Counseling Center, Inc.
927 Palmayra Street
Jackson, MS 39205

New Life for Women Inc
814 North Congress Street
Jackson, MS 39202

Veterans' Affairs Medical Center Chemical Dependence Treatment Program
1500 East Woodrow Wilson
Unit 116B1
Jackson, MS 39216

KESSLER AFB

Kessler Air Force Base Substance Abuse Program
81 MDOS/SGOMH
301 Fisher Street, Room 1A-132
Keesler AFB, MS 39534-2519

LAUREL

South Central Regional Medical Center
1220 Jefferson Street
Laurel, MS 39441

MCCOMB

Southwest Mississippi MH/MR Complex Regional Alcohol and Drug Services
1701 White Street
McComb, MS 39648

MENDENHALL

New Roads Residential Treatment Center
1060 Smith Road
Mendenhall, MS 39114

MERIDIAN

Adult Male Alcohol and Drug Services Unit
4555 Highland Park Drive
Meridian, MS 39302

Laurel Wood Center
5000 Highway 39 North
Meridian, MS 39303

Weems Mental Health Center
Alcohol and Drug Program
Weems Lifecare
1415 Junior College Road
Meridian, MS 39304

OCEAN SPRINGS

Home of Grace Men's Program
14200 Jericho Road
Ocean Springs, MS 39565

OLIVE BRANCH

Charter Parkwood
8135 Goodman Road
Olive Branch, MS 38654

OXFORD

Communicare Alcohol and Drug Program Haven House
152 Highway 7th Street
Oxford, MS 38655

PARCHMAN

Mississippi Department of Corrections Alcohol and Drug Abuse Program
Parchman, MS 38738

PHILADELPHIA

Choctaw Community Mental Health Mississippi Band of Choctaw Indians
Route 7
Choctaw Health Center
Philadelphia, MS 39350

TUPELO

North Mississippi Medical Center
830 South Gloster Street
Tupelo, MS 38801

Region III Community Mental Health Center
2434 South Eason Boulevard
Tupelo, MS 38801

VICKSBURG

Marian Hill Chemical Dependency Center
100 McAuley Drive
Vicksburg, MS 39180

Warren/Yazoo Mental Health Service
3444 Wisconsin Avenue
Vicksburg, MS 39180

WHITFIELD

Mississippi State Hospital Chemical Dependency Unit
Building 84
Whitfield, MS 39193

MISSOURI

ALBANY

Family Guidance Center for Behavioral Healthcare
302 North Smith Street
Albany, MO 64402

AVA

South Central Missouri Rehab Center, Inc.
Douglas County Courthouse
Ava, MO 65608

BELLE

Missouri Alcohol Assessment Consultants, Inc.
206 South Church Street
Belle, MO 65013

BELTON

Midwest ADP Center Belton Site CIP/Outpatient
17136 Bel Ray Place
Belton, MO 64012

BETHANY

North Central Missouri Mental Health Center
3405 Miller Street
Bethany, MO 64424

BOONVILLE

Boonville Valley Hope
1415 Ashley Road
Boonville, MO 65233

Family Counseling Center of Missouri, Inc. Outpatient Clinic
211 Main Street
Boonville, MO 65233

BRANSON

Tri-Lake Sigma House
360 Rinehart Road
Branson, MO 65616

BROOKFIELD

North Central Missouri Mental Health Center
1 Center Drive
Brookfield, MO 64628

Preferred Family Healthcare Inc Brookfield Office
1 Center Drive
Brookfield, MO 64628

CAMERON

Family Guidance Center for Behavioral Healthcare
502 Northland Plaza
Cameron, MO 64429

CANTON

Hannibal Council on Alcohol and Drug Abuse
413 College Street
Canton, MO 63435

CAPE GIRARDEAU

Family Counseling Center, Inc. Women's CSTAR
20 South Sprig Street
Suite 2
Cape Girardeau, MO 63701

Gibson Recovery Center, Inc.
1112 Linden Street
Cape Girardeau, MO 63703

CARUTHERSVILLE

Correctional Counseling, Inc.
1210 West Highway 84
Caruthersville, MO 63830

CHILLICOTHE

North Central Missouri Mental Health Center
705 Webster Street
Chillicothe, MO 64601

CLINTON

Pathways
1800 Community Drive
Clinton, MO 64735

COLUMBIA

Arthur Center
103-B Corporate Lake Drive
Columbia, MO 65203

**Charter Behavioral Health
System of Columbia**
200 Portland Street
Columbia, MO 65201

DRD Columbia Medical Clinic
1415 Paris Road
Columbia, MO 65201

**Family Counseling Center of
Missouri, Inc.**
Alcohol/Drug Treatment Services
117 North Garth Street
Columbia, MO 65203

CSTAR McCambridge Center
201 North Garth Street
Columbia, MO 65203

**Harry S. Truman Memorial
Veterans Hospital**
800 Hospital Drive
Columbia, MO 65201

**Mid-Missouri Mental Health
Center Alcohol and Drug
Abuse Unit**
3 Hospital Drive
Columbia, MO 65201

**Phoenix Programs, Inc.
Residential Program**
607 South 5th Street
Columbia, MO 65201

CRESTWOOD

**Southeast Missouri Community
Treatment Center Accredited
Family Clinic**
9264 Waston Road
Crestwood, MO 63126

CREVE COUER

Edgewood Program
615 South New Ballas Road
Creve Coeur, MO 63141

DESOTO

COMTREA, Inc.
3343 Armbruster Road
DeSoto, MO 63020

EL DORADO SPRINGS

**Pathways Community
Behavioral Healthcare, Inc. El
Dorado Springs Outpatient**
107 West Broadway Street
El Dorado Springs, MO 64744

EXCELSIOR SPRINGS

Northland Community Center
106 Elizabeth Street
Excelsior Springs, MO 64024

FARMINGTON

**Southeastern Missouri
Treatment Center**
Aquinas Center
5336 Highway 32 East
Farmington, MO 63640

FESTUS

**Community Treatment, Inc.
(COMTREA)**
227 Main Street
Festus, MO 63028

FLORISSANT

Christian Hospital Northwest
1225 Graham Road
Florissant, MO 63031

**Eastern Missouri Alternative
Sentencing Services EMA/
Flourissant CIP/Outpatient**
19 Florissant Oaks Street
Florissant, MO 63031

FORDLAND

**Ozark Correctional Center OTP
Avalon Community Services,
Inc.**
Route 2
Fordland, MO 65652

FORT LEONARD WOOD

**Alcohol and Drug Abuse
Prevention and Control
Program Community
Counseling Center**
MCXP-BM-AD Building 310
Fort Leonard Wood, MO 65473

FULTON

Fulton State Hospital
Alcohol and Drug Treatment Unit
600 East 5th Street
Fulton, MO 65251

**Hannibal Council on Alcohol
and Drug Abuse Recovery
Center**
502 North Nichols Street
Fulton, MO 65251

GAINESVILLE

**South Central Missouri Rehab
Center, Inc. Ozark County
Health Center**
304 West 3rd Street
Gainesville, MO 65655

GALLATIN

**North Central Missouri Mental
Health Center**
109 East Jackson Street
Gallatin, MO 64640

GLADSTONE

Columbia Health Systems, Inc.
6910 North Holmes Street
Suite 148
Gladstone, MO 64118

HAMILTON

**North Central Missouri Mental
Health Center**
1 Cross Street
Hamilton, MO 64644

HANNIBAL

**Hannibal Council on Alcohol/
Drug Abuse, Inc.**
146 Communications Drive
Hannibal, MO 63401

HARRISONVILLE

Community Mental Health Consultants, Inc.
Cass County Psychological Services
306 South Independence Street
Harrisonville, MO 64701

Pathways Community Behavioral Healthcare, Inc.
300 Galaxie Avenue
Harrisonville, MO 64701

HAYTI

Correctional Counseling, Inc.
806 East Washington Street
Hayti, MO 63851

Family Counseling Center, Inc.
Highway J North
Hayti, MO 63851

HOUSTON

Southeast Missouri Community Treatment Center
SEMO/Houston Office
Texas City Health
201 South First Street
Houston, MO 65483

INDEPENDENCE

Comprehensive Mental Health Services
10819 Winner Road
Independence, MO 64052

CSTAR Program
10901 Winner Road
Independence, MO 64052

Midwest Addiction, Inc.
4231 South Hocker Street
Building 13, Suite 250
Independence, MO 64055

JEFFERSON CITY

Capital Region Medical Center Chemical Dependency Recovery Program
1600 Southwest Boulevard
Capitol Region Medical Center
Jefferson City, MO 65102

Family Counseling Center of Missouri, Inc.
Jefferson City Outpatient
502 East McCarty Street
Jefferson City, MO 65101

Fulton State Hospital Capital City ADA Outpatient
211 Oscar Drive, Suite A
Jefferson City, MO 65101

Jefferson City Correctional Center Intensive Therapeutic Community
631 State Street
Jefferson City, MO 65101

JOPLIN

Family Self Help Center, Inc. DBA Lafayette House/CSTAR
1809 Connor Avenue
Joplin, MO 64804

Ozark Center New Directions
Acute Adult Substance Abuse Treatment Program
530 East 34th Street
Joplin, MO 64801

CSTAR
Substance Abuse Unit
2808 Picher Street
Joplin, MO 64803

Scott Greening Center for Youth Dependency, Inc.
1315 East 20 Street
Joplin, MO 64804

KANSAS CITY

Baptist Medical Center
6601 Rockhill Road
8th Floor
Kansas City, MO 64131

Benilde Hall Program
1600 Paseo Boulevard
Kansas City, MO 64108-1623

DRD Kansas City Medical Clinic
723 East 18 Street
Kansas City, MO 64108

Gateway Foundation, Inc. Intensive Outpatient Services
1734 East 63rd Street, Suite 301
Kansas City, MO 64110

Kansas City Community Center (KCCC)
1534 Campbell Street
Kansas City, MO 64108

Kansas City Free and Clean Gateway Foundation, Inc.
1734 East 63rd Street, Suite 301
Kansas City, MO 64110

Marillac Center
2826 Main Street
Kansas City, MO 64108

Midwest ADP Center Outpatient Program
1212 McGee Street
Kansas City, MO 64108

Missouri Dept of Labor/Industrial Relations
North Clinic/Residential
Women's Place
5840 Swope Parkway
Kansas City, MO 64130

North Star Recovery Research Mental Health Services
2801 Wyandotte Street, 6th Floor
Kansas City, MO 64108

Residential Unit
3220 East 23 Street
Kansas City, MO 64127

Rodgers South
2701 East 31 Street
Kansas City, MO 64128

Salvation Army Missouri Shield of Service
5100 East 24th Street
Kansas City, MO 64127

Scott Greening Center, Inc. Western Region Unit
2750 Cherry Street
Kansas City, MO 64108-3140

Truman Medical Center East
Administrative Site
7900 Lees Summit Road
Kansas City, MO 64139

Behavioral Health/Relapse
Program
221 Charlotte Street
Kansas City, MO 64108

**Western Missouri Mental Health
Center**
Paseo Comprehensive Rehab Clinic
2211 Charlotte Street
Kansas City, MO 64108

KENNETT

Family Counseling Center, Inc.
1109 Jones Street
Kennett, MO 63857

KIRKSVILLE

**Preferred Family Healthcare,
Inc.**
1101 South Jamison Street
Kirksville, MO 63501-0767

KIRKWOOD

**Saint Louis Foundation for
Alcohol and Related
Dependencies**
Exodus Program
135 West Adams Street, Suite 203
Kirkwood, MO 63122

LEES SUMMIT

**Research Mental Health
Services**
901 NE Independence Avenue
Lees Summit, MO 64063

LINN CREEK

**Family Counseling Center of
Missouri, Inc. Cedar Ridge
Treatment Center**
Route 1
Linn Creek, MO 65052

LOCKWOOD

**Community Mental Health
Consultants, Inc. Dade County
Psychological Services**
1111 South Main Street
Lockwood, MO 65682

LOUISIANA

Hannibal Council on Alcohol
3516 Georgia Street
Louisiana, MO 63353

MACON

Preferred Family Healthcare
907 State Route
Macon, MO 63552

MALDEN

Correctional Counseling Inc.
110 East Main Street
Malden, MO 63863

MARSHALL

**David R Rasse and Associates,
Inc.**
78 West Arrow Street
Marshall, MO 65340

**Fulton State Hospital Marshall
ADA Outpatient Clinic**
Marshall Habilitation Center
700 East Slater
Marshall, MO 65340

MARYVILLE

Family Guidance Center
301 East Summit Drive
South Hills Medical Building
Maryville, MO 64468

MEXICO

**Hannibal Council on Alcohol/
Drug Abuse, Inc.**
Mexico Area Recovery Center
1130 South Elmwood Street
Mexico, MO 65265

MILAN

**North Central Missouri Mental
Health Center**
217 East Second Street
Milan, MO 63556

MOBERLY

Better Choices
102 East Rollins Street
Moberly, MO 65270

**Escape Outpatient Chemical
Dependency Center**
501 North Ault Street
Moberly, MO 65270

MONETT

**Clark Community Mental
Health Center**
307 4th Street
Monett, MO 65708

MOUNTAIN GROVE

**South Central Missouri Rehab
Ctr Inc Grace and Glory
Church**
1104 North Main Street
Mountain Grove, MO 65711

MOUNTAIN VIEW

**South Central Missouri Rehab
Ctr Inc United Methodist
Church**
106 East 3rd Street
Mountain View, MO 65548

MOUNT VERNON

**The University of MO
Crossroads Prog DBA MO
Rehabilitation Center**
600 North Main Street
Mount Vernon, MO 65712

NEOSHO

Ozark Center New Directions
214 North Washington Street
Neosho, MO 64850

1011 West Hill Street
Neosho, MO 64850

NEVADA

**Community Mental Health
Consultants**
815 South Ash Street
Nevada, MO 64772

North Complex
427 North Cedar Street
Nevada, MO 64772

**Pathways Comm Behav
    Healthcare Inc Nevada
    Outpatient**
2203 North Elm Street
Nevada, MO 64772

NEW MADRID

Correctional Counseling, Inc.
315 Main Street
New Madrid, MO 63869

ODESSA

**Pathways Commmunity
    Behavioral Healthcare, Inc.
    Odessa Outpatient**
301 North 2nd Street
Odessa, MO 64076

OVERLAND PARK

**Wubbenhorst and
    Wubbenhorst, Inc. DBA
    Madison Avenue Psychologial
    Services**
8826 Santa Fe Street, Suite 207
Overland Park, MO 66212

PERRYVILLE

Gibson Recovery Center, Inc.
300 Perry Plaza, Suite F
Perryville, MO 63775

POPLAR BLUFF

Diversified Treatment Services
New Era/Westwood Center
Weekend Intervention Program
Route 11
Poplar Bluff, MO 63901

**Doctors Regional Medical
    Center**
419 Oak Boulevard
Poplar Bluff, MO 63901

Family Counseling Center, Inc.
400 Vine Street
Poplar Bluff, MO 63901

POTOSI

**Southeast Missouri Community
    Treatment Center**
108 Thistle Street Austin Plaza
Potosi, MO 63664

ROCK PORT

**Family Guidance Center for
    Behavioral Healthcare**
201 East Highway 169
Rock Port, MO 64482

ROLLA

**Southeast Missouri Community
    Treatment Center**
1702 East 10th Street
Rolla, MO 65401

SAINT CHARLES

**Bridgeway Counseling Services,
    Inc.**
1601 Old South River Road
Saint Charles, MO 63303

SAINT JOSEPH

Saint Joseph Youth Center
702 Felix Street
Saint Joseph, MO 64501

SAINT LOUIS

Alexian Brothers Hospital
3800 South Broadway
Saint Louis, MO 63118

Archway Communities, Inc.
5652 Pershing Avenue
Saint Louis, MO 63112

**Black Alcohol/Drug Service
    Info. Center (BASIC)**
CSTAR
1221 Locust Street
Suite 800
Saint Louis, MO 63103

**Christian Hospital Recovery
    Center**
605 Old Ballas Road
Saint Louis, MO 63141

Dart, Inc.
Administrative Unit
Medication Unit
Outpatient Unit
1307 Lindbergh Plaza Center
Saint Louis, MO 63132

East Unit
1027 South Vandeventer Street
Saint Louis, MO 63110

Gateway Foundation Inc
1430 Olive Street Suite 300
Saint Louis, MO 63103-2303

Community Release Center
1621 North First Street
Saint Louis, MO 63102

DBA GFI Services
Gateway Free And Clean
1430 Olive Street Suite 305
Saint Louis, MO 63103-2303

Harris House Foundation
8327 South Broadway
Saint Louis, MO 63111

Hyland Center
10020 Kennerly Road
Saint Louis, MO 63128

**Metropolitan Saint Louis
    Psychiatric Center**
5351 Delmar Boulevard
Saint Louis, MO 63112

New Beginnings CSTAR Inc
Adolescent CSTAR
1408 North Kings Highway
Saint Louis, MO 63113

Alternative Care
625 North Euclid Street, 5th Floor
Saint Louis, MO 63108

**Provident Counseling Family
    Care Program**
9109 Watson Street
Saint Louis, MO 63126

Queen of Peace Center
325 North Newstead Street
Saint Louis, MO 63108

Saint Patrick Center
1200 North 6th Street
Saint Louis, MO 63106

Salvation Army
CSTAR Program
10740 Page Boulevard
Saint Louis, MO 63132

Harbor Light Center
3010 Washington Avenue
Saint Louis, MO 63103

SAINT PETERS

**Missouri Valley Alcohol and
Drug Program**
1125 Cave Springs Estate Drive
Suite F
Saint Peters, MO 63376

SALEM

**Southeast Missouri Community
Treatment Center Salem
Center**
203 North Grand Street
Salem, MO 65560

SEDALIA

**Pathways Community
Behavioral Healthcare, Inc.**
State Fair Shopping Center
Sedalia, MO 65301

SPRINGFIELD

**Bridgeway Substance Abuse
Program**
2828 North National Avenue
Springfield, MO 65803

Burrell, Inc.
CSTAR Program
1300 Bradford Parkway
Springfield, MO 65804

**Carol Jones Recovery Center for
Women**
2411 West Catalpa Street
Springfield, MO 65807

**Center for Addictions Cox
Health Systems**
1423 North Jefferson Street
Springfield, MO 65802

DRD Springfield Medical Clinic
1046 West Sunshine Street
Springfield, MO 65807

Sigma House, Inc.
800 South Park Avenue
Springfield, MO 65802

TRENTON

**North Central Missouri Mental
Health Center**
Administrative Unit
Substance Abuse Program
1601 East 28 Street
Trenton, MO 64683

**Preferred Family Healthcare,
Inc.**
703 Main Street
Trenton, MO 64683

UNION

Meramec Recovery Center, Inc.
115 South Oak Street
Union, MO 63084

**Missouri Alcohol Assessment
Consultants, Inc.**
206 South Church Street
Union, MO 63084

UNIONVILLE

**North Central Missouri Mental
Health Center**
132 North 19th Street
Unionville, MO 63565

VANDALIA

Gateway Foundation, Inc.
Women's Eastern Reception/
Diagnostic
1101 East Highway 54
Vandalia, MO 63382

WARRENSBURG

**Pathways Community
Behavioral Healthcare, Inc.
Warrensburg Recovery Center**
703 North Devasher Street
Warrensburg, MO 64093

WASHINGTON

**Clayton Concepts, Inc. New
Hope**
516 Jefferson Street
Washington, MO 63090

WAYNESVILLE

Piney Ridge Center, Inc.
1000 Hospital Road
Waynesville, MO 65583

WEST PLAINS

**South Central Missouri Rehab
Center**
1015 Lanton Road
West Plains, MO 65775

WINDSOR

Royal Oaks Hospital
307 North Main Street
Windsor, MO 65360

WOODSON TERRACE

**Saint Louis Metro Treatment
Center, Inc.**
4024 Woodson Road
Woodson Terrace, MO 63134

MONTANA

ANACONDA

Deer Lodge County Alcohol and Drug Services of Anaconda
100 West Park Street
Anaconda, MT 59711

BILLINGS

Journey Recovery Program
1245 North 29 Street
Billings, MT 59103

Rimrock Foundation
1231 North 29 Street
Billings, MT 59101

BOX ELDER

Rocky Boys Chemical Dependency Center
Rural Route 1
Box Elder, MT 59521

BOZEMAN

Alcohol/Drug Services of Gallatin County
502 South 19 Street
Suite 302
Bozeman, MT 59715

BUTTE

Butte/Silver Bow Chemical Dependency Services
125 West Granite Street
Butte, MT 50701

Montana Chemical Dependency Center
2500 Continental Drive
Butte, MT 59701

North American Indian Alliance Chemical Dependency Program
100 East Galena Street
Butte, MT 59701

DEER LODGE

Chemical Dependency and Family Counseling, Inc.
304 Milwaukee Avenue
Deer Lodge, MT 59722

FORT BENTON

TLC Recovery, Inc.
1308 Frankin Street
Court House Annex
Fort Benton, MT 59442

FORT HARRISON

VAMAM/ROC
Fort Harrison, MT 59636-1500

GLENDIVE

District II Alcohol and Drug Program
119 South Kendrick Street
Glendive, MT 59330

GREAT FALLS

Benefits Health Care
500 15th Avenue South
Great Falls, MT 59405

Montana Deaconess Medical Center Chemical Dependency Unit
1101 26 Street South
Great Falls, MT 59405

Gateway Recovery Center
401 3 Avenue North
Great Falls, MT 59401

HAMILTON

Crossroads/Ravalli County Chemical Dependency Services
214 Pinckney Street
Hamilton, MT 59840

HARLEM

Fort Belknap Chemical Dependency Program
Fort Belknap Reservation
Route 1
Harlem, MT 59526

HAVRE

Northern Montana Chemical Dependency Program
1410 First Avenue
Havre, MT 59501

HELENA

Boyd Andrew Chemical Dependency Care Center
Arcade Building Unit 1-E
Helena, MT 59601

KALISPELL

Flathead Valley Chemical Dependency Clinic, Inc.
1312 North Meridian Road
Kalispell, MT 59901

Pathways Treatment Center Kalispell Regional Medical Center
200 Heritage Way
Kalispell, MT 59901

LEWISTOWN

Alcohol and Drug Services of Central Montana
505 West Main Street
Suite 418
Lewistown, MT 59457

LIBBY

Recovery Northwest/Lincoln County Main Office
418 Main Avenue
Libby, MT 59923

LIVINGSTON

Southwest Chemical Dependency Program
414 East Callendar Street
Livingston, MT 59047

MALSTROM AFB

Malmstrom Air Force Base Substance Abuse Program
341 MDG/SGOMH
468 74 Street North
Malmstrom AFB, MT 59402-6780

MALTA

High Plains Chemical Dependency Services
105 1/2 South 2nd Street East
Malta, MT 59538

MARION

Wilderness Treatment Center
200 Hubbart Dam Road
Marion, MT 59925

MILES CITY

Eastern Montana Mental Health Substance Abuse and Dependency Services
2200 Box Elder
Miles City, MT 59301

MISSOULA

Missoula Indian Center
2300 Regent Street
Missoula, MT 59801

Saint Patrick Hospital Addiction Treatment Program
500 West Broadway
Missoula, MT 59802

Western Montana Regional Mental Health Turning Point
500 North Higgins Street
Suite 101
Missoula, MT 59802

POLSON

Lake County Chemical Dependency Program
12 5th Avenue East
Polson, MT 59860

SAINT IGNATIUS

Confederated Salish/Kootenai Tribes Addiction Treatment Program
402 Mission Drive
Saint Ignatius, MT 59865

NEBRASKA

AINSWORTH

Sandhills Mental Health and Substance Abuse Services, Inc.
312 North Main Street
Ainsworth, NE 69210

ALLIANCE

Human Services, Inc.
419 West 25 Street
Alliance, NE 69301

AUBURN

Blue Valley Mental Health Center
1121 15th Street
Auburn, NE 68305

BEATRICE

Blue Valley Mental Health Center
1200 South 9 Street
Beatrice, NE 68310

BELLEVUE

Lutheran Family Services/ Bellevue
1318 Federal Square Drive
Bellevue, NE 68005

Rainbow Hope Counseling and Recovery Services
1103 Galvin Road South
Bellevue, NE 68005-3031

Renaissance Program
703 West 24th Avenue
Bellevue, NE 68005

COLUMBUS

Mid-East Nebraska Behavioral Health Care Services
3314 26th Street
Columbus, NE 68601

Sunrise Place
4432 Sunrise Place
Columbus, NE 68602

CRETE

Blue Valley Mental Health Center
225 East 9th Street, Suite 1
Crete, NE 68333

DAVID CITY

Blue Valley Mental Health Center
367 E Street
David City, NE 68632

FAIRBURY

Blue Valley Mental Health Center
521 E Street
Fairbury, NE 68352

FALLS CITY

Blue Valley Mental Health Center
116 West 19th Street
Falls City, NE 68355

FREMONT

Alegent Health Behavioral Services
2350 North Clarkson Street
Fremont, NE 68025

Pathfinder Alcohol/Drug Outpatient Clinic
658 North H Street
Fremont, NE 68025

GENEVA

Blue Valley Mental Health Center Alcohol and Drug Abuse Services
831 F Street
Geneva, NE 68361

GORDON

Northeast Panhandle Substance Abuse Center
305 Foch Street
Gordon, NE 69343

GRAND ISLAND

Friendship House, Inc.
406 West Koenig Street
Grand Island, NE 68801

Mid-Plains Center Behavioral Healthcare, Inc.
914 Bauman Street
Grand Island, NE 68801

Milne Detoxification Center
406 West Koenig Street
Grand Island, NE 68801

Saint Francis Alcoholism/Drug Treatment Center
2116 West Faidley Avenue
Grand Island, NE 68803

Veterans' Affairs Medical Center Substance Abuse Treatment Program
2201 North Broadwell Street
Grand Island, NE 68803

HASTINGS

Hastings Regional Center Chemical Dependency Unit
Hastings, NE 68901

South Central Counseling
Hastings Clinic
616 West 5th Street
Hastings, NE 68901

The Bridge, Inc.
922 North Denver Street
Hastings, NE 68901

HEBRON

Blue Valley Mental Health
Thayer County Courthouse
Hebron, NE 68370

HOLDREGE

South Central Behavioral Services Holdrege Clinic
701 4th Avenue
Johnson Center, Suite 7
Holdrege, NE 68949

IMPERIAL

Region II Alcoholism and Drug Abuse Center
East Highway 6
Weir Building
Imperial, NE 69033

KEARNEY

Richard Young Hospital Chemical Dependency Unit
4600 17th Avenue
Kearney, NE 68847

South Central Counseling Substance Abuse Treatment Program
3810 Central Avenue
Kearney, NE 68847

Christopher House
2521 Central Avenue
Kearney, NE 68847-4547

LEXINGTON

Heartland Counseling and Consulting Clinic
307 East 5th Street
Lexington, NE 68850

LINCOLN

Antlers
2501 South Street
Lincoln, NE 68502

Bryan LGH Medical Center West Independence Center
1650 Lake Street
Lincoln, NE 68502

Center Pointe
Administration/Outpatient Offices
1000 South 13th Street
Lincoln, NE 68502

Adult Residential Program
610 J Street
Lincoln, NE 68508

Community Mental Health of Lancaster County
2200 Saint Mary's Avenue
Lincoln, NE 68502

Cornhusker Place
Detoxification Program
721 K Street
Lincoln, NE 68508

First Step
2231 Winthrop Road
Lincoln, NE 68502

Houses of Hope of Nebraska, Inc.
2015 South 16th Street
Lincoln, NE 68502

Lincoln Medical Education Foundation School Community Intervention Program
4608 Valley Road
Lincoln, NE 68510

Lincoln Valley Hope Alcohol and Drug Counseling and Referral Center
3633 O Street
Lincoln, NE 68510

Lincoln/Lancaster County Child Guidance Adolescent Substance Abuse Program
215 Centennial Mall South
312 Lincoln Center Building
Lincoln, NE 68508

**Lutheran Family Social Services
Substance Abuse Program**
4620 Randolph Street
Lincoln, NE 68510

Saint Monica's
Project Mother and Child
2109 South 24th Street
Lincoln, NE 68510

Residential and Outpatient
Services
6420 Colby Street
Lincoln, NE 68505

**Veterans' Affairs Medical Center
Chemical Abuse Services**
600 South 70 Street
Unit 116A
Lincoln, NE 68510

MACY

Macy Counseling Center
100 Main Street
Macy, NE 68039

**Macy Youth and Family
Services**
Macy, NE 68039

MCCOOK

**Heartland Counseling and
Consulting Clinic**
1012 West 3rd Street
McCook, NE 69001

NEBRASKA CITY

**Blue Valley Mental Health
Center**
1903 4 Corso
Nebraska City, NE 68410

Oak Arbor Recovery Center
1314 3 Avenue
Nebraska City, NE 68410

NIOBRARA

**Santee Sioux Tribe of
Nebraska/Health Education
Addictions Recovery Training
(HEART)**
Route 2
Niobrara, NE 68760

NORFOLK

Faith Regional Health Services
East Campus
1500 Koenigstein Avenue
Norfolk, NE 68701

Norfolk Regional Center
1700 North Victory Road
Norfolk, NE 68701

Odyssey III Counseling Services
401 South 17th Street
Norfolk, NE 68701-4724

Ponca Tribe of Nebraska
1310 Norfolk Avenue, Suite B
Norfolk, NE 68701

The Link, Inc.
1001 Norfolk Avenue
Norfolk, NE 68701

Well Link, Inc.
305 North 9 Street
Norfolk, NE 68702

NORTH PLATTE

**Great Plains Regional Medical
Center**
601 West Leota Street
North Platte, NE 69101

Lutheran Family Services
1300 East 4th Street
North Platte, NE 69101

**New Horizons Detoxification
Unit**
110 North Bailey Street
North Platte, NE 69101

**Region II Human Services
Heartland Counseling/
Consulting Clinic**
110 North Bailey Street
North Platte, NE 69101

O'NEILL

**Valley Hope Alcoholism
Treatment Center**
1421 North 10th Street
O'Neill, NE 68763

OGALLALA

**Heartland Counseling and
Consulting Clinic**
103 East 10th Street
Ogallala, NE 69153

OMAHA

A and A Assessments
4780 South 130th Street
Omaha, NE 68137

**Adlerian Center for Therapy
Consultation and Education**
11911 Arbor Street
Omaha, NE 68144-2970

**Alcoholics Resocialization
Conditioning Help (ARCH Inc)**
604 South 37th Street
Omaha, NE 68105

**Alegant Health Behavioral
Services**
6901 North 72nd Street
Omaha, NE 68122

**Arbor Family Counseling
Associates, Inc.**
11605 Arbor Street, Suite 106
Omaha, NE 68144-2934

Catholic Charities
Outpatient
Saint Gabriel's Center
Sheehan Center
3300 North 60th Street
Omaha, NE 68104

Chicano Awareness Center
4821 South 24th Street
Omaha, NE 68107

Discovery Center
2937 South 120th Street
Omaha, NE 68144

**Family Services/South Omaha
Counseling**
2900 O Street
Livestock Exchange Building
Suite 521
Omaha, NE

Greater Omaha Community Action Alcohol and Drug Outpatient Services
2406 Fowler Street
Omaha, NE 68111

Intertribal Treatment Center
2301 South 15th Street
Omaha, NE 68108

Lydia House
3030 North 21st Street East
Omaha, NE 68110

Methodist Richard Young Behavioral Health Unit
415 South 25th Avenue
Omaha, NE 68105

Nova Therapeutic Community
Partial Care Center
1915 South 38th Street
Omaha, NE 68105

Residential Center
3473 Larimore Avenue
Omaha, NE 68111

Omaha Psychiatric Associates
2132 South 42nd Street
Omaha, NE 68105

Pathway Counseling
5036 South 136th Street, Suite A
Omaha, NE 68137-1622

Santa Monica, Inc.
103 North 39th Street
Omaha, NE 68131

Sienna/Francis House
1702 Nicholas Street
Omaha, NE 68102

Stephens Center
2723 Q Street
Omaha, NE 68107

Therapy Resource Associates
10855 West Dodge Road
Suite 180
Omaha, NE 68154

United Behavioral Systems, Inc.
11717 Burt Street, Suite 104
Omaha, NE 68154

University Alcohol and Alcohol Program
2205 South 10th Street
Omaha, NE 68108

Veterans' Affairs Medical Center Substance Abuse Treatment Center
4101 Woolworth Avenue
Omaha, NE 68105

O'NEILL

Sandhills Mental Health and Substance Abuse Services, Inc.
204 East Everett Street
O'Neill, NE 68763

Valley Hope Alcoholism Treatment Center
1421 North 10 Street
O'Neill, NE 68763

PAPILLION

Lutheran Family Services Papillion Clinic
120 West 2nd Street
Papillion, NE 68046

PAWNEE CITY

Blue Valley Mental Health Center
701 I Street
Pawnee City, NE 68420

PLATTSMOUTH

Lutheran Family Services Cass Family Clinic
542 Main Street
Plattsmouth, NE 68048

SCHUYLER

Pathfinder Clinic
802 A Street
Schuyler, NE 68661

SCOTTSBLUFF

Human Services, Inc. Detoxification Center
15 West 16th Street
Scottsbluff, NE 69361

Panhandle Mental Health Center Substance Abuse Program
4110 Avenue D
Scottsbluff, NE 69361

Regional West Medical Center Behavioral Health Services
3700 Avenue B
Scottsbluff, NE 69361

SEWARD

Blue Valley Mental Health Center
729 Seward Street
Seward, NE 68434

SIDNEY

Memorial Health Center
835 15th Avenue
Sidney, NE 69162

SOUTH SIOUX CITY

Heartland Counseling Services, Inc.
917 West 21st Street
South Sioux City, NE 68776

SUPERIOR

Family Resource Center
344 North Dakota Street
Superior, NE 68978-1843

VALENTINE

Sandhills Mental Health and Substance Abuse Services, Inc.
325 North Victoria Street
Presbyterian Church
Valentine, NE 69201

WAHOO

Blue Valley Mental Health Center
543 North Linden Street
Wahoo, NE 68066

WEST POINT

Pathfinder Clinic Alcohol and Drug Outpatient Clinic
434 North Lincoln Street
West Point, NE 68788

WHITE CLAY

Hands of Faith Ministry
Whiteclay, NE 69365

WINNEBAGO

Chee Woy Na Zhee Halfway House
Highway 77
Winnebago, NE 68071

Indian Health Service Drug Dependency Unit
Highway 77-75
Winnebago, NE 68071

YORK

Blue Valley Mental Health Center
727 Lincoln Avenue
York, NE 68467

Family Counseling Center
1100 Lincoln Avenue, Suite C-3
York, NE 68467-1743

NEVADA

CARSON CITY

Carson City Community Counseling Center
625 Fairview Drive
Suite 111
Carson City, NV 89701

Carson Treatment Center
120 North Harbin Avenue
Carson City, NV 89701

ELKO

Ruby View Counseling Center Outpatient
401 Railroad Street, Suite 301
Elko, NV 89801

Vitality Center
Residential Treatment
3740 East Idaho Street
Elko, NV 89801

Teen Discovery
1297 Idaho Street
Elko, NV 89801

ELY

Bristlecone Counseling Service Outpatient
995 Campton Street
Ely, NV 89301

FALLON

Basic Recovery Associates, Inc.
141 Keddie Street
Fallon, NV 89406

Churchill Council Alcohol and Drug Treatment
165 North Carson Street
Fallon, NV 89406

LAS VEGAS

Bridge Counseling Associates Outpatient
1701 West Charleston Boulevard
Las Vegas, NV 89104

Center for Behavioral Health/ Nevada Methadone Outpatient Treatment Center
3050 East Desert Inn Road
Suite 117
Las Vegas, NV 89121

Clark County Health District Addiction Treatment Clinic/ Methadone
625 Shadow Lane
Las Vegas, NV 89127

Clark County Juvenile Court Services Family Based Drug Treatment Program
3401 East Bonanza Road
Las Vegas, NV 89101

Community Counseling Center
1120 Almond Tree Lane
Las Vegas, NV 89104

Community Health Centers of South Nevada
916 West Owens Avenue
Las Vegas, NV 89106

Economic Opportunity Board of Clark County
Treatment Center
522 West Washington Street
Las Vegas, NV 89106

Emotional Health Services
919 East Bonneville Street
Las Vegas, NV 89101-2305

Family Preservation Services
4220 South Maryland Street
Las Vegas, NV 89119

Healthy Families Project
2500 Apricot Lane
Las Vegas, NV 89108

Las Vegas Indian Center
2300 West Bonanza Road
Las Vegas, NV 89106

Mesa Family Counseling
1000 South 3rd Street
Las Vegas, NV 89101

Nevada Community Enrichment Program
2820 West Charleston Boulevard
Suite D-37
Las Vegas, NV 89102

Nevada Treatment Center
1721 East Charleston Boulevard
Las Vegas, NV 89104

New Life Medical Center
1750 Industrial Road
Las Vegas, NV 89102

Southwest Passage
1101 North Decatur Boulevard
Las Vegas, NV 89108-1220

Westcare, Inc.
Adult Detox
930 North 4th Street
Las Vegas, NV 89101

Community Involvement Center
401 South Martin Luther King
  Boulevard
Las Vegas, NV 89106

Harris Springs Ranch
Las Vegas, NV 89016

LOVELOCK

Lovelock Counseling Clinic
775 Cornell Street
Lovelock, NV 89419

MESQUITE

Mesquite Mental Health Center
416 Riverside Road
Mesquite, NV 89024

NIXON

**Pyramid Lake Health
  Department Sumunumu
  Substance Abuse Program**
705 Highway 446
Nixon, NV 89424

NORTH LAS VEGAS

**Salvation Army Las Vegas Adult
  Rehabilitation Program**
211 Judson Street
North Las Vegas, NV 89030

OWYHEE

**Owyhee Community Health
  Facility Shoshone Paiute
  Substance Abuse Program**
Nevada State Highway 225
Owyhee, NV 89832

PAHRUMP

**Westcare, Inc. Pahrump Youth
  Outpatient**
1670 East Heritage Street
Pahrump, NV 89048

RENO

**Basic Recovery Associates, Inc.
  Psychotherapeutic and
  Educational Ctr**
1085 South Virginia Street
Suite C and D
Reno, NV 89502

**Center for Behavioral Health of
  Nevada**
160 Hubbard Way, Suite A
Reno, NV 89502

**Family Counseling Service of
  Northern Nevada**
575 East Plumb Lane
Reno, NV 89501

Reno Treatment Center
750 Kuenzli Street
Reno, NV 89502

Ridge House
57 Vine Street
Reno, NV 89503

Sagewind
1725 South McCarran Boulevard
Reno, NV 89510-1491

Step Two
3220 Coronado Street
Suite 380
Reno, NV 89503

SPARKS

**Family Counseling Service of
  Northern Nevada, Inc.**
480 Gallette Way
Building 9 Room 40
Sparks, NV 89431

**Northern Area Substance Abuse
  Council Chemical
  Dependency Unit/Detox**
480 Galletti Way
Buildings 3 and 4 Second Floor
Sparks, NV 89431

TONOPAH

Tonopah Counseling Center
1100 Erie Main Street
Tonopah, NV 89049

WEST WENDOVER

Great Basin Counseling Service
915 Wells Street
West Wendover, NV 89883

WINNEMUCCA

**Silver Sage Counseling Service
  Outpatient Services**
530 Melarkey Street
Winnemucca, NV 89445

YERINGTON

**Lyon Council Alcohol and
  Drugs Yerington Project**
26 Nevin Way
Yerington, NV 89447

NEW HAMPSHIRE

BEDFORD

Bedford Counseling Associates
25 South River Road
Bedford Commons
Bedford, NH 03110

BERLIN

**Founders Hall Androscoggin
    Valley MHC**
13 Green Square
Berlin, NH 03570-3860

**Tri-County Community Action
    Program, Inc.**
361 School Street
Berlin, NH 03570

CANTERBURY

Odyssey Family Center
367 Shaker Road
Canterbury, NH 03224

CLAREMONT

Bailey House
18 Bailey Avenue
Claremont, NH 03743

COLEBROOK

**Upper Connecticut Mental
    Health and Developmental
    Services**
34 Colby Street
Colebrook, NH 03576

CONCORD

**Community Services Council
    Merrimack County Alcohol
    and Drug Intervention**
2 Industrial Park Drive
Suite 5
Concord, NH 03301

**Concord Hospital Fresh Start
    Program**
250 Pleasant Street
Concord, NH 03301

**Summit Behind the Walls New
    Hampshire State Prison**
281 North State Street
Concord, NH 03301

DOVER

**Prospects Frisbie Strafford
    Guidance**
130 Central Avenue
Dover, NH 03820

**Southeastern New Hampshire
    Services**
272 Country Farm Crossroad
Dover, NH 03820

DUBLIN

**Beech Hill Hospital Substance
    Abuse Services**
New Harrisville Road
Dublin, NH 03444

Marathon House
Adolescent Program
Long Term Residential
1 Pierce Road
Dublin, NH 03444

EXETER

**Southeastern New Hampshire
    Services**
24 Front Street
Exeter, NH 03833

HENNIKER

**Contoocook Valley Counseling
    Center**
9 Hall Avenue
Henniker, NH 03242

KEENE

**Cheshire Medical Center Mental
    Health Unit**
580 Court Street
Keene, NH 03431

**Marathon Behavioral Treatment
    Center**
106 Roxbury Street
Keene, NH 03431

**Monadnock Region Substance
    Abuse Services, Inc.**
310 Marlboro Street
Keene, NH 03431

LACONIA

Horizons Counseling Center
Village West, Building
Laconia, NH 03246

**Lakes Region General Hospital
    Nathan Brody Chemical
    Dependency Program**
80 Highland Street
Laconia, NH 03246

LEBANON

Brill, Jacqueline
106 Hanover Street
Lebanon, NH 03766

**Community Support Services
    Horizon House**
85 Mechanic Street, Suite 360
Lebanon, NH 03766

Headrest
14 Church Street
Lebanon, NH 03766

**West Central Services
    Counseling Center**
2 Whipple Place
Suite 202
Lebanon, NH 03766

20 West Park
Lebanon, NH 03766

LITTLETON

**White Mountain Mental Health
    Center Substance Abuse
    Services**
29 Maple Street
Littleton, NH 03561

MANCHESTER

Farnum Center
235 Hanover Street
Manchester, NH 03104

Manchester Office of Youth Services
50 Bridge Street, Suite 308
Manchester, NH 03101

Mental Health Center of Greater Manchester Co-Occurring Disorders Treatment Program
43 Walnut Street
Manchester, NH 03104

Riverway Center for Recovery
100 McGregor Street
Manchester, NH 03102

Tirrell House
15–17 Brook Street
Manchester, NH 03104

Veterans Affairs Medical Center Substance Abuse Treatment Program (SATP)
718 Smyth Road Building 5
Manchester, NH 03104

NASHUA

Charter Brookside Behavioral Health Systems
29 Northwest Boulevard
Nashua, NH 03063

Gateway Family Health Center
268 Main Street
Nashua, NH 03060

Greater Nashua Council on Alcoholism Pine Street Extension
Keystone Hall
Nashua, NH 03060

Nashua Youth Council
112 West Pearl Street
Nashua, NH 03060

Saint Joseph's Hospital New Start
172 Kinsley Street
Nashua, NH 03061

NEW LONDON

Kearsarge Counseling Center
Seamans Road
New London, NH 03257-1101

NEWPORT

West Central Services Counseling Center of Newport
167 Summer Street
Newport, NH 03773

PORTSMOUTH

Child and Family Services
1 Junkins Avenue
Portsmouth, NH 03801

Southeastern New Hampshire Services at Portsmouth
151 Court Street
Portsmouth, NH 03801

ROCHESTER

Southeastern New Hampshire Services
32 Wakefield Street
Rochester, NH 03867

WOLFEBORO

Carroll County Mental Health
Wolfeboro, NH 03894

NEW JERSEY

ABSECON

Family Service Association
312 East Whitehorse Pike
Absecon, NJ 08201

Thomas E. Hand Professional Associates
283 East Jimmie Leeds Road
Absecon, NJ 08201

ASBURY PARK

Jersey Shore Addiction Services, Inc. T/A Asbury Park Drug Treatment Center
1200 Memorial Drive
Asbury Park, NJ 07712

ATLANTIC CITY

Archway Associates for Life Enhancement
26 South New York Avenue
Atlantic City, NJ 08401

Atlanticare Behavioral Health
210-B Maryland Avenue
Atlantic City, NJ 08401

Institute for Human Development (IHD)
1315 Pacific Avenue
Atlantic City, NJ 08401

ATLANTIC HIGHLANDS

Matonti, Alane E., BSW CADC NCAC
64 7th Avenue
Atlantic Highlands, NJ 07716

BASKING RIDGE

Bresnahan, Jeremiah, ACSW CAC, and Maureen Bresnahan, MS CADC
36 Manchester Drive
Basking Ridge, NJ 07920

BAYONNE

Community Psychotherapy Associates
479 Avenue C
Bayonne, NJ 07002

New Pathway Counseling Services, Inc.
995 Broadway Street
Bayonne, NJ 07002

Private Counseling Service
510 Broadway Street
Bayonne, NJ 07002

BELLE MEAD

Carrier Foundation Addiction Unit
Belle Mead, NJ 08502

BELLEVILLE

Community Healthcare Network of Belleville, Bloomfield, Nutley
570 Belleville Avenue
Belleville, NJ 07109

Marriage and Family Counseling Center
387 Union Avenue
Belleville, NJ 07109

BLAIRSTOWN

Little Hill/Alina Lodge
Paulinskill River and Squires Road
Blairstown, NJ 07825

BOONTON

Saint Clare's Health Services
130 Powerville Road
Boonton, NJ 07005

BOUND BROOK

Family Counseling Service of Somerset County Addiction Services
339 West 2nd Street
Bound Brook, NJ 08805-1833

BRANT BEACH

Saint Francis Community Center
4700 Long Beach Boulevard
Brant Beach, NJ 08008

BRICK

Ocean Counseling and Referral Services
35 Beaverson Boulevard
Lion's Head Office Park
Building 9B
Brick, NJ 08723

BRIDGETON

Cumberland County Alcoholism and Drug Treatment
72 North Pearl
Bridgeton, NJ 08302

Faith Farm, Inc.
21 Stretch Road
Bridgeton, NJ 08302

South Jersey Drug Treatment Center
Cumberland Drive
Bridgeton, NJ 08302

BRIDGEWATER

Catholic Charities Comprehensive Family Addiction Treatment
540–550 Route 22 East
Bridgewater, NJ 08807

Cedar House
520 North Bridge Street
Bridgewater, NJ 08807

Richard Hall CMHC Outpatient Substance Abuse Services
500 North Bridge Street
Bridgewater, NJ 08807

BURLINGTON

Catholic Charities of Burlington
206 High Street
Burlington, NJ 08016

Amity House for Men
1004 High Street
Burlington, NJ 08016

Family Enrichment Institute, Inc.
415 Keim Boulevard, Suite 1-B
Burlington, NJ 08016

CALDWELL

The Bridge, Inc.
14 Park Avenue
Caldwell, NJ 07006

CAMDEN

Camden County Division of Alcohol and Substance Abuse Step-Up Program
2600 Mount Ephraim Avenue
Camden, NJ 08104

Cooper House
225 South 6th Street
Camden, NJ 08103

Hispanic Family Center of Southern New Jersey La Esperanza
35 Church
Camden, NJ 08103

Sikora Center, Inc.
613-615 Clinton Street
Camden, NJ 08103

Substance Abuse Center of Southern Jersey, Inc.
413 Broadway
Segaloff Treatment Center
Camden, NJ 08103

CAPE MAY

Employee Care
Bank Street Commons
Suite 130
Cape May, NJ 08204

CAPE MAY COURT HOUSE

Burdette Tomlin Hospital Outpatient Counseling
Stone Harbor Boulevard
Route 9
Cape May Court House, NJ 08210

Cape May County Youth Shelter Substance Abuse Services
151 Crest Haven Road
Cape May Court House, NJ 08210

CEDAR GROVE

Turning Point, Inc.
125 Fairview Avenue
Cedar Grove, NJ 07009

CHERRY HILL

Kennedy Memorial Hospital/ Cherry Hill Division Substance Abuse Services/ Detox and Outpatient
Chapel Avenue and Cooperlanding Road
Cherry Hill, NJ 08034

UMDNJ/University Behavioral Health Care
498 Marlboro Avenue
Cherry Hill, NJ 08002

CLIFTON

Clifton Counseling Services
60 Hadley Avenue
Suite A
Clifton, NJ 07011

COLLINGSWOOD

Genesis Counseling Center Alcoholism Outpatient Services
636 Haddon Avenue
Collingswood, NJ 08108

CRANFORD

Catholic Community Services Mount Carmel Guild
505 South Avenue
Cranford, NJ 07016

DENVILLE

OPT Counseling Services
61 Broadway
Denville, NJ 07834

DOVER

Hope House Outpatient Services
19–21 Belmont Avenue
Dover, NJ 07802

EAST ORANGE

East Orange General Hospital Alcohol Rehab/Family Treatment
300 Central Avenue
East Orange, NJ 07018-2819

East Orange Substance Abuse Treatment Program
160 Halsted Street
East Orange, NJ 07018

Veterans' Affairs Medical Center
Drug Dependency Treatment Program
385 Tremont Avenue
East Orange, NJ 07019

EDISON

Edison Catholic Charities Substance Abuse Program
26 Safran Avenue
Edison, NJ 08837

JFK Center for Behavioral Health
65 James Street
Edison, NJ 08818

EGG HARBOR TOWNSHIP

Atlanticare Behavioral Health
6010 Black Horse Pike
Egg Harbor Township, NJ 08234

ELIZABETH

Bridgeway, Inc.
615 North Broad Street
Elizabeth, NJ 07208-3409

Elizabeth General Medical Center Substance Abuse Services
655 East Jersey Street
3rd Floor
Elizabeth, NJ 07201

Essex Substance Abuse Treatment Center Elizabeth Clinic
850 Woodruff Lane
Elizabeth, NJ 07201

Flynn Christian Fellowship
1089–1091 East Jersey Street
Elizabeth, NJ 07201

Proceed, Inc. Addiction Services
815 Elizabeth Avenue
Elizabeth, NJ 07201

Seton Center for Chemical Dependency
225 Williamson Street
Saint Elizabeth Hospital
Elizabeth, NJ 07207

ENGLEWOOD

Community Centers for Mental Health, Inc. Substance Abuse Services
93 West Palisade Avenue
Englewood, NJ 07631

The Van Ost Institute for Family Living, Inc.
150 East Palisade Avenue
Englewood, NJ 07631

Contini, Richard A.
26-07 Route 4
Fair Lawn, NJ 07410

FLEMINGTON

Catholic Charities Substance Abuse Services Care Program
6 Park Avenue
Flemington, NJ 08822

Good News Home for Women
33 Bartles Corner Road
Flemington, NJ 08822

Hunterdon Drug Awareness Program
8 Main Street
Suite 7
Flemington, NJ 08822

Hunterdon Medical Center Addictions Treatment Services
2100 Wescott Drive
Mental Health Center
Flemington, NJ 08822

**Hunterdon Youth Services
Inside Out Program**
Rural Route 2
322 Highway 12
Flemington, NJ 08822

**National Council on Alcoholism
and Drug Dependence/
Hunterdon County**
153 Broad Street
Flemington, NJ 08822

FORT DIX

**McGuire Air Force Base
Substance Abuse Program**
305 MDOS/SGOMH
5250 New Jersey Avenue
Fort Dix, NJ 08640

FORT LEE

**Behavioral Counseling
Associates**
1580 Lemoine Avenue
Suite 8
Fort Lee, NJ 07024

FORT MONMOUTH

Community Counseling Center
Building 864 Selfm-Ad
Fort Monmouth, NJ 07703

FREEHOLD

**Freehold Community
Counseling Service**
30 Jackson Mills Road
Freehold, NJ 07728

**Monmouth County Division of
Social Services**
Project Transition, Unit 505
Freehold, NJ 07728

**New Hope Foundation, Inc.
Outpatient**
51 Throckmorton Street
Freehold, NJ 07728

GLASSBORO

**Together, Inc. Drug Treatment
Program**
7 State Street
Glassboro, NJ 08028

HACKENSACK

**Alternatives to Domestic
Violence Substance Abuse
Unit**
21 Main Street
Room 111W
Hackensack, NJ 07601

**Bergen County Div of Family
Guidance Adolescent
Substance Abuse Program**
21 Main Street, Room 110
Hackensack, NJ 07602

**Department of Health Services
Addiction Recovery Program**
151 Hudson Street
Hackensack, NJ 07601

**Hackensack Medical Center
Addiction Treatment Center/
Outpatient**
60 2nd Street, First Floor
Hackensack, NJ 07601-1271

**Monsignor Wall Social Service
Center**
149 Hudson Street
Hackensack, NJ 07601

HACKETTSTOWN

Hackettstown Community
Hospital Substance Abuse
Department
651 Willow Grove Street
Hackettstown, NJ 07840

HADDONFIELD

**Addiction Recovery Trt and
Service**
118 North Haddon Avenue
Haddonfield, NJ 08033-2306

HAZLET

**Bradley, Carolyn A., LCSW
CADC CPS**
1 Bethany Road
Suite 30-A, Building 2
Hazlet, NJ 07730-1663

Women's Center of Monmouth
County, Inc. Outpatient Alcohol
Counseling
1 Bethany Road
Building 3 Suite 42
Hazlet, NJ 07730

HOBOKEN

**Saint Mary's CMHC Substance
Abuse Unit**
314 Clinton Street
Hoboken, NJ 07030

Saint Mary's Hospital Giant
Steps/Adolescent Substance Abuse
Program
527 Clinton Street
Hoboken, NJ 07030

HOLMDEL

Bayshore Counseling Center
719 North Beers Street
Holmdel, NJ 07733

HOWELL

**Howell Township Youth and
Family Counseling Services**
425 Adelphia Street
Howell, NJ 07731

IRVINGTON

**L and L Clinics, Inc. Methadone
Maintenance and Detox**
57–59 New Street
Irvington, NJ 07111

JERSEY CITY

Catholic Community Services
249 Virginia Avenue
Jersey City, NJ 07304

Counseling Resources Center
176 Palisade Avenue
Jersey City, NJ 07306

Hogar Crea
79 Cornelison Avenue
Jersey City, NJ 07302

Jersey City Medical Center Dept of Psychiatry Addiction Services
50 Baldwin Avenue, 11 Center
Jersey City, NJ 07304-3154

Salvation Army Adult Rehab
Center/Inpatient and Outpatient
248 Erie Street
Jersey City, NJ 07302

Spectrum Health Care, Inc.
74–80 Pacific Avenue
Jersey City, NJ 07304

KEANSBURG

Awareness Counseling Drug and Alcohol Rehabilitation Center, Inc.
23 Church Street
Keansburg, NJ 07734

KEARNY

Inter County Council on Drug/
Alcohol Abuse Administration/
Drug Free Counseling
416 Kearny Avenue
Kearny, NJ 07032

KEYPORT

Endeavor House
6 Broadway
Keyport, NJ 07735

LAFAYETTE

Sunrise House Foundation, Inc. Alcohol Residential Program
Sunset Inn Road
Intersection of Routes 15 and 94
Lafayette, NJ 07848

LAKEWOOD

Counseling Center for Self Discovery
222 River Avenue
Route 9 South
Lakewood, NJ 08701

Preferred Behavioral Health of New Jersey
700 Airport Road
Lakewood, NJ 08701

LEONARDO

Middletown Office of Substance Abuse Services
900 Leonardville Road
Croydon Hall
Leonardo, NJ 07737

LINWOOD

Recovery Counseling Services
Office 1 Central Square
Linwood, NJ 08221

LIVINGSTON

Saint Barnabas Behavioral Health Network
5 Regent Street, Suite 522
Livingston, NJ 07039

LYNDHURST

Comprehensive Behavioral Health Center
516 Valley Brook Avenue
Lyndhurst, NJ 07071

MANALAPAN

Manalapan Community and Family Services
120 Route 522
Manalapan, NJ 07726

MARGATE CITY

Gegner, Murray, LCSW
210 North Rumson Avenue
Margate City, NJ 08402

MARLBORO

Discovery Institute for Addictive Disorders
Route 5, Cottage 15
Marlboro, NJ 07746

New Hope Foundation, Inc. Substance Abuse Services
Route 520
Marlboro, NJ 07746

MATAWAN

Community YMCA
166 Main Street
Matawan, NJ 07747

MAYS LANDING

Lighthouse/Recovery Services of New Jersey
5034 Atlantic Avenue
Mays Landing, NJ 08330

MEDFORD

Elm Lifelines
23 South Main Street, Suite 1
Medford, NJ 08055

Fox Counseling Associates
1 North Main Street
Suite 3B
Medford, NJ 08055

MENDHAM

Daytop Village
80 West Main Street
Mendham, NJ 07945

MILLTOWN

Trautz Associates
134 North Main Street
Milltown, NJ 08850

MONTCLAIR

Mountainside Hospital Alcoholism Treatment Unit
Bay and Highland Avenues
Montclair, NJ 07042

Cope Center, Inc.
104 Bloomfield Avenue
Montclair, NJ 07042

MORRIS PLAINS

New Views Treatment Program, Inc.
Central Avenue
Morris Plains, NJ 07950-9068

MORRISTOWN

Atlantic Behavioral Health Morristown Memorial Hospital Outpatient Addictive Service
95 Mount Kemble Avenue
Morristown, NJ 07962

Morris County Addictions Recovery Center
30 Schuyler Place, 2nd Floor
Morristown, NJ 07963-0900

Morristown Memorial Hospital Juvenile Evaluation and Treatment Services
100 Madison Avenue
Morristown, NJ 07960

Mrs. Wilson's Halfway House
56 Mount Kemble Avenue
Morristown, NJ 07960

MOUNT HOLLY

Amity House, Inc.
211 Garden Street
Mount Holly, NJ 08060

Burlington Comp. Counseling, Inc.
75 Washington Street
Mount Holly, NJ 08060

NEPTUNE

Jersey Shore Medical Center
1945 Highway 33
Neptune, NJ 07753

NEWARK

American Habitare
687 Frelinghuysen Avenue
Newark, NJ 07114

Choices, Inc.
169 Roseville Avenue
Newark, NJ 07107

Community United for Rehabilitation of Addiction, Inc. (CURA)
35 Lincoln Park
Newark, NJ 07102

Essex Substance Abuse Treatment Center, Inc.
164 Blanchard Street
Newark, NJ 07105

461 Frelinghuysen Avenue
Newark, NJ 07144

Integrity House, Inc.
103 Lincoln Park
Newark, NJ 07102

Mount Carmel Guild
Halfway House
56 Freeman Street
Newark, NJ 07105

Addiction Treatment Services
1160 Raymond Boulevard
Newark, NJ 07102

Newark Renaissance House, Inc. Youth and Family Treatment Center
62-80 Norfolk Street
Newark, NJ 07103

NEW BRUNSWICK

Damon House, Inc. Residential and Outpatient
105 Joyce Kilmer Avenue
New Brunswick, NJ 08901

New Brunswick Counseling Center
84 New Street
New Brunswick, NJ 08901

Open Door Alcoholism Treatment Program
2–4 Kirkpatrick and New Street
New Brunswick, NJ 08901

Program for Addictions Consultation and Treatment (PACT)
254 Easton Avenue
New Brunswick, NJ 08901

Saint Peter's Medical Center
Center for Treatment of Pregnancy and Addiction
288 Livingstone Avenue
New Brunswick, NJ 08903

NEW LISBON

Burlington County Health Department Post House
610 Pemberton/Browns Mills Road
New Lisbon, NJ 08064

NEWTON

Center for Mental Health
175 High Street
Newton, NJ 07860

Decide Program
35 High Street
Newton, NJ 07860

Newton Memorial Hospital
Alcohol and Substance Abuse Program
175 High Street
Newton, NJ 07860

Professional Counseling Associates
35 High Street
Newton, NJ 07860

Riser Sommer Tolliver Corp.
40 Park Place
Newton, NJ 07860

NORTH BERGEN

Palisades General Hospital Counseling Center
7101 Kennedy Boulevard
North Bergen, NJ 07047

NORTHVALE

Bergen County Community Action Program Ladder Project
35 Piermont Road, Building N
Northvale, NJ 07647

OLD BRIDGE

Extracare Health Services
201 Route 34
Old Bridge, NJ 08857

ORADELL

**Professional Counseling
    Associates**
370 Kinderkamack Road
Oradell, NJ 07649

ORANGE

**City of Orange Drug/Alcohol
    Abuse Program**
439 Main Street
Orange, NJ 07050

Family Connections
395 South Center Street
Orange, NJ 07050

PARAMUS

Bergen Pines County Hospital
Evergreen Treatment Center
Monsignor Wall Social Service
    Center
230 East Ridgewood Avenue
Paramus, NJ 07652

**Mid-Bergen Mental Health
    Center**
610 Industrial Avenue
Paramus, NJ 07652

PASSAIC

**Hispanic Information Center
    Alcohol Outreach Program for
    Minorities**
186 Gregory Street
Passaic, NJ 07055

PATERSON

Eva's Shelter and Kitchen
393 Main Street
Paterson, NJ 07505

**Paterson Counseling Center,
    Inc.**
321 Main Street
Paterson, NJ 07505

Straight and Narrow
508 Straight Street
Paterson, NJ 07501

PHILLIPSBURG

**Catholic Charities/Warren
    ADAPT**
700 Sayre Avenue
Phillipsburg, NJ 08865

**Warren Hospital Alcohol/Drug
    Recovery Center/Detox**
185 Roseberry Street
Phillipsburg, NJ 08865

**Warren Hospital MICA
    Program/ Inpatient**
185 Roseberry Street
Mental Health Unit 2 South
Phillipsburg, NJ 08865

PICATINNY ARSENAL

**US Army Armament Resource
    Development Center
    Employee Assistance Office**
Amsta AR MWR
Building 120
Picatinny Arsenal, NJ 07806-5001

PISCATAWAY

Specialized Addiction Services
667 Hoes Lane
Piscataway, NJ 08854

PLAINFIELD

Organization for Recovery
519 North Avenue
Plainfield, NJ 07060

Project Alert
930 Putnam Avenue
Plainfield, NJ 07060

**Union County Psychiatric Clinic
    Adolescent Alcohol Program**
117–119 Roosevelt Avenue
Plainfield, NJ 07062

**Steps Recovery Center
    Muhlenberg Regional Medical
    Center**
Park Avenue and Randolph Road
Plainfield, NJ 07060

POMPTON LAKES

Matthew E. Collins CDC CRPS
Counseling and Relapse Prevention
    Services
109 Beech Avenue
Pompton Lakes, NJ 07442

POMPTON PLAINS

New Bridge Service, Inc.
21 Evans Place
Pompton Plains, NJ 07444-1428

PRINCETON

Cornerhouse
369 Witherspoon Street
Valley Road Building
Princeton, NJ 08540

**Family/Children Service of
    Central New Jersey Outpatient
    Alcoholism Counseling and
    Education**
120 John Street
Princeton, NJ 08542

RANCOCAS

**Hampton Behavioral Health
    Center**
650 Rancocas Road
Rancocas, NJ 08073

RANDOLPH

Morris County Aftercare Center
Outpatient/Drug Free and
    Methadone
1574 Sussex Turnpike
Randolph, NJ 07869

RED BANK

CPC Behavioral Health Care
270 Highway 35
Red Bank, NJ 07701

Ruane, Mary Anne, MSW CAC
30 Linden Place
Red Bank, NJ 07701

Barbetta, Philip
30 Linden Place, Suite A-1
Red Bank, NJ 07701-1817

Riverview Medical Center Addiction Recovery Services
48 East Front Street
Red Bank, NJ 07701

RIDGEWOOD

Seligson, Henry, Ph.D. and Bryan Granelli, Ph.D.
112 Prospect Street
Ridgewood, NJ 07452

RINGWOOD

Sandra A. Carlson Counseling
11 Sunset Road
Ringwood, NJ 07456

RIVERSIDE

Zurbrugg Memorial Health Facility
Hospital Plaza
Riverside Division
Riverside, NJ 08075

RIVERTON

Healthmark Counseling
101 Route 130
Madison Building, Suite 321
Riverton, NJ 08077

SADDLE BROOK

High Focus Centers
299 Market Street, Suite 110
Saddle Brook, NJ 07663

SALEM

Maryville, Inc. Outpatient Services
567 Salem Quinton Road
Salem, NJ 08079

SEABROOK

Seabrook House
Polk Lane
Seabrook, NJ 08302

SECAUCUS

Integrity, Inc.
575 County Avenue, Building C-3
Secaucus, NJ 07096

SKILLMAN

Crawford House, Inc. Halfway House for Women Alcoholics
362 Sunset Road
Skillman, NJ 08558

SOMERS POINT

Amethyst Addictions Services
1409 Roberts Avenue
Somers Point, NJ 08244

SOMERVILLE

Samaritan Homeless Interim Program
67 West High Street
Somerville, NJ 08876

Somerset Medical Center
Specialized Treatment for
Addictions Recovery Program
(STAR)
111 Courtyard Drive
Somerville, NJ 08876

Somerset Treatment Services
256 East Main Street
Somerville, NJ 08876

SOUTH AMBOY

Hynes, Jack MA
South Amboy, NJ 08879

Stevens, Inc.
169 North Stevens Avenue
South Amboy, NJ 08879

Strathmore Treatment Associates
1 Lower Main Street, Route 35
South Amboy, NJ 08879

SOUTH RIVER

Memorial Medical Center
77 Water Street
South River, NJ 08882

SPRINGFIELD

Overlook Hospital Addictive Health System
530 Morris Avenue
Springfield, NJ 07081

SUMMIT

Charter Behavioral Health Systems of New Jersey
19 Prospect Street
Summit, NJ 07901

TOM'S RIVER

Alternatives Counseling Center, Inc.
96 East Water Street
Tom's River, NJ 08754

Counseling and Referral Services of Ocean County, Inc.
247 Main Street
Toms River, NJ 08753

Easter Seal Substance Abuse Treatment Services
1595 Route 9
Toms River, NJ 08755

Healy Counseling Associates
1108 Hooper Avenue
Tom's River, NJ 08753

TRENTON

Catholic Charities Alcoholism/ Addictions Program
47 North Clinton Avenue
Trenton, NJ 08607

Family Guidance Center of
Mercer County Substance Abuse
Recovery Program
2300 Hamilton Avenue
Trenton, NJ 08619

Fort Dix Community Counseling Center
Building 5203
Maryland Avenue
Trenton, NJ 08640-5140

Greater Trenton CMHC Outpatient MICA Services
132 North Warren Street
Trenton, NJ 08607

Mercer Street Friends Center Outpatient Drug and Alcohol Treatment Service
1201 West State Street
Trenton, NJ 08618

**New Horizon Treatment
Services, Inc.**
132 Perry Street
2nd Floor
Trenton, NJ 08618

Rescue Mission of Trenton
98 Carroll Street
Trenton, NJ 08604

**United Progress, Inc.
Detoxification Center**
541 East State Street
Trenton, NJ 08609

VENTNOR CITY

**Jewish Family Services
Addiction Services**
3 South Weymouth Avenue
Ventnor City, NJ 08406

VINELAND

Hendricks House for Men
542 Northwest Boulevard
Vineland, NJ 08360

Lloyd Reynolds Associates
733 Elmer Street
Vineland, NJ 08360

VOORHEES

Reality House, Inc.
1 Alpha Avenue
Suite 43
Voorhees, NJ 08043

WALL

**Wall Youth Center and
Community Services**
1824 South M Street
Wall, NJ 07719

WASHINGTON

**Family Guidance Center of
Warren Outpatient Substance
Abuse Treatment Program**
492 Route 57 West
Washington, NJ 07882

WAYNE

Wayne Counseling Center
475 Valley Road
Wayne, NJ 07470

WEST NEW YORK

**Mental Health and Addictive
Services**
5301 Broadway Street
West New York, NJ 07093

WESTVILLE

**Maryville Alcoholism Rehab
Center Outpatient Program**
156 Broadway
Westville, NJ 08093

WHITING

**America's Keswick Keswick
Colony Division**
601 Route 530
Whiting, NJ 08759

WILDWOOD

**Cape Counseling Services, Inc.
Drug and Alcohol Unit**
2604 Pacific Avenue
Wildwood, NJ 08260

WILLIAMSTOWN

Maryville, Inc.
1403 Grant Avenue
Williamstown, NJ 08094

WOODBURY

Services to Overcome Drug
Abuse Among Teenagers of New
Jersey, Inc. (SODAT, Inc.)
124 North Broad Street
Woodbury, NJ 08096

NEW MEXICO

ALAMOGORDO

Counseling Center, Inc.
1900 East 10th Street
Alamogordo, NM 88310

**Otero County Council on
Alcohol Abuse and
Alcoholism**
850 Wright Road
Alamogordo, NM 88310

ALBUQUERQUE

**Albuquerque Health Care for
the Homeless**
805 Tijenas Street
Albuquerque, NM 87102

Aliviar Counseling Service
1121 Kent NW
Albuquerque, NM 87102

**All Indian Pueblo Council, Inc.
Two Worlds Project**
3939 San Pedro Street NE
Suite D
Albuquerque, NM 87190

**Charter Heights Behavioral
Health Services Substance
Abuse Services**
103 Hospital Loop NE
Albuquerque, NM 87108

**Citizens' Council on Alcoholism
and Drug Abuse**
7711 Zuni Road SE
Albuquerque, NM 87108

Conflict Management, Inc.
3900 Georgia Street NE
Albuquerque, NM 87110

**Counseling and Psychotherapy
Institute**
803 Tijeras Street NW
Albuquerque, NM 87194

Hogares, Inc.
1218 Griegos Road NW
Albuquerque, NM 87107

Kaseman Presbyterian
8300 Constitution Street NE
Albuquerque, NM 87110

Lifestyle Recovery
3306 4th Street NW
Albuquerque, NM 87107

**Lovelace Park Center Substance
   Abuse Services**
5655 Jefferson Street NE
Albuquerque, NM 87109

**Memorial Hospital Addictive
   Disease Program**
806 Central Street SE
Albuquerque, NM 87102

**New Mexico Monitored
   Treatment Program**
9204 Menaul Boulevard NE
Suite 6
Albuquerque, NM 87112

**Saint Martin's Hospitality
   Center**
1201 3 Street
Albuquerque, NM 87125

Turquoise Lodge
6000 Isleta Boulevard SW
Albuquerque, NM 87105

University of New Mexico
Milagro Program
1007 Stanford Road NE
Albuquerque, NM 87131

Center on Alcoholism Substance
   Abuse and Addictions
2350 Alamo Drive SE
Albuquerque, NM 87106-3202

Veterans' Affairs Medical Center
Substance Abuse Treatment
   Program
2100 Ridgecrest Drive SE
Albuquerque, NM 87108

**Western Clinical Health
   Services of New Mexico**
Silver Street Clinic
4105 Silver Street SE
Albuquerque, NM 87108

ANTHONY

BERNALILLO

**Five Sandoval Indian Pueblos,
   Inc.**
1043 Highway 313
Bernalillo, NM 87004

La Buena Vida, Inc.
872 Camino Del Pueblo
Bernalillo, NM 87004

CARLSBAD

**Carlsbad Mental Health
   Association Villa de
   Esperanza**
914 North Canal Street
Carlsbad, NM 88220

CLAYTON

**Golden Spread Rural Frontier
   Coalition**
200 Aspen Street
Clayton, NM 88415

CLEVELAND

Rio Grande Treatment Center
Cleveland, NM 87715

CLOVIS

Mental Health Resources, Inc.
919 Rencher Street
Clovis, NM 88101

CROWNPOINT

**Navajo Nation Behavioral
   Health Services]**
Crownpoint, NM 87313

CUBA

**Presbyterian Medical Services
   Cuba Health Center**
State Road 44
Cuba, NM 87013

DEMING

**Border Area Mental Health
   Services**
901 West Hickory Street
Deming, NM 88030

DULCE

**Jicarilla Apache Tribe Multi
   Service Center**
Jicarilla Reservation, Building 23
Dulce, NM 87528

EMBUDO

**Rio Grande Alcoholism
   Treatment Program, Inc.**
Embudo, NM 87531

ESPANOLA

**Ayudantes, Inc. Espanola
   Northern Clinic**
810-F Riverside Drive
Espanola, NM 87533

Hoy Alcoholism Program
1102-A North Paseo De Onate
Espanola, NM 87532

FARMINGTON

Presbyterian Medical Services
Community Counseling Center
1001 West Broadway
Farmington, NM 87410

**San Juan Detoxification
   Services**
Four Winds Addiction Recovery
   Center
1313 Mission Avenue
Farmington, NM 87401

FORT BAYARD

Fort Bayard Medical Center
Yucca Lodge
Fort Bayard, NM 88036

GALLUP

**Na Nihzhoozhi Center, Inc.
   (NCI)**
2205 East Boyd Street
Gallup, NM 87301

Rehobeth McKinley Christian Health Care Services
650 Vanden Bosch Parkway
Gallup, NM 87301

GRANTS

Valencia Counseling Services, Inc. Cibola Counseling
210 East Santa Fe Street
Grants, NM 87020

HOBBS

Guidance Center of Lea County Treatment Center
920 West Broadway
Hobbs, NM 88240

Palmer Drug Abuse Program of Lea County
200 East Snyder Street
Hobbs, NM 88241

HOLLOMAN AFB

Holloman Air Force Base Substance Abuse Program
49 MDOS/SGOMH
1022 Fifth Street
Holloman AFB, NM 88330-8039

ISLETA

Pueblo of Isleta Alcoholism and Drug Program
Isleta, NM 87022

JEEZ PUEBLO

Behavioral Health Program
Jemez Pueblo, NM 87024

LAGUNA

Pueblo of Laguna Service Center
Laguna, NM 87026

LAS CRUCES

DWI Drug Court Treatment Program
642 South Alameda Street
Las Cruces, NM 88005

Families and Youth, Inc.
221 North Downtown Mall
Las Cruces, NM 88004

Mesilla Valley Hospital Residential Unit
3751 Del Rey Boulevard
Las Cruces, NM 88005

Southwest Counseling Center, Inc.
2401 South Espina Street
Las Cruces, NM 88005

Serenity House
1050 Monte Vista Avenue
Las Cruces, NM 88001

LAS VEGAS

Ayudantes, Inc.
803 Grand Avenue
Las Vegas, NM 87701-4252

LORDSBURG

Border Area Mental Health Services Lordsburg Counseling Center
500 East 13th Street
Medical Complex
Lordsburg, NM 88045

LOS ALAMOS

Los Alamos Family Council
1505 15th Street, Suite A
Los Alamos, NM 87544

LOS LUNAS

Valencia Counseling Services
735 Don Pasqual Road
Los Lunas, NM 87301

LOVINGTON

Guidance Center of Lea County, Inc.
1115 West Avenue, Suite D
Lovington, NM 88260

MAGDALENA

Alamo Alcoholism Program Outpatient and Prevention
Alamo Navajo Reservation
Magdalena, NM 87825

MESCALERO

Mescalero Tribal Human Services
107 Sunset Loop
Mescalero, NM 88340

MORA

Helping Hands, Inc.
North 15 Highway
Mora, NM 87732

PORTALES

Mental Health Resources, Inc. Substance Abuse Services/ Outpatient
300 East First Street
Portales, NM 88130

QUESTA

Presbyterian Medical Services Questa Health Center
Questa, NM 87556

RAMAH

Ramah Navajo Behavioral Health Services
Southside of Pinehill Street School Campus
Ramah, NM 87321

ROSWELL

Counseling Associates, Inc.
109 West Bland Street
Roswell, NM 88201

New Mexico Rehabilitation Center Chemical Dependency Unit
31 Gail Harris Avenue
Roswell, NM 88201

RUIDISO DOWNS

The Counseling Center, Inc. Substance Abuse Services
206 Sudderth Drive
Ruidoso Downs, NM 88346

SAN FELIPE PUEBLO

San Felipe Behavioral Health Substance Abuse and Prevention Program
San Felipe Pueblo Street
San Felipe Pueblo, NM 87001

SAN FIDEL

Acoma Canoncito Laguna Hospital New Sunrise Regional Treatment Center
San Fidel, NM 87049

SAN JUAN PUEBLO

Delancey Street/New Mexico, Inc.
40 Old Alcalde Road
San Juan Pueblo, NM 87566

Eight Northern Indian Pueblos Behavioral Health Program
Lower Alcada Road
San Juan Pueblo, NM 87566

SANTA FE

Ayudantes, Inc. Santa Fe Northern Clinic
1316 Apache Street
Santa Fe, NM 87504

Life Link
2325 Cerrillos Road
Santa Fe, NM 87505

Pinon Hills Hospital Substance Abuse Services
313 Camino Alire
Santa Fe, NM 87501

Recovery of Alcoholics Program, Inc.
4100 Lucia Lane
Santa Fe, NM 87505

Saint Vincent Hospital Substance Abuse Services
455 Saint Michael's Drive
Santa Fe, NM 87501

SANTA ROSA

Greater Santa Rosa Council on Alcohol
The Sure House
130 South 4th Street
Santa Rosa, NM 88435

SANTA TERESA

Alliance Hospital of Santa Teresa Rio Valle
100 Laurel Court
Santa Teresa, NM 88008

SANTO DOMINGO PUEBLO

Santo Domingo Substance Abuse Program
San Ildefonso Street
Santo Domingo Pueblo, NM 8705

SHIPROCK

Four Corners Regional Adolescent Treatment Center
Yucca Street Dorm 2
Shiprock, NM 87420

Shiprock Outpatient Treatment Center
Old PHS Hospital Building
Shiprock, NM 87420

SILVER CITY

Border Area Mental Health Substance Abuse Services
315 South Hudson Street
Silver City, NM 88061

SOCORRO

Socorro Mental Health Foundation
204-B Heel Avenue
Socorro, NM 87801

TAOS

Taos Alcohol and Drug Program
413 Sipapu Road
Taos, NM 87571

TRUTH OR CONSEQUENCES

Southwest Counseling Center, Inc.
118 Broadway
Truth Or Consequences, NM 87901-2830

TUCUMCARI

Mental Health Resources, Inc.
300 South 2nd Street
Tucumcari, NM 88401

ZUNI

Teambuilders Counseling Services, Inc.
Tucumcari, NM 88401

NEW YORK

ALBANY

Albany Citizens Council on
Alcohol and Other Chemical
   Dependence, Inc.
Alcohol Crisis Center
75 New Scotland Avenue Unit G
Capital District Psychiatric Center
Albany, NY 12208

90 McCarty Avenue
Albany, NY 12202

Albany County Substance Abuse
   Prevention Clinic
845 Central Avenue East 1
Albany, NY 12206

Altamont Program Inc
575 Broadway Street
Albany, NY 12204

Arbor Hill Alcoholism Program
(AHAP) Supportive Living Facility
250 Clinton Avenue
Albany, NY 12206

Eight Twenty River Street, Inc.
   Eleanor Young Clinic
134 Franklin Street
Albany, NY 12202

Equinox Counseling Center
306 Central Avenue
Albany, NY 12210

Hospitality House Therapeutic
   Community, Inc./Residential
271 Central Avenue
Albany, NY 12206

La Salle School, Inc.
391 Western Avenue
Albany, NY 12203

Pearl Street Counseling Center,
   Inc. Drug Free Clinic
42 South Pearl Street
Albany, NY 12207

Saint John's Project Lift, Inc.
Alcoholism Community Residence
37 South Ferry Street
Albany, NY 12202

Drug Abuse Services
45 South Ferry Street
Albany, NY 12202

Saint Peter's Addiction
   Recovery Center (SPARC)
Acute Care Unit
315 South Manning Boulevard
Cusack Pavilion
Albany, NY 12208

64 2nd Avenue
Albany, NY 12202

The Next Step, Inc. Recovery
   Home for Women
276 Sherman Street
Albany, NY 12206

Trinity Institution Homer
   Perkins Center, Inc.
76-82 2nd Street
Albany, NY 12210

Visiting Nurse Assoc. of Albany,
   Inc. Geriatric Alcohol
   Program
35 Colvin Avenue
Albany, NY 12206

Whitney M. Young, Jr. Health
   Center, Inc.
Family Alcoholism/Chemical
   Dependency Treatment Services
900 Lark Drive
Albany, NY 12207

Rehabilitation Clinic Methadone
   Maintenance Treatment
   Program
10 Dewitt Street
Albany, NY 12207-1306

ALBION

Unity Behavioral Health
   Chemical Dependency
   Services
168 South Main Street
Medical Arts Center
Albion, NY 14411

ALDEN

Brylin Hospitals Addiction
   Medical Services
11438 Genesee Street
Alden, NY 14004

ALTAMONT

Eight Twenty River Street, Inc.
   The Altamount House/Alcohol
   Inpatient Rehab
1180 Berne Altamont Road Route
   156
Altamont, NY 12009

AMHERST

Sisters of Charity Hospital Star
   Outpatient Services
4512 Main Street
Amherst, NY 14226

AMITYVILLE

Long Island Home at South
   Oaks Hospital
Alcoholism Outpatient and Drug
   Clinic
Bailey House Alcohol Inpatient
Detox Unit
Robbins Inpatient Alcoholism
Rehab Center
400 Sunrise Highway
Amityville, NY 11701

Town of Babylon Division of
   Drug And Alcohol Services
400 Broadway
Amityville, NY 11701

AMSTERDAM

Saint Mary's Hospital
Alcoholism Inpatient Rehab
Program
427 Guy Park Avenue
Amsterdam, NY 12010

Comprehensive Alcohol
Outpatient Clinic
76 Guy Park Avenue
Amsterdam, NY 12010

APPLETON

**Fellowship House, Inc.
Somerset House/Alcohol
Halfway House**
7397 Lake Road
Appleton, NY 14008

ASTORIA

**Hanac Substance Abuse
Program**
31-14 30 Avenue
Astoria, NY 11102

AUBURN

**Recovery Counseling Services
Alcoholism Outpatient Clinic**
188 Genesee Street
Auburn, NY 13021

**Unity House of Cayuga County,
Inc. Grace House**
56 Osborne Street
Auburn, NY 13021

**Confidential Help for Alcohol
Drugs (CHAD)**
Alcoholism Outpatient Clinic
75 Genesee Street
Piccolo Building
Auburn, NY 13021

BABYLON

**Crossings Recovery Program,
Inc.**
Crossings Alcoholism Outpatient
Clinic
133 East Main Street
Berger Professional Plaza Suite 1B
Babylon, NY 11702

BALDWIN

**Baldwin Council Against Drug
Abuse (BCADA) Outpatient
Drug Free**
950 Church Street
Baldwin, NY 11510

BALDWINSVILLE

**Confidential Counseling and
Evaluation Services**
2115 Downer Street
Baldwinsville, NY 13027

BALLSTON SPA

**Clinical Services and
Consulting, Inc. Ballston SPA
Alcohol Clinic**
433 Geyser Road
Ballston Spa, NY 12020

Hedgerow House
994 Route 67
Ballston Spa, NY 12020

BARRYVILLE

**New Hope Manor, Inc.
Residential Unit**
35 Hillside Road
Barryville, NY 12719

**Veritas Therapeutic
Community, Inc. Lucy Rudd
House**
375 Route 55
Barryville, NY 12719

BATAVIA

**Genesee Council on Alcohol and
Substance Abuse, Inc.**
Drug Abuse Services
Substance Abuse Outpatient
30 Bank Street
Batavia, NY 14020

**Mercy Hall Chemical
Dependency Treatment
Program**
16 Bank Street
Batavia, NY 14020

BATH

Kinship Community Residence
130 Rumsey Street
Bath, NY 14810

**Steuben County Alcoholism and
Substance Abuse Services**
115 Liberty Street
Bath, NY 14810

BAY SHORE

**Family Consultation Service,
Inc. Family Alcoholism
Treatment Center**
38 Park Avenue
Bay Shore, NY 11706

**Southside Hospital Substance
Abuse Detoxification Services**
Montauk Highway
Bay Shore, NY 11706

BAYSIDE

Long Island Jewish Hillside
Medical Center Family
Treatment Program Outpatient
Alcohol Clinic
212-02 41st Avenue
Bayside, NY 11364

BEACON

Saint Francis Hospital
Alcohol Outpatient Clinic
Turning Point/Acute Care
Turning Point/Inpatient
Rehabilitation
60 Delavan Avenue
Beacon, NY 12058

Beacon Counseling Center
223 Main Street
Beacon, NY 12508

BEDFORD HILLS

**Renaissance Project, Inc.
Bedford Hills Unit**
524-26 North Bedford Road
Bedford Hills, NY 10507

BELLPORT

**Outreach Development
Corporation Outreach Project**
11 Farber Drive, Unit D
Bellport, NY 11713

BETHPAGE

**Bethpage Adolescent
Development Associates
(BADA)**
936 Stewart Avenue
Bethpage, NY 11714

Bridge Back to Life Center, Inc. Drug Abuse Outpatient Clinic
4271 Hempstead Turnpike
Bethpage, NY 11714

BINGHAMTON

Addictions Center of Broome County, Inc.
455 State Street
Binghamton, NY 13901

Alternatives Counseling Center, Inc.
37 Mill Street
Binghamton, NY 13903

Broome County Chemical Dependency Services
168 Water Street
Binghamton, NY 13901

Fairview Recovery Services
Alcohol Crisis Center
247 Court Street
Binghamton, NY 13904

Fairview Halfway House
110 Fairview Avenue
Binghamton, NY 13904

Merrick Halfway House
1 Merrick Street
Binghamton, NY 13904

United Health Services, Inc.
New Horizons Alcohol Inpatient
Rehab Unit
New Horizons Detox Program
New Horizons Chemical
Dependency
Mitchell Avenue
Binghamton General Hospital
Binghamton, NY 13903

YWCA Clear Visions for Women Halfway House
80 Hawley Street
Binghamton, NY 13901

BLAUVELT

Daytop Village, Inc. Rockland Outreach Center
620 Route 303
Blauvelt, NY 10913

BOHEMIA

Catholic Charities (Talbot House) Alcohol Crisis Center
30-C Carlough Road
Bohemia, NY 11716

BOICEVILLE

Catskill Mountain Counseling
4080 Route 28
Boiceville, NY 12412

BRADFORD

Kinship House
3261 State Route 226
Bradford, NY 14815

BRENTWOOD

A Program Planned For Life Enrichment, Inc. (APPLE)
600 Suffolk Avenue, Suite A
Brentwood, NY 11717

Charles K Post Addiction Treatment Center
Pilgrim Psychiatric Center
Building 1
Brentwood, NY 11717

Outreach Development Corporation Outreach II
400 Crooked Hill Road
Brentwood, NY 11717

Town of Islip Dept. of Human Services Access
Division of Drugs and Alcohol
452 Suffolk Avenue
Brentwood, NY 11717

BRIDGEHAMPTON

Catholic Charities of Rockville Centre Outpatient Alcohol Clinic
2442 Main Street
Bridgehampton, NY 11932

BRONX

Albert Einstein College of Medicine Division of Substance Abuse
Melrose Unit
1764 Randall Avenue
Bronx, NY 10473

HUB 1/2/3
368 East 149 Street
Bronx, NY 10455

Yeshiva University/Melrose
260 East 161 Street
Bronx, NY 10451

Trailer 1
1500 Waters Place
Bronx, NY 10461

Van Etten Hospital Clinic
Morris Park and Seminole Avenue
Wing A
Bronx, NY 10461

Alternatives Youth Programs Chemical Dependency for Youth Clinic
324 East 149th Street
1st and 2nd Floor
Bronx, NY 10455

Argus Community Inc.
Harbor House
402 East 156th Street
Bronx, NY 10456

Basics/Franklin House
1064 Franklin Avenue
Bronx, NY 10456

Bronx Alcoholism Treatment
Center Alcoholism Rehabilitation
Unit
1500 Waters Place
Building 13
Bronx, NY 10461

Bronx Citizens Committee, Inc.
1668 Webster Avenue
Bronx, NY 10457

City Probation Programs
480 East 185th Street
Bronx, NY 10458

Bronx/Lebanon Hospital Center
Alcoholism Halfway House
Alcoholism Outpatient Clinic
321 East Tremont Street
Bronx, NY 10457

Alcoholism Halfway House
742-44 Kelly Street
Bronx, NY 10456

Alcoholism Inpatient Rehab
Dept. of Psychiatry Detox Unit
1276 Fulton Avenue
Bronx, NY 10456

Methadone Maintenance
Treatment Program/KEEP
3100 3rd Avenue
Bronx, NY 10451

City Probation Programs
480 East 185th Street
Bronx, NY 10458

Concourse Medical Methadone Treatment Clinic
880 Morris Avenue
Bronx, NY 10451

Cosmetic Executive Women Residence at Casa Rita
284 East 151st Street
Bronx, NY 10451

Daytop Village, Inc.
Medically Supervised Drug Clinic
Bronx, NY 10461

Dr. Martin Luther King, Jr. Health Center Alcoholism Outpatient Clinic
3565 3rd Avenue, Suite B-1
Bronx, NY 10456

Hunt's Point Multi-Service
Substance Abuse Treatment
Program
785 Westchester Avenue
Bronx, NY 10455

Alcoholism Outpatient Clinic
Chemical Dependency Probation
Program
630 Jackson Avenue
Bronx, NY 10455

Jacobi Medical Center Comprehensive Alcoholism Treatment Center
Morris Park Avenue and Seminole
Avenue
Bronx, NY 10461

La Casita
834 East 156th Street
Bronx, NY 10455

Learning for the Living Center
760 East 160th Street
Bronx, NY 10456

Lincoln Medical and Mental
Health Center Alcoholism
Outpatient Clinic
349 East 140 Street
Bronx, NY 10454

Montefiore Medical Center
SATP Unit I
3550 Jerome Avenue
Bronx, NY 10467

SATP Unit II
SATP Unit III
2005 Jerome Avenue
Bronx, NY 10453

Mrs A's Day Program
966 Prospect Avenue
Bronx, NY 10459

Narco Freedom, Inc.
Children and Families Together
391 East 149th Street
Bronx, NY 10455

Key Extended Entry Program
487 Willis Avenue
Bronx, NY 10455

Alternatives Drug/Free Treatment
Prog
Independence Alcohol Treatment
Program
477–479 Willis Avenue
Bronx, NY 10455

Methadone Maintenance
Treatment Program
477–479 Willis Avenue
Bronx, NY 10455

250 Grand Concourse
1st Floor
Bronx, NY

Regeneration Women and Children
Residential Treatment Program
2640-2652 3rd Avenue
2nd Floor
Bronx, NY 10454

Neighborhood Youth and Family Services
4137 3 Avenue
Bronx, NY 10457

Osborne Association Treatment Services
807-09 Westchester Avenue
Bronx, NY 10455

Our Lady of Mercy Medical Center
4401 Bronx Boulevard
Bronx, NY 10470

Phoenix House
Phelan Place
1851 Phelan Place
Bronx, NY 10453

Police Athletic League, Inc. Youhlink Program
2255 Webster Avenue, 3rd Floor
Bronx, NY 10457

Project Return Foundation, Inc.
Discovery Program
Exdous House Homeless Unit
1600 Macombs Road
Bronx, NY 10452

Womens Day Treatment Program
1484 Inwood Avenue 1st Floor
Bronx, NY 10452

Promesa, Inc.
Drug Treatment
1776 Clay Avenue
Bronx, NY 10457

Riverdale Mental Health Association
5676 Riverdale Avenue
Bronx, NY 10471

Saint Barnabas Hospital
Alcohol Detox Program
Alcoholism Outpatient Rehab
Program
3rd Avenue and East 183rd Street
Bronx, NY 10457

Methadone Maintenance
Treatment Program
4535-39 3rd Avenue
Bronx, NY 10457

**Samaritan Village, Inc.
Residential Drug Free
Program**
1381 University Avenue
Bronx, NY 10452

**Scan New York Volunteer
Parent**
Aides Assoc. Family Renewal
Center Drug Abuse Treatment
1075 Grand Concourse
Bronx, NY 10452

Soundview Throgs Neck CMHC
1967 Turnbull Avenue
Bronx, NY 10473

South Bronx Mental Health
Council, Inc. CMHC Alcoholism
Outpatient Clinic
1241 Lafayette Street
Bronx, NY 10474

Sports Foundation, Inc.
391 East 149 Street
Room 317
Bronx, NY 10455

**Tri-Center, Inc. Drug Abuse
Treatment**
2488 Grand Concourse
Bronx, NY 10458

**Veterans Affairs Medical Center
Substance Abuse Program**
130 West Kingsbridge Road
Bronx, NY 10468

**VIP Community Services Drug
Free Day Treatment**
770 East 176th Street
Bronx, NY 10460

Methadone Maintenance
Treatment Program
1910 Arthur Avenue, 7th Floor
Bronx, NY 10457

VIP Women's Residence
1946 Bathgate Avenue, 4th Floor
Bronx, NY 10457

**Vocational Instruction Project
Community Services
Alcoholism Halfway House**
671 East 231st Street
Bronx, NY 10466

Willow Shelter Program
781 East 135th Street
Bronx, NY 10454

BROOKLYN

ARTC Brooklyn
Medically Supervised Outpatient/
Probation
937 Fulton Street
Brooklyn, NY 11238

Brooklyn Clinic 11/Fort Greene
937 Fulton Street
Brooklyn, NY 11238

Brooklyn Clinic 13/Bushwick
1149-55 Myrtle Avenue
Brooklyn, NY 11206

Brooklyn Clinic 14/Brownsville
494 Dumont Avenue
Brooklyn, NY 11207

**Bedford Stuyvesant
Comprehensive Alcoholism
Treatment Center**
1121 Bedford Avenue
Brooklyn, NY 11216

**Bensonhurst Mental Health
Clinic, Inc.**
Drug Abuse Services
Outpatient/Prevention
86-20 18 Avenue
Brooklyn, NY 11214

**Beth Israel Medical Center
MMTP**
Cumberland Clinic
98 Flatbush Avenue
Brooklyn, NY 11217

**Break Free Russian Adolescent
Project Midwood Adolescent
Project**
2020 Coney Island Avenue
Brooklyn, NY 11223

Bridge Back to Life Center, Inc.
6823 5th Avenue
Brooklyn, NY 11220

**Builders for Family and Youth
Flatbush Addiction Treatment
Center**
1463 Flatbush Avenue
Brooklyn, NY 11210

Canarsie Aware, Inc.
Day Service
Outpatient/Prevention
1310 Rockaway Parkway
Brooklyn, NY 11236

**Church Avenue Merchants'
Block**
Assoc., Inc. Drug Abuse Prevention
Services
2211 Church Avenue
Brooklyn, NY 11226

Coney Island Hospital
Alcoholism and Drug Treatment
Program
2601 Ocean Parkway
Brooklyn, NY 11235

**Counseling Service of Eastern
District New York, Inc.**
186 Montague Street
Brooklyn, NY 11201

Cumberland Diagnostic and
Treatment Center Alcoholism
Treatment Program
100 North Portland Avenue
Brooklyn, NY 11205

CSEDNY REDI Program
185 Montague Street, 4th Floor
Brooklyn, NY 11201

Damon House New York, Inc.
Bushwick Homeless Drug Abuse
Residential Center
1154-1156 Dekalb Avenue
Brooklyn, NY 11221

Williamsburg Homeless Program
310 South First Street
Brooklyn, NY 11211

**Daytop Village, Inc. Brooklyn
Outreach Center**
401 State Street
Brooklyn, NY 11201

Discipleship Outreach Ministries
Exodus Treatment Center
5220 4th Avenue
Brooklyn, NY 11220

District 3 Youth and Adult, Inc. Outpatient Drug Free
271 Melrose Street
Brooklyn, NY 11206

EL Regreso Foundation, Inc.
Drug Abuse Treatment
189–191 South 2 Street
Brooklyn, NY 11211

232 Metropolitan Avenue
Brooklyn, NY 11211

Health Science Center Brooklyn/Kings County
Polydrug Unit 1
600 Albany Avenue
Building K Box 9 Code 26
Brooklyn, NY 11203

HHC New York City Kings County Hospital
600 Albany Avenue
Brooklyn, NY 11204

HHC/Woodhill Medical CMH
Center Chemical Dependency
Services Drug Detox Unit
760 Broadway
Brooklyn, NY 11206

Interfaith Medical Center
1545 Atlantic Avenue
Brooklyn, NY 11213

Bushwick Clinic
Methadone Maintenance
Treatment Program
555 Prospect Place
Ambulatory Building
Brooklyn, NY 11238

Kings County Hospital Center
Acute Detox
Alcohol Outpatient
600 Albany Avenue
Brooklyn, NY 11203

Comprehensive Alcoholism
Outpatient Clinic
591 Kingston Avenue
Brooklyn, NY 11203

Kingsboro Addiction Treatment Center
754 Lexington Avenue
Brooklyn, NY 11215

Long Island College Hospital
Outpatient Clinic
255 Duffield Street
Brooklyn, NY 11201

Lutheran Medical Center
Alcoholism Outpatient Clinic
Drug Abuse Treatment
514 49 Street
Brooklyn, NY 11220

Acute Care Addiction Program
150 55th Street
Brooklyn, NY 11220

Mid-Brooklyn Health Society, Inc. Alcohol Crisis Center
599 Ralph Avenue
Brooklyn, NY 11233

Narco Freedom/Court Street Clinic
217 Court Street
Brooklyn, NY 11201

New Directions Alcohol and Substance Abuse Treatment Program
202-206 Flatbush Avenue
Brooklyn, NY 11217

NYC Department of Probation Tri Center Unit III
175 Remsen Street
Brooklyn, NY 11201

Paul J. Cooper Center for Human
Services Outpatient Alcoholism
Clinic
106 New Lots Avenue
Brooklyn, NY 11212

Saint Martin de Porres Alabama Avenue Clinic
480 Alabama Avenue
Brooklyn, NY 11207

Saint Mary's Hospital
Substance Abuse Treatment
635 Classon Avenue
Brooklyn, NY 11238

1480 Prospect Place
Brooklyn, NY 11213

229 Powell Street
Brooklyn, NY 11212

Saint Vincent's Services, Inc. Alcoholism Outpatient Clinic
333 Atlantic Avenue, 1st Floor
Brooklyn, NY 11201

Serendipity
977 Bedford Avenue
Brooklyn, NY 11205

South Brooklyn Medical Administrative Services Methadone Maintenance Program
685 3 Avenue
Brooklyn, NY 11232

SUNY Health Science Center of Brooklyn Family Youth Center
604 Winthrop Street
Building F, 5th Floor
Brooklyn, NY 11203

Villa II, Inc. Alcoholism and Drug Abuse Outpatient Clinic
175 Remsen Street, 10th Floor
Brooklyn, NY 11201

Tri-Center, Inc. Drug Abuse Treatment
175 Remsen Street
Brooklyn, NY 11201

Urban Resource Institute Marguerite Saunders Urban Center for Alcohol Services
937 Fulton Street
Brooklyn, NY 11238

Victim Services Agency Outpatient Drug Abuse Clinic
3021 Atlantic Avenue
Brooklyn, NY 11208

Woodhull Medical and Mental Center
Chemical Dependency Services
Alcohol and Drug Detox Unit
760 Broadway
Brooklyn, NY 11206

BUFFALO

**Alcohol and Drug Dependency
    Services Inc.**
Alcohol Crisis Program
Inpatient Rehabilitation Services
291 Elm Street
Buffalo, NY 14203

Casa de Vita Halfway House/
    Women
200 Albany Street
Buffalo, NY 14213

Chemical Dependency Program
for Youth/LT
920 Harlem Road
Buffalo, NY 14224

Outpatient Clinic
210 Franklin Street
Buffalo, NY 14202

Men's Halfway House
2025 Broadway
Buffalo, NY 14213

**Beacon Center Alcoholism and
    Drug Outpatient Clinic**
695 Ellicot Square
Buffalo, NY 14150

Brylin Hospitals, Inc.
Drug Abuse Treatment Unit
Outpatient Unit
2625 Delaware Avenue
Buffalo, NY 14216

Williamsville Outpatient Clinic
5225 Sheridan Drive
Buffalo, NY 14221

**Buffalo General Health Care
    System**
Addiction Services
80 Goodrich Street
Buffalo, NY 14203

Deconess Center Alcoholism Clinic
1001 Humboldt Parkway
Buffalo, NY 14208

Buffalo General Hospital
Alcohol Outpatient
1001 Humboldt Parkway
Buffalo, NY 14201

**CAO/Dart Drug Abuse Research
    and Treatment Program**
1237 Main Street
Buffalo, NY 14209

**Cazenovia Recovery Systems,
    Inc.**
Cazenovia Manor
486 North Legion Drive
Buffalo, NY 14210

New Beginnings Community
    Residence
376 Dewitt Street
Buffalo, NY 14213

Supportive Living Program
923 Sycamore Street
Buffalo, NY 14212

**City of Buffalo DSAS Fillmore/
    Leroy Counseling Center**
2255 Fillmore Avenue
Buffalo, NY 14214

Ellicott/Masten Counseling Clinic
425 Michigan Avenue
Sheehan Memorial Hospital
Buffalo, NY 14203

Elmwood Counseling Clinic
656 Elmwood Avenue
Suite 201
Buffalo, NY 14222

Genesee/Moselle Clinic
1532 Genesee Street
Buffalo, NY 14211

Lakeshore Behavioral Health
El Comienzo Hispanic Alcoholism
    Outpatient Clinic
508 Niagara Street
Buffalo, NY 14201

Erie County Medical Center
Alcoholism Acute Care Program
Detoxification Unit
Chemical Dependency Program
462 Grider Street
Buffalo, NY 14215

West Eagle Clinical Services
134 West Eagle Street, Room 500
Buffalo, NY 14202

Erie Niagara Counseling
Associates Alcoholism Outpatient
    Clinic
6245 Sheridan Drive
Buffalo, NY 14221

Health Care Plan Inc
899 Main Street
Buffalo, NY 14203

Horizon Health Services
Addictions Outpatient/Bailey
3297 Bailey Avenue
Buffalo, NY 14215

Addictions Outpatient/Black Rock
699 Hertel Avenue
Buffalo, NY 14207

Addictions Outpatient/Central
    Park
60 East Amherst Street
Buffalo, NY 14214

**Mid-Erie Mental Health
    Services, Chemical
    Dependency Program**
1520 Walden Avenue
Buffalo, NY 14225

Alcoholism Outpatient Clinic
1131 Broadway Street
Buffalo, NY 14212

**Monsignor Carr Institute
    Ambulatory Substance Abuse
    Services**
76 West Humboldt Parkway
Buffalo, NY 14214

**Northwest Community Mental
    Health Center**
Elmwood Avenue Unit
2495 Elmwood Avenue
Buffalo, NY 14217

Niagara Street Unit
1300 Niagara Street
Buffalo, NY 14213

**Research Institute on
    Addictions Clinical Research
    Center**
1021 Main Street
Buffalo, NY 14203

Sheeham Memorial Hospital
Chemical Dependency Treatment
425 Michigan Avenue
Buffalo, NY 14203

Sisters of Charity Hospital Star Alcoholism Outpatient Clinic
1500 Union Road
Buffalo, NY 14224

Spectrum Human Services
New Alternatives
1235 Main Street
Buffalo, NY 14201

South Buffalo Counseling Center
2040 Seneca Street
Buffalo, NY 14210

Stutzman Alcoholism Treatment
Center Alcoholism Inpatient Rehab
Unit
360 Forest Avenue
Buffalo, NY 14213

Veterans' Affairs Medical Center Substance Abuse Program
3495 Bailey Avenue
Unit 116G
Buffalo, NY 14215

CAMILLUS

Professional Counseling Services Alcoholism Outpatient Clinic
5099 West Genesee Street
Camillus, NY 13031

CANAAN

Berkshire Alcoholism Outpatient Clinic
Route 22
Canaan, NY 12029

CANADAIGUA

Kim, Chong, M.D. VAMC Substance Abuse Services
400 Fort Hill Avenue
Canandaigua, NY 14424

Clifton Springs Hospital Alcoholism Outpatient Clinic
11 North Street
Canandaigua, NY 14424

Ontario County Division of Substance Abuse Services
3019 County Complex Drive
Canandaigua, NY 14424

CANTON

North Country Freedom Homes
The Canton House/Halfway House
25 Dies Street
Canton, NY 13617

Saint Lawrence County Alcohol and Substance Abuse Services Alcoholism Outpatient Clinic
University Shopping Plaza
Canton, NY 13617

CARMEL

Arms Acres, Inc.
Alcoholism Inpatient/Outpatient
Carmel, NY 10512

Putnam Family and Community Services
47 Brewster Avenue
Carmel, NY 10512

CARTHAGE

Carthage Clinic of Community Center for Alcoholism
410 State Street
Carthage, NY 13619

CASSADAGA

Tri-County Chemical Dependency
33 North Main Street
Cassadaga, NY 14718

CATSKILL

Twin County Alcohol and Substance Abuse Services, Inc.
66 William Street
Catskill, NY 12414

CENTER MORICHES

Greater Hamptons Interfaith Outpatient Drug Abuse Clinic
529 Main Street
School Special Education Admin.
Bldg.
Center Moriches, NY 11934

Transitions Counseling Center, Inc. Alcoholism Outpatient Clinic
408 Main Street
Center Moriches, NY 11934

COBLESKILL

New Directions Schoharie County Substance Abuse Program
150 East Main Street
Cobleskill, NY 12043

Schoharie County Community
Services Program for Alcoholism
Recovery
150 East Main Street
Cobleskill, NY 12043

COLD SPRING HARBOR

Huntington Youth Bureau/Drug
and Alcohol Cold Spring Harbor
YDA
82 Turkey Lane
Cold Spring Harbor High School
Cold Spring Harbor, NY 11724

COMMACK

Huntington Youth Bureau/Drug
and Alcohol Commack YDA/ Long
Acre School
Sarina Drive and Betty Lane
Commack, NY 11725

Catholic Charities of Rockville Centre Outpatient Alcohol Clinic/Commack
155 Indian Head Road
Commack, NY 11725

CORAM

Passages Counseling Center
Alcoholism Outpatient Clinic/
   Montauk
3680 Route 112
Coram, NY 11727

YMCA Family Services
6 Middle Country Road
Coram, NY 11727

CORNING

**Catholic Charities of the
   Southern Tier Transitions
   Counsel for Healthy Living**
65 East First Street
Corning, NY 14830

**Steuben Council Alcohol and
   Substance Abuse Services**
114 Chestnut Street
Corning, NY 14830

CORTLAND

**Alcohol Services Inc. Cortland
   Alcoholism Outpatient Clinic**
17 Main Street
Cortland, NY 13045

Catholic Charities of Cortland
County The Charles Street
   Halfway House
29 Charles Street
Cortland, NY 13045

**Family Counseling Services of
   Cortland County**
Alcoholism Outpatient Clinic
10 North Main Street
Cortland, NY 13045

CORTLAND MANOR

**Hudson Valley Hospital Center
   Methadone Maintenance
   Treatment Program**
1980 Crompond Road
Cortlandt Manor, NY 10567

DANSVILLE

Livingston County Council/
Alcoholism Alcoholism Outpatient
   Clinic
Red Jacket Street
Dansville, NY 14437

DELMAR

**Addiction Counseling Center of
   Bethlehem Crossroads**
4 Normanskill Boulevard
Delmar, NY 12054

DOUGLASTON

**Jewish Board of Family/
   Children Services Pride of
   Judea Mental Health Center**
243-02 Northern Boulevard
Douglaston, NY 11362

DOVER PLAINS

**Saint Francis Hospital Eastern
   Dutchess Counseling Center**
Reimer and Mill Streets Chemical
   Dependency Clinic
Dover Plains, NY 12522

DUNKIRK

Chautauqua County Dept. Of
Mental Health Alcohol and
   Substance Abuse Clinic
319 Central Avenue, 2nd floor
Dunkirk, NY 14048

EAST GREENBUSH

Seton Addiction Services
743 Columbia Turnpike
East Greenbush, NY 12061

EAST HAMPTON

A Program Planned for Life
Enrichment, Inc. (APPLE)/East
95 Industrial Road
East Hampton, NY 11937

Hampton Outpatient
43 Main Street
East Hampton, NY 11937

EAST MEADOW

**Family Service Association East
   Meadow Substance Abuse
   Outpatient**
1975 Hempstead Turnpike, Suite
   405
East Meadow, NY 11554

**Nassau County Dept of Drug
   and Alcohol Addiction Drug
   Counseling Program**
2201 Hempstead Turnpike
Nassau County Med Center
Bldg K, 2nd Floor
East Meadow, NY 11554

Nassau County Medical Center
Alcoholism Outpatient Unit
Detox Unit
2201 Hempstead Turnpike
Nassau County Medical Center
Building K
East Meadow, NY 11554

**Nassau County Substance
   Alternative Clinic Methadone
   Maintenance Treatment
   Program**
2201 Hempstead Turnpike
Nassau CO Medical Center
Building Z
East Meadow, NY 11554

EAST NORTHPORT

**Huntington Youth Bureau/Drug
   and Alcohol Northport/East
   Northport YDA**
7 Diane Court
East Northport, NY 11731

EDEN

**Turning Point House Recovery
   Home**
9136 Sandrock Road
Eden, NY 14057

ELIZABETHTOWN

Saint Joseph's Rehabilitation
Center Inc. Alcoholism and
   Substance Abuse Outpatient
   Cinic
Maple Avenue
Elizabethtown, NY 12932

ELLENVILLE

Ellenville Community Hospital
Acute Care Program
Outpatient Services
Route 209
Ellenville, NY 12428

Renaissance Project, Inc.
Ellenville Residential Facility
767 Cape Road
Ellenville, NY 12428

Samaritan Village, Inc.
751 Briggs Highway
Ellenville, NY 12428

Ulster County Mental Health
Services Ellenville Alcohol Abuse
  Outpatient Clinic
50 Center Street
Trudy Resnick Farber Center
Ellenville, NY 12428

ELMIRA

Economic Opportunity Program,
Inc.
Alcoholism and Drug Rehab Clinic
310 West 3 Street
Elmira, NY 14901

Our House Community
Residence
401 Division Street
Elmira, NY 14901

Saint Joseph's Hospital
Southern Tier Alcoholism Rehab
  Services (STARS)
555 East Market Street
Elmira, NY 14902

Schuyler/Chemung/TIOGA
Boces Workplace Intervention/
  Alcoholism EAP
495 Philo Road
Elmira, NY 14903

ELMONT

Long Island Counseling Center
ACT Chemical Dependency
Program
570 Elmont Road, 3rd Floor
Elmont, NY 11003

Long Island Jewish Medical
Center
Elmont Treatment Center
40 Elmont Road
Elmont, NY 11003

EVANS MILLS

Credo Foundation, Inc.
24180 County Road 16
Evans Mills, NY 13637

FARMINGVILLE

Suffolk County Division of
Alcohol and Substance Abuse
Services Farmingville
Alcoholism Outpatient Clinic
15 Horse Block Place
Farmingville, NY 11738

FAR ROCKAWAY

South Shore Alcoholism
Outpatient Program
718-720 Beach 20th Street
Far Rockaway, NY 11691

Saint John's Episcopal Hospital
South Shore Alcohol Detox
  Program
327 Beach 19th Street
Far Rockaway, NY 11691

Task Force on Integrated Projects/
  Mica
718-720 Beach 20th Street
Far Rockaway, NY 11691

FISHKILL

Mid-Hudson Alcoholism
Recovery Center Florence
Manor Community Residence
2977 Route 9
Fishkill, NY 12524

FLUSHING

Aurora Concept, Inc.
160-40 78 Road
Flushing, NY 11366

ELMCOR Youth and Adult
Activities, Inc.
Day Service Drug Treatment
  Program
107-20 Northern Boulevard
Flushing, NY 11368

Homeward Bound Program
107-10 Northern Boulevard
Flushing, NY 11368

Elmhurst Halfway House
81-30 Baxter Avenue
Flushing, NY 11373

Elmhurst Hospital Center
Methadone Maintenance
Treatment Program
79-01 Broadway
Flushing, NY 11373

Human Service Centers, Inc.
Alcoholism Outpatient Clinic
87-08 Justice Avenue, Suite 1-G
Flushing, NY 11373

Jewish Board of Family/Child
Services Living Free Drug
Program
97-45 Queens Boulevard
Flushing, NY 11374

Mental Health Providers of
Western Queens, Inc. Alcoholism
  Services
62-07 Woodside Avenue
Flushing, NY 11377

New York Hospital/Medical
Center Queens Alcoholism
Outpatient Clinic
174-11 Horace Harding
  Expressway
Flushing, NY 11365

Saint Barnabas Hospital
Correctional Health Affiliate
Keep
18-18 Hazen Street
Flushing, NY 11370

FRANKLIN SQUARE

Community Counseling Services of West Nassau
Alcoholism Outpatient Clinic
Outpatient Drug Free
1200-A Hempstead Turnpike
Franklin Square, NY 11010

FREEPORT

Operation Pride Outpatient Drug Free
33 Guy Lombardo Avenue
Freeport, NY 11520

Mercy Medical Center
Mercy Hill HWH/Women
95 Pine Street
Freeport, NY 11520

Women's Day Rehabilitation Services
90 Mill Road
Freeport, NY 11520

South Shore Child Guidance
Center Care Alcoholism Program
87 Church Street
Freeport, NY 11520

FULTON

Alcoholism Services in Oswego County
153 North 2nd Street
Fulton, NY 13069

Farnham, Inc. Drug Abuse Outpatient Clinic
120 Cayuga Street, Suite B
Fulton, NY 13069

GARDEN CITY

Medical Arts Samaritan, Inc. Cornerstone Continuous Care
233 7th Street
Garden City, NY 11530

Mercy Hospital Association
Family Counseling Alcoholism Outpatient Clinic
385 Oak Street
Garden City, NY 11530

Mercy Hospital New Hope Primary Care Program
8 Street Avenue P
Mitchel Field Complex
Garden City, NY 11530

GENEVA

Geneva General Hospital 3 South Detox Unit
196 North Street
Geneva, NY 14456

GLEN COVE

Angelo J. Melillo Center for
Mental Health, Inc. Alcoholism Counseling Services
30A Glen Street
Glen Cove, NY 11542

North Shore University Hospital at Glen Cove
Adolescent Substance Abuse Program
Women's/Children's Program
Substance Abuse Program
Saint Andrew's Lane
Glen Cove, NY 11542

GLENS FALLS

Human Resource Center
46 Elm Street
Glens Falls, NY 12801

GLOVERSVILLE

Fulton County Comm. Services
Board Fulton County Alcoholism Services
34 West Fulton Street
Gloversville, NY 12078

Fulton Friendship House, Inc. Victorian Manor
8-10 First Avenue
Gloversville, NY 12078

Saint Mary's Hospital Alcoholism Services
73 North Main Street
Gloversville, NY 12078

GOSHEN

New York State Office of Children/Family Services Drug Abuse Residential Treatment Program
Goshen Secusre Center
Cross Road
Goshen, NY 10924

Pius XII Chemical Dependency Program Substance Abuse Clinic
224 Main Street
Goshen, NY 10924

GOWANDA

Tri-County Memorial Hospital
Alcoholism Inpatient/Outpatient Program
Chemical Dependency Programs
100 Memorial Drive
Gowanda, NY 14070

GREAT NECK

Great Neck Community
Organization for Parents and Youth (COPAY)/Outpatient DE
21 North Station Plaza
2nd Floor
Great Neck, NY 11021

GREENLAWN

Huntington Youth Bureau/Drug and Alcohol Harbor Fields Elwood YDA
8 Gates Street
Greenlawn, NY 11740

GREENPORT

Eastern Long Island Hospital
Quannacut Alcoholism Inpatient Rehab Program
201 Manor Place
Greenport, NY 11944

GROTON

Ithaca Alpha House Center, Inc. Outpatient Drug Abuse Clinic
101 Cayuga Street
Groton, NY 13073

GUILDERLAND

Saint Peter's Addiction Recovery
Center (SPARC) Inpatient Rehabilitation Program
2232 Western Avenue
Guilderland, NY 12084

HAMDEN

Delaware County Alcohol and Drug Abuse Services
Route 10
Hamden, NY 13782

Delaware County Comm. Services
Board De County Alcohol Drug Abuse Services/Hamden
Road 1
Hamden, NY 13782

HAMPTON BAYS

Greater Hamptons Interfaith Council Outpatient Drug Abuse Clinic
154-5 West Montauk Highway
Hampton Bays, NY 11946

Long Island Center for Recovery, Inc.
Alcohol Primary Care
Alcoholism and Drug Abuse Inpatient Rehabilitation
320 Montauk Highway
Hampton Bays, NY 11946

HARRIS

Comm. General Hospital of
Sullivan County Biochemical Dependency Unit
Bushville Road
Harris, NY 12742

HARRISON

Saint Vincent's Westchester Alcoholism Treatment and Outpatient Program
275 North Street
Harrison, NY 10528

HAUPPAUGE

A Program Planned for Life Enrichment, Inc. (APPLE)
220 Veterans Highway
Hauppauge, NY 11788

1373-40 Veterans Highway
Hauppauge, NY 11788

North County Complex Methadone Maintenance Treatment Program
Building 151
415 Oser Avenue
Hauppauge, NY 11788-3620

Suffolk County Dept of Alcohol/ Substance Abuse
Methadone Maintenance and Keep Program
1330 Motor Parkway
Hauppauge, NY 11788

Outpatient Drug Abuse Clinic
Veterans Memorial Highway
North County Complex
Bldg 16, 1st Floor
Hauppauge, NY 11788

HAVERSTRAW

Open Arms, Inc. Halfway House
57-59 Sharp Street
Haverstraw, NY 10927

Village of Haverstraw Counseling Center/Reachout
40 New Main Street
Haverstraw, NY 10927

HAWTHORNE

Cortland Treatment Center of Saint Vincent's
4 Skyline Drive
Hawthorne, NY 10532

HEMPSTEAD

Counseling Service of Eastern
District New York, Inc. Drug Abuse Treatment
175 Fulton Avenue
Suite 301C
Hempstead, NY 11501

EAC, Inc. Outpatient Clinic
250 Fulton Avenue 2nd Floor
Hempstead, NY 11550

Family Services Association of Nassau County
Alcohol Treatment Center
Drug Treatment Center
126 North Franklin Street
Hempstead, NY 11550

Hempstead General Hospital Medical Center Acute Care Alcoholism Program
800 Front Street
Hempstead, NY 11550

Hispanic Counseling Center
Outpatient Drug Free Unit
250 Fulton Avenue
Hempstead, NY 11500

Alcoholism Outpatient Clinic
175 Fulton Avenue, Suite 500
Hempstead, NY 11550

HERKIMER

Herkimer County Alcoholism Services
301 North Walsh Street
Herkimer, NY 13350

HICKSVILLE

Central Nassau Guidance and Counseling Services, Inc.
950 South Oyster Bay Road
Hicksville, NY 11801

Family Service Association
Drug Program
Hicksville Alcoholism Outpatient Clinic
385 West John Street
Hicksville, NY 11801

HIGHLAND

Step One
106 Vineyard Avenue
Highland, NY 12528

Ulster County Mental Health Services Highland/New Paltz Alcohol Abuse Outpatient
560 Route 299 East
Highland, NY 12528

HOGANSBURG

Saint Regis Mohawk Tribe Health Services
St. Regis Road
Hogansburg, NY 13655

HOLTSVILLE

Transitions Counseling Center, Inc. Alcoholism Outpatient Clinic
1150 Portion Road
Holtsville, NY 11742

HORNELL

Saint James Mercy Hospital
Mercycare Alcoholism Treatment Center
1 Bethesda Drive
Hornell, NY 14843

HUDSON

Twin County Alcohol and Substance Abuse Services, Inc. Alcoholism Outpatient Clinic
419 Warren Street
Hudson, NY 12534

Catholic Charities of Columbia County/Supervised Outpatient
431 East Allen Street
Hudson, NY 12534

Columbia County Schools Community Services Project
71 North 3 Street
Hudson, NY 12534

HUDSON FALLS

Family Treatment Center for Alcoholism of
Glen Falls Hospital Alcohol Outpatient Clinic
418 Lower Main Street
Hudson Falls, NY 12839

HUNTINGTON

Huntington Youth Bureau/Drug and Alcohol
Counseling Center
423 Park Avenue
Huntington, NY 11743

HUNTINGTON STATION

Daytop Village, Inc.
Suffolk Outreach
2075 New York Avenue
Huntington Station, NY 11746

Huntington Youth Bureau/Drug and Alcohol
Huntington Station YDA
4 Railroad Street
Huntington Station, NY 11746

South Huntington YDA
300 West Hills Road
Huntington Station, NY 11746

Half Hollow Hills YDA
525 Half Hollow Road
Huntington Station, NY 11746

Long Island Center, Inc. Alcoholism Outpatient Clinic
11 Dawson Street
Huntington Station, NY 11746

Saint Christopher Ottilie Morning Star Community
151 Burrs Lane
Huntington Station, NY 11746

Suffolk County Dept. of
Alcoholism and Substance Abuse Services Huntington Station MMTP Clinic
689 East Jericho Turnpike
Huntington Station, NY 11746

HURLEY

Never Alone, Inc.
20 Crofts Road
Hurley, NY 12443

INDIAN LAKE

Hamilton County Community
Services Alcoholism
Counseling and Prevention Services
83 White Birch Lane
Indian Lake, NY 12842

IRVING

Cattaraugus Indian Reservation Health Center Human Services Unit
1510 Route 438
Irving, NY 14081

ISLIP

Town of Islip Dept. of Human Services
Drug Counseling Services
Outpatient Drug Free
401 Main Street
Islip, NY 11751

ITHACA

Alcoholism and Substance Abuse Council of Tompkins County
201 East Green Street
Suite 500
Ithaca, NY 14850

Ithaca Alpha House Center, Inc. Outpatient Center
102 The Commons
Ithaca, NY 14850

JAMAICA

Beth Israel Medical Center MMTP Queens Clinic
82-68 164 Street
3C1 Bldg. T, Dept. Medicine
Jamaica, NY 11432

Counseling Services of EDNY Heights Recovery Center
89-31 161st Street, Suite 708
Jamaica, NY 11432

Creedmoor Addiction Treatment Center Alcoholism Inpatient Rehab Program
80-45 Winchester Boulevard
Building 19(D)
Jamaica, NY 11427

Daytop Village, Inc. Queens
91-01 Merrick Boulevard
Jamaica, NY 11432

Interline Employee Assistance Program, Inc. Alcoholism Outpatient Clinic
89-00 Sutphin Boulevard
Suite 409
Jamaica, NY 11435

J/CAP Day Services
162-04 South Road
Jamaica, NY 11433

Mary Immaculate Hospital MMTP Clinic
147-18 Archer Avenue
Jamaica, NY 11435

New Spirit Outpatient Alcoholism Clinic
162-04 South Road
Jamaica, NY 11433

Phoenix House, Inc. Portal
175-15 Rockaway Avenue
Jamaica, NY 11434

Queens Child Guidance Center, Inc. Jamaica Family Center
89-56 162nd Street, 3rd Floor
Jamaica, NY 11432

Queens Hospital Center
Alcoholism Clinic
Alcoholism Consultation Team
Alcoholism Inpatient Detox Unit
82-68 164 Street
Jamaica, NY 11432

Stop DWI Program
114-2 Guy Brewer Boulevard
Suite 216
Jamaica, NY 11434

Queens Village Commission for Mental Health
J CAP, Inc./Safe Kids
146-15 Rockaway Boulevard
Jamaica, NY 11433

J CAP Residential Unit
177-33 Baisley Boulevard
Jamaica, NY 11434

Samaritan Village, Inc.
MTA Ambulatory/Residential
130-15 89 Road
Jamaica, NY 11419

MTA Residential Drug Free
Outpatient
Program
88-83 Van Wyck Expressway
Jamaica, NY 11435

JAMESTOWN

Chautauqua County Dept. of
Mental Health Alcohol and
Substance Abuse Clinic
73 Forest Avenue
Jamestown, NY 14901

WCA Hospital
Alcoholism Rehab Program
51 Glasgow Avenue
Jamestown, NY 14701

JOHNSON CITY

Southern Tier Drug Abuse Treatment Center
Outpatient Methadone Treatment
Clinic
40 Arch Street
Johnson City, NY 13790

JOHNSTOWN

New York State Office of Children/Family Services Drug Abuse Residential Treatment Program
Tryon Residential Center
881 County Highway 107
Johnstown, NY 12095

KATONAH

Four Winds Hospital, Inc. Choices Alcoholism Outpatient Clinic
800 Cross River Road
Katonah, NY 10536

KENMORE

Northern Erie Clinical Services
2282 Elmwood Avenue
Kenmore, NY 14217

KERHONKSON

Veritas Villa, Inc.
Alcoholism and Drug Abuse
Inpatient
Rehabilitation
5 Ridgeview Road
Kerhonkson, NY 12446

KINGSTON

The Bridge Back of FRMH
30 Broadway Street, Suite 205
Kingston, NY 12401

Kingston Hospital Alcohol Acute Care Program
396 Broadway Street
Kingston, NY 12401

Ulster County Mental Health Services
Alcohol Day Rehab/Evening
Intensive Program
Drug Free Clinic
Drug Free Jail Program
Kingston Alcohol Abuse
Outpatient Clinic
Methadone Maintenance and
Rehab Program/Outpatient
239 Golden Hill Drive
Kingston, NY 12401

LAKE GROVE

Lake Grove Treatment Centers of New York Alcoholism Outpatient Clinic
921 Hawkins Avenue
Lake Grove, NY 11755-1306

Chemical Dependency for Youth Clinic
111 Moriches Road
Lake Grove, NY 11755-1306

LATHAM

Clinical Services and Consulting Inc. Latham Alcoholism Clinic
636 New London Road
Latham, NY 12110

LAWRENCE

Committee on Drug Abuse (CODA) Outpatient Drug Free
270 Lawrence Avenue
Lawrence, NY 11559

Peninsula Counseling Center Alcoholism Counseling Service
270 Lawrence Avenue
5 Towns Community Center
Lawrence, NY 11559

LEVITTOWN

Yours Ours Mine Community Center, Inc.
Adolescent and Family Alcohol Program
Outpatient Ambulatory Drug Free Unit
152 Center Lane Village Green
Levittown, NY 11756

LEWISTON

Mount Saint Mary's Hospital Clearview Treatment Services
5300 Military Road
Lewiston, NY 14092

LIBERTY

Inward House Substance Abuse Treatment
Upper Ferndale Road
Liberty, NY 12754

Sullivan County Alcohol and Drug Abuse Services
Outpatient Clinic
710 Infirmary Road 2nd Floor
Liberty, NY 12754

LIVERPOOL

Conifer Park, Inc. Outpatient Alcoholism Clinic
526 Old Liverpool Road, Suite 4
Liverpool, NY 13088

Family Services Associates Alcohol Outpatient Clinic
7445 Morgan Road
Suite 100
Liverpool, NY 13090

LIVONIA

Livingston County Council on Alcohol and Substance Abuse
30 Commerical Street
Livonia, NY 14487

LOCKPORT

Alcoholism Council in Niagara
County Alcoholism Outpatient Clinic
41 Main Street
Lockview Plaza
Lockport, NY 14094

Reflections Recovery Center
521 East Avenue
Suite 4S
Lockport, NY 14094

LONG BEACH

Long Beach Medical Center
FACTS Alcoholism Outpatient Clinic
455 East Bay Drive
Long Beach, NY 11561

Long Beach Reach
Drug Abuse Clinic
26 West Park Avenue
Long Beach, NY 11561

LONG ISLAND CITY

A Way Out, Inc. II Day Service
10–34 44 Drive
Long Island City, NY 11101

Bridge Plaza Treatment and
Rehab Clinic Education and Methadone Treatment Unit
41-15 27 Street
Long Island City, NY 11101

Phoenix House
Vernon Boulevard Unit
34-25 Vernon Boulevard
Long Island City, NY 10023

Marcy II Unit
2900 Northern Boulevard
Long Island City, NY 11101

LOWVILLE

Lewis County Alcoholism and
Substance Abuse Treatment
Center Alcoholism Outpatient Clinic
7514 South State Street
Lowville, NY 13367

LYNBROOK

Link Counseling Center, Inc. Outpatient Drug Free
21 Langdon Place
Lynbrook, NY 11563

LYONS

Clifton Springs Outpatient Alcoholism Clinic
122 Broad Street
Lyons, NY 14489

Wayne County Substance Abuse Services
1519 Nye Road
Lyons, NY 14489

MADRID

North Country Freedom Homes John E. Murphy Community Residence
3702 Circle 14
Madrid, NY 13660

MALONE

Citizen Advocates, Inc. North Star Substance Abuse Services
16 4th Street
Malone, NY 12953

Saint Joseph Rehabilitation
Center, Inc. Alcoholism Outpatient
Clinic/Malone
214 East Main Street
Malone, NY 12953

MANHASSET

LIJ/HMC Manhasset Clinic
Daycare Unit
Outpatient Drug Free Unit
1355 Northern Boulevard
Manhasset, NY 11030

North Shore University Hospital
Drug Treatment Center
400 Community Drive
Manhasset, NY 11030

MASSAPEQUA

**Yes Community Counseling
Center Outpatient Medically
Supervised**
30 Broadway
Massapequa, NY 11758

MASSENA

Canadian/American Youth
Services, Inc. Rose Hill Treatment
Center
2 Elizabeth Drive
Massena, NY 13662

MATTITUCK

**Eastern Long Island Hospital
Quannacut Outpatient
Services**
7555 Main Road
Mattituck, NY 11952

MELVILLE

**Seafield Services, Inc. Alcohol
and Drug Abuse Treatment
Unit**
900 Walt Whitman Road
Suite 102
Melville, NY 11747

MERRICK

Tempo Group Outpatient Clinic
1260 Meadowbrook Road
Merrick, NY 11566

MEXICO

**Harbor Lights Chemical
Dependency Services
Alcoholism Outpatient Clinic**
3358 Main Street
Mexico, NY 13114

MIDDLE ISLAND

**Family Recovery Center
Alcoholism Outpatient Clinic**
514 Middle Country Road
Middle Island, NY 11953

MIDDLETOWN

Emergency Housing Group, Inc.
Middletown Alcohol Crisis Center
Middletown Psychiatric Center
Building 8
Middletown, NY 10940

**Horton Family Program
Outpatient Clinic for Youth**
406 East Main Street
Middletown, NY 10940

**Pius XII Youth and Family
Services**
10 Orchard Street
Middletown, NY 10940

**Regional Economic Community
Action Recap Alcoholism
Outpatient Rehab Program**
40 Smith Street
Middletown, NY 10940

**Restorative Management
Corporation Outpatient Drug
Clinic**
15 King Street
Middletown, NY 10940

**Richard C. Ward Addiction
Treatment Center**
141 Monhagen Avenue
Middletown, NY 10940

MILLBROOK

**Saint Francis Hospital
Millbrook Counseling Center**
Oak Summit Road
Millbrook, NY 12545

MINEOLA

**Long Island Jewish Hillside
Medical Center**
Family Consultation Center
Alcoholism Outpatient
366 Jericho Turnpike
Mineola, NY 11501

Nassau Counseling, Inc.
Outpatient Program
450 Jericho Turnpike, Suite 206
Mineola, NY 11501

**Seafield Center, Inc. Mineola
Alcoholism Outpatient Clinic**
110 Main Street
Mineola, NY 11501

MONROE

**Pius XII Chemical Dependency
Program**
Monroe Clinic/Outpatient Drug
Free
Monroe Alcoholism Outpatient
Clinic
520 Route 17-M
Monroe, NY 10950

MONTICELLO

**Sullivan County Council on
Alcohol/Drug Abuse, Inc.**
17 Hamilton Avenue
Monticello, NY 12701

MORICHES

**Passages Counseling Center
Alcoholism Outpatient Clinic**
Montauk Highway Monarch Center
Suite 109
Moriches, NY 11955

MOUNT KISCO

**The Weekend Center, Inc.
Alcoholism Outpatient Clinic**
24 Smith Avenue
Mount Kisco, NY 10549

MOUNT VERNON

Mount Vernon Hospital Methadone Maintenance Treatment Clinic
3 South 6th Avenue
Mount Vernon, NY 10550

Renaissance Project, Inc. Mount Vernon Unit
3 South 6 Street
Mount Vernon, NY 10550

Westchester Community
Opportunity Program Mount
Vernon Open Door Program
34 South 6 Avenue
Mount Vernon, NY 10550

Yonkers General Hospital Archway Alcoholism Outpatient Clinic
100 East First Street, 6th Floor
Mount Vernon, NY 10550

NEWARK

Finger Lakes Alcoholism
Counseling Referral Agency
Alcoholism Outpatient Clinic
301 West Union Street
Newark, NY 14513

NEWBURGH

Pius XII Chemical Dependency
Program Newburgh Clinic/
Outpatient Drug Free
62 Grand Street
Newburgh, NY 12550

Saint Luke's Hospital of Newburgh
479 Broadway
Newburgh, NY 12550

Alcohol Outpatient
Methadone Maintenance
Treatment Program
3 Commercial Place
Newburgh, NY 12550

NEW HARTFORD

Center for Addiction Recovery,
Inc. Alcoholism Outpatient Clinic
4299 Middle Settlement Road
New Hartford, NY 13413

NEW HYDE PARK

Long Island Jewish Medical Center
Daehrs Outpatient Drug Free
270-05 76 Avenue
Building 5
New Hyde Park, NY 11042

NEW ROCHELLE

Guidance Center, Inc.
Chemical Dependency Treatment
Center
403-5 North Avenue
New Rochelle, NY 10801

Renaissance Project, Inc.
New Rochelle Unit
Re-Entry Unit/Storefront
350 North Avenue
New Rochelle, NY 10801

United Hospital Alcoholism Outpatient Clinic
3 The Boulevard
New Rochelle, NY 10801

Volunteers of America
395 Webster Avenue
New Rochelle, NY 10801

Westchester Community
Opportunity Program New
Rochelle Outreach Center
33 Lincoln Avenue
Suite 2
New Rochelle, NY 10801

NEW YORK

Adolescent Health Center of The Mount Sinai Medical Center
312 East 94th Street
New York, NY 10128

Alcoholism Outpatient Clinic
19 Union Square West, 7th Floor
New York, NY 10003

Alianza Dominicana, Inc.
2410 Amsterdam Avenue
New York, NY 10033

American Indian Community Substance Abuse Services
708 Broadway
New York, NY 10003

Areba Casriel, Inc.
Alcoholism Inpatient Rehab
Program
Inpatient Drug Detox Program
Inpatient Primary Alcohol
Program
500 West 57th Street, 2nd Floor
New York, NY 10019

Drug Outpatient Program
Substance Abuse Outpatient Clinic
145 West 45th Street
New York, NY 10019

ARMS Acres, Inc. Alcoholism
Outpatient Services of Manhattan
1841 Broadway
3rd floor
New York, NY 10023

ARTC
Manhattan Clinic 21
Starting Point
136 West 125th Street
6th Floor
New York, NY 10027

Manhattan Clinic 22
Kaleidoscope
136 West 125th Street
New York, NY 10027

Manhattan Clinic 23
Third Horizon
2195 3rd Avenue
New York, NY 10035

Beth Israel Medical Center
Alcoholism Acute Care
Program
10 Nathan D Perlman Place
Bernstein Pavilion
New York, NY 10003

Drug Detoxification Program
1-9 Nathan D Perlman Place
New York, NY 10003

Stuyvesant Square Chemical
Dependency Program
380 2nd Avenue, 10th Floor
New York, NY 10010

Stuyvesant Square Chemical
Dependency Program
1st Avenue at 16th Street
New York, NY 10003

Beth Israel Medical Center Methadone Maintenance Treatment Program
Avenue A Clinic
26 Avenue A
New York, NY 10009

Clinics 1/2/3/6/7
Interium Clinic
103 East 125th Street
New York, NY 10035

Clinics IE/2F/3G
429 2nd Avenue
New York, NY 10003

Clinic 2C
435 2nd Avenue
New York, NY 10010

Clinic 3C
435 2nd Avenue
New York, NY 10010

Clinic 4, Units 1/2
21 Old Broadway
Basement
New York, NY 10027

Clinics 8/8D
140 West 125th Street
New York, NY 10027

Gouverneur Clinic
109 Delancy Street
New York, NY 10002

Coney Island Clinic
215 Park Avenue South, 15th
    Floor
New York, NY 10003

Saint Vincent's Clinic
201 West 13th Street
New York, 10011

Bliss Poston the Second Wind, Inc.
152 Madison Avenue
Suite 505
New York, NY 10016

Bowery Residents Committee, Inc. Alcoholism Outpatient Clinic
191 Chrystie Street
New York, NY 10002

Boys Harbor, Inc. Alcohol Outpatient Unit
1 East 104th Street
New York, NY 10029

BRC Human Services Corporation Alcohol Crisis Center
324 Lafayette Street
New York, NY 10012

Cabrini Medical Center Start
137 2nd Avenue
New York, NY 10003

Carnegie Hill Institute Methadone Treatment Center
116 East 92nd Street
New York, NY 10028

Center for Comp. Health Practice, Inc.
1900 2nd Avenue
12th Floor
New York, NY 10029

163 East 97th Street
New York, NY 10029

Central Harlem Emergency Care Services Alcohol Crisis Center
419 West 126th Street
New York, NY 10027

Chinatown Alcoholism Services
253 South Street 2nd Floor
New York, NY 10002-7827

CIS Counseling Center, Inc. CIS Addiction Services
150 Nassau Street, Room 1100
New York, NY 10038

Cornell University Medical
College Midtown Center for
    Treatment and Research
55 West 44th Street
New York, NY 10036

Create, Inc.
121 West 111th Street
New York, NY 10026

Daytop Village, Inc.
Federal Parole
132 West 83rd Street
New York, NY 10024

Education Alliance
25 Avenue D
New York, NY 10009

Project Contact
Outpatient Program
315 East 10th Street
New York, NY 10009

Enter, Inc.
Alcoholism Community Residence
2009 3rd Avenue
New York, NY 10029

Alcoholism Outpatient Clinic
302–306 East 111 Street
2nd Floor
New York, NY 10029

Exponents Treatment Exchange
151 West 26th Street, 3rd Floor
New York, NY 10001

First Step to Recovery
330 West 58th Street, Suite 609
New York, NY 10019

Freedom Institute, Inc. Alcoholism Outpatient Clinic
515 Madison Avenue
35th Floor
New York, NY 10022

Gracie Square Hospital
416 East 76th Street
New York, NY 10021

Gramercy Park Medical Group
253-55 3rd Avenue
New York, NY 10010

Greenwich House Counseling Center
80 5th Avenue
10th Floor
New York, NY 10011

Greenwich House, Inc.
Alcohol and Drug Treatment
    Program
55 5th Avenue
New York, NY 10003

Alcohol Treatment Program
312 Bowery
New York, NY 10012

Greenwich House MMTP
Cooper Square
50 Cooper Square
New York, NY 10003

Greenwich House West MMTP
24 West 20th Street
New York, NY 10011

Harlem Hospital
Alcohol Detoxification Unit
Harlem Hospital Center
K Building Mezzanine
136 Street and 5th Avenue
New York, NY 10037

Alcoholism Treatment Center
22-44 West 137th Street 4th Floor
New York, NY 10037

Methadone Treatment Clinic
15 West 136th Street K Building
New York, NY 10037

Methadone Maintenance
    Treatment Program
264 West 118th Street
New York, NY 10026-1620

Harold L. Trigg Clinic
543 Cathedral Parkway
New York, NY 10025

Hazelden New York
Inpatient Drug Abuse Rehab
    Program
Outpatient Drug Abuse Clinic
233 East 17th Street
New York, NY 10003

HHC Bellevue Hospital
Methadone Maintenance
    Treatment Program
27th Street and 1st Avenue
Buildings C and D
New York, NY 10016

Alcoholism Outpatient Clinic
462 1st Avenue at 27th Street
New York, NY 10016

**HHC/Metropolitan Hospital
    Center**
Drug Detoxification Program
Methadone Treatment Program
1900 2nd Avenue, 2nd Floor
New York, NY 10029

Immigrant Social Services, Inc.
137 Henry Street
New York, NY 10002

Inter Care, Ltd.
51 East 25th Street
Suite 400
New York, NY 10010

**International Center for the
    Disabled (TCD) Chemical
    Dependency Services/
    Outpatient Clinic**
340 East 24 Street
New York, NY 10010

**Inwood Community Services,
    Inc.**
Comprehensive Outpatient
    Alcoholism Program
Get Centered/Outpatient
651 Academy Street, 2nd Floor
New York, NY 10034

**Koeppel, Richard, M.D.
    Methadone Maintenance
    Treatment**
311 West 35th Street
New York, NY 10001

**Lesbian and Gay Community
    Services Center**
Project Connect
208 West 13th Street
New York, NY 10011

Lower Eastside Service Center
Drug Abuse Prevention Services
127 West 22nd Street
New York, NY 10011

Methadone Maintenance
    Treatment Program Unit 1
Outpatient Day Clinic
46 East Broadway
New York, NY 10002

Methadone Maintenance
    Treatment Program Unit 2
7 Governeur Slip East
New York, NY 10002

Methadone Maintenance
    Treatment Program Unit 3
62 East Broadway
New York, NY 10002

Su Casa Methadone Maintenance
    Treatment Program
157 Chambers Street 8th Floor
New York, NY 10007

**Manhattan Addiction Treatment
    Center**
600 East 125th Street
Wards Island
New York, NY 10035

Medical Arts Center Hospital
57 West 57th Street
New York, NY 10019

**Medically Supervised
    Ambulatory Substance Abuse
    Clinic**
19 Union Square West, 7th Floor
New York, NY 10003

Metropolitan Hospital Center
Drug Addiction Clinic
Methadone Maintenance
    Treatment Program
1900 2nd Avenue
Psychiatric Pavilion
New York, NY 10029

Mount Sinai Hospital
Narcotics Rehab Center
17 East 102nd Street
New York, NY 10029

Narco Freedom Program
337 West 51st Street
New York, NY 10019

458 West 50th Street
New York, NY 10019-6501

National Recovery Institute
458 West 50th Street
New York, NY 10019

**New York City Department of
    Probation Tri-Center Unit**
Alcoholism Outpatient Clinic
Drug Abuse Treatment
575 8th Avenue, 7th Floor
New York, NY 10018

New York Foundling
3280 Broadway Street
New York, NY 10027

New York Hospital Methadone Maintenance Treatment Clinic
401 East 71st Street
New York, NY 10021

New York Presbyterian Hospital Adolescent Development Program
411 East 69th Street
New York, NY 10021

New York Society for The Deaf Substance Abuse Clinic
817 Broadway Street, 7th Floor
New York, NY 10003

New York State Association for Retarded Children Sobriety Services Clinic
200 Park Avenue South, 3rd Floor
New York, NY 10003

New York University Downtown Hospital Methadone Maintenance Treatment Program
74 Trinity Place
New York, NY 10006

North General Hospital
Alcoholism Detoxification Unit
1879 Madison Avenue
New York, NY 10035

Alcoholism
   Treatment Center
1824 Madison Avenue
New York, NY 10035

NRL Resources, Inc.
450 South Park Avenue
Suite 402
New York, NY 10016

Odyssey House, Inc. of New York
Odyssey House Adult Program
Wards Island
Mabon Building 13
New York, NY 10035

Phase Piggy Back, Inc.
Adult Resocialization Unit
507 West 145th Street
New York, NY 10031

Project Okhute
1780-1784 Amsterdam Avenue
New York, NY 10031

Striver House
202-204 Edgecomb Avenue
New York, NY 10030

Parallax Center, Inc.
145 East 32nd Street, 6th Floor
New York, NY 10016

Phoenix House
164 West 74th Street
New York, NY 10023

Pride Site I Male Only Site
371 East 10th Street
New York, NY 10009

Project Green Hope Services for Women
Drug Abuse Services
448 East 119th Street
New York, NY 10035

Project Renewal Alcohol Crisis Center
8 East 3rd Street, 4th Floor
New York, NY 10003

Project Return Foundation, Inc.
814-816 Amsterdam Avenue
New York, NY 10025

Chelsea Tribeca Institute
Continuing Care Treatment
   Program
740 Broadway, 6th Floor
New York, NY 10003

Dreitzer Residence for Women and
   Children
315-317 East 115th Street
New York, NY 10029

Project Return Parole
814 Amsterdam Avenue
New York, NY 10025

Transitional Treatment Program
2112 2nd Avenue
New York, NY 10029

Reality House, Inc
Drug Free Outpatient
MTA Day Service
637 West 125th Street
New York, NY 10027

Saint Clare's Hospital Health Center Methadone Treatment Services
426 West 52nd Street
New York, NY 10019

Saint Luke's/Roosevelt Hospital Center
Alcoholism Halfway House
306 West 102nd Street
New York, NY 10025

Alcoholism Inpatient Detox Unit
Amsterdam Avenue at 114th
   Street
New York, NY 10025

Alcoholism Outpatient Clinic
411 West 114th Street
New York, NY 10025

Smithers Alcoholism Outpatient
   Clinic
Substance Abuse Program/
   Narcotics
1000 10th Avenue
New York, NY 10019

Smithers Inpatient Rehabilitation
   Unit
56 East 93rd Street
New York, NY 10028

Saint Marks Place Institute Outpatient Alcoholism Program
57 Saint Marks Place
New York, NY 10003

Samaritan Village, Inc.
Residential Drug Free
225-27 East 53rd Street
New York, NY 10022

Drug Residential Treatment
   Program
327 West 43rd Street
New York, NY 10036

Settlement Health Association, Inc. Rush Program
1775 3rd Avenue
New York, NY 10029

Silbermann, Eugene. M.D., Outpatient Methadone Clinic
2369 2nd Avenue
New York, NY 10035

22 East 110th Street
New York, NY 10029

**Upper Manhattan Mental Health
Center Alcoholism Program**
1727 Amsterdam Avenue
New York, NY 10031

**Veritas Therapeutic
Community, Inc.**
Residential Drug Treatment
Program
912 Amsterdam Avenue
New York, NY 10025

Infants and Toddlers Program
119 West 106th Street
New York, NY 10025

Veterans' Affairs Medical Center
Alcohol/Drug Dependence
Treatment Program
523 East 22nd Street
New York, NY 10010

Villa OPC II, Inc.
Alcoholism Outpatient Clinic
290 Madison Avenue 6th Floor
New York, NY 10017

**Women in Need Alcoholism and
Drug Abuse Services**
115 West 31st Street
New York, NY 10001

NIAGARA FALLS

**Alcohol Council in Niagara
County**
First Step Chemical Crisis Center
1560 Buffalo Avenue
Niagara Falls, NY 14303

Fellowship House, Inc.
Alcoholism Halfway House
431 Memorial Parkway
Niagara Falls, NY 14303

Fellowship House Supportive
Living
625 Buffalo Avenue
Niagara Falls, NY 14303

Horizon Health Services
Addictions Outpatient Drug Clinic
Alcoholism Outpatient Clinic
6560 Niagara Falls Boulevard, 2nd
Floor
Niagara Falls, NY 14304

**Milestones Alcoholism Services
Alcoholism Outpatient Clinic**
501 10 Street
Niagara Falls, NY 14301

**Niagara County Mental Health
Department Alcoholism
Outpatient Clinic**
1001 11th Street
Niagara Falls, NY 14301

Niagara Drug Abuse Program
Methadone Maintenance
Treatment Program
Outpatient Services
1001 11th Street
Trott Access Center
Niagara Falls, NY 14301

NORTH BABYLON

**Suffolk County Dept of Health
Services Division of Alcohol
and Substance Abuse Services**
1121 Deer Park Avenue
North Babylon, NY 11703

NORTH MERRICK

**Tempo Group, Inc. Drug Abuse
Outpatient Clinic**
1260 Meadowbrook Road
North Merrick, NY 11566

NORTHPORT

Concepts For Narcotics
Prevention, Inc. The Place/
Outpatient Drug Free
324 Main Street
Northport, NY 11768

NORTH TONAWANDA

**Bry-Lin Hospitals Alcoholism
Services**
3571 Niagara Falls Boulevard
North Tonawanda, NY 14120

**Mount Saint Mary's Hospital
Clearview Alcoholism
Outpatient Services**
66 Mead Street
North Tonawanda, NY 14120

NORWICH

**Chenango County Alcohol and
Drug Services**
Alcoholism Outpatient
105 Leilanis Way
Norwich, NY 13815

NYACK

Nyack Hospital
Alcoholism Acute Care Program
Alcoholism Inpatient Rehab
Program
160 North Midland Avenue
Nyack, NY 10960

**Nyack/Orangeburg Outreach to
Youth**
42 Burd Street
Nyack, NY 10960

OAKDALE

**Sanctuary East, Ltd. Outpatient
Drug Abuse Clinic**
One Berard Boulevard
Oakdale, NY 11769

OCEANSIDE

**Oceanside Counseling Center,
Inc.**
Alcoholism Services
Medically Supervised Outpatient
Drug Free
71 Homecrest Court
Oceanside, NY 11572

OGDENSBURG

**Saint Lawrence Addiction
Treatment Center**
1 Chimney Point Drive
Hamilton Hall
Ogdensburg, NY 13669

Saint Lawrence County Comm.
Services Board Alcoholism
Outpatient Clinic/Ogdensburg
1 Chimney Point Drive
Pritchard Pavilion
Ogdensburg, NY 13669

OLEAN

Cattaraugus County Council on
Alcoholism and Substance Abuse,
   Inc.
201 South Union Street
Olean, NY 14760

ONEIDA

Mancusco Counseling Services
123 Phelps Street
Oneida, NY 13421

Maxwell House
Next Step Apartments
312 Main Street
Oneida, NY 13421

ONEONTA

Otsego County Community
Services Otsego Chemical
   Dependencies Clinic
31 Main Street
Oneonta, NY 13820

ORANGEBURG

**Blaisdell Alcoholism Treatment
   Center Inpatient
   Rehabilitation Unit**
Rockland Psychiatric Center
   Campus
Building 28
Orangeburg, NY 10962

ORCHARD PARK

Spectrum Human Services
Southtowns Counseling
227 Thorn Avenue
Orchard Park, NY 14127

OSSINING

**Phelps Alcohol Treatment
   Services**
22 Rockledge Avenue
Ossining, NY 10562

OSWEGO

**Farnham, Inc. Outpatient
   Services**
33 East First Street
Oswego, NY 13126

**Oswego County Council on
   Alcoholism**
Alcoholism Outpatient Clinic
53 East 3rd Street
Oswego, NY 13126

**Tioga County Alcohol and Drug
   Services**
175 Front Street
Owego, NY 13827

Substance Abuse Outpatient Clinic
1277 Taylor Road
Wash Glad Building
Owego, NY 13827

OVID

**Dick Van Dyke Addiction
   Treatment Center Alcoholism
   Inpatient Rehab Unit**
1330 County Road, Suite 132
Ovid, NY 14521-9716

OYSTER BAY

Youth and Family Counseling
Agency of Oyster Bay/East
   Norwich, Inc.
193A South Street
Oyster Bay, NY 11771

PATCHOGUE

**Crossings of Long Island, Inc.
   Alcohol and Drug Treatment
   Programs**
450 Waverly Avenue, Suite 5
Patchogue, NY 11772

Brookhaven Health Center
365 East Main Street
Patchogue, NY 11772

PEARL RIVER

**Nyack Hospital Alcoholism
   Outpatient Clinic**
2 Blue Hill Plaza
Pearl River, NY 10965

PEEKSKILL

**Peekskill Area Health Center,
   Inc.**
Alcoholism Outpatient Clinic
Peekskill Pathways
1037 Main Street
Peekskill, NY 10566

PLAINVIEW

**Nassau County Dept. of Drugs
   and Alcohol Addiction**
1425 Old Country Road
Plainview, NY 11803

Plainview/Old Bethpage CSD
Youth Activities Council/
Reflection/Prevention
777 Old Country Road
Plainview, NY 11803

PLATTSBURGH

**Champlain Valley Family
   Center Drug Treatment Youth
   Services Inc.**
20 Ampersand Drive
Plattsburgh, NY 12901

**Clinton County Alcoholism
   Program**
16 Ampersand Drive
Plattsburgh, NY 12901

**Clinton County Mental Health
   Association**
Twin Oaks Alcoholism Halfway
   House
79 Oak Street
Plattsburgh, NY 12901

**Conifer Park, Inc. Alcoholism
   Outpatient Clinic**
13 Latour Avenue
Plattsburgh, NY 12901

POMONA

**Rockland County Dept of
   Mental Health Alcoholism
   Detoxification Unit**
Dr Robert L Yeager Health Center
Building C
Pomona, NY 10970

PORT CHESTER

Renaissance Project, Inc. Port Chester Center
4 Poningo Street
Port Chester, NY 10573

United Hospital Substance Abuse Detoxification Unit
406 Boston Post Road
Port Chester, NY 10573

WCMHB Saint Vincent's Hospital
Methadone Maintenance Treatment Program/Outpatient
350 North Main Street
Port Chester, NY 10573

PORT JEFFERSON

Saint Charles Hospital and Rehab Center Alcoholism Inpatient Rehab Program
200 Belle Terre Road
Port Jefferson, NY 11777

PORT JEFFERSON STATION

Crossings Recover Center
5225 Route 347
Davis Professional Park, Suite 40
Port Jefferson Station, NY 11776

John T. Mather Memorial Hospital Mather Outpatient Alcoholism Clinic
208 Route 112
Port Jefferson Station, NY 11776

PORT JERVIS

Crossroads At Mercy Community
Hospital Crossroads Acute Care Alcoholism Program
160 East Main Street
Port Jervis, NY 12771

Support Center, Inc. Substance Abuse Treatment Program
181 Route 209
Port Jervis, NY 12771

PORT WASHINGTON

Port Counseling Center, Inc.
225 Main Street
Port Washington, NY 11050

POTSDAM

Canton/Potsdam Hospital
Alcoholism Detoxification Unit
50 Leroy Street
Potsdam, NY 13676

Saint Lawrence County Alcohol and Substance Abuse Services Outpatient Clinic
State University of New York at Potsdam
Van Housen Hall
Potsdam, NY 13676

POUGHKEEPSIE

Astor School Based Clinic Alcoholism Youth Clinic
350 Dutchess Turnpike
Poughkeepsie, NY 12603

Dutchess County Dept. of Mental Hygiene
Alcohol Abuse Clinic
20 Manchester Road
Poughkeepsie, NY 12603

Dutchess County Methadone Clinic Outpatient
230 North Road
Poughkeepsie, NY 12601

Dutchess County Substance Abuse Clinic
20 Manchester Road
Poughkeepsie, NY 12603

Josephs House Alcoholism Supportive Living Facility
4 Fallkill Place
Poughkeepsie, NY 12601

Mid-Hudson Alcoholism Recovery Center
Alcoholism Primary Care Program
Branch B. Ryon Hall
Poughkeepsie, NY 12601

Bolger House Community Residence
260 Church Street
Poughkeepsie, NY 12601

New Hope Manor, Inc. Re-Entry House
141 South Avenue
Poughkeepsie, NY 12601

Waryas House Rehab Programs, Inc.
101 Inwood Avenue
Poughkeepsie, NY 12603

QUEENSBURY

Baywood Center
551 Bay Road
Queensbury, NY 12804

REGO PARK

Long Island Consultation Center, Inc. Alcoholism Outpatient Clinic
97-29 64th Road
Rego Park, NY 11374

Psychiatric and Addictions Recovery Services (PARS)
92-29 Queens Boulevard
Suite 2-E
Rego Park, NY 11374

RHINEBECK

Cornerstone of Rhinebeck
500 Milan Hollow Road
Rhinebeck, NY 12572

Daytop Village, Inc.
Fox Hollow Road
Rhinebeck, NY 12572

Saint Francis Hospital Rhinebeck Counseling Center
14 Springbrook Avenue
Rhinebeck, NY 12572

RICHMOND HILL

New York City Department of Probation Outreach Family Services
117-11 Myrtle Avenue
Richmond Hill, NY 11418-1751

RICHVILLE

Canton Potsdam Hospital Alcoholism Outpatient Clinic
The Richville Clinic
Richville, NY 13681

RIDGEWOOD

Outreach House I
16-14 Weirfield Street
Ridgewood, NY 11385

RIVERHEAD

Seafield Services
Alcoholism Outpatient Program
Drug Abuse Treatment Unit
212 West Main Street
Riverhead, NY 11091

Alternatives East Counseling Center
540 East Main Street
Riverhead, NY 11901

Suffolk County Dept of Alcohol and Substance Abuse Services
300 Center Drive County Center
Riverhead, NY 11901

ROCHESTER

Anthony L. Jordan Health Center Alcoholism Outpatient Clinic
30 Hart Street
Rochester, NY 14603

Bry-Lin Hospitals
Outpatient Alcoholism Program
2741 Ridge Road West
Rochester, NY 14626

Catholic Charities/Rochester
Catholic Family Center
Outpatient/Intensive Outpatient
Restart Alcoholism Outpatient
Clinic
55 Troup Street
Plymouth Park West
Rochester, NY 14608

CFC/Restart Substance Abuse Services
Liberty Manor
1111 Joseph Avenue
Rochester, NY 14621

81 Barberry Terrace
Rochester, NY 14621

Community Alcoholism Services Clinic
150 North Clinton Avenue
Rochester, NY 14604

Conifer Counseling Services
1150 University Avenue
Rochester, NY 14607

Crossroads Apartment Program
758 South Avenue
Rochester, NY 14620

East House Corporation
269 Alexander Street
Rochester, NY 14607

239 Alphonse Street
Rochester, NY 14621

50 Browncroft boulevard
Rochester, NY 14609

Crossroads III/Cody House
407 Frederick Douglas Street
Rochester, NY 14608

Family Services of Rochester, Inc.
Administrative Unit
Alcoholism Outpatient Clinic
Avon Drug Abuse Prevention Unit
30 North Clinton Avenue
Rochester, NY 14604

Genesee Hospital Dept. of
Psychiatry Genesee Alcohol
Treatment Center
580 South Avenue
Rochester, NY 14607

Huther/Doyle Memorial Institute
Alcoholism Outpatient Clinic
Drug Abuse Treatment Unit
360 East Avenue
Rochester, NY 14604

John L. Norris Alcoholism Treatment Center
Alcoholism Inpatient Rehab Unit
1732 South Avenue
Rochester Psychiatric Center,
Howard I
Rochester, NY 14620

Main Quest Treatment Center
184 Alexander Street
Rochester, NY 14607

287 Wellington Avenue
Rochester, NY 14611

Alcoholism Inpatient Rehab Unit
Comprehensive OP Alcoholism
Clinic
Supportive Living
774 West Main Street
Rochester, NY 14611

Burlington Community Residence
380 Barrington Street
Rochester, NY 14620

West Avenue Community
Residence
383 West Avenue
Rochester, NY 14611

Park Ridge Chemical Dependency, Inc.
Brighton Alcoholism Outpatient
Clinic
Drug Abuse Treatment
2000 South Winton Road
Building 2
Rochester, NY 14618

Adolescent Community Residence
2654 Ridgeway Avenue
Rochester, NY 14626

Unity Health System
1565 Long Pond Road
Rochester, NY 14626

Women's Community Residence
2650 Ridgeway Avenue
Rochester, NY 14626

Park Ridge Hospital
Chemical Dependency Unit
Short Term Rehab Unit
1565 Long Pond Road
Rochester, NY 14626

Outpatient Substance Abuse Clinic
81 Lake Avenue
Rochester, NY 14608

Pathway Houses of Rochester
Alcoholism Supportive Living
Facility
353 University Avenue
Rochester, NY 14607

Sisters of Charity Hospital
435 East Henrietta Road
Rochester, NY 14620

Supportive Living Facility
440 Fredrick Douglas Street
Rochester, NY 14608

Rochester Mental Health Center
Alcoholism Outpatient Clinic
Drug Treatment Services/
MSASATP
490 East Ridge Road
Rochester, NY 14621

**Saint Joseph's Villa of
Rochester, Inc.**
Life Program/Residential Chemical
Dependency Services/Youth/
Long Term
3300 Dewey Avenue
Rochester, NY 14616

**University of Rochester/Strong
Memorial Hospital**
Methadone Maintenance
Treatment Clinic
Drug Dependency Outpatient
300 Crittenden Boulevard
Rochester, NY 14642

Veterans' Affairs Medical Center
465 Westfall Road, Suite 116-6
Rochester, NY 14614

**Volunteers of America of
Western New York
Alcoholism Halfway House**
175 Ward Street
Rochester, NY 14606

Westfall Associates, Inc.
919 Westfall Road
Suite C-120
Rochester, NY 14618

**YWCA of Rochester/Monroe
County**
Alcohol Clinic
Steppingstone Drug Program
Supported Living Program
175 North Clinton Avenue
Rochester, NY 14604

ROCKVILLE CENTRE

Mercy Medical Center
Hospital Intervention Services
1000 North Village Avenue
Rockville Centre, NY 11570

Rockville Center Narcotics/Drug
Abuse Confide/Outpatient Drug
Free
30 Hempstead Avenue
Suite H-6
Rockville Centre, NY 11570

ROME

Rome Memorial Hospital
Community Recovery Center
Alcoholism Outpatient
264 West Dominick Street
Rome, NY 13440

RONKONKOMA

**A Program Planned for Life
Enrichment, Inc. (APPLE)**
161 Lake Shore Road
Ronkonkoma, NY 11779

153 Lake Shore Drive
Ronkonkoma, NY 11779

**Community Counseling Services
of Ronkonkoma Alcoholism
Outpatient Clinic**
3275 Veterans Memorial Highway
Suite B-1
Ronkonkoma, NY 11779

Passages Counseling Center
650 Hawkins Avenue
Ronkonkoma, NY 11779

**Professional Addiction
Counseling and Education**
3555 Veterans Highway
Suite E
Ronkonkoma, NY 11779

ROOSEVELT

**Nassau County Department of
Drug and Alcohol Addiction**
42 East Fulton Avenue
Roosevelt, NY 11575

Roosevelt Education Alcoholism
Counseling Treatment Center
React Alcoholism Outpatient Clinic
27A Washington Place
Roosevelt, NY 11575

SAINT ALBANS

**Queens Village Commission for
Mental Health**
JCAP Inc.,
177-33 Baisley Boulevard
Saint Albans, NY 11434

SALAMANCA

**Lionel R John Health Center
Human Services Unit**
987 R C Hoag Drive
Salamanca, NY 14779

SANBORN

**Horizon Village Drug Free
Residential Treatment**
6301 Inducon Drive East
Sanborn, NY 14132

SARANAC LAKE

**Saint Joseph's Rehabilitation
Center, Inc.**
Alcoholism Inpatient
Rehabilitation Program
Glenwood Estates
Saranac Lake, NY 12983

Alcoholism and Drug Outpatient
Clinic
50 Woodruff Street
Saranac Lake, NY 12983

SARATOGA SPRINGS

Saratoga County Alcoholism
Services Alcoholic Outpatient
Clinic
254 Church Street
Saratoga Springs, NY 12866

Saratoga Springs Office of
Abused Substances and
Intervention Services, Inc.
517 Broadway
Saratoga Springs, NY 12866

SCHENECTADY

Alcoholism and Substance Abuse Council of Schenectady County, Inc.
834 Emmett Street
Schenectady, NY 12307

575 Lansing Street
Schenectady, NY 12303

406-408 Summit Avenue
Schenectady, NY 12307

302 State Street
Schenectady, NY 12305

Bridge Center of Schenectady, Inc.
Residential Drug Treatment
70–72 Union Street
Schenectady, NY 12308

Carver Community Counseling Services Medically Supervised Outpatient
949 State Street
Schenectady, NY 12307

Lifestart Ambulatory Substance Abuse Program
1356 Union Street
Schenectady, NY 12308

Seton Addiction Services
1594 State Street
Schenectady, NY 12304

SCOTIA

Conifer Park, Inc.
Alcoholism and Drug Abuse
Services
79 Glenridge Road
Scotia, NY 12302

SEAFORD

Seaford Union Free School District Drug Abuse Program
1575 Seamans Neck Road
Seaford, NY 11783

SHRUB OAK

Phoenix Academy
Stoney Street
Shrub Oak, NY 10588

SMITHTOWN

Employee Assistance Resource Services, Inc. (EARS)
278 East Main Street
Smithtown, NY 11787

Saint John's Episcopal Hospital
Smithtown Alcohol Detoxification
Unit
498 Smithtown Bypass
Smithtown, NY 11787

Town of Smithtown/Horizons Counseling and Education Center
124 West Main Street
Smithtown, NY 11787

SOUTHAMPTON

Alternatives Counseling Center
291 Hampton Road
Southampton, NY 11968

SOUTH KORTRIGHT

Phoenix House
County Road 513
Old Route 10 Belle Terre
South Kortright, NY 13842

SOUTH OZONE PARK

Faith Mission Alcohol Crisis Center, Inc.
114-40 Van Wyck Expressway
South Ozone Park, NY 11420

SPRING VALLEY

Rockland County Dept of Mental Health Alcoholism Outpatient Clinic
50A South Main Street
Spring Valley, NY 10977

Town of Ramapo Youth
Counseling Services Outpatient
Drug Free
296 North Main Street
Spring Valley, NY 10977

STATEN ISLAND

Amethyst House, Inc. Alcoholism Halfway House
75 Vanderbilt Avenue
Staten Island, NY 10304

Bayley Seton Hospital, Inc.
Alcoholism Acute Care Unit
75 Vanderbilt Avenue
Staten Island, NY 10304

Bridge Back to Life Center, Inc. Staten Island Drug Abuse Treatment
1688 Victory Boulevard
Staten Island, NY 10314

Camelot of Staten Island, Inc.
Adolescent Drug Abuse Prog.
Outpatient Adult Program
263 Port Richmond Avenue
Staten Island, NY 10302

Drug Free Residential
273 Heberton Avenue
Staten Island, NY 10302

Tier 2
1111 Front Capadanno Boulevard
Staten Island, NY 10306

Chemical Dependency North/ SIUH
450 Seaview Avenue
Staten Island, NY 10305

Project Hospitality, Inc.
Women's Recovery Program
100 Central Avenue
Staten Island, NY 10301

Saint Vincent's Hospital Medical Center
Alcoholism Outpatient Clinic/DWI
Program
1794 Richmond Road
Staten Island, NY 10306

Seamens Society for Children and Families Substance Abuse Treatment Services
25 Hyatt Street
Staten Island, NY 10301

Sisters of Charity Healthcare, Inc.

Bayley Seton Campus Outpatient
75 Vanderbilt Avenue
Staten Island, NY 10304

Saint Vincents Campus Richmond
427 Forest Avenue
Staten Island, NY 10301

South Beach Alcoholism Treatment Center

777 Seaview Avenue
South Beach Psychiatric Center
Building A
Staten Island, NY 10305

Staten Island Children's Council, Inc. Drug Free Outpatient

420 Target Street
Staten Island, NY 10304

Staten Island University Hospital

Drug Free Services
Key Extended Entry Program
Methadone Maintenance
Treatment Program
392 Seguine Avenue
Staten Island, NY 10309

Chemical Dependancy Rehab
Alcohol and Drug Detox
375 Seguine Avenue
Staten Island, NY 10309

Alcoholism Outpatient Clinic
376 Seguine Avenue
Staten Island, NY 10309

YMCA of Greater New York

Staten Island YMCA Counseling
Services
3902 Richmond Avenue
Staten Island, NY 10312

SUFFERN

Good Samaritan Hospital of Suffern

Alcoholism Clinic
Drug Abuse Treatment Unit
255 Lafayette Avenue
Suffern, NY 10901

SWAN LAKE

Daytop Village, Inc.

Route 55
Swan Lake, NY 12783

SYOSSET

North Shore University Hospital at Plainview Alcoholism Acute Care Program

221 Jericho Turnpike
Syosset, NY 11791

Syosset Central School District Drug Abuse Program

South Woods Road
Syosset High School
Syosset, NY 11791

Syosset Counseling Center, Inc. Neighborhood SCAN/Drug Free Outpatient

23 Willis Avenue, Suite 300
Syosset, NY 11791

Kenneth Peters Center for Recovery Outpatient Alcoholism Clinic

6800 Jericho Turnpike, Suite
122-W
Syosset, NY 11791

SYRACUSE

Alcohol Services, Inc. Alcoholism Outpatient Clinic

247 West Fayette Street
Syracuse, NY 13202

Bright Path Counseling Center

7266 Buckley Road
Syracuse, NY 13212

Clinical Counseling Services Alcoholism Outpatient Clinic

70 James Street, Suite 215
Syracuse, NY 13202

Crouse Hospital

Intervention Services
Alcoholism Outpatient Clinic
Drug Free Outpatient Unit
Methadone Maintenance
Treatment Program
410 South Crouse Avenue
Syracuse, NY 13210

Crouse Health, Inc.
Commonwealth Place
6010 East Molloy Road
Syracuse, NY 13211

Alcoholism Acute Care Unit
Hospital Intervention Services
736 Irving Avenue
Syracuse, NY 13210

Forensic Consultants, Ltd. Alcoholism Outpatient Clinic

State Tower Building, Suite 700
Syracuse, NY 13202

Pelion of Central New York, Inc.

Alcoholism Outpatient Clinic
Chronic Disorders Outpatient
500 South Salina Street
Suite 218
Syracuse, NY 13202

Recovery Counseling Services

508 State Tower Building
Syracuse, NY 13202

Syracuse Behavioral Healthcare

Outpatient Services
518 James Street
Syracuse, NY 13203

The Willows Alcoholism Inpatient
Program
Si Van Duyn Street
Onondaga Hill
Syracuse, NY 13215

Syracuse Brick House, Inc.

Men's Halfway House
121 Green Street
Syracuse, NY 13203

Women's Halfway House
3606 James Street
Syracuse, NY 13206

Syracuse Community Health Center

Alcoholism Outpatient Clinic
Ambulatory Substance Abuse
Services
819 South Salina Street
Syracuse, NY 13202

Veterans' Affairs Medical Center

800 Irving Avenue
Syracuse, NY 13210

Yost, Inc. Center for Individual and Family Development
205 South Salina Street, 2nd Floor
Syracuse, NY 13202

TARRYTOWN

Phelps Memorial Hospital Center Alcoholism Inpatient Rehabilitation Program
701 North Broadway Street
Tarrytown, NY 10591

Phelps Mental Health Center Threshold Program/Alcohol Outpatient Clinic
38 Beekman Avenue
Tarrytown, NY 10591

TICONDEROGA

Saint Josephs Rehabilitation Center Alcoholism Halfway House
Moses Ludington Hospital Pavilion
Wicker Street
Ticonderoga, NY 12883

TONAWANDA

Beacon Center
Alcoholism Outpatient Clinic
Drug Abuse Outpatient Clinic
2440 Sheridan Drive
Tonawanda, NY 14150

Horizon Health Services, Inc.
Addictions Outpatient
1370 Niagara Falls Boulevard
Tonawanda, NY 14150

TROY

Hudson Mohawk Recovery Center Alcoholism and Drug Outpatient Clinic
16 First Street
Troy, NY 12180

Pahl, Inc. Drug Abuse Treatment Services
106–108 9th Street
Troy, NY 12180

Pahl Transitional Apartments
2239–2243 5th Avenue
Troy, NY 12180

Rensselaer County Mental Health Unified Services
Outpatient Drug Free Program
7 Avenue and State Street
County Office Building
Troy, NY 12180

Samaritan Hospital Detoxification Service
2215 Burdett Avenue
Troy, NY 12180

Seton Addiction Services at Saint Marys Hospital
1300 Massachusetts Avenue
Troy, NY 12180

TRUMANSBURG

Ithaca Alpha House Center, Inc. Residential
6625 Route 227
Trumansburg, NY 14886

TUCKAHOE

The Maxwell Institute of St. Vincent's Hospital
92 Yonkers Road
Tuckahoe, NY 10707

TUPPER LAKE

Saint Josephs Rehabilitation Center Alcoholism Outpatient Clinic
114 Wawbeek Avenue
Tupper Lake, NY 12986

UTICA

Dam Counseling Services Drug Abuse Clinic
250 Genesee Street, Suite 306
Utica, NY 13502

Insight House Chemical Dependency Services
500 Whitesboro Street
Utica, NY 13501

McPike Alcoholism Treatment
Center Alcoholism Inpatient Rehab Unit
1213 Court Street
Mohawk Valley Psychiatric Center
Utica, NY 13502

Rescue Mission of Utica, Inc. Alcohol Crisis Center
210 Lansing Street
Utica, NY 13501

VALHALLA

Weekend Center, Inc. Generations Alcoholism Outpatient Clinic
7-11 Legion Drive
Valhalla, NY 10595

Westchester County Medical Center
Behavioral Health Clinic
Valhalla Campus
Valhalla, NY 10595

VALLEY STREAM

Friends of Bridge, Inc. Drug Abuse Treatment Program
5–11 Pflug Place
Valley Stream, NY 11580

WALTON

Delaware Valley Hospital
Alcoholism Inpatient Rehabilitation
1 Titus Place
Walton, NY 13856

WAMPSVILLE

Madison County Alcohol and Drug Abuse Program
North Court Street
Veterans Memorial Building
Wampsville, NY 13163

WANTAGH

Southeast Nassau Guidance Center (SNG)
Alcoholism Counseling and Treatment
3401 Merrick Road
Wantagh, NY 11793

WARSAW

Allegany Rehab Associates, Inc.
Wyoming County Chemical Abuse
    Treatment Program
422 North Main Street
Warsaw, NY 14569

WARWICK

Sleepy Valley Center
Alcoholism Inpatient/Outpatient
    Rehabilitation Unit
117 Sleepy Valley Road
Warwick, NY 10990

WATERLOO

**Seneca County Community
    Counseling Center Alcoholism
    Outpatient Clinic**
31 Thurber Drive
Waterloo, NY 13165

WATERTOWN

**Community Center for
    Alcoholism of Jefferson
    County**
Alcoholism Outpatient Clinic
595 West Main Street
Watertown, NY 13601

Men's Halfway House
417 Washington Street
Watertown, NY 13601

Women's Halfway House
1130 State Street
Watertown, NY 13601

**Credo Foundation, Inc. Drug
    Treatment Program**
138 Winthrop Street
Watertown, NY 13601

WAVERLY

**Tioga County Alcohol and Drug
    Services Satellite**
284 Route 17-C
Waverly, NY 14892

WEBSTER

**Delphi Drug and Alcohol
    Council**
Drug Free Outpatient
55 East Main Street
Webster, NY 14580

WELLSVILLE

**Allegany Area Council on
    Alcoholism**
Trapping Brook House
3084 Trapping Brook Road
Wellsville, NY 14895

Drug Abuse Outpatient Clinic
76 Park Avenue
Wellsville, NY 14895

WEST BABYLON

Nepenthe, Inc.
1 Farmingdale Road, Route 109
West Babylon, NY 11704

WESTBURY

**North Shore Child/Family
    Guidance Association**
Chemical Dependency for Youth
50 Sylvester Street
Westbury, NY 11590

WESTHAMPTON BEACH

**Greater Hamptons Interfaith
    Council Outpatient Drug
    Abuse Clinic**
Main Street
Beinecke Building
Westhampton Beach, NY 11978

**Seafield Center, Inc. Alcoholism
    Inpatient Rehabilitation Unit**
7 Seafield Lane
Westhampton Beach, NY 11978

WEST HEMPSTEAD

**Long Island Jewish Hillside
    Hospital Medical Center**
Project Outreach
600 Hempstead Turnpike
West Hempstead, NY 11552

WESTON MILLS

Cattaraugus County Council on
Alcohol and Substance Abuse
    Program/Weston's Manor
Route 417
Weston Mills, NY 14788

WEST POINT

**US Army MEDDAC Department
    of U.S. Army**
Building 684
West Point, NY 10996-1197

WEST SENECA

**Health Care Plan, Inc.
    Alcoholism Outpatient Clinic**
130 Empire Drive
West Seneca, NY 14224

WHITE PLAINS

Greenburgh Open Door
5 Prospect Avenue, 2nd Floor
White Plains, NY 10607

Halfway Houses of Westchester,
Inc. Hawthorne House Alcoholism
    Halfway House
14 Longview Avenue
White Plains, NY 10605

**Innovative Health Systems Inc
    (IHS) Drug Abuse Treatment
    Unit**
7 Holland Avenue
White Plains, NY 10603

**New York and Presbyterian
    Hospital**
Alcoholism Inpatient/Outpatient
Rehabilitation Unit
21 Bloomingdale Road
White Plains, NY 10605

**Saint Agnes Hospital Inpatient
    Substance Abuse Detox**
305 North Street/Two Gaisman
White Plains, NY 10605

**Treatment Center of
    Westchester Alcoholism
    Outpatient Clinic**
10 Mitchell Place
White Plains, NY 10601

West Help Greenburgh
1 West Help Drive
White Plains, NY 10603

**White Plains Hospital Medical
Center Methadone
Maintenance Treatment
Program**
Davis Avenue East Post Road
White Plains, NY 10601

**Yonkers General Hospital
Greenburgh Alcohol
Treatment Services**
30 Manhattan Avenue
White Plains, NY 10607

WILLARD

**New York Services Department
of Correctional Services**
Willard Drug Treatment Campus
7116 County Route 132
Willard, NY 14588

WOODMERE

Tempo Group, Inc.
Drug Abuse Treatment/Intensive
Program
Outpatient Drug Free Unit
Prevention Unit
112 Franklin Place
Woodmere, NY 11598

YONKERS

Renaissance Project, Inc.
Chemical Dependency Treatment
Facility
42 Warburton Avenue
Yonkers, NY 10701

Saint Joseph's Hospital
Drug Free Counseling
107 South Broadway
Yonkers, NY 10701

Methadone Maintenance
Treatment Program
8 Guion Street
Yonkers, NY 10701

**Weekend Center, Inc.
Generations Alcoholism
Outpatient Clinic**
70 Ashburton Avenue
Yonkers, NY 10701

Yonkers General Hospital
Alcoholism Acute Care Program
Substance Detox
2 Park Avenue
Yonkers, NY 10703

Methadone Maintenance
Treatment Program
70 Ashburton Avenue
Yonkers, NY 10701

Yonkers Residential Center
Breakaway Alcoholism Outpatient
Clinic
317 South Broadway
Yonkers, NY 10705

Residential Treatment Program for
Youth
100 North Broadway Street
Yonkers, NY 10705

NORTH CAROLINA

AHOSKIE

**Roanoke/Chowan Human
Services Center**
Route 3, Box 22A
Ahoskie, NC 27910

ALBEMARLE

Albemarle House, Inc.
242 North 2nd Street
Albemarle, NC 28001

**Piedmont Behavioral
Healthcare**
1000 North 1st Street, Suite 1
Albemarle, NC 28001-2833

ASHEBORO

Alpha House, Inc.
1006 Sunset Avenue
Asheboro, NC 27203

**Randolph County Mental
Health/**
DD and Substance Abuse Services
Program
110 West Walker Road
Asheboro, NC 27203

ASHEVILLE

ARP/Phoenix LLP
129 Biltmore Avenue
Asheville, NC 28801

**Blue Ridge Center Adult
Substance Abuse Program**
283 Biltmore Avenue
Asheville, NC 28801

Horizon Recovery
31 College Place, Suite 304-D
Asheville, NC 28801-2483

Mountain Treatment Center
260 Merrimon Avenue
Asheville, NC 28801

Neil Dobbins Center
277 Biltmore Avenue
Asheville, NC 28801

**Veterans' Affairs Medical Center
Substance Abuse Treatment
Program**
1100 Tunnel Road
Asheville, NC 28805

BELMONT

**Carolinas Counseling
Consulting**
35 North Main Street
Belmont, NC 28012-3155

BLACK MOUNTAIN

**Alcohol and Drug Abuse
Treatment Center**
301 Tabernacle Road
Black Mountain, NC 28711

Robert Swain Recovery Center
1280 Old U.S. 70
Black Mountain, NC 28711

BOONE

**New River Behavioral Health
    Services**
132 Poplar Grove Connector
Boone, NC 28607

**Yadkin Valley Extended
    Services**
252 East King Street
Boone, NC 28607-4042

BREVARD

**Bridgeway/A Division of
    Transylvania Community
    Hospital, Inc.**
Hospital Drive
Brevard, NC 28712

BRYSON CITY

**Smoky Mountain Counseling
    Center**
80 Academy Street
Bryson City, NC 28713-0181

BUIES CREEK

**Lee/Harnett Mental Health
    Center**
5841 U.S. 421 South
Buies Creek, NC 27506

BURLINGTON

**Alamance Caswell Area MH/DD
    and Substance Abuse
    Program**
319 North Graham Hopedale Road
Suite A
Burlington, NC 27217

**Alamance Regional Medical
    Center**
1240 Huffman Mill Road
Burlington, NC 27215

**Residential Treatment Services
    of Alamance**
136 Hall Avenue
Burlington, NC 27215

BURNSVILLE

New Hope Counseling
525 West Main Street, Suite 1
Burnsville, NC 28714-2834

BUTNER

**Alcohol and Drug Abuse
    Treatment Center**
101 North Broad Street
Butner, NC 27509

CAMP LEJEUNE

**Naval Hospital Alcohol
    Rehabilitation Department**
Building 326
Camp Lejeune, NC 28542

CANDLER

**First Step Farm of Western
    North Carolina, Inc.**
214 Black Oak Cove Road
Candler, NC 28715

CARRBORO

**Orange/Person/Chatham Mental
    Health Center Substance
    Abuse Services**
101 East Weaver Street Suite 300
Carrboro, NC 27510

CARTHAGE

Sandhills Teen Challenge
444 Farm Life School Road
Carthage, NC 28327-9126

CHAPEL HILL

Freedom House Recovery Center
1477 Airport Road
Chapel Hill, NC 27514

CHARLESTON AFB

**Charleston Air Force Base
    Substance Abuse Program**
437 MDOS/SGOMH
204 West Hill Boulevard
Charleston AFB, NC 29404-4704

CHARLOTTE

Amethyst Charlotte, Inc.
1715 Sharon Road West
Charlotte, NC 28210

Assessment Dynamics
3127 Eastway Drive, Suite 212
Charlotte, NC 28205-5643

Behavioral Health Center Mercy
2001 Vail Avenue
Charlotte, NC 28207

Charlotte Rescue Mission
907 West First Street
Charlotte, NC 28202

Charter Pines Hospital
3621 Randolph Road
Charlotte, NC 28211

Chemical Dependency Center
100 Billingsley Road
Charlotte, NC 28211

**Dillworth Center for Chemical
    Dependency**
429 East Boulevard
Charlotte, NC 28203

**McLeod Addictive Disease
    Center**
145 Remount Road
Charlotte, NC 28203

**Mecklenburg County Area
    Mental**
Health Authority Substance Abuse
    Services
429 Billingsley Road
2nd Floor
Charlotte, NC 28211

**New Beginnings of Southern
    Piedmont LLC**
1508 Cleveland Avenue
Charlotte, NC 28203

Serenity Counseling Services
1409 East Boulevard
Charlotte, NC 28203

CHEROKEE

Cherokee Health Systems A Ye Ka Chemical Dependency Unit
Hospital Road
Cherokee, NC 28719

Unity Regional Youth Treatment Center
Sequoyah Trail Drive
Cherokee, NC 28719

CHERRY POINT

Substance Abuse Counseling Center MCAS Cherry Point
C Street, Building 294, Wing 7
Cherry Point, NC 28533

CONCORD

Cabarrus Family Recovery Center Substance Abuse Services
845 Church Street Commons, Suite 308
Concord, NC 28025

Serenity House, Inc.
172 Spring Street SW
Concord, NC 28025

Thrailkill Counseling
231 Branchview Drive NE, Suite C
Concord, NC 28025-3416

DOBSON

Hope Valley, Inc.
105 Country Home Road
Dobson, NC 27017

DURHAM

Duke Alcoholism and Addiction Program
2213 Elba Street
Durham, NC 27710

Durham Community Guidance Clinic
Turner Building
Trent and Elba Streets
Durham, NC 27705

Durham Regional Hospital Oakleigh
309 Crutchfield Street
Durham, NC 27704

Men and Women in Crisis Counseling Service
1413 Broad Street
Durham, NC 27705

Substance Abuse Services
304 West Main Street
Durham, NC 27701

Veterans' Affairs Medical Center Substance Abuse Program
508 Fulton Street
Durham, NC 27705

ELIZABETH CITY

Albemarle Mental Health Center
305 East Main Street
Elizabeth City, NC 27909

ELIZABETHTOWN

Bladen County Mental Health Center Alcoholism Program
East McKay Street
Elizabethtown, NC 28337

ELKIN

Crossroads Behavioral Health
130-A Hawthorne Lane
Elkin, NC 28621

FAYETTEVILLE

Behavioral Health Care
1830 Owen Drive, Suite 103
Fayetteville, NC 28304

Cardinal Clinic
351 Wagoner Drive, Suite 400
Fayetteville, NC 28303-4608

Cumberland County Mental
Health Center Family Recovery Services
109 Bradford Avenue
4th Floor
Fayetteville, NC 28301

Raintree Clinic
804 Stamper Road, Suite 201
Fayetteville, NC 28303

Roxie Avenue Center Substance Abuse Services
1724 Roxie Avenue
Fayetteville, NC 28304

FRANKLIN

Smoky Mountain Counseling Center
100 Thomas Heights Road
Franklin, NC 28734

GASTONIA

Family Service, Inc.
214 East Franklin Boulevard
Gastonia, NC 28052

Flynn Fellowship Home of Gastonia, Inc.
311 South Marietta Street
Gastonia, NC 28052

McLeod Addictive Disease Center
418 West Main Avenue
Gastonia, NC 28053-0596

New Beginnings of Gaston County
430 West Franklin Boulevard
Gastonia, NC 28052

GOLDSBORO

Carolina Care Center
206 North Spence Avenue
Goldsboro, NC 27534

Department of Corrections DART Cherry Facility
West Ash Street
Goldsboro, NC 27533

Wayne County Mental Health Center
301 North Herman Street
County Office Building
Goldsboro, NC 27530

GRAHAM

Family Consultants, Inc.
219 East Elm Street
Graham, NC 27253

GREENSBORO

Alcohol and Drug Services of Guilford
312 North Eugene Street
Greensboro, NC 27401

301 East Washington Street
Suite 101
Greensboro, NC 27403

Alternative Counseling Center
5415 West Friendly Street
Greensboro, NC 27410

Assessment Counseling and Testing Services
320 South Eugene Street
Greensboro, NC 27401

Employee Counseling Associates, Inc.
612 Pasteur Drive Suite 207
Greensboro, NC 27403

Fellowship Hall
5140 Dunstan Road
Greensboro, NC 27405

Guilford County Mental Health Center Substance Abuse Program
201 North Eugene Street
Greensboro, NC 27401

Jacqueline W Trotter Associates, Inc.
612 Pasteur Drive, Suite 104
Greensboro, NC 27403-1120

Ringer Center
213 East Bessemer Avenue
Greensboro, NC 27401-1415

Southeastern Counseling Center
1207 West Bessemer Avenue
Suite 227
Greensboro, NC 27408

TRC Counseling
1401 Sunset Drive, Suite 203
Greensboro, NC 27408-7230

GREENVILLE

Hatteras House
215 South Meade Street
Greenville, NC 27858

Pitt County Mental Health Center
203 Government Circle
Greenville, NC 27834

Side By Side Recovery Program
315 South Evans Street, Suite B
Greenville, NC 27858-1832

W. B. Jones Alcohol and Drug Abuse Treatment Center
2577 West Fifth Street
Greenville, NC 27834

HENDERSON

Franklin/Granville/Vance/
Warren Area Mental Health Program
125 Emergency Road
Henderson, NC 27536

HENDERSONVILLE

Horizon Recovery
132-B 3rd Avenue East
Hendersonville, NC 28792-4302

Trend Community Mental Health Services
800 Fleming Street
Hendersonville, NC 28739

HICKORY

Alcohol and Drug Abuse Services of Catawba County
120 Fairgrove Church Road SE
Suite 23
Hickory, NC 28602

Phoenix Lawhon
910 Tate Boulevard SE
Suite 102
Hickory, NC 28602

HIGH POINT

Alcohol and Drug Services of Guilford
119 Chestnut Drive
High Point, NC 27262

Adult Residential
5209 West Wendover
High Point, NC 27260

High Point Behavioral Health
601 North Elm Street
High Point, NC 27261-1899

Incentives, Inc.
212 East Green Drive
High Point, NC 27260-6654

JACKSONVILLE

Bryann Marr Behavioral Healthcare Systems
192 Village Drive
Jacksonville, NC 28546

Chemical Dependency Training Evaluation and Guidance, Inc.
230 New Bridge Street
Jacksonville, NC 28540

Onslow County Behavioral Health Services
215 Memorial Drive
Jacksonville, NC 28546

U.S. Marine Corp Substance Abuse Counseling Center
Marine Corps Air Station New River
Jacksonville, NC 28540-5000

JAMESTOWN

Alcoholics Home, Inc.
5884 Riverdale Road
Jamestown, NC 27282

KENANSVILLE

Chemical Dependency Training Evaluation and Guidance
106 South Street, Suite E
Kenansville, NC 28349

Duplin/Sampson Area MH/DD/ SAS Kenansville and Clinton Division Outpatient
117 Beasley Street
Kenansville, NC 28349

KERNERSVILLE

Twin City Counseling Center Inc
119 South Main Street
Kernersville, NC 27284

KINSTON

Lenoir Area MH/MR Substance Abuse Program
2901 North Heritage Street
Kinston, NC 28501

LAURINGURG

Scotland County Mental Health Center Substance Abuse Services
1224 Biggs Street
Laurinburg, NC 28352

LENOIR

Foothills Mental Health Center
901 Ashe Avenue
Lenoir, NC 28645

LEXINGTON

Davidson Alcoholic Care, Inc.
1675 East Center Street
Lexington, NC 27292

Davidson Assessment and Counseling
110-C Cotton Grove Road
Lexington, NC 27292

LINCOLNTON

Acts in Recovery, Inc.
326 East Main Street
Lincolnton, NC 28092

LOUISBURG

Franklin County Mental Health Clinic
107 Industrial Drive, Suite B
Louisburg, NC 27549

Genesis Substance Abuse Services
167 Highway 56 East
Louisburg, NC 27549-9449

LUMBERTON

Carolina Manor Treatment Center
1100 Pine Run Drive
Lumberton, NC 28358

Robeson County Mental Health Clinic
Non-Hospital Detoxification Center
450 Country Club Road
Lumberton, NC 28359

207 West 29th Street
Lumberton, NC 28358

MARBLE

Smoky Mountain Counseling Center
Highway 19
Marble, NC 28905

MARION

Foothills Mental Health Program
122 South Main Street
Marion, NC 28752

McDowell Council on Alcohol and Drug Abuse
17 North Garden Street
Marion, NC 28752

MONROE

Friendship Home, Inc.
2111 Stafford Street Extension
Monroe, NC 28110

New Beginnings of Southern Piedmont LLC
5719 Highway 74 West
Monroe, NC 28110

Piedmont Behavioral Health Union Center
1190 West Roosevelt Boulevard
Monroe, NC 28110

Union Regional Medical Center Behavorial Health Center/ First Step
600 Hospital Drive
Monroe, NC 28110

MOREHEAD CITY

Carteret Counseling Services, Inc.
105 North 10th Street
Morehead City, NC 28557

MORGANTON

Broughton Hospital
1000 South Sterling Street
Morganton, NC 28655

Foothills Area Mental Health Center
1001 B East Union Street
Morganton, NC 28655

Foothills Detox/Crisis Program
2130 NC 18/U.S. 64
Morganton, NC 28655

TLC Human Resources, Inc.
132 South Sterling Street
Evion Building
Morganton, NC 28680-1447

MOUNT AIRY

Crossroads Behavioral Health Center
351 Riverside Drive
Mount Airy, NC 27030

Delphi Counseling Services
201 North Main Street, Suite 307
Mount Airy, NC 27030

NEW BERN

Assessment and Counseling Services,Inc.
249 Craven Street
New Bern, NC 28560

Child Family Psychological
1425 South Glenburnie Road, Suite 1
New Bern, NC 28562-2610

New Bern Family Services Substance Abuse Services
403 George Street
New Bern, NC 28563

NEWLAND

New River Mental Health Center Avery Cares Center
636 Cranberry Street
Newland, NC 28657

NEWTON

Doris Lasley and Associates Abuse Services
116 North College Avenue
Newton, NC 28658-3237

NORTH WILKESBORO

New River Mental Health Wilkesboro Detox Unit
118 Peace Street
North Wilkesboro, NC 28659

PEMBROKE

Robeson Health Care Corp Our House
302 East 3rd Street
Pembroke, NC 28372

PILOT MOUNTAIN

Hope Valley/Women's Division
136 Hope Valley Road
Pilot Mountain, NC 27041

PINEHURST

Moore Regional Hospital Pinehurst Treatment Center
Page Road
Pinehurst, NC 28374

PITTSBORO

Chatham Counseling Center
40 Camp Drive
Pittsboro, NC 27312

POPE AFB

Pope Air Force Base Substance Abuse Program
23 MDOS/SGOMH
383 Maynard Street
Pope AFB, NC 28308-2383

RALEIGH

Charter Behavioral Health System Holly Hill/Charter Behavioral Health
3019 Falstaff Road
Raleigh, NC 27610

Jamie Norton and Associates Keys to Recovery
1110 Navaho Drive
Tower One Building, Suite 103
Raleigh, NC 27609

PSI Solution Center
801 Jones Franklin Road
Suite 210
Raleigh, NC 27606-3381

Pathways Counseling Center
2809 Highwoods Boulevard
Suite 103
Raleigh, NC 27604

Recovery Partnership, Inc.
3900 Barrett Drive
Suite 301
Raleigh, NC 27609

Southlight, Inc. Community Treatment Project Lifeplus
2101 Old Garner Road, Suite 111
Raleigh, NC 27610

Wake County Alcoholism Treatment Center
3000 Falstaff Road
Raleigh, NC 27610

REIDSVILLE

Rockingham County Mental
Health Center Substance Abuse Services
405 NC 65
Reidsville, NC 27320

ROANOKE RAPIDS

Riverstone Counseling and Personal Development
210 Smith Church Road
Roanoke Rapids, NC 27870

ROBBINSVILLE

Smoky Mountain Counseling Center
217 South Main Street
Robbinsville, NC 28771

ROCKINGHAM

Recovery Associates
208 East Franklin Street, Suite C
Rockingham, NC 28379-3640

Samaritan Colony
136 Samaritan Drive
Rockingham, NC 28379

ROCKY MOUNT

Edgecombe/Nash Mental Health Center Substance Abuse Program
500 Nash Medical Arts Mall
Rocky Mount, NC 27804

Urton Associates
3300 Sunset Avenue
Rocky Mount, NC 27804-3571

ROXBORO

Person County Mental Health Center
204 West Barden Street
Roxboro, NC 27573

SALISBURY

Rowan Regional Medical Lifeworks Center
612 Mocksville Avenue
Salisbury, NC 28144

Veterans' Affairs Medical Center Substance Abuse Treatment Program
1601 Brenner Avenue
Unit 4-2B (116A3)
Salisbury, NC 28144

SANFORD

Harbor Clinic
138 South Steele Street
Sanford, NC 27330-4201

SELMA

Day by Day Treatment Center
1110 River Road
Selma, NC 27576

SHALLOTTE

Coast Behavioral Health Services
624 Village Road, Suite 1
Shallotte, NC 28470

SHELBY

Cleveland Center
917 First Street
Shelby, NC 28150

New Beginnings of Southern Piedmont
115 North Lafayette Street
Shelby, NC 28150-4445

Wellness Training Association, Inc.
217 North Lafayette Street
Shelby, NC 28150

SMITHFIELD

Johnston Substance Abuse
Program Treatment and Rehabilitation
521 Bright Leaf Boulevard
Smithfield, NC 27577

SOUTHERN PINES

Recovery Associates
770 NW Broad Street
Southern Pines, NC 28387

SPARTA

New River Mental Health Center
West Doughton Street
Sparta, NC 28675

SPINDALE

Rutherford Substance Abuse Services
271 Callahan Koon Road
Spindale, NC 28160-2207

STATESVILLE

Carolina Psychiatric Group
515 Brookdale Drive
Statesville, NC 28677

Counseling Center of Iredell
125 West Bell Street
Statesville, NC 28677

Steps to Success
211 South Center Street
City Center Building, 4th Floor
Statesville, NC 28677-5258

TARBORO

Urton Associates
102 East Granville Street
Tarboro, NC 27886-5002

TAYLORSVILLE

Foothills Mental Health Center Alcohol and Drug Abuse Program
326 First Avenue SW
Taylorsville, NC 28681

THOMASVILLE

Davidson County MH/DD and Substance Abuse Services
205 Old Lexington Road
Thomasville, NC 27360

Green Center of Growth Development
25 West Guilford Street
Thomasville, NC 27360-3945

WARRENTON

John A. Hyman Substance Abuse Services
Rural Route 3
Warrenton, NC 27589-9803

WASHINGTON

Tideland Mental Health Center Substance Abuse Division
1308 Highland Drive
Washington, NC 27889

WAYNESVILLE

Gateway
1406 Dellwood Road
Waynesville, NC 28786

Smokey Mountain Counseling Center
131 Walnut Street
Waynesville, NC 28786

Smoky Mountain Area Mental Health Haywood County Center
1207 East Street
Waynesville, NC 28786

WEST END

Sandhills Mental Health Center Substance Abuse Services
7 Lakes Drive
West End, NC 27376

WEST JEFFERSON

Yadkin Valley Extended Services
106 Jefferson Drive
West Jefferson, NC 28694-7245

WHITEVILLE

Columbus County Mental Health Center
306 Jefferson Street
Whiteville, NC 28472

WHITTIER

Smoky Mountain Center for MH/MR/SA Services Substance Abuse Services Program
1450 Smoky Cove Road
Whittier, NC 28789

WILKESBORO

New River Substance Abuse Services Wilkes County
1226 School Street
Wilkesboro, NC 28697

Yadkin Valley Extended Services
Wilkesboro, NC 28697

WILMINGTON

Coastal Horizons Center Outpatient Treatment Services
721 Market Street, 3rd Floor
Wilmington, NC 28401

Harvest of Wilmington, Inc.
3805 Wrightsville Avenue, Suite 17
Wilmington, NC 28403-8464

Kelly House East Coast Solutions
1507 Martin Street
Wilmington, NC 28401-6483

Recovery Center of Richmond
2520 Troy Drive
Wilmington, NC 28401

Southeastern Center for Mental Health/DD Substance Abuse Services
2023 South 17 Street
Wilmington, NC 28401

Stepping Stone Manor
416 Walnut Street
Wilmington, NC 28401

WILSON

Alternatives
2122 West Nash Road
Wilson, NC 27893-1728

Wilson/Greene Substance Abuse Center
208 North Goldsboro Street
Wilson, NC 27895

WINSTON SALEM

Addiction Recovery Care Association
1931 Union Cross Road
Winston Salem, NC 27107

Behavioral Health Resources Novant Health Resources Network
3333 Silas Creek Parkway
Winston Salem, NC 27103

Centerpoint Substance Abuse Services
725 North Highland Avenue
Winston Salem, NC 27101

First, Inc.
316 North Spring Street
Winston Salem, NC 27101

Friendship House
533 Summit Street
Winston Salem, NC 27101

Lifeskills
1001 South Marshall Street
Winston-Salem, NC 27101

Step One, Inc.
665 West 4th Street
Winston Salem, NC 27101

WINTERVILLE

Community Wellness Center Recovery Place
108 West Firetower Road, Suite H
Winterville, NC 28590

YADKINVILLE

Surry Yadkin Area MH/DD/SA Authority
320 East Lee Avenue
Yadkinville, NC 27055

Yadkin Valley Counseling Services
202 East Main Street
Yadkinville, NC 27055

NORTH DAKOTA

BELCOURT

Turtle Mountain Counseling Center
Highway 5
Belcourt, ND 58316

BISMARCK

Basaraba, Rose, LAC Counseling Services
433 East Bismarck Expressway, Suite 3
Bismarck, ND 58504-6511

Burleigh County Detoxification Center
514 East Thayer Avenue
Burleigh County Sheriff's Department
Bismarck, ND 58501

De Counseling Service
418 East Rosser Avenue, Suite E
Bismarck, ND 58501

Heartview Foundation
105 East Broadway
Bismarck, ND 58501

New Freedom Center
2101 East Broadway
Bismarck, ND 58501

North Dakota State Penitentiary Addiction Treatment Program
Bismarck, ND 58502

West Central Human Service Center Chemical Dependency Program
600 South 2 Street
Bismarck, ND 58504

Whole Person Recovery Center
1138 Summit Boulevard
Bismarck, ND 58504

DEVILS LAKE

Alternatives to High Risk Substance Use
UND/Lake Region
1801 College Drive North
Devils Lake, ND 58703-1111

Lake Region Human Service Center Chemical Dependency Program
Highway 2 West
Devils Lake, ND 58301

DICKINSON

Badlands Human Service Center Chemical Dependency Program
Dickinson State University Campus
Pulver Hall
Dickinson, ND 58601

Heart River Alcohol/Drug Abuse Services
7 1st Avenue West, Suite 101
Dickinson, ND 58601

Prairie Echoes Counseling Services
135 West Villard Street
Dickinson, ND 58601-5121

FARGO

Centre, Inc.
123 North 15th Street
Fargo, ND 58107

Drake and Burau Counseling Services
1202 23rd Street South, Suite 6
Fargo, ND 58103

Human Services Associate
806 6th Avenue North
Fargo, ND 58102

Meritcare Hospital Psychiatric Services/Partial Hospitalization
720 4th Street North
Fargo, ND 58102

Meritcare Neuroscience Clinic
700 South First Avenue
Fargo, ND 58103

Prairie Psychiatric Center
510 4th Street South
Fargo, ND 58107-0827

Share House
4227 9th Avenue SW
Fargo, ND 58103

Southeast Human Service Center Alcohol and Drug Abuse Unit
2624 9 Avenue South
Fargo, ND 58103

Veterans' Affairs Medical Center Substance Abuse Treatment Program
2101 Elm Street North
Fargo, ND 58102

FORT TOTTEN

Spirit Lake Nation Recovery and Wellness Program
Fort Totton, ND 58335

FORT YATES

Standing Rock Nation Comprehensive Chemical Prevention Program
Main Street
Fort Yates, ND 58538

GARRISON

Ron Stanley Counseling Service
36 3 Avenue NW
Garrison, ND 58540

GRAFTON

MAB Counseling Services
625 Hill Avenue
Grafton, ND 58237

GRAND FORKS

Alcohol and Drug Services, Inc.
311 South 4th Street, Suite 1
Grand Forks, ND 58201-4726

Altru Hospital
1200 South Columbia Road
Grand Forks, ND 58201-6007

Wright, Katy Substance Abuse Counseling
1407 South 24 Avenue
Suite 214
Grand Forks, ND 58201

Northeast Human Service Center Chemical Dependency Program
1407 24 Avenue South
Grand Forks, ND 58201

Northridge Counseling Center, Inc.
215 North 3 Street, Suite 100
Grand Forks, ND 58203

JAMESTOWN

Alcohol/Families and Children
Jamestown Mall, Suite 221
Jamestown, ND 58401

DUI Seminar Program
624 9th Avenue SE
Jamestown, ND 58401

North Dakota State Hospital Chemical Dependency Unit
Jamestown, ND 58402

Northern Prairie Consultants
115 2nd Street SW
Jamestown, ND 58401

South Central Human Service Center Chemical Dependency Program
520 3rd Street NW
Jamestown, ND 58402

MANDAN

North Dakota Youth Counseling Program
701 16th Avenue SW
Mandan, ND 58554

MINOT

Bachmeier Counseling
1809 South Broadway Street
Minot, ND 58701

Dakota Boys' Ranch
6301 19th Avenue NW
Minot, ND 58702

Gateway Counseling Center
315 South Main Street
Suite 307-A
Minot, ND 58701

Mental Health Addiction Services Trinity Hospital
Burdick Expressway Main Street
Minot, ND 58702-5020

North Central Human Service
Center Chemical Dependency Program
400 22 Avenue NW
Minot, ND 58701

Unimed Medical Center Chemical Dependency Services
600 17th Avenue SE
Minot, ND 58701

MINOT AFB

Minot Air Force Base Substance Abuse Program
5 MDOS/SGOMH
10 Missile Avenue
Minot AFB, ND 58705-5024

NEW TOWN

Three Affiliated Tribes Circle of Life Alcohol Program
302 North Breslin Addition Street
New Town, ND 58763

TRENTON

Native American Resource Center
Trenton, ND 58853

WILLISTON

Mercy Recovery Center
1213 15 Avenue West
Williston, ND 58801

Northwest Human Service Center Chemical Dependency Program
316 2 Avenue West
Williston, ND 58801

OHIO

AKRON

Adolescent Counseling and Treatment, Inc.
Akron, OH 44319

Akron Health Department Alcoholism Division
177 South Broadway
Akron, OH 44308

Akron Urban Minority Alcohol and Drug Abuse Outreach Program, Inc. Addiction Treatment Services
665 West Market Street, Suite F
Akron, OH 44303

Community Drug Board
Women's Recovery Center
725 East Market Street
Akron, OH 44305

Genesis Program
386 South Portage Path
Akron, OH 44320

Ramar Center
380 South Portage Path
Akron, OH 44320

Family Services of Summit County
212 East Exchange Street
Akron, OH 44304

Interval Brotherhood Homes, Inc. Alcohol Rehabilitation Center
3445 South Main Street
Akron, OH 44319

Oriana House
ADM Crisis Center
15 Frederick Street
Akron, OH 44304

Adolescent Residential Center
885 East Buchtel Avenue
Akron, OH 44305

Community Based Correctional Facility
264 Crosier Street
Akron, OH 44311

Glenwood Site
40 East Glenwood Avenue
Akron, OH 44304

Residential Correction Center
222 Power Street
Akron, OH 44304

Senior Workers' Action Program Chemical Dependency Services
415 Portage Path
Akron, OH 44320

Tri-County Employee Assistance Program
450 Grant Street
Suite 2411
Akron, OH 44311

Urban Ounce of Prevention Services, Inc.
1501 Smith Hawkins Avenue
Akron, OH 44320

ALLIANCE

Quest Recovery Services, Inc. Alliance Division
724 South Union Street
Alliance, OH 44601

ALVORDTON

Fresh Start Home I
109 West Main Street
Alvordton, OH 43501

Fresh Start Home II
405 East Main Street
Alvordton, OH 43501

ASHLAND

Appleseed CMHC
1126 Cottage Street
Ashland, OH 44805

Ashland County Council on Alcoholism and Drug Abuse, Inc.
310 College Avenue
Ashland, OH 44805

ASHTABULA

Lake Area Recovery Center
Outpatient Drug Free Program
2801 C Court
Ashtabula, OH 44004

Turning Point
2711 Donohoe Drive
Ashtabula, OH 44004

ATHENS

Health Recovery Services, Inc.
Athens County Outpatient Clinic
100 Hospital Drive
Athens, OH 45701

Bassett House
10050 Bassett Road
Athens, OH 45701

Rural Women's Recovery Program
9908 Bassett Road
Athens, OH 45701

BAINBRIDGE

Lighthouse Youth Center Paint Creek Alcohol and Drug Outpatient Treatment
1071 Tong Hollow Road
Bainbridge, OH 45612

BATAVIA

Clermont Recovery Center, Inc.
Outpatient Services
2379 Clermont Center Drive
Batavia, OH 45103

Jail Program
4700 Filager Road
Batavia, OH 45103

Family Service of the Cincinnati Area
Clermont Center
2085-A Front Wheel Drive
Batavia, OH 45103

BEACHWOOD

Glenbeigh Center of Beachwood Alcohol/Drug Outpatient Treatment
3789-B South Green Road
Beachwood, OH 44122

Jewish Family Services Assoc. of
Cleveland Alcoholism/Chemical Dependency
24075 Commerce Park Road
Beachwood, OH 44122

Laurelwood Counseling Center of Beachwood Outpatient Program
25200 Chagrin Road
Water Tower Plaza
Beachwood, OH 44122

North East Ohio Health Services Alcohol and Drug Outpatient Treatment
23210 Chagrin Boulevard
Building One, Suite 400
Beachwood, OH 44122

BELLAIRE

Crossroads Counseling Service
First National Bank Building
Suite 210–211
Bellaire, OH 43906

BELLEFONTAINE

Logan/Champaign Consolidated Care
1513 Township Road, Suite 235
Bellefontaine, OH 43311

BELMONT

Awakenings
116 Main Street
Belmont, OH 43718

BIDWELL

Family Addiction Community Treatment Services
1770 Jackson Pike
Bidwell, OH 45614

BOWLING GREEN

Behavioral Connections of Wood County
320 West Gypsy Lane Road
Bowling Green, OH 43402

Women's Residence Program
1033 Devlac Grove
Bowling Green, OH 43402

BRECKSVILLE

Veterans Addiction Recovery Center Alcohol/Drug Dependence Treatment Program
10000 Brecksville Road
Suite 116-B
Brecksville, OH 44141

BROADVIEW HEIGHTS

New Directions Alcohol and Drug Outpatient Treatment
6640 Harris Road
Broadview Heights, OH 44147

BROOK PARK

Freedom House I Counter Attack DIP
Budget Inns of America
14043 Brook Park Road
Brook Park, OH 44142

BRUNSWICK

Alcohol and Drug Dependency
Services of Medina County/ Brunswick Office
4274 Manhattan Circle Drive
Brunswick, OH 44212

BRYAN

Five County Alcohol/Drug Program
125 East South Street
Bryan, OH 43506

BUCYRUS

Community Counseling Services, Inc. Bucyrus Office
820 Plymouth Street
Bucyrus, OH 44820

CADIZ

Crossroads Counseling Service
239 West Warren Street
Cadiz, OH 43907

CALDWELL

**Noble Drug Abuse and
Alcoholism Council, Inc.**
48 Olive Street
Caldwell, OH 43724

CAMBRIDGE

**Guernsey Health Choices, Inc.
Drug Addiction Treatment
Center Outpatient**
111 North 7th Street
Cambridge, OH 43725

CANTON

Community Treatment and
Correction Center Inc./ Substance
Abuse Program
1200 Market Avenue South
Canton, OH 44707

**Crisis Intervention Center of
Stark County, Inc.**
2421 13 Street NW
Canton, OH 44708

Quest Recovery Services, Inc.
1341 Market Avenue North
Canton, OH 44714

Quest Deliverance House/Women's
Residential Treatment
626 Walnut Avenue NE
Canton, OH 44702

Quest Recovery House
215 Newton Avenue NW
Canton, OH 44703

Stark County TASC
1375 Raff Road SW
Canton, OH 44710

**Veterans Addiction Recovery
Center Alcohol Dependency
Treatment Unit**
221 3rd Street SE
Canton, OH 44702

CELINA

Gateway Outreach Center
Nonresidential Alcohol Safety
Program
Outpatient Services
800 Pro Drive
Celina, OH 45822

CHAGRIN FALLS

**BHC Windsor Hospital Alcohol
and Drug Treatment Program**
115 East Summit Street
Chagrin Falls, OH 44022

CHARDON

**Lake Geauga Center on
Alcoholism and Drug Abuse**
200 Center Street
Chardon, OH 44024

**Ravenwood Center Drug and
Alcohol Treatment Services**
12557 Ravenwood Drive
Chardon, OH 44024

**Stillwater Adolescent Intensive
Outpatient Treatment
Program**
695 South Street, Suite 6
Chardon, OH 44024

CHILLICOTHE

Great Seal Family Care Center
425 Chestnut Street
Suite 6
Chillicothe, OH 45601

**Ross Correctional Institute
Substance Abuse Program**
16149 State Route 104
Chillicothe, OH 45601

**Scioto Paint Valley Mental
Health Center**
Martha Cottrill Clinic
4449 State Route 159
Chillicothe, OH 45601

**Veterans' Affairs Medical Center
Substance Abuse Treatment
Program**
17273 State Route 104
116-A3
Chillicothe, OH 45601

CINCINNATI

**Alcoholism Council of
Cincinnati Area**
Alice Paul House
118 East William Howard Taft
Road
Cincinnati, OH 45219

Mount Airy Shelter Program
2660 Diehl Road
Cincinnati, OH 45223

Beekman Work Release Center
2438 Beekman Street
Cincinnati, OH 45214

**Bethesda Alcohol and Drug
Treatment**
619 Oak Street
Cincinnati, OH 45206

**Center for Comprehensive
Alcoholism Treatment**
830 Ezzard Charles Drive
Cincinnati, OH 45214

**Central Community Health
Board Drug Services**
5240 North Bend Road
Cincinnati, OH 45239

532 Maxwell Avenue
Cincinnati, OH 45219

**Crossroads Center Outpatient
Treatment Services**
311 Martin Luther King Drive
C Building
Cincinnati, OH 45219

**Family Services of the
Cincinnati Area**
205 West 4 Street
Cincinnati, OH 45202

Hyde Park Counseling Center
2727 Madison Road Suite 303
Cincinnati, OH 45209

Sharonville Counseling Center
4050 Executive Park Drive
Suite 404
Cincinnati, OH 45241

First Step Home, Inc.
2118 Saint Michael Street
Cincinnati, OH 45204

Fransiscan Behavioral Health Services Chemical Dependency Program
2446 Kipling Avenue
Cincinnati, OH 45239

Ikron Corporation Alcohol and Drug Treatment Program
2347 Vine Street
Cincinnati, OH 45219

Jewish Hospital of Cincinnati, Inc. Adolescent Chemical Dependency Unit
3200 Burnet Avenue
Cincinnati, OH 45229

Norcen Behavioral Health Systems Adolescent Recovery Program
7710 Reading Road, Suite 300
Cincinnati, OH 45237

Ohio River Valley, Inc.
115 West McMicken Street
Cincinnati, OH 45210

Prospect House
682 Hawthorne Avenue
Cincinnati, OH 45205

Shaffer House
583 Grand Avenue
Cincinnati, OH 45205

Shelterhouse Volunteer Group, Inc. Drop-In Center
217 West 12 Street
Cincinnati, OH 45210

Talbert House
3123 Woodburn Avenue
Cincinnati, OH 45207

Adapt
3009 Burnet Avenue
Cincinnati, OH 45219

Adapt for Women
3595 Washington Avenue
Cincinnati, OH 45229

Adolescent Services/Alternatives
3009 Burnet Avenue
Cincinnati, OH 45219

Cornerstone
2216 Vine Street
Cincinnati, OH 45219

Extended Treatment Program
1617 Reading Road
Cincinnati, OH 45202

McMillan House for Young Men
3123 Woodburn Avenue
Cincinnati, OH 45207

Outpatient Adult Services
308 Reading Road
Cincinnati, OH 45202

SA/MI Day Treatment
2433 Iowa Avenue
Cincinnati, OH 45206

Spring Grove Center
3129 Springrove Avenue
Cincinnati, OH 45225

Talbert House for Women
1617 Reading Road
Cincinnati, OH 45207

Talbert House Turning Point
2605 Woodburn Avenue
Cincinnati, OH 45206

Veterans Affairs Medical Center Chemical Dependence Treatment Program
3200 Vine Street
Building 1 8S 151
Cincinnati, OH 45220

CIRCLEVILLE

Haven House of Pickaway County, Inc.
1180 North Court Street, Suite G
Circleville, OH 43113

Pickaway Area Recovery Services
210 Sharon Road
Circleville, OH 43113

Scioto Paint Valley Mental Health Center Pickaway County Office
145 Morris Road
Circleville, OH 43113

CLEVELAND

Alcoholism Services of Cleveland
East Unit
2490 Lee Boulevard
Suite 320
Cleveland, OH 44118

Homeless Project
2219 Payne Avenue
Cleveland, OH 44114

Probation Recovery Project
1200 Ontario Avenue Court Tower
7th Floor
Cleveland, OH 44118

Bellefaire/Jewish Children's Bureau Pact Program
22001 Fairmount Boulevard
Cleveland, OH 44118

Berea Children's Home Wrap Around Family Service Center
3235 Prospect Avenue
Cleveland, OH 44115

Buckeye Health Center Ann Nelson Perinatal Substance Abuse Program
11819 Buckeye Road
Cleveland, OH 44120

Catholic Charities Services
Hispanic Program
2012 West 25th Street, Suite 516
Cleveland, OH 44113

DePaul Family Center
2320 East 24th Street
Cleveland, OH 44115

Matt Talbot Inn
2270 Professor Avenue
Cleveland, OH 44113

Catholic Social Services Counseling of Cuyahoga County
3135 Euclid Avenue, Suite 202
Cleveland, OH 44115

Center for Families and Children
1468 West Ninth Street
Cleveland, OH 44113

AIDS Initiative Project
2728 Euclid Avenue
Cleveland, OH 44115

Cares Plus Alcohol and Drug
    Counseling
3955 Euclid Avenue
Cleveland, OH 44115

Hispanic Counseling
4115 Bridge Avenue Suite 309
Cleveland, OH 44113

Safe Harbor Alcohol/Drug
    Treatment
1145 Galewood Drive
Cleveland, OH 44110

**Cleveland Clinic Alcohol and
    Drug Recovery Center**
9500 Euclid Avenue, Desk P-48
Cleveland, OH 44106

**Cleveland Health Department
    Center Point I**
3030 Euclid Avenue
Cleveland, OH 44114

**Cleveland Treatment Center,
    Inc.**
1127 Carnegie Avenue
Cleveland, OH 44115

**Community Action Against
    Addiction, Inc.**
5209 Euclid Avenue
Cleveland, OH 44103

**Community Assessment
    Program**
5163 Broadway Avenue
Cleveland, OH 44127

Southeast Women's Center
7835 Harvard Avenue
Cleveland, OH 44127

**Covenant Adolescent CD
    Treatment and Prevention
    Center**
1688 Fulton Road
Cleveland, OH 44113

**Cuyahoga Dept Justice Affairs
    Division of Youth Services/
    Aftercare**
1276 West 3rd Street, Suite 319
Cleveland, OH 44113

**East Cleveland Straight Talk
    Alcohol and Drug Outpatient
    Treatment**
12921 Euclid Avenue
Cleveland, OH 44112

Freedom House, Inc.
Alcohol and Drug Treatment
    Programs
12160 Triskett Road
Cleveland, OH 44111

Halfway House Treatment
    Program
2121 West 117th Street
Cleveland, OH 44111

East Side Catholic Shelter
11811 Shaker Boulevard
Cleveland, OH 44120

**Fresh Start Alcohol and Drug
    Outpatient Treatment**
4807 Cedar Avenue
Cleveland, OH 44103

Fresh Start II
16801 Euclid Avenue
Cleveland, OH 44112

Fresh Start III
1809 East 89th Street
Cleveland, OH 44120

Fresh Start IV
11811 Shaker Boulevard, Suite
    411
Cleveland, OH 44120

Harbor Light Substance Abuse
Division Outpatient/Detox Unit 1
1710 Prospect Avenue
Cleveland, OH 44115

Hispanic Urban Minority
Alcoholism and Drug Abuse
    Outreach Program
3305 West 25 Street
Suite 517
Cleveland, OH 44113

Hitchcock Center for Women
1227 Ansel Road
Cleveland, OH 44108

**HUMADAOP/Casa Alma/Casa
    Maria**
3387 Fulton Road
Cleveland, OH 44109

**Laurelwood Counseling Center
    of University Circle**
1909 East 101st Street, Suite 203
Cleveland, OH 44106

**McIntyre Foundation Driver
    Intervention Program**
4805 Pearl Road
Cleveland, OH 44109

**Meridia Euclid Hospital
    Recovery Center**
18901 Lakeshore Boulevard
Cleveland, OH 44119

Meridia Health System
6700 Beta Drive Suite 200
Cleveland, OH 44143

**Meridia Huron Hospital
    Recovery Center**
13951 Terrace Road
Cleveland, OH 44112

**Metrohealth Medical Center
    Alcohol CD Services**
2500 Metrohealth Drive
Hamann Building 842
Cleveland, OH 44104

**Miracle Village Chemical
    Dependency Treatment
    Program**
2500 East 79th Street
Metrohealth Clement Center
Cleveland, OH 44104

**Murtis H Taylor Multi-Service
    Center STAAR Program**
13411 Union Avenue
Cleveland, OH 44120

**Neighborhood Counseling
    Service SAMI Program**
1702 West 28th Street
Cleveland, OH 44113

New Directions
30800 Chagrin Boulevard
Cleveland, OH 44124

Northeast Ohio Health Services
1909 East 101st Street Suite 201
Cleveland, OH 44106

**Northeast Pre-Release Center
    Substance Abuse Services**
2675 East 30 Street
Cleveland, OH 44101

Project East
22001 Fairmount Boulevard
Cleveland, OH 44118

Recovery Resources
3950 Chester Avenue
Cleveland, OH 44114-4625

Prep Program
3950 Chester Avenue
Cleveland, OH 44114-4625

Women/Children's Center
Metzenbaum Children's Center
3343 Community College Avenue
Cleveland, OH 44115

**Saint John West Shore Hospital
Area Healthcare System**
2351 East 22nd Street
Cleveland, OH 44115

**Southwest General Health
Center Oakview Program**
18697 Bagley Road
Cleveland, OH 44130

**Stella Maris Washington Avenue
Unit**
1320 Washington Avenue
Cleveland, OH 44113

**University MacDonald Women's
Hospital Ann Nelson
Perinatal Substance Abuse**
11100 Euclid Avenue
Cleveland, OH 44106

Veterans' Addiction Recovery
Center Alcohol/Drug Dependence
Treatment Unit
10701 East Boulevard
Cleveland, OH 44106

**Women's Center of Greater
Cleveland**
6209 Storer Avenue
Cleveland, OH 44102

Y Haven/Its A New Day
3210 Franklin Boulevard
Cleveland, OH 44113

Y Haven II
6001 Woodland Avenue
Cleveland, OH 44104

CLEVELAND HEIGHTS

**Center for Families and
Children Rap Art Center**
1941 South Taylor Road
Cleveland Heights, OH 44118

CLINTON

Barberton Rescue Mission
6694 Taylor Road
Clinton, OH 44216

COLUMBUS

**Africentric Personal
Development Shop ATOP/
Alcohol/Drug Outpatient
Treatment**
1409 Livingston Avenue, Suite 104
Columbus, OH 43205

**Columbus Area Community
Mental Health Center Alcohol
and Drug Abuse Treatment**
3035 West Broad Street
Columbus, OH 43204

Columbus Health Department
Alcoholism and Drug Abuse
Programs
181 Washington Boulevard
Columbus, OH 43215

Community Counseling Centers
3025 West Broad Street
Columbus, OH 43204

COMPDRUG Corporation
Alvis House
Outpatient Services
700 Bryden Road
Columbus, OH 43215

Vita Treatment Center/Methadone
Services
156 Parsons Avenue
3rd Floor
Columbus, OH 43215

**Comprehensive Offender
Program Effort DBA Ralph W
Alvis House**
1991 Bryden Road
Columbus, OH 43205

**Crittenton Family Services
Cedars Branch**
1414 East Broad Street
Columbus, OH 43205

**Department Youth Services
Freedom Center**
1414 East Broad Street
Columbus, OH 43205

**Directions for Youth Alcohol
and Drug Treatment Program**
1515 Indianola Avenue
Columbus, OH 43201

**Diversified Community Services
Community Based
Therapeutic Services**
1651 East Main Street
Columbus, OH 43205

**Franklin Pre-Release Center
Residential Substance Abuse
Program**
1800 Harmon Avenue
Columbus, OH 43223

House of Hope for Alcoholics
177 West Hubbard Avenue
Columbus, OH 43215

Stevens House
1320 Parsons Avenue
Columbus, OH 43206

Maryhaven, Inc.
217 South Hamilton Road
Columbus, OH 43213

**Mount Carmel Behavioral
Healthcare**
2238 South Hamilton Road
Columbus, OH 43232

**NCC Associates North Central
Mental Health**
338 Granville Street
Columbus, OH 43230

Neighborhood House, Inc.
Alcohol/Drug Counseling Program
1000 Atcheson Street
Columbus, OH 43203

North Central Mental Health Services

Drug and Alcohol Treatment Program
1301 North High Street
Columbus, OH 43201

3035 West Broad Street
Columbus, OH 43204

Family Focus
40 Spruce Street
Columbus, OH 43215

Fowler House
422 East Lane Avenue
Columbus, OH 43201

Soaring Sober Day Options
595 East Rich Street
Columbus, OH 43215

North Community Counseling Centers, Inc.

The Bridge
4897 Karl Road
Columbus, OH 43229

1495 Morse Road, Suite B-3
Columbus, OH 43229

Northwest Counseling Services
1560 Fishinger Road
Columbus, OH 43221

Parenthesis Behavioral Healthcare Alcohol and Drug Outpatient Treatment
2242 South Hamilton Road
Suite 200
Columbus, OH 43232

Parkside Recovery Services
349 Olde Ridenour Road
Columbus, OH 43230

Project Linden
1500 East 17 Avenue
Columbus, OH 43219

Rosemont Center Marian Hall Dual Diagnosis Program
2440 Dawnlight Avenue
Columbus, OH 43211

Southeast, Inc.
217 South Hamilton Road
Columbus, OH 43213

Alcohol/Drug Outpatient
16 West Long Street
Columbus, OH 43215

1455 South 4th Street
Columbus, OH 43207

Substance Abuse Services, Inc.
3556 Sullivan Avenue, Room 106
Columbus, OH 43205

Syntaxis Youth Homes Joyce Group Home
2824 Joyce Avenue
Columbus, OH 43211

Talbot Hall at Park Medical Center
1492 East Broad Street
Columbus, OH 43205

Traumatic Brain Injury Network Alcohol/Drug Outpatient Treatment
1581 Dodd Drive
106 McCampbell Hall
Columbus, OH 43210-9110

United Behavioral Health Alcohol and Drug Outpatient Treatment
6096 East Main Street, Suite 110
Columbus, OH 43213

Wellness Group, Inc.
1660 NW Professional Plaza
Suite E
Columbus, OH 43220

COSHOCTON

Coshocton County
Drug and Alcohol Council, Inc.
140 1/2 South 6th Street
Coshocton, OH 43812

Coshocton Counseling Center
710 Main Street
Coshocton, OH 43812

CRESTLINE

Community Counseling Services Inc
224 North Seltzer Street
Crestline, OH 44827

MedCentral Crestline Hospital Freedom Hall
291 Heiser Court
Crestline, OH 44827

CUYAHOGA FALLS

Family solutions
Alcohol and Drug Outpatient
2100 Front Street
Cuyahoga Falls, OH 44221

DAYTON

Alvis House Alcohol and Drug Outpatient Treatment
42 Arnold Place
Dayton, OH 45407

Born Free
Miami Valley Hospital Turning Point
Dayton, OH 45409

Combined Health District Center for Alcohol and Drug Addiction Services
4100 West 3rd Street
VA Medical Center Building 410
3rd Floor
Dayton, OH 45428

600 Wayne Avenue Oregon Plaza
Dayton, OH 45410-1122

Day Mont Behavioral Health Care Substance Abuse Services
1520 Germantown Street
Dayton, OH 45408

Dayton Correctional Institute Project Rebound
4104 Germantown Street
Dayton, OH 45417

Diversion Alternatives for Youth
330 South Ludlow Street
Dayton, OH 45402

Eastway Behavioral Healthcare
600 Wayne Avenue
Dayton, OH 45410

Eastway Corporation Pathways Residential Program
4950 Northcutt Place
Dayton, OH 45414

Franciscan Stress Care Center Alcohol and Drug Treatment
One Franciscan Way
Dayton, OH 45408

Grandview Hospital Careview Chemical Dependency Program
405 Grand Avenue
Dayton, OH 45405-4796

Monday Community Correctional Institution Alcohol/Drug Outpatient Treatment
1951 South Gettysburg Avenue
Dayton, OH 45418-2313

Nova House Association Treatment Program
732 Beckman Street
Dayton, OH 45410

Project Cure, Inc.
1800 North James H. McGee Boulevard
Dayton, OH 45427

South Community, Inc. Alcohol/ Drug Treatment Program
238 Yuma Court
Dayton, OH 45458

Wright State University School of Medicine RRTC on Drugs and Disability
Dayton, OH 45438

DEFIANCE

Community Counseling of Northwest Ohio
1103 Holgate Avenue
Defiance, OH 43512

Five County Alcohol/Drug Program
418 Auglaize Street
Defiance, OH 43512

DELAWARE

Delaware Area Recovery Resources, Inc.
540 U.S. Route 36 East
Delaware, OH 43015

Ohio Department of Youth Services Scioto Juvenile Correctional Center
5993 Home Road
Delaware, OH 43015

DUBLIN

Dublin Counseling Center
6077 Frantz Road
Suite 103
Dublin, OH 43017

EASTLAKE

North Coast Student Assistance Corp. Alcohol and Drug Outpatient Treatment
34050 Glen Drive
Eastlake, OH 44095

EATON

Preble County Recovery Center, Inc.
100 East Somers Street
Eaton, OH 45320

ELYRIA

Lorain County Alcohol and Drug Abuse Services
215 Court Street
Elyria, OH 44035

230 4 Street
Elyria, OH 44035

FAIRBORN

Community Network, Inc.
919 South Central Street
Fairborn, OH 45324

FOSTORIA

Firelands Community Hospital Counseling and Recovery
301 South Main Street
Fostoria, OH 44830

Fostoria Alcohol/Drug Center
114 West North Street
Fostoria, OH 44830

FREMONT

Firelands Community Hospital Counseling and Recovery
675 Bartson Road
Fremont, OH 43420

GALION

Community Counseling Services, Inc. Galion Office
269 Portland Way South
Galion, OH 44833

GEORGETOWN

Brown County Counseling
75 Banting Drive
Georgetown, OH 45121

GRAFTON

Lorain Correctional Institution Substance Abuse Services
2075 South Avon/Beldon Road
Grafton, OH 44044

GREENVILLE

Darke County Recovery Services
134 West 4 Street
Greenville, OH 45331

GROVE CITY

Wellness Group, Inc. Learn Driver Intervention Program
Ramada Inn South
1879 Stringtown Road
Grove City, OH 43123

HAMILTON

Alcohol and Chemical Abuse Council of Butler County Ohio, Inc.
111 Buckeye Street
Hamilton, OH 45011

Butler County Mental Health Center Harbor House
140 Buckeye Street
Hamilton, OH 45011

Fort Hamilton Hughes Memorial Hospital Center Horizon Services
630 Eaton Avenue
Hamilton, OH 45013

Sojourner Home
449 North 3 Street
Hamilton, OH 45011

Herland Family Center
520 High Street
Hamilton, OH 45011

Intensive Outpatient Program
625 High Street
Hamilton, OH 45011

Southwestern Ohio Serenity Hall, Inc.
439 South 2 Street
Hamilton, OH 45011

24 North 7th Street
Hamilton, OH 45011

Transitional Living Drug/ Alcohol Addiction Disorder Program
117 Park Avenue
Hamilton, OH 45013

HILLSBORO

Family Recovery Services for Alcohol and Drug Abuse, Inc.
Driver Intervention Program
972 West Main Street
Hillsboro, OH 45133

Scioto Paint Valley Mental Health Center Highland County Office
108 Erin Court
Hillsboro, OH 45133

HOLLAND

Comprehensive Addiction Service System (COMPASS)
1150 South McCord Street, Suite 101
Holland, OH 43528

HUDSON

Youth Development Center Genesis Program
996 Hines Hill Road
Hudson, OH 44236

INDEPENDENCE

Marycrest
7800 Brookside Road
Independence, OH 44131

Saint Vincent Charity Hospital
Rosary Hall
6701 Rockside Road
Independence, OH 44131

IRONTON

River Valley Health System
2228 South 9th Street
Ironton, OH 45638

KENTON

Tri-Star Community Counseling
718 East Franklin Street
Kenton, OH 43326

LAKEWOOD

River Valley Health System
2228 South 9th Street
Ironton, OH 45638

Alcoholism Services of Cleveland
14805 Detroit Avenue, Suite 320
Lakewood, OH 44107

LANCASTER

Center for Families and Children Mental Health Counseling
14701 Detroit Avenue, Suite 620
Lakewood, OH 44107

LEBANON

Center of Warren/Clinton Counties
107 Oregonia Road
Lebanon, OH 45036

Warren Detention Center
550 Justice Drive
Lebanon, OH 45036

Talbert House Community Correctional Center
5234 State Route 63
Lebanon, OH 45036

Warren Correctional Institution Recovery Services Department
State Route 63
Lebanon, OH 45036

LIBERTY CENTER

Maumee Youth Center
RFD 2
Liberty Center, OH 43532

LIMA

Northwest Family Services
DBA Family Resource Centers Project Inroads
799 South Main Street
Lima, OH 45804

Saint Rita's Medical Center Addiction Services
730 West Market Street
Lima, OH 45801

Tri-Star Community Counseling, Inc. Recovery Services
530 South Main Street
Lima, OH 45804

LISBON

Columbiana County Mental Health Center Substance Abuse Program
40722 State Route 154
Lisbon, OH 44432

Family Recovery Center
Outpatient Program
964 North Market Street
Lisbon, OH 44432

Vista Centre Outpatient Treatment
100 Vista Drive
Lisbon, OH 44432

LOGAN

**Health Recovery Services, Inc.
Hocking County Outpatient
Clinic**
4 East Hunter Street
Logan, OH 43138

LONDON

**London Correctional Institution
Recovery Services**
State Route 56
London, OH 43140

Madison Correctional Institute
1851 State Route 56
London, OH 43140

**Madison County Alcohol and
Drug Services**
210 North Main Street
London, OH 43140

LORAIN

Compass House
2130 East 36 Street
Lorain, OH 44055

1440 Lexington Avenue
Lorain, OH 44052

**Lorain County Alcohol and
Drug Abuse Services**
225 West 6th Street
Lorain, OH 44052

625 Reid Avenue
Lorain, OH 44052

**Recovery Resources Juvenile
Offenders/Pairs Program**
203 West 8th Street
Lorain, OH 44053

LOUDONVILLE

**Mohican Youth Center
Substance Abuse Program**
741 West Main Street, Suite 1
Loudonville, OH 44842

LOUISVILLE

**Stark Regional Community
Correction Center Alcohol
and Drug Outpatient
Treatment**
4433 Lesh Street NE
Louisville, OH 44641

LUCASVILLE

**Southern Ohio Correctional
Facility Substance Abuse
Program**
Lucasville-Minford Road
Lucasville, OH 45699

MANSFIELD

**Center for Individual and
Family Services Drug Abuse
Program**
741 Scholl Road
Mansfield, OH 44907

**Mansfield Correctional
Institution Innervisions**
1150 North Main Street
Mansfield, OH 44901

**Mansfield Urban Minority
Alcoholism and Drug Abuse
Outreach Program**
400 Bowman Street
Mansfield, OH 44901

Richland Hospital
Serenity Hall
Substance Abuse Services
1451 Lucas Road
Mansfield, OH 44901

**Volunteers of America Central
Ohio, Inc.**
290 North Main Street
Mansfield, OH 44901

MAPLE HEIGHTS

**Center for Families and
Children Cleveland CARES/
Southgate**
5398 Northfield Road
Maple Heights, OH 44137

MARIETTA

Marietta College
210 Thomas Hall
Marietta, OH 45750

**Marietta Memorial Hospital
Substance Abuse Services**
401 Matthew Street
Marietta, OH 45750

MARION

Marion Area Counseling Center
Alcohol and Drug Program
320 Executive Drive
Marion, OH 43302

Crossroads Recovery
286 Patterson Street
Marion, OH 43302

Professional Treatment Systems
310 Executive Drive
Marion, OH 43302

MARTINS FERRY

**East Ohio Regional Hospital
Touchstones Treatment
Center**
90 North 4th Street
Martins Ferry, OH 43935

MARYSVILLE

Charles B. Mills Center
715 South Plum Street
Marysville, OH 43040

**COMPDRUG Corporation
Tapestry/TC Program**
1479 Collins Avenue
Ohio Reformatory for Women
Marysville, OH 43040

MASON

**Center of Warren/Clinton
Counties**
201 Reading Road
Mason, OH 45040

MASSILLON

Longford Health Sources of Massillon Community Hospital
875 8th Street NE
Massillon, OH 44648

Massillon Division of Quest Recovery Services
325 3rd Street SE
Massillon, OH 44646

Nova Behavioral Health
39 Tremont Avenue SW
Massillon, OH 44646

MAUMEE

Professional Systems Addiction Treatment Service
1627 Hen Thorn Drive
Maumee, OH 43537

MCCONNELSVILLE

Morgan Behavioral Health Choices Morgan Drug and Alcohol Council
915 South Riverside Drive
Morgan County Prep Center
McConnelsville, OH 43756

MEDINA

Alcohol and Drug Dependency Services of Medina County, Inc.
246 Northland Drive
Suite 140
Medina, OH 44256

MENTOR

Crossroads Counseling Services, Inc. Adolescent Counseling Service
8445 Munson Road
Mentor, OH 44060

Lake Geauga Center on Alcohol and Drug Abuse, Inc.
8827 Mentor Avenue
Mentor, OH 44060

Laurelwood Counseling Center of Mentor
7060 Wayside Drive
Mentor, OH 44060

MIDDLEPORT

Health Recovery Services, Inc. Meigs County Clinic
138 North 2nd Avenue
Middleport, OH 45760

MIDDLETOWN

Comprehensive Counseling Service Intensive Outpatient Treatment
1659 South Breiel Boulevard
Middletown, OH 45044

Fort Hamilton Hospital Horizon Services
829 Elliott Drive
Middletown, OH 45042

MILFORD

Cincinnati Teen Challenge, Inc.
1466 Route 60
Milford, OH 45150

Kids Helping Kids
6070 Branch Hill Guinea Pike
Milford, OH 45150

MILLERSBURG

Human Resource Center
186 West Jackson Street
Millersburg, OH 44654

MINGO JUNCTION

Jefferson Behavioral Health System Care Network/ Residential Facility
202 Township Road
Route 164
Mingo Junction, OH 43938

MOUNT GILEAD

Morrow County Council on Alcohol and Drugs, Inc.
950 Meadow Drive
Mount Gilead, OH 43338

Drugs/Jail Outpatient Treatment Program
Morrow County Jail
State Route 42
Mount Gilead, OH 43338

MOUNT ORAB

Brown County Counseling Service Alcohol/Drug Program
13679 State Route 68
Mount Orab, OH 45154

MOUNT VERNON

Alcohol and Drug Freedom Center of Knox County
106 East Gambier Street
Mount Vernon, OH 43050

NAPOLEON

Five County Alcohol/Drug Program
444 Independence Drive
Suite 110
Napoleon, OH 43545

Henry County Hospital Help Center
11-600 State Road 424
Napoleon, OH 43545

NELSONVILLE

Hocking Correctional Facility Substance Abuse Department
16759 Snake Hollow Road
Nelsonville, OH 45764

Septa Correctional Facility Alcohol and Drug Outpatient Clinic
7 West 29 Drive
Nelsonville, OH 45764

NEWARK

Licking County Alcoholism Prevention Program
Outpatient Services
62 East Stevens Street
Newark, OH 43055

**Shepherd Hill Hospital
   Substance Abuse Services**
200 Messimer Drive
Newark, OH 43055

Spencer Halfway House, Inc.
69 Granville Street
Newark, OH 43055

NEW LEXINGTON

**Perry County Alcohol and Drug
   Abuse Council, Inc.**
227 North Main Street
New Lexington, OH 43764

NEW PHILADELPHIA

Harbor House, Inc.
Shelter House
New Philadelphia, OH 44663

Outpatient for Women
349 East High Street
New Philadelphia, OH 44663

NILES

**Glenbeigh Center of Niles
   Alcohol/Drug Outpatient
   Treatment**
29 North Road SE
Niles, OH 44446

NORTH CANTON

**Walsh University Counselor in
   Residence**
2020 Easton Street NW
North Canton, OH 44720

NORWALK

**Firelands Community Hospital
   Counseling and Recovery
   Services**
292 Benedict Avenue
Norwalk, OH 44857

OAK HARBOR

**Giving Tree, Inc. Mental Health
   and Drug Addiction Services**
11969 WSR 105
Oak Harbor, OH 43449

ORIENT

Correctional Reception Center
11271 State Route 762
Orient, OH 43146

**Pickaway Correctional
   Institution**
Oasis Therapeutic Community
   Prison Project
11781 State Route 762
Orient, OH 43146

ORRVILLE

**Education and Counseling
   Services, Inc.**
Wayne County Residential
   Program
1022 West High Street
Orrville, OH 44667

**Wayne County Alcoholism
   Services**
1710 West Paradise Road
Orrville, OH 44667

OTTAWA

Pathways Counseling Center
117 Court Street
Ottawa, OH 45875

PAINESVILLE

**Catholic Services of Lake
   County**
8 North State Street Room 455
Painesville, OH 44077

**Lake Geauga Center on Alcohol/
   Drug Abuse, Inc.**
Lake House
42 East Jackson Street
Painesville, OH 44077

Oak House
796 Oak Street
Painesville, OH 44077

PARMA

**Center for Families and
   Children Southwest Alcohol/
   Drug Counseling**
5955 Ridge Road
Parma, OH 44129

PAULDING

**Paulding County Alcohol and
   Drug Services Council, Inc.**
501 McDonald Pike
Paulding, OH 45879

PERRYSBURG

**Behavioral Connections of
   Wood County, Inc.**
27072 Carronade Street
Suite A and B
Perrysburg, OH 43551

PICKERINGTON

**Fairfield County Drug/Alcohol
   Recovery Center Pickerington
   Office**
437 Hill Road North
Pickerington Professional Park
Pickerington, OH 43147

PIQUA

**Miami County Alcoholism
   Program**
Outpatient Services
423 North Wayne Street
Piqua, OH 45356

PORT CLINTON

**Bayshore Counseling Services,
   Inc. Ottawa County Outpatient
   Office**
201 West Madison Street
Port Clinton, OH 43452

**Giving Tree, Inc. Dual
   Diagnosis Alcohol/Drug
   Treatment**
335 Buckeye Boulevard
Port Clinton, OH 43452

PORTSMOUTH

**James T. Marsh Male Halfway
   House**
1216 4th Street
Portsmouth, OH 45662

River Valley Health System Behavioral Health Services
2201 25th Street
Behavioral Health Services Campus
Portsmouth, OH 45662-3252

Stepping Stone House
1409 2nd Street
Portsmouth, OH 45662

PROCTORVILLE

Family Guidance Center
209 State Street
Proctorville, OH 45669

RAVENNA

Townhall II
Serenity Halfway House
151 East Spruce Avenue
Ravenna, OH 44266

Alcohol and Drug Outpatient Treatment
223 West Main Street
Ravenna, OH 44266

Horizon Halfway House
147 East Spruce Avenue
Ravenna, OH 44266

REYNOLDSBURG

NCC Reynoldsburg North Central Mental Health
6432 East Main Street
Reynoldsburg, OH 43068

RIPLEY

Brown County Counseling Services Alcohol/Drug Program
Early Childhood Resource Center
500 South Second Street
Ripley, OH 45167

RITTMAN

Your Human Resource Center
51 North Main Street
Rittman, OH 44270

ROCK CREEK

Glenbeigh Health Sources
2863 State Route 45
Rock Creek, OH 44084

ROCKY RIVER

Glenbeigh Center of Rocky River Alcohol Drug Outpatient Treatment
20800 Center Ridge Road
Suite 202
Rocky River, OH 44116

SAINT CLAIRSVILLE

Crossroads Counseling Service
255 West Main Street
Saint Clairsville, OH 43950

SANDUSKY

Bayshore Counseling Services, Inc. Erie County Outpatient Office
1218 Cleveland Road, Suite B
Sandusky, OH 44870-4787

Firelands Community Hospital Firelands Center
2020 Hayes Avenue
Sandusky, OH 44870

Providence Hospital Alcohol and Drug Detox and Outpatient Treatment
1912 Hayes Avenue
Sandusky, OH 44870

SHELBY

Cornell Abraxas Group
2775 State Route 39
Shelby, OH 44875

SIDNEY

Shelby County Counseling Center Alcohol and Drug Outpatient Treatment
500 East Court Street
Sidney, OH 45365

SMITHVILLE

Boys Village, Inc. Alcohol/Drug Treatment Program
2803 State Route 585
Smithville, OH 44677

SOLON

Center for Families and Children Reach Out Program
33995 Bainbridge Road
Solon, OH 44139

SOUTH POINT

Family Guidance Center
305 North 4th Street
South Point, OH 45680

Ironton/Lawrence County CAO River Valley Driver Intervention Program
103 East 4th Street
South Point, OH 45680

SPRINGBORO

Center of Warren/Clinton Counties Greenwood Center
50 Greenwood Lane
Springboro, OH 45066

SPRINGFIELD

Alcohol/Drug Abuse Programs For Treatment (ADAPT)
825 East High Street
Springfield, OH 45501

Matt Talbot House
809 South Limestone Street
Springfield, OH 45505

McKinley Hall, Inc.
Inpatient Program
225 East Street
Springfield, OH 44505

Outpatient Program
1101 East High Street
Springfield, OH 45505

Mental Health Services for Clark County
Outpatient Adolescent Recovery
1835 Miracle Mile
Springfield, OH 45504

Outpatient Adult Recovery/Jail
120 North Fountain Boulevard
Springfield, OH 45501

Mercy Memorial Hospital Mercy Reach Substance Abuse Program
1343 North Fountain Boulevard
Springfield, OH 45501-1380

Youth Challenges
CAF Street
Springfield, OH 45504

STEUBENVILLE

Jefferson Behavioral Health System Drug and Alcohol Outpatient Treatment
200 North 4th Street
Steubenville, OH 43952

Trinity Medical Center West Addiction Recovery Program
4000 Johnson Road
Steubenville, OH 43952

TIFFIN

Firelands Community Hospital Firelands Counseling and Recovery
181 East Perry Street
Tiffin, OH 44883

TOLEDO

Adelante
Los Ninos Substance Abuse Prevention
520 Broadway
Toledo, OH 43602

Boysville of Michigan, Inc. Saint Anthony Villa
2740 West Central Avenue
Andre Hall
Toledo, OH 43606

Comprehensive Addiction Services Systems (COMPASS)
3001 Hill Avenue
Toledo, OH 43607

Fresh Attitude, Inc. Alcohol and Drug Halfway House
3211 Mayo Street
Toledo, OH 43620

3212 Chase Street
Toledo, OH 43611

Outpatient Treatment
2700 Monroe Street, Suite K
Toledo, OH 43606

Rescue Mental Health Services
3350 Collingwood Boulevard
Toledo, OH 43610

Saint Charles Hospital
Westgate Outpatient Behavioral Services
3140 West Central Avenue
Toledo, OH 43606

Saint Paul's Community Center Intervention Program
230 13 Street
Toledo, OH 43624

Substance Abuse Services, Inc.
701 Adams Street
Toledo, OH 43624

Outpatient Services
1832 Adams Street
Toledo, OH 43624

Talbot Outpatient Center
732 South Main Street
Toledo, OH 43605

Toledo Hospital Alcohol and Drug Treatment Center
2142 North Cove Boulevard
Toledo, OH 43606

Unison Behavioral Health Group Dual Recovery Program
1425 Starr Avenue
Toledo, OH 43605

TROY

Dettmer Recovery Services
3130 North Dixie Drive
Troy, OH 45373

Miami County Mental Health Center Choices/Troy Satellite
1059 North Market Street
Troy, OH 45373

UPPER SANDUSKY

Firelands Community Hospital Firelands Counseling and Recovery
132 East Wyandot Avenue
Upper Sandusky, OH 43351

URBANA

Logan/Champaign Alcohol and Drug Addiction Services
40 Monument Square
Suite 301
Urbana, OH 43078

Mercy Memorial Hospital Mercy Substance Abuse Program
904 Scioto Street
Urbana, OH 43078

VAN WERT

Fountainview Center
120 West Main Street
2nd Floor
Van Wert, OH 45891

WADSWORTH

Alcohol and Drug Dependency Services of Medina County/ Wadsworth Office
180 High Street
Wadsworth, OH 44281

WAPAKONETA

Tri-Star Community Counseling
15 Willipie Street
Wapakoneta, OH 45895

WARREN

Saint Joseph Health Center
667 Eastland Avenue
Warren, OH 44484

Saint Joseph Riverside Hospital New Start Treatment Center
1370 Tod Avenue NW
Warren, OH 44485

Two North Park, Inc.
720 Pine Avenue SE
Warren, OH 44481

York Avenue Church of God Treatment Center Alcohol/ Drug Outpatient Treatment
872 York Avenue
Warren, OH 44485

WASHINGTON COURT HOUSE

Scioto Paint Valley Mental Health Center Fayette County Office
1300 East Paint Street
Washington Court House, OH 43160

WAUSEON

Five County Alcohol/Drug Program
125 North Fulton Street
Wauseon, OH 43567

Fulton County Health Center
725 South Shoop Avenue
Wauseon, OH 43567

Fulton Stress Unit Fulcare Daytox Alcohol and Drug Treatment
725 South Shoop Avenue
Wauseon, OH 43567

WAVERLY

Pike County Recovery Outpatient Services
111 North High Street
Waverly, OH 45690

Scioto Paint Valley Mental Health Center Pike County Office
102 Dawn Lane
Waverly, OH 45690

WESTERVILLE

Concord Counseling Services, Inc.
924 Eastwind Drive
Westerville, OH 43081

WESTLAKE

Saint John West Shore Hospital Serenity Center
29000 Center Ridge Road
Westlake, OH 44145

WEST LIBERTY

L/C Consolidated Care, Inc.
1521 North Detroit Street
West Liberty, OH 43357

WILLARD

Firelands Community Hospital Firelands Counseling and Recovery
302 Woodland Avenue
Willard, OH 44890

WILLOUGHBY

Laurelwood Hospital Addictive Disease Unit
35900 Euclid Avenue
Willoughby, OH 44094

WILMINGTON

Center of Warren/Clinton Counties
Alcohol and Drug Treatment Programs/Hopewell BHCS
610 West Main Street
Floor 2 East
Wilmington, OH 45177

Wilmington Center
1216 West Locust Street
Wilmington, OH 45177

WOODSFIELD

Crossroads Counseling Services
37984 Airport Road
Woodsfield, OH 43793

WOOSTER

College of Wooster Alcohol/ Drug Prevention Project
Wooster, OH 44691

Human Resource Center
2692 Akron Road
Wooster, OH 44691

Wayne County Alcoholism Services
Beacon House
732 Spink Street
Wooster, OH 44691

Pathway House
550 North Grant Street
Wooster, OH 44691

WORTHINGTON

Focus Health Care
5701 North High Street Suite 8
Worthington, OH 43085

Harding Hospital Adult and Adolescent Services
445 East Dublin Granville Road
Worthington, OH 43085

XENIA

Stepping In Recovery (SIR) Alcohol and Drug Outpatient Treatment
39 Greene Street
Xenia, OH 45385

TCN Behavioral Health
476 West Market Street
Xenia, OH 45385

Greene County Jail Outpatient Treatment
77 East Market Street
Xenia, OH 45385

Women's Recovery Center
515 Martin Drive
Xenia, OH 45385

YOUNGSTOWN

Addiction Programs of Mahoning County, Inc.
Donofrio Alcoholism Rehabilitation Center
1161 McGuffey Road
Youngstown, OH 44505

Donofrio Womens Center
64 Ridge Street
Youngstown, OH 44507

Alcoholism Programs of Mahoning County
Alma L Field 3/4 House
145 Illinois Avenue
Youngstown, OH 44505

Bodnar 3/4 Way Home
2516 Market Street
Youngstown, OH 44507

Community Corrections Association, Inc.
Community Corrections Facility
1740 Market Street
Youngstown, OH 44507

Residential Treatment Center I
1764 Market Street
Youngstown, OH 44507

Residential Treatment Center II
1620 Market Street
Youngstown, OH 44507

Neil Kennedy Recovery Clinic
2151 Rush Boulevard
Youngstown, OH 44507-1598

Northside Medical Center Adolescent Recovery Services
500 Gypsy Lane
Youngstown, OH 44501

Parkside Behavioral Healthcare Parkside Counseling Services
7536 Market Street
Youngstown, OH 44501-0240

Chemical Abuse Center, Inc.
5211 Mahoning Avenue, Suite 110
Youngstown, OH 44515

ZANESVILLE

Genesis Recovery Program
716 Adair Avenue
Zanesville, OH 43701

Good Samaritan Medical Center Alcoholism and Drug Recovery Treatment Program
716 Adair Avenue
Zanesville, OH 43701

Muskingum Behavioral Health
575 Harding Road
Zanesville, OH 43701

OKLAHOMA

ADA

Ada Area Chemical Dependency Center
727 Arlington Street
Ada, OK 74820

Rolling Hills Hospital Substance Abuse Services
1000 Rolling Hills Lane
Ada, OK 74820

ALTUS

New Hope Halfway House of Division of New Hope of Mangum
710 East Southerland Street
Altus, OK 73521

ALTUS AIR FORCE BASE

Altus Air Force Base Substance Abuse Program
97 MDOS/SGOMH
301 North First Street
Altus AFB, OK 73523-5005

U.S. Air Force Hospital Altus
Altus Air Force Base
Altus AFB, OK 73523

ALVA

Freedom Ranch, Inc. CBTI
Route 1, Box 48
Alva, OK 73717

ANADARKO

Consortium Against Substance Abuse
115 East Broadway
Anadarko, OK 73005

ANTLERS

Oaks Behavioral Center
414 West Main Street
Antlers, OK 74523-2661

ARCADIA

Drug Recovery Adolescent Program
505 North Broadway
Arcadia, OK 73007

ARDMORE

Arbuckle Drug and Alcohol Information Center, Inc.
1219 K Street NW
Ardmore, OK 73401

Broadway House, Inc.
214 North Washington Street
Ardmore, OK 73403

Mental Health Services of Southern Oklahoma Vantage Pointe
2530 South Commerce Street
Building C
Ardmore, OK 73401

ATOKA

Oaks Behavioral Center
211 East Court Street
Atoka, OK 74525-2000

BARTLESVILLE

Alcohol and Drug Center, Inc.
615 SE Frank Phillips Boulevard
Bartlesville, OK 74003

BROKEN ARROW

Healthcare Management Alliance, Inc. DBA Recovery Plus
817 South Elm Place, Suite 105
Broken Arrow, OK 74012

CHANDLER

Gateway to Prevention Recovery
102 East 7th Street
Chandler, OK 74834-2820

CHICKASHA

**Southwest Youth and Family
Services, Inc.**
198 East Almar Drive
Chickasha, OK 73023

CHOCTAW

**Tri-City Youth and Family
Center, Inc.**
14625 NE 23 Street
Choctaw, OK 73020

CLAREMORE

**Rogers County Drug Abuse
Program, Inc.**
118 West North Seminole Street
Claremore, OK 74018

CLINTON

**Opportunities, Inc.
Rehabilitation Center
Behavioral Care Services**
720 South 8th Street
Clinton, OK 73601

COALGATE

Oaks Behavioral Health Center
2 South Main Street
Coalgate, OK 74538-2829

CONCHO

**Cheyenne/Arapaho Substance
Abuse**
700 North Black Kettle Drive
Concho, OK 73022

CUSHING

**Valley Hope Alcoholism
Treatment Center**
100 South Jones Avenue
Cushing, OK 74023

DURANT

Kiamichi Council Alcoholism
307 West Elm Street, Suite 2
Durant, OK 74701-4109

EDMOND

**Edmond Family Services, Inc.
Outpatient Drug/Alcohol
Services**
7 North Broadway, Suite E
Edmond, OK 73034-1085

EL RENO

**Chisholm Trail Counseling
Services Substance Abuse
Services**
200 North Choctaw Street
Suite 110
El Reno, OK 73036

ENID

**Wheatland Mental Health
Center, Inc.**
702 North Grand Street
Enid, OK 73701

EUFAULA

Oaks Behavioral Health Center
119 McKinley Street
Eufaula, OK 74432-2853

FORT SILL

**Alcohol and Drug Abuse
Prevention and Control
Program (ADAPCP)**
2870-B Craig Road
Fort Sill, OK 73503-5100

FORT SUPPLY

**Western State Psychiatric
Center**
Highway 270 East
Fort Supply, OK 73841

GROVE

House of Hope, Inc.
East 32 South 625 Road
Grove, OK 74344

GUTHRIE

**Eagle Ridge Family Treatment
Center**
1916 East Perkins Street
Guthrie, OK 73044

**Logan County Youth and Family
Service**
4710 South Division Street
Guthrie, OK 73044

**Wheatland Mental Health
Center**
1923 South Division Street
Guthrie, OK 73044

GUYMON

Next Step Network
1004 Highway 54 NE
Guymon, OK 73942

HOMINY

Hominy Health Services, Inc.
211 East 5th Street
Hominy, OK 74035

HUGO

**Kiamichi Council on
Alcoholism and Other Drug
Abuse, Inc.**
308 East Jefferson Street
Hugo, OK 74743

IDABEL

**Kiamichi Council on
Alcoholism and Other Drug
Abuse, Inc.**
104 North East Avenue A
Idabel, OK 74745

People Plus, Inc.
103 NE Avenue A
Idabel, OK 74745

KINGFISHER

**Wheatland Mental Health
Center**
124 East Sheridan Street Suite
200
Kingfisher, OK 73750

LAWTON

Comanche County Memorial Hospital Memorial Pavilion
3401 West Gore Boulevard
Lawton, OK 73505

1602 SW 82nd Street
Lawton, OK 73505

Jim Taliaferro CMHC
602 SW 38 Street
Lawton, OK 73505

New Pathways Halfway House
1401 NE Laurie Tatum Road
Lawton, OK 73502

Roadback, Inc.
1502 D Street SW
Suite 4
Lawton, OK 73501

LONE WOLF

Southwestern Oklahoma Adolescent Addiction Rehab Ranch, Inc. (SOAARR)
Route 1, Box 69
Lone Wolf, OK 73655

MANGUM

New Hope of Mangum Chemical Dependency Unit
2 Wickersham Drive
Mangum, OK 73554

MARIETTA

Morning Star Adolescent Treatment Unit
Route 1, Box 14
Marietta, OK 73448

MCALESTER

Brown Schools of Oklahoma
1401 East Cherokee Avenue
McAlester, OK 74501-5635

Carl Albert Community Mental Health Center
1101 East Monroe Street
McAlester, OK 74502

The Oaks Rehabilitative Services Center
628 East Creek Street
McAlester, OK 74501

MCLOUD

Kickapoo Alcohol and Substance Abuse Program
State Highway 102
McLoud, OK 74851

MIAMI

Inter Tribal Substance Abuse/ Prevention and Treatment Center
101 South Main Street
Miami, OK 74354

Northeastern Oklahoma Council on Alcoholism
316 Eastgate Boulevard
Miami, OK 74355

MUSKOGEE

Green Country Behavioral Health Services, Inc. Alcohol and Drug Abuse Services
619 North Main Street
Muskogee, OK 74401

Monarch Incorporated
501 Fredonia Street
Muskogee, OK 74403

Muskogee County Council of Youth Services
4409 Eufaula Avenue
Muskogee, OK 74401

Recovery Plus
1805 North York Street, Suite G
Muskogee, OK 74403-1442

NORMAN

Central Oklahoma CMHC
909 East Alameda Street
Norman, OK 73071

NAIC/Center for Oklahoma Alcohol and Drug Services, Inc.
215 West Linn Street
Norman, OK 73069

Norman Alcohol and Drug Treatment Center
East Main Street and State Drive
Norman, OK 73071

Norman Regional Hospital Behavioral Medicine Services
708 24th Avenue NW
Norman, OK 73069

NOWATA

Grand Lake Mental Health Center, Inc. Alcohol and Drug Abuse Services
114 West Delaware Street
Nowata, OK 74048

Recovery Way, Inc. Inpatient Program
237 South Locust Street
Nowata, OK 74048

OKEMAH

Gateway to Prevention Recovery
119 South 1st Street
Okemah, OK 74859

OKLAHOMA CITY

A Chance to Change Foundation
5228 Classen Boulevard
Oklahoma City, OK 73118

Alcohol Training and Education, Inc.
2800 NW 36 Street
Suite 101
Oklahoma City, OK 73112

Carver Correction Center
2801 SW 3 Street
Oklahoma City, OK 73108

Community Counseling Center
1140 North Hudson Street
Oklahoma City, OK 73103

Community House
1501 NE 11th Street
Oklahoma City, OK 73117

Cope, Inc.
3033 North Walnut Street
Suite 200-W
Oklahoma City, OK 73105

Deaconess Hospital
5501 North Portland Avenue
Oklahoma City, OK 73112-2099

Drug Recovery, Inc.
415 NW 7 Street
Oklahoma City, OK 73102

Ivanhoe Facility
415 NW 8th Street
Oklahoma City, OK 73102-2603

Outpatient
425 NW 7th Street
Oklahoma City, OK 73101-1256

Integris Mental Health Integris Recovery Network
3300 NW Expressway
Oklahoma City, OK 73112

Mercy Health Center Outpatient Alcohol Treatment Program
4300 West Memorial Road
Oklahoma City, OK 73120

Moore Alcohol/Drug Center, Inc.
624 NW 5th Street
Oklahoma City, OK 73160

New Direction Centers of America
3115 North Lincoln Boulevard
Oklahoma City, OK 73105

North Care Center Substance Abuse Services
6300 North Classen Boulevard
Building A
Oklahoma City, OK 73118

Oklahoma County Crisis Intervention Center
1200 NE 13th Street
Oklahoma City, OK 73117

Oklahoma Halfway House, Inc.
517 SW 2 Street
Oklahoma City, OK 73109

Orange Quarters, Inc. DBA The Life Improvement Center
1017 10th Street NW
Oklahoma City, OK 73107

Phoenix House
824 East Drive
Oklahoma City, OK 73105

Red Rock Behavioral Health Services Substance Abuse Services
4400 North Lincoln Boulevard
Oklahoma City, OK 73105

Referral Center for Alcohol and Drug Service of Central Oklahoma
1215 NW 25th Street
Oklahoma City, OK 73106

Saint Anthony Hospital Recovery and Treatment (START)
1000 North Lee Street
Oklahoma City, OK 73101

Veterans' Affairs Medical Center Substance Abuse Treatment
921 NE 13 Street
116C
Oklahoma City, OK 73104

Total Life Counseling TLC Foundation
5900 Mostellar Drive, Suite 333
Oklahoma City, OK 73112

Turning Point South
1607 SW 15th Street
Oklahoma City, OK 73108

Valley Hope Alcoholism and Drug Center of Oklahoma City
5010 North Drexel Boulevard
Oklahoma City, OK 73112

OKMULGEE

Behavioral Health Services of the Creek Nation
410 West 6th Street
Okmulgee, OK 74447

PAWHUSKA

Osage Nation Counseling Center Substance Abuse Program
518 Leahy Street
Pawhuska, OK 74056

PAWNEE

Community Alcoholism Services
600 Denver Street
Pawnee, OK 74058

PONCA CITY

Bridgeway, Inc.
620 West Grand Street
Ponca City, OK 74602

Edwin Fair Mental Health Center Alcohol and Drug Abuse Unit
1500 North 6 Street
Ponca City, OK 74601

Native American Women's Alcohol Rehabilitation Center
5856 South Highway 177
Ponca City, OK 74601

Social Development Center
Route 1, Box 1595
Ponca City, OK 74601

PRYOR

The Brown Schools at Shadow Mountain
5 South Vann
Pryor, OK 74361

RED ROCK

Otoe/Missouria Tribe Substance Abuse Program
Route 1
Red Rock, OK 74651

SAPULA

Freedom Ranch CBTI
14 South Water Street
Sapulpa, OK 74066

SEMINOLE

Tri-City Substance Abuse Center
214 East Oak Street
Seminole, OK 74868

SHAWNEE

Absentee Shawnee Tribe Substance Abuse Program
2025 South Gordon Cooper Drive
Shawnee, OK 74801

Gateway to Prevention and Recovery
1010 East 45 Street
Shawnee, OK 74802

Native American Center of Recovery, Inc.
420 North Kickapoo Street
Shawnee, OK 74802

STILLWATER

CBTI Drug Court Program
217 West 5th Avenue, Suite 7
Stillwater, OK 74074-4005

Payne County Counseling Services
801 South Main Street
Suite 5
Stillwater, OK 74074

Payne County Youth Services, Inc.
2224 West 12 Street
Stillwater, OK 74074

Recovery Plus
2324 North Perkins Road
Stillwater, OK 74075

Starting Point II, Inc.
608 Highpoint Drive
Stillwater, OK 74075

TAHLEQUAH

Jack Brown Regional Treatment Center
Tahlequah, OK 74465

Jim Taliaferro Community Mental Health and Substance Abuse Centers
1200 West 4th Street
Tahlequah, OK 74465

TALIHINA

Chi Hullo Li Choctaw Nation of Oklahoma
Route 2 Box 1774
Talihina, OK 74571

Choctaw Nation Recovery Center
Route 2
Talihina, OK 74571

TINKER AFB

Tinker Air Force Base Substance Abuse Program
72 MDOS/SGOMH
5700 Arnold Street
Tinker AFB, OK 73145-8102

TISHOMINGO

Oaks Behavioral Health Center
117 West Main Street
Tishomingo, OK 73460

TONKAWA

Alpha II, Inc.
1608 North Main Street
Tonkawa, OK 74653

Tonkawa Tribe Substance Abuse Program
Tonkawa, OK 74653

TULSA

Browns School of Oklahoma
6262 South Sheridan Street
Tulsa, OK 74133

CBTI Tulsa Freedom Ranch
6126 East 32nd Place
Tulsa, OK 74135

Children's Medical Center
5300 East Skelly Drive
Tulsa, OK 74135-6599

Davis Counseling Program
1419 East 15th Street
Tulsa, OK 74120-5840

First Wings of Freedom
12 East 12th Street
Tulsa, OK 74119

Hillcrest Behavioral Services
1120 South Utica Street
Tulsa, OK 74104

Hillcrest Health Care System l Behavioral Health Services of Tulsa
1418 East 71st Street, Suite E
Tulsa, OK 74136-5060

How Foundation Rehabilitation Center of Oklahoma, Inc.
5649 South Garnett Road
Tulsa, OK 74146

Indian Health Care Resource Center of Tulsa
915 South Cincinnati Street
Tulsa, OK 74119

Life Improvement Center
5550 South Garnet Street
Tulsa, OK 74147-1903

Metro Tulsa Counseling Services
1602 North Cincinnati Avenue
Tulsa, OK 74106

New Choice and Associates
4833 South Sheridan Road
Suite 408
Tulsa, OK 74135

Parkside, Inc.
1620 East 12 Street
Tulsa, OK 74120

Street School, Inc.
1135 South Yale Avenue
Tulsa, OK 74112

Tulsa Regional Medical Center Chemical Dependency Unit
744 West 9 Street
Tulsa, OK 74127

Twelve and Twelve, Inc.
6333 East Skelley Drive
Tulsa, OK 74135

1214 South Baltimore Avenue
Tulsa, OK 74119-2820

Veterans' Affairs Medical Center Outpatient Clinic
635 West 11th Street
Tulsa, OK 74127

VANCE AFB

Vance Air Force Base Substance Abuse Program
527 Gott Road
Building 606
Vance AFB, OK 73705-5105

VINITA

Vinita Alcohol and Drug Treatment Center
Vinita, OK 74301

Vinita Alcohol and Drug Treatment Center
Vinita, OK 74301

WALTERS

Jim Taliaferro Community Mental Health and Substance Abuse Centers
319 South 3rd Street
Walters, OK 73572

WATONGA

Opportunities, Inc. Chemical Dependency/Treatment Center
117 East First Street
Watonga, OK 73772

WAURIKA

Jim Taliaferro Community Mental Health and Substance Abuse Centers
431 East C Avenue
Waurika, OK 73573-2435

WETUMKA

Wetumka General Hospital Second Chance Substance Abuse Services
325 South Washita Street
Wetumka, OK 74883

WEWOKA

Mental Health Services of Southern Oklahoma
110 North Wewoka Street
Wewoka, OK 74884

Seminole Nation of Oklahoma Alcohol/Substance Abuse Program
400 South Brown Street
Wewoka, OK 74884

WILBURTON

Oaks Behavioral Health Center
113 West Ada Avenue
Wilburton, OK 74578-4008

WOODWARD

Western States Psychiatric Center
1222 10 Street
Suite 211
Woodward, OK 73801

OREGON

ALBANY

Addiction Counseling and Education Services, Inc. (ACES)
1856 Grand Prairie Road SE
Albany, OR 97321

Catherine Freer Wilderness Therapy Expeditions
420 SW 3rd Street
Albany, OR 97321

Linn County Alcohol and Drug Treatment Program
104 SW 4th Street
Albany, OR 97321

Serenity Lane
1209 Shortridge SE
Albany, OR 97321

ALOHA

BI, Inc.
18475 SW Alton Street
Aloha, OR 97006

ASHLAND

Community Works Lithia Springs Programs
695 Mistletoe Road, Suite H
Ashland, OR 97520

ASTORIA

Alcohol/Drug Programs
10 6th Street, Suite 103
Astoria, OR 97103

Clatsop Behavioral Health Center
10 6th Street
Astoria, OR 97103

Heron Outpatient Counseling Services
53 Portway Street
Astoria, OR 97103

BAKER CITY

Elkhorn Adolescent Treatment Center
3700 Midway Street
Baker City, OR 97814

New Directions Baker House
2330 5TH Street
Baker City, OR 97814

Powder River Alcohol and Drug Treatment Program
3600 13 Street
Baker City, OR 97814

BEAVERTON

Evans and Sullivan
97660 SW Beaverton-Hillsdale Highway
Beaverton, OR 97005

BEND

Central Oregon Extended Unit for Recovery
644 NE Greenwood Avenue
Bend, OR 97701

Deschutes County Human Services Substance Abuse Services
409 NE Greenwood Avenue
Suite 2
Bend, OR 97701

Serenity Lane
601 NW Harmon Street
Bend, OR 97701

BROOKINGS

Southcoast Addictions Program
505 Hemlock Street
Brookings, OR 97415

BURNS

**Harney Counseling and
Guidance Services**
415 North Fairview Street
Burns, OR 97720

Wada Tika Health Center
HC-71 100 Pasigo Street
Burns, OR 97720

CANBY

Oregon Chicano Concilio
139 SW 2nd Avenue
Canby, OR 97013

CENTRAL POINT

Genesis Recovery Center
600 South 2nd Street
Central Point, OR 97502

CONDON

**Mid-Columbia Center For
Living Gilliam County Office**
422 North Main Street
Condon, OR 97823-0705

COOS BAY

**Ambit Southwestern Oregon
Community Action Committee**
2110 Newmark Street
Coos Bay, OR 97420

Better Options to Corrections
320 Central Street
Suite 408
Coos Bay, OR 97420

**Coos Lowen Umpqua and
Siuslaw Alcohol and Drug
Program**
338 Wallace Street
Coos Bay, OR 97420

Coquille Indian Tribe
Coos Bay, OR 97420

CORVALLIS

**Addiction Counseling and
Education Services, Inc.**
885 NW Grant Street
Corvallis, OR 97330

**Benton County Alcohol
Treatment Program**
530 NW 27 Street
Public Service Building
Corvallis, OR 97330

Discovery Counseling
260 SW Madison Street, Suite 101
Corvallis, OR 97339

**Milestones Family Recovery
Program**
306 SW 8 Street
Corvallis, OR 97333

Outpatient Services
5185 SW 3rd Street
Corvallis, OR 97333

DALLAS

**Polk County Mental Health
Alcohol and Drug Treatment
Program**
182 SW Academy Street
Suite 304
Dallas, OR 97338

**Valley Community Hospital
Addiction Health Services**
550 SE Clay Street
Dallas, OR 97338

ENTERPRISE

**Wallowa County Mental Health
Clinic Alcohol and Drug
Program**
207 SW 1st Street
Enterprise, OR 97828

EUGENE

**Addiction Counseling and
Education Services, Inc.
(ACES)**
84 Centennial Loop
Eugene, OR 97401

Bridge Program
1040 Oak Street
Eugene, OR 97401

Buckley Detoxification Services
605 West 4th Street
Eugene, OR 97402

Building Recovery
1210 Pearl Street
Eugene, OR 97401

Centro Latino Americana
944 West 5th Street
Eugene, OR 97402

**Eugene Center for Family
Development**
1258 High Street
Eugene, OR 97401

**Lane County Alcohol/Drug/
Offender Program**
135 East 6 Avenue
Eugene, OR 97401

**Looking Glass Adolescent
Recovery Program**
1675 West 11th Street
Eugene, OR 97401

Passages
1079 Alder Street
Eugene, OR 97401

Pathways
2391 Centennial Boulevard
Eugene, OR 97401

**Prevention and Recovery
Northwest**
1188 Olive Street
Eugene, OR 97401

Serenity Lane, Inc. New Hope
2133 Centennial Plaza
Eugene, OR 97401

**White Bird Clinic Chrysalis
Program**
332 East 12 Street
Eugene, OR 97401

**Willamette Family Treatment
Services**
1420 Green Acres Road
Eugene, OR 97408

Women's Outpatient Program
687 Cheshire Street
Eugene, OR 97402

FOREST GROVE

Pacific Alcohol and Drug Counseling, Inc.
2021 Hawthorne Street
Forest Grove, OR 97116

GOLD BEACH

Curry County Substance Abuse Treatment Program
29821 Colvin Street
Gold Beach, OR 97444

GRAND RONDE

Confederated Tribes of Grand Ronde Human Services Division Alcohol and Drug Program
9615 Grand Ronde Road
Grand Ronde, OR 97347

GRANTS PASS

Adapt
424 NW 6th Street, Suite 102
Grants Pass, OR 97526

Choices Counseling Center
310 6th Street NW
Grants Pass, OR 97526

Genesis Recovery Center
124 NW Midland Avenue
Suite 104
Grants Pass, OR 97526-1269

Josephine County Community Corrections
304-306 D Street
Grants Pass, OR 97526

GRESHAM

Change Point
1217 NE Burnside Street
Gresham, OR 97030-5771

Network Project Stop
515 North East Roberts Street
Gresham, OR 97030

HEPPNER

Morrow/Wheeler Behavioral Health Alcoholism Services
120 South Main Street
Heppner, OR 97836

HERMISTON

Umatilla County Mental Health Services
405 North 1st Street, Suite 111
Hermiston, OR 97838-1843

HILLSBORO

Oregon Human Development Corporation Ayuda Community Services
441 South 1st Avenue
Hillsboro, OR 97123

Tuality Counseling and Addiction Services Alcohol and Drug Outpatient Program
848 SE Baseline Street
Hillsboro, OR 97123

Youth Contact
447 SE Baseline Street
Hillsboro, OR 97123

HOOD RIVER

Gorge Counseling/Treatment Services of Hood River Memorial Hospital
216 Columbia Avenue
Hood River, OR 97031

Mid-Columbia Center for Living Hood River Alcohol and Drug Program
1235 State Street
Hood River, OR 97031

JEFFERSON

Pacific Ridge
1587 Pacific Ridge Lane SE
Jefferson, OR 97352-9654

JOHN DAY

Grant County Center for Human Development
166 SW Brent Street
John Day, OR 97845

KLAMATH FALLS

Consortium Jail Treatment Program
3300 Vandenberg Road
Klamath Falls, OR 97603-3730

Corrections Annex Treatment
220 Main Street
Klamath Falls, OR 97601

Klamath Alcohol and Drug Abuse, Inc. (KADA)
310 South 5 Street
Klamath Falls, OR 97601

Klamath Consortium
296 Main Street
Klamath Falls, OR 97601

Lutheran Family Services
2545 North Eldorado Avenue
Klamath Falls, OR 97601

LINCOLN CITY

Discovery Counseling
1424 SE 51st Street
Room 202-A
Lincoln City, OR 97367

MADRAS

Chenan, Inc. Counseling and Intervention
27 D Street SE
Madras, OR 97741

MARYLHURST

Clackamas County Mental Health Center Alcohol and Drug Program
Marylhurst Campus Education Hall
Marylhurst, OR 97036

MCMINNVILLE

Yamhill County Mental Health Chemical Dependency Program
627 North Ford Street
McMinnville, OR 97128

MEDFORD

Jackson County Substance Abuse Program
338 North Front Street
Medford, OR 97501

KlLPIA Counseling Services
111 Genessee Street
Medford, OR 97504

Ontrack, Inc.
221 West Main Street
Medford, OR 97501

3397 Delta Waters Road
Medford, OR 97501

Rogue Valley Addictions Recovery Center
1003 West Main Street
Medford, OR 97501

MILTON FREEWATER

Umatilla County Mental Health Milton Freewater Clinic
810 South Main Street
Milton Freewater, OR 97862

NEWBERG

Springbrook Northwest, Inc.
2001 Crestview Drive
Newberg, OR 97132

NEWPORT

Discovery Counseling
1628 North Coast Highway
Seatowne Shopping Center
Newport, OR 97365

Lincoln County Alcohol and Drug Program
255 SW Coast Highway
Newport, OR 97365

Lincoln County Council on Alcohol and Drug Abuse
155 SW High Street
Newport, OR 97365

Lincoln County Human Services Alcohol/Tobacco and Other Drugs Program
36 SW Nye Street
Newport, OR 97365-3823

Reconnections
1164 SW Coast Highway
Suites I and J
Newport, OR 97365

NORTH BEND

Center for Holistic Therapy
625 Oconnell Street
North Bend, OR 97459

Coos County Correctional Treatment Program
1975 McPherson Street
North Bend, OR 97459

ONTARIO

Lifeways Behavioral Health Counseling Center
1108 SW 4th Street
Ontario, OR 97914

Malheur County Alcohol and Drug Authority Alcohol Recovery Center
686 NW 9 Street
Ontario, OR 97914

OREGON CITY

Clackamas County Mental Health Center Alcohol and Drug Program
821 Main Street
Oregon City, OR 97045

Network Addiction Treatment Project Stop
1001 Molalla Avenue
Oregon City, OR 97045

Northwest Treatment Services
702 Main Street
Oregon City, OR 97045

PENDLETON

Brady and Associates
4705 NW Pioneer Place
Pendleton, OR 97801

Eastern Oregon Alcoholism Foundation
216 SW Hailey Avenue
Pendleton, OR 97801

Umatilla County Mental Health Program Substance Abuse Treatment Unit
721 SE 3 Street, Suite B
Pendleton, OR 97801

Yellow Hawk Tribal Health Center Chemical Dependency Program
Pendleton, OR 97801

PHOENIX

Phoenix Counseling Service
153 South Main Street
Phoenix, OR 97535

PORTLAND

Addictions Recovery Association
Letty Owings Center
2545 NE Flanders Street
Portland, OR 97232

Alpha Family Treatment Center
1427 SE 182nd Street
Portland, OR 97233

Annand Counseling Center
7320 SW Hunziker Road
Suite 200
Portland, OR 97223-2301

ASAP Treatment Services, Inc.
2130 SW 5th Avenue
Portland, OR 97201

BHC Pacific Gateway Hospital
1345 SE Harney Street
Portland, OR 97202

Caremark Chemical Dependency
3001 North Gantenbein Avenue
Portland, OR 97227

Cedar Hills Plaza Chemical Dependency Services
10300 SW Eastridge Road
Providence Cedar Hills Plaza
Portland, OR 97225

Center for Community Mental Health
3716 NE Martin Luther King Boulevard
Portland, OR 97211

Changepoint Diversion Association
1949 SE 122nd Avenue
Portland, OR 97233

Comprehensive Options for Drug Abusers CODA)
1027 East Burnside Street
Portland, OR 97214

Columbia River Correctional Institution Turning Point
9111 NE Sunderland Avenue
Portland, OR 97211

De Paul Adult Treatment Center
1320 SW Washington Street
Portland, OR 97205

De Paul Youth Treatment Center
4411 NE Emerson Street
Portland, OR 97218

General Health, Inc.
2600 SE Belmont Street
Portland, OR 97212

Hooper Detox
20 NE Martin Luther King Boulevard
Portland, OR 97232

Legacy Emanuel Hospital Project Network
2631 North Mississippi Avenue
Portland, OR 97227

Native American Rehabilitation
Association of The Northwest,Inc.
17645 NW Saint Helens Highway
Portland, OR 97231

Network Behavioral Healthcare
Addiction Treatment Services
2415 SE 43rd Avenue,Suite 200
Portland, OR 97206

Harmony House
2270 SE 39th Avenue
Portland, OR 97214

Northwest Treatment Services
9370 SW Greenburg Road
Suite 601
Portland, OR 97223

948 NE 102 Street
Suite 101
Portland, OR 97220

OHSU Behavioral Health Services
621 SW Alder Street, Suite 520
Portland, OR 97205-3620

Oregon Chicano Concilio
1732 NE 43rd Street
Portland, OR 97213

Pacific Alcohol and Drug Counseling Inc
11515 SW Durham Road
Suite E-8
Portland, OR 97224

Portland Addictions/ Acupuncture Center
120 SW Morrison Street
Portland, OR 97205

Project for Community Recovery
3525 NE Martin Luther King Jr. Blvd.
Portland, OR 97212

Providence Medical Center Addictions Treatment Services
5211 NE Glisan Street
Portland, OR 97213

Providence Milwaukie Hospital Chemical Dependency Services
10150 SE 32nd Avenue
Portland, OR 97222

Ram Clinic
3610 NE 82nd Avenue, Suite 100
Portland, OR 97220

Serenity Lane
9414 SW Barbur Boulevard
Suite B
Portland, OR 97219

Stay Clean, Inc.
1223 Alberta Street NE
Portland, OR 97211

Tualatin Valley Centers
14600 NW Cornell Road
Portland, OR 97229

9111 Sunderland Road NE
Portland, OR 97211

2130 SW 5th Avenue, Suite 210
Portland, OR 97201-4934

Volunteers of America
Mens Residential Center
2318 NE Martin Luther King Boulevard
Portland, OR 97212

Women's Residential Center
200 SE 7th Street
Portland, OR 97214

Woodland Park Behavioral Health Service
10300 NE Hancock Street
Portland, OR 97220

PRINEVILLE

Lutheran Family Services Crook County Mental Health Program
203 North Court Street
Prineville, OR 97754

Rimrock Trails
1333 NW 9th Street
Prineville, OR 97754

REDMOND

Visions of Hope Recovery Center
676 Negus Way
Redmond, OR 97756

REEDSPORT

Adapt
2785 Frontage Road
Reedsport, OR 97467-1814

ROSEBURG

Adapt
548 SE Jackson Street, Suite 1
Roseburg, OR 97470

Deer Creek Adolescent Treatment Center
2064 Douglas Street SE
Roseburg, OR 97470

Roseburg Recovery Services
727-B Southeast Main Street
Roseburg, OR 97470

Crossroads
3099 NE Diamond Lake Boulevard
Roseburg, OR 97470

SAINT HELENS

Columbia Community Mental Health
105 South 3rd Street
Saint Helens, OR 97051

SALEM

Bridgeway
3325 Harold Street NE
Salem, OR 97305

Chemawa Alcoholism Education Center
3760 Chemawa Road NE
Salem, OR 97305

Hillcrest Youth Correctional Facility
2450 Strong Road SE
Salem, OR 97310

Inside Out Care, Inc.
780 Commercial Street SE
Suite 105
Salem, OR 97302

Marion County Health Department
3180 Center Street NE
Room 2274
Salem, OR 97301

Multicultural Consultants, Ltd.
3760 Market Street NE 316
Salem, OR 97301

Nanitch Sahallie Treatment Center
5119 River Road NE
Salem, OR 97303

Network, Inc. Harmony House of Marion County
3040 Center Street NE
Salem, OR 97301

New Step Behavioral Health
1655 Capitol Street NE, Suite 1
Salem, OR 97303

Pacific Alcohol and Drug, Inc. Step Program
4005 Aumsville Highway SE
Salem, OR 97301

Pacific Recovery
1235 Woodrow Street NE
Salem, OR 97303

Seasons
1582 Lancaster Drive NE
Salem, OR 97301

Serenity Lane
910 Capitol Street NE
Salem, OR 97301

Tahana Whitecrow Foundation
2350 Wallace Road NW
Salem, OR 97304-2127

SANDY

Sandy Family Services, Inc.
39365 Proctor Boulevard
Sandy, OR 97055

SCAPPOOSE

Heart to Heart Counseling Center
52700 North East 1st Street
Scappoose, OR 97056

SILETZ

Siletz Tribal Council Alcohol and Drug Program
201 SW Swan Street
Siletz, OR 97380

SILVERTON

Seasons
209 C Street
Silverton, OR 97381

STAYTON

Stayton Counseling
223 Locust Street
Stayton, OR 97383

THE DALLES

Mid-Columbia Center for Living
400 East 5 Street
Room 207
The Dalles, OR 97058

TIGARD

Tigard Recovery Center
10362 SW McDonald Road
Tigard, OR 97224

WARM SPRINGS

Confederated Tribes of Warm Springs Alcohol and Drug Abuse Program
Warm Springs, OR 97761

WOODBURN

Bridgeway, Inc.
399 Young Street
Woodburn, OR 97071

PENNSYLVANIA

AKRON

Recovery Unlimited, Inc.
115 North 9th Street
Akron, PA 17501-1341

ALIQUIPPA

**Drug and Alcohol Services of
Beaver Valley**
524 Franklin Avenue
Aliquippa, PA 15001

Gateway Rehabilitation Center
Economy Village
Road 2
Aliquippa, PA 15001

Linmar Terrace
1200 Tyler Street Rental Office
Aliquippa, PA 15001

Mount Washington Homes
Pleasantview Homes
Moffett Run Road
Aliquippa, PA 15001

Tom Rutter House
100 Moffet Run Road
Aliquippa, PA 15001

ALLENTOWN

Family House
112 North 9th Street
Allentown, PA 18102

Florence Child Guidance Center
1812 Allen Street
Allentown, PA 18104

Livengrin Counseling Center
961 Marcon Boulevard Suite 304
Allentown, PA 18103

**Saint Luke's Addictions Service
Halfway Home of Lehigh
Valley**
121 North 8th Street
Allentown, PA 18101

**Saint Luke's Hospital Allentown
Campus**
1736 Hamilton Street
Allentown, PA 18104

32 North 18th Street
Allentown, PA 18104

Recovery Center
33 North Saint George Street
Allentown, PA 18104

Treatment Trends, Inc.
Confront Program
1130 Walnut Street
Allentown, PA 18102

Keenan House
18-22 South 6th Street
Allentown, PA 18105

White Deer Run of Allentown
1132 Hamilton Street, Suite 300
Allentown, PA 18101

ALLENWOOD

White Deer Run
Devitt Camp Road
Allenwood, PA 17810

ALTOONA

**Altoona Hospital Mental Health
Alcohol and Drug Services**
620 Howard Avenue
Altoona, PA 16601

AMP/CEP Group Homes, Inc.
T/A Right Turn
901 6 Avenue
Altoona, PA 16602

830 6 Avenue
Altoona, PA 16602

825 1/2 7th Avenue
Altoona, PA 16603

**Blair County Community Action
Program Substance Abuse
Services**
2100 6th Avenue
Altoona, PA 16601

**Home Nursing Agency
Community Support
Alternatives**
500 East Chestnut Avenue
Altoona, PA 16601

AMBLER

**Northwestern Human Services
of Montgomery County**
600 North Bethlehem Pike
Ambler, PA 19002

ARDMORE

**Jewish Family and Children's
Service of Philadelphia**
133 Coulter Avenue
Ardmore, PA 19003

**Lower Merion Counseling
Services**
7 East Lancaster Avenue
Ardmore, PA 19003

Womanspace
120 Ardmore Avenue
Ardmore, PA 19003

ASHLAND

**Gaudenzia at Fountain Springs
Women and Children
Program**
95 Broad Street
Ashland, PA 17921

AUDUBON

Saint Gabriel's Hall
1300 Pawlings Road
Audubon, PA 19407

BANGOR

**Community Psychological
Center Inc**
715 Pennsylvania Avenue
Bangor, PA 18013

BEAVER

**Drug and Alcohol Services of
Beaver Valley, Inc.**
697 State Street
Beaver, PA 15009

BEAVER FALLS

Gateway Rehabilitation Center
Harmony Dwellings
Rent Office 9th Street
Beaver Falls, PA 15010

Morada Dwellings
Apartment 136, Morada Dwellings
Beaver Falls, PA 15010

BELLEFONTE

Comprehensive Recovery Care, Inc.
323 West High Street
Bellefonte, PA 16823-1303

Counseling Services, Inc.
Drug and Alcohol Program
441 North Spring Street
Bellefonte, PA 16823

BENSALEM

De Lasalle Vocational
Street Road and Bristol Street
Bensalem, PA 19020

Libertae, Inc.
5245 Bensalem Boulevard
Bensalem, PA 19020

Livengrin Foundation Inc
4833 Hulmeville Road
Bensalem, PA 19020-3099

BERLIN

Twin Lakes Center
426 Main Street
Berlin, PA 15530

BERWICK

Berwick's Recovery System
701 East 16th Street
Berwick, PA 18603

BETHLEHEM

Hogar Crea of Bethlehem
1409 Pembroke Road
Bethlehem, PA 18017-7198

Saint Luke's Addictions Treatment Services Incorporated
50 East Broad Street
Bethlehem, PA 18018

1107 Eaton Avenue
Bethlehem, PA 18018

Step By Step, Inc.
623 West Union Boulevard
Bethlehem, PA 18018

BIRDSBORO

Center for Mental Health
201 East Main Street
Birdsboro, PA 19508

BLOOMSBURG

Behavioral Health Resource Group of Bloomsburg
603 West Main Street
Bloomsburg, PA 17815

Bloomsburg Hospital New Hope Drug And Alcohol Services
480 Central Road
Bloomsburg, PA 17815

BOYERTOWN

Inner Direction Counseling Center
400 Sweinhart Road
Boyertown, PA 19512

BRADDOCK

UPMC Braddock
400 Holland Avenue
Braddock, PA 15104

BRADFORD

Alcohol and Drug Abuse Services Bradford Unit
2 Main Street
Seneca Building, Suite 600
Bradford, PA 16701

Bradford Regional Medical Center Mentally/Chem Add/ Dual Diag/Psych Unit
116-156 Interstate Parkway
Bradford, PA 16701-1097

BRISTOL

Livengrin
1270 New Rogers Road
Bristol, PA 19007

Lower Bucks Hospital Mental Health Services
501 Bath Road
Bristol, PA 19007

BUTLER

Butler Memorial Hospital
Regional Recovery Program/ Outpatient
911 East Brady Street
Butler, PA 16001

Regional Recovery Program
911 East Brady Street
Butler, PA 16001

Charter Outpatient Recovery Center
118 South Church Street
Butler, PA 16001

Irene Stacy Community Mental Health Center
112 Hillvue Drive
Butler, PA 16001

Veterans' Affairs Medical Center Substance Abuse Treatment Unit (SATU)
325 New Castle Road
Butler, PA 16001

CAMP HILL

Guidance Associates
412 Erford Road
Camp Hill, PA 17011

Holy Spirit Hospital Drug and Alcohol Medical Service Unit
503 North 21 Street
Camp Hill, PA 17011

Roxbury in Camp Hill Intensive Outpatient/Outpatient
3300 Trindle Road
Camp Hill, PA 17011

Russell, Russell and Associates, Inc.
1940 Market Street
Camp Hill, PA 17011

CANONSBURG

Gateway Greentree
6000 Waterdam Plaza Drive
Suite 260
Canonsburg, PA 15317

CARBONDALE

Drug and Alcohol Treatment Service
9 North Main Street
Carbondale, PA 18407-2316

CARLISLE

Carlisle Area Counseling Services
700 Clay Street
Carlisle, PA 17013

Carlisle Hospital
246 Parker Street
Carlisle, PA 17013

Stevens Center
401 East Louther Street
Carlisle, PA 17013

CHAMBERSBURG

Manito, Inc.
7564 Browns Mill Road
Chambersburg, PA 17201

Twin Lakes Center Drug and Alcohol Rehabilitation
166 South Main Street
Kerrstown Square Suite 202
Chambersburg, PA 17201

CHESTER

Ches Penn Health Services, Inc.
619 Welsh Street
Chester, PA 19013

1300 West 9th Street
Chester, PA 19015

Crozer Chester Medical Center
CHS Methadone Program
CHS Outpatient Service
2600 West 9th Street
Chester, PA 19013

UHS Keystone Center
2001 Providence Road
Chester, PA 19013

CLARION

Clarion County Counseling Center
Drug/Alcohol Administration
214 South 7 Avenue
Clarion, PA 16214

CLARKS SUMMIT

Lourdesmont Good Shepherd Youth and Family Services
537 Venard Road
Clarks Summit, PA 18411

CLIFTON HEIGHTS

Family and Community Service of Delaware County
37 North Glenwood Avenue
Clifton Heights, PA 19018

COATESVILLE

Continuum, Inc.
131 Harmony Street
Coatesville, PA 19320

Samara House YWCA
423 East Lincoln Highway
Coatesville, PA 19320

Veterans Affairs Medical Center Substance Abuse Treatment Program
1400 Black Horse Hill Road
Coatesville, PA 19320-2097

COLUMBIA

Lancaster General Hospital Susquehanna Division Addictions Center
306 North Seventh Street
Columbia, PA 17512-0926

CONNELLSVILLE

Fayette County Drug and Alcohol Commission, Inc.
1032 Morrell Avenue
Connellsville, PA 15425

COUDERSPORT

Charles Cole Memorial Hospital Alcohol and Drug Abuse Services
107 East Second Street
Coudersport, PA 16915

CRANBERRY TOWNSHIP

Butler Regional Recovery Evening Program
20421 Route 19 Suite 100
Butler Centre
Cranberry Township, PA 16066-7514

Discovery House
326 Thomson Park Drive
Building 300
Cranberry Twp, PA 16066

Irene Stacy CMHC Drug and Alcohol Unit
Butler Center
20421 Route 19, Suite 310
Cranberry Township, PA 16066

Saint Francis Medical Center North Center for Addiction Services
1 Saint Francis Way
Cranberry Township, PA 16066-5119

CRUM LYNNE

Teencare
1124 Chester Pike First Floor
Crum Lynne, PA 19022

DANVILLE

Penn State Geisinger Health System Alcohol/Chemical Dependency Outpatient Services
12 Poplar Street
Danville, PA 17822

Psychological Services Clinic
405 Bloom Street
Danville, PA 17821

DELTA

**Adams Hanover Counseling
Services Delta**
5 Pendyrus Street
Delta, PA 17314

DOYLESTOWN

Aldie Counseling Center
228 North Main Street
Doylestown, PA 18901

**Bucks County Correctional
Facility Drug and Alcohol
Unit**
1730 South Easton Road
Doylestown, PA 18901

**Bucks County Council on
Alcoholism and Drug
Dependence**
Routes 313 and 611
252 West Swamp Road/Unit 33
Doylestown, PA 18901

Livengrin Counseling Center
275 South Main Street, Suite 11
Terrace Office Center
Doylestown, PA 18901

DREXEL HILL

**Delaware County Memorial
Hospital Alcoholism and
Addiction Treatment Center**
501 North Lansdowne Avenue
Drexel Hill, PA 19026

DU BOIS

**Concerns Counseling and
Consultation Firm**
90 Beaver Drive
Du Bois, PA 15801

EAGLEVILLE

**Eagleville Hospital Inpatient
Program**
100 Eagleville Road
Eagleville, PA 19408

EASTON

**Saint Luke's Addiction
Treatment Services, Inc.**
158-160 South 3rd Street
Easton, PA 18042

Twin Rivers Medical Inc
158 South 3rd Street
Easton, PA 18042-4518

EAST PETERSBURG

**Lancaster Area Psychological
Services**
6079 Main Street
East Petersburg, PA 17520-1267

EBENSBURG

**Home Nursing Agency
Community Services**
594 Manor Drive
Ebensburg, PA 15931

ELIZABETHTOWN

HSA Counseling Inc
11 Center Square
Elizabethtown, PA 17022

Naaman Center
4600 East Harrisburg Pike
Elizabethtown, PA 17022

ELKINS PARK

**Jewish Family and Children's
Service of Philadelphia**
7607 Old York Road Lower Level
Elkins Park, PA 19027

ELKLAND

Laurel Health Center
103 Forestview Drive
Elkland, PA 16920

ELLWOOD CITY

**Drug and Alcohol Community
Treatment Services, Inc.**
720 Lawrence Avenue
Ellwood City, PA 16117

ELWYN

ChesPenn Health Services
176 South Middletown Road
Elwyn, PA 19063

EMPORIUM

Alcohol and Drug Abuse Center
107 South Cherry Street
Emporium, PA 15834

EPHRATA

Terraces
1170 South State Street
Ephrata, PA 17522

ERIE

**Charter Behavior Health System
at Cove Forge/Frontier Place**
1371 West 6th Street
Erie, PA 16505

Community House, Inc.
521 West 7 Street
Erie, PA 16502

Cornell Abraxas II
502 West 6th Street
Erie, PA 16502

Crossroads/Serenity Hall
414 West 5 Street
Erie, PA 16507

**Dr. Daniel S. Snow Recovery
House**
361 West 5th Street
Erie, PA 16507

**Family Services of Northwestern
Pennsylvania**
121 West 10th Street
Erie, PA 16501

Perseus House, Inc.
132 West 26 Street
Erie, PA 16508

516 West 7 Street
Erie, PA 16502

Saint Vincent Health Center Serenity Recovery Center for Substance Abuse Outpatient Program
2409 State Street
Erie, PA 16544

Stairways Mental Health Drug and Alcohol Unit
531 West 10th Street
Erie, PA 16504

Veterans Affairs Medical Center Substance Abuse Treatment Program
135 East 38th Street
Psychology Service 116-B
Erie, PA 16504

EXTON

Alcoholism and Addictions Council Holcomb Behavioral Health
930 East Lancaster Avenue
Suite 220
Exton, PA 19341

UHS Recovery Foundation, Inc. Key Recovery Center
319 North Pottstown Pike
Suite 102
Exton, PA 19341

FARRELL

Insights Chemical Dependency Program Outpatient/Shenango
1980 Green Street
Farrell, PA 16121

FORD CITY

Ministries of Eden Inc
837 5th Avenue
Ford City, PA 16226

FORT WASHINGTON

Livengrin Counseling Center
520 Pennsylvania Avenue
Fort Washington, PA 19034

FRANKLIN

Family Services and Children's Aid Society Society Drug Alcohol Program
1243 Liberty Street
Franklin, PA 16323

GETTYSBURG

Adams Hanover Counseling Services, Inc.
44 South Franklin Street
Gettysburg, PA 17325

Cornerstone Counseling and Education Services
108 North Stratton Street
Gettysburg, PA 17325

The Recovery Place
69 West Middle Street
Gettysburg, PA 17325

GLENSIDE

Milestones
614 North Easton Road
Glenside, PA 19038

GREENSBURG

CSAS, Inc. Myriad Program
211 Huff Avenue, Suite D
Greensburg, PA 15601

GREENVILLE

Insights Chemical Dependency Program Outpatient/ Greenville
60 South Race Street
Greenville, PA 16125

GROVE CITY

George Junior Republic
200 George Junior Road
Grove City, PA 16127-5058

Horizon Hospital Insights Chemical Dependency Program
430 Hillcrest Avenue
Grove City, PA 16127

HANOVER

Adams Hanover Counseling Services, Inc.
625 West Elm Avenue
Hanover, PA 17331

Cornerstone Counseling and Education Services
11 York Street Suite 101
Hanover, PA 17331

HARRISBURG

Another Chance Counseling
200 Shell Street
Harrisburg, PA 17109

Conewago Place Outpatient
2901 North 6th Street
Harrisburg, PA 17110

Discovery House
99 South Cameron Street
Harrisburg, PA 17101

Gaudenzia
Chambers Hill Adolescent Program
3740 Chambers Hill Road
Harrisburg, PA 17111

Common Ground
2835 North Front Street
Harrisburg, PA 17110

90 Concept
Spruce Road
Harrisburg State Hospital Building
21 Harrisburg, PA 17105

Outpatient Services
2039 North 2nd Street
Harrisburg, PA 17102

Harrisburg Area Counseling Services
3907 Derry Street
Harrisburg, PA 17111

Hoffman Psychological Associates
3029 North Front Street
Suite 102
Harrisburg, PA 17110-1220

Pinnacle Health Psychological Associates
205 South Front Street
Harrisburg, PA 17105

Riegler Shienvold and Associates
2151 Linglestown Road, Suite 200
Harrisburg, PA 17110-9455

Teen Challenge
1421 North Front Street
Harrisburg, PA 17102

Tressler Greater Harrisburg Alcohol and Drug Counseling
3309 Spring Street, Suite 204
Harrisburg, PA 17109

Weaver Counseling
4607 Locust Lane
Harrisburg, PA 17109

HAVERTOWN

Mercy Haverford Hospital Substance Abuse Services
2000 Old West Chester Pike
Havertown, PA 19083

HAZLETON

A Better Today, Inc.
21 North Church Street
Hazleton, PA 18201

Northeast Counseling Services
750 East Broad Street
Hazleton, PA 18201

Serento Gardens Alcohol and Drug Services
145 West Broad Street, 2nd Floor
Hazleton, PA 18201

HENRYVILLE

Greenway Center
State Route 715-314
Henryville, PA 18332

HERMITAGE

Sharon Regional Health System Behavioral Health Services
2375 Garden Way
Hermitage, PA 16148

HERSHEY

Bennett, Timothy
825 Fishburn Road
Hershey, PA 17033

Guidance Associates of Pennsylvania
475 West Governor Road
Hershey, PA 17033

University Recovery Center Department of Psychiatry
500 University Drive
Hershey, PA 17033

HILLER

Fayette County Drug and Alcohol Commission Inc
903 First Street
Hiller, PA 15444

HOMESTEAD

Caty Services Family Recovery Center
120 East 9th Street
Homestead, PA 15120

HUMMELSTOWN

Conewago Place
424 Nye Road
Hummelstown, PA 17036

HUNTINGDON

Mainstream Counseling
1001 Washington Street
Huntingdon, PA 16652

HYNDMAN

Twin Lakes Center for Drug and Alcohol Rehabilitation
Hyndman Area Health Center
Hyndman, PA 15545

INDIANA

The Open Door, Inc.
20 South 6 Street
Indiana, PA 15701

Twin Lakes
840 Philadelphia Street
Indiana, PA 15701

JEANNETTE

Adelphoi Village McKee Home
109 North 2nd Street
Jeannette, PA 15644

Monsour Medical Center
70 Lincoln Way East
Jeannette, PA 15644-3167

JOHNSTOWN

Croyle Psychological Associates
1450 Scalp Avenue, Suite 209
Johnstown, PA 15904

New Visions/Mercy Hall Drug and Alcohol Program
1020 Franklin Street
Johnstown, PA 15905

Peniel Drug and Alcohol Treatment Facility
760 Copper Avenue
Johnstown, PA 15906

Twin Lakes Center for Drug Alcohol Rehabilitation
406 Main Street, Suite 408
Johnstown, PA 15901

KANE

Alcohol and Drug Abuse Services Kane Unit
16 Greeves Street
Kane, PA 16735

Kane Community Hospital Detox Program
North Fraley Street
Kane, PA 16735

Nelson Behavioral Center
Presbyterian Church Greene Street
Kane, PA 16735

KEMPTON

Blue Mountain House of Hope
8284 Leaser Road
Kempton, PA 19529-0067

KENNETT SQUARE

Bowling Green Inn Brandywine
1375 Newark Road
Kennett Square, PA 19348

NHS Help Counseling Division
500 North Walnut Street
Kennett Square, PA 19348

KING OF PRUSSIA

Rehabilitation After Work
700 South Henderson Road
Suite 10 Merion Building
King of Prussia, PA 19406

KINGSTON

Choices A Divsion of Community Counseling Services
518 Wyoming Avenue
Kingston, PA 18704

Clem/Mar House, Inc.
540-542 Main Street
Kingston, PA 18704

KITTANNING

Armstrong County Memorial Hospital Alcohol and Drug Services
1 Nolte Drive
Kittanning, PA 16201

Armstrong County Council On Alcohol and Other Drugs, Inc./ARC Manor
200 Oak Avenue
Kittanning, PA 16201

KUTZTOWN

Center for Mental Health Care
Trexler and Noble Street
Kutztown, PA 19530

LANCASTER

Drug and Alcohol Rehab Service, Inc. Manos Residential Therapeutic Community
121 South Prince Street
Lancaster, PA 17603

Family Service of Lancaster County
630 Janet Avenue
Lancaster, PA 17601

HSA Counseling, Inc.
48 North Queen Street, 3rd Floor
Lancaster, PA 17603

Lancaster Clinical Counseling Assoc.
131 East Orange Street
2nd Floor/Rear
Lancaster, PA 17602

Lancaster Freedom Center
436 North Lime Street
Lancaster, PA 17602

Nuestra Clinica of Saca Da Program
545 Pershing Avenue
Lancaster, PA 17602

T.W. Ponessa Associates Counseling
448 Murry Hill Circle
Lancaster, PA 17601-4141

White Deer Run of Lancaster
53-55 North West End Avenue
Lancaster, PA 17604

LANGHORNE

Jewish Family and Children's Service of Philadelphia
340 East Maple Avenue
Suite 107
Langhorne, PA 19047

LANSDALE

Help Line Center, Inc.
306 A Madison Avenue
Lansdale, PA 19446

LEBANON

Another Chance Counseling
607 South 14th Avenue
Lebanon, PA 17042-8805

Renaissance Counseling
701 Chestnut Street
Lebanon, PA 17042

Veterans' Affairs Medical Center Substance Abuse Treatment Unit (SATU)
1700 South Lincoln Avenue
Lebanon, PA 17042

LEHIGHTON

Carbon/Monroe/Pike Drug/ Alcohol Commission, Inc.
128 South First Street
Lehighton, PA 18235

LEWISTOWN

Clear Concepts
218 Electric Avenue
Lewistown, PA 17044

N/P Health Services
400 Highland Avenue
Lewistown, PA 17044-1198

LITITZ

Hear, Inc. Gate House for Men
649 East Main Street
Lititz, PA 17543

LOCK HAVEN

Green Ridge Counseling Center
Unit IV
25 West Main Street
Lock Haven, PA 17745

MALVERN

Malvern Institute
940 King Road
Malvern, PA 19355

MANSFIELD

Laurel Health Center
40 West Wellsboro Street
Mansfield, PA 16933

MARIENVILLE

Abraxas Foundation, Inc. Abraxas I
Blue Jay Village
Marienville, PA 16239

MARS

Gateway North Hills
1559 Route 228
Mars, PA 16046

MCKEESPORT

Center for Substance Abuse
120 5 Avenue
McKeesport, PA 15132

**Mon Yough Women and Family
 Center**
515 Sinclair Street
McKeesport, PA 15132

**Whales Tale Substance Abuse
 Treatment Services**
416 Olive Street
McKeesport, PA 15132

MCKEES ROCKS

**Northern Southwest Community
 MH/MR/DA Services**
McKees Rocks Center
710 Thompson Avenue
McKees Rocks, PA 15136

MEADVILLE

**Crawford County Drug and
 Alcohol Executive
 Commission**
898 Park Avenue
Suite 12
Meadville, PA 16335

**Meadville Medical Center
 Stepping Stones**
1034 Grove Street
Meadville, PA 16335

MECHANICSBURG

**Gaudenzia Foundation Inc.
 West Shore Outpatient
 Program**
6 State Road
Suite 115
Mechanicsburg, PA 17055

MEDIA

**Family and Community Service
 of Delaware County**
100 West Front Street
Media, PA 19063

Focus Counseling Center, Inc.
700 North Jackson Street
Media, PA 19063-2527

Mirmont Treatment Center
100 Yearsley Mill Road
Media, PA 19063

MIFFLINTOWN

Clear Concepts
Rural Route 4
Mifflintown, PA 17059

MILFORD

**Carbon/Monroe/Pike Drug/
 Alcohol Commission Pike
 County Clinic**
10 Buist Road
Milford, PA 18337

MILTON

Bethesda Day Treatment Center
Milton Center 49 Lower Market
 Street
Milton, PA 17847

**Green Ridge Counseling Center
 Unit I**
28 North Front Street
Milton, PA 17847

MOHNTON

Rose Kearney Halfway House
225 East Wyomissing Avenue
Mohnton, PA 19540

MONESSEN

**CSAS, Inc. Mon Valley Drug
 and Alcohol Program**
8 Eastgate Street
Monessen, PA 15062-1385

MONONGAHELA

Whale's Tale Freedom
1290 Chess Street
Monongahela, PA 15063

Monongahela Valley Hospital
Country Club Road
Monongahela, PA 15063

MONROEVILLE

Gateway/Monroeville
4327 Northern Pike
Monroeville, PA 15146

**Saint Francis Medical Center
 Center for Chemical
 Dependency**
2550 Mosside Boulevard
Medical Arts Building, Suite 212
Monroeville, PA 15146

MONTROSE

Trehab Center, Inc.
10 Public Avenue
Montrose, PA 18801

MORRISVILLE

Good Friends, Inc.
868 West Bridge Road
Morrisville, PA 19067

MOUNTAINHOME

Performance Strategies, Inc.
Route 390
Mountainhome, PA 18342

MOUNTVILLE

Gatehouse for Women
465 West Main Street
Mountville, PA 17554-0403

NANTICOKE

Northeast Counseling Services
130 West Washington Street
Nanticoke, PA 18634

NATRONA HEIGHTS

**Butler Regional Recovery
 Program Outpatient**
1301 Carlisle Street
Natrona Heights, PA 15065

NEW BLOOMFIELD

Perry Human Services
New Bloomfield, PA 17068

NEW CASTLE

Drug and Alcohol Community Treatment Services, Inc.
332 Highland Avenue
New Castle, PA 16101

Essawi Counseling Services
343 East Washington Street
New Castle, PA 16101

Highland House
312 Highland Avenue
New Castle, PA 16101

Saint Francis Hospital Detox Unit
1000 South Mercer Street
New Castle, PA 16101

NEW CUMBERLAND

New Insights, Inc.
R 320 Bridge Street
Suite 96
New Cumberland, PA 17070

NEW KENSINGTON

Alle Kiski Pavilion
4th and 17th Avenue
New Kensington, PA 15068

Csas Alle Kiski Drug and Alcohol Program
2120 Freeport Road
New Kensington, PA 15068

Greenbriar Treatment Center
251 7th Street, Suite F
New Kensington, PA 15068

NEWTOWN

Today, Inc.
1990 North Woodbourne Road
Newtown, PA 18940-0841

NORRISTOWN

Family House/Norristown
901 Dekalb Street
Norristown, PA 19401

Montgomery County Methadone Center
316 Dekalb Street
Norristown, PA 19401

Montgomery County MH/MR Emergency Service
50 Beech Drive
Norristown, PA 19401

Programs in Counseling
20 West Main Street
Norristown, PA 19401

Valley Forge Medical Center and Hospital
1033 West Germantown Pike
Norristown, PA 19403

OIL CITY

Northwest Medical Center Drug and Alcohol Program
174 East Bissell Avenue
Oil City, PA 16301

Northwest Medical Center
136 East Bissell Avenue
Oil City, PA 16301

PAOLI

Center for Addictive Diseases
21 Industrial Boulevard, Suite 200
Paoli, PA 19301

Constructive Living
63 Chestnut Road, Suite 3
Paoli, PA 19301

Rehab After Work
1440 Russell Road
Paoli, PA 19301

PHILADELPHIA

Abbottsford Community Health Center
3205 Defense Terrace
Philadelphia, PA 19129

Achievement Through Counseling and Treatment
1745 North 4th Street
Philadelphia, PA 19122

Alcohol and Mental Health Associates
1200 Walnut Street
2nd Floor
Philadelphia, PA 19107

Alleghany University
Hanneman Division
Institute for Addictive Disorders
Youth Opportunity Program
511 North Broad Street
Philadelphia, PA 19123

Asociacion de Puertorriquenos En Marcha Inc.
2147 North 6th Street
Philadelphia, PA 19122

Proyecto Borinquen
520 West Venango Street
Philadelphia, PA 19140

Proyecto Nueva Vida
2143 North 6th Street
Philadelphia, PA 19122

Beacon House at Episcopal Hospital
100 East Lehigh Avenue
Philadelphia, PA 19125

Bowling Green/Center City
1420 Walnut Street Suite 1212
Philadelphia, PA 19102-4017

Caring Together Perinatal Addictions Program
3300 Henry Avenue
Philadelphia, PA 19129

Community Council for Mental Health and Mental Retardation
4900 Wyalusing Avenue
Philadelphia, PA 19131

Consortium, Inc. University City Counseling Center
451 University Avenue
Philadelphia, PA 19104

Cora Services
Community Services Division
733 Susquehanna Road
Philadelphia, PA 19111-1399

Neumann Program
Adams Avenue and Orthodox Road
Philadelphia, PA 19124

De Lasalle in Towne
25 South Van Pelt Street
Philadelphia, PA 19103

Diagnostic and Rehabilitation Center
Main Clinic
229 Arch Street
Philadelphia, PA 19106

Hutchinson Place
3439 West Hutchinson Street
Philadelphia, PA 19140

Dr. Warren E. Smith Community Substance Abuse Centers, Inc.
1315 Windrim Avenue
Philadelphia, PA 19141

Family Center
1201 Chestnut Street 11th Floor
Philadelphia, PA 19107

Family Preservation Program
4219 Chester Avenue
Philadelphia, PA 19104

Frankford Hospital
First Days Program
Frankford Avenue and Wakeling Street
Philadelphia, PA 19124

Friends Hospital
4641 Roosevelt Boulevard
Philadelphia, PA 19124

Gaudenzia
5401 Wayne Avenue
Philadelphia, PA 19144

1415 North Broad Street
Room 116
Philadelphia, PA 19122

1300 East Tulpehocken Street
Philadelphia, PA 19138

3025 North Broad Street
Philadelphia, PA 19132

1834 West Tioga Street
Philadelphia, PA 19140

Genesis II, Inc.
1214 North Broad Street
Philadelphia, PA 19121

Caton House
1239 Spring Garden Street
Philadelphia, PA 19123

Girard Medical Center Return Program/Forensic Intensive Rehab
8th and Girard Avenue
Philadelphia, PA 19122

Horizon House
Outpatient Substance Abuse Program
120 South 30th Street
5th Floor
Philadelphia, PA 19104

Susquehanna Park Residential Community
2137 North 33rd Street
Philadelphia, PA 19121

Hospitality House Outpatient Services
2134 North Hancock Street
Philadelphia, PA 19122

Hutchinson Place
3439 North Hutchinson Street
Philadelphia, PA 19140

Intercommunity Action, Inc. (Interac) Alcohol/Education/ and Family Counseling Program
6122 Ridge Avenue
Philadelphia, PA 19128

Interim House West
4150-52 Parkside Avenue
Philadelphia, PA 19104

Interim House West II
4234 Parkside Avenue
Philadelphia, PA 19104

Interphase Recovery System
814 East Allegheny Avenue
Philadelphia, PA 19134-2402

Jefferson Intensive Outpatient Program
Jefferson Methadone Clinic
21 Street and Washington Avenue
Philadelphia, PA 19146

Jefferson Outreach Drug and Alcohol Program
Central District
1201 Chestnut Street
14th Floor
Philadelphia, PA 19107

JEVS/ACT Achievement Through Counseling and Treatment
5820 Old York Road
Philadelphia, PA 19141-2598

Jewish Family and Children's Service Project Pride
10125 Verree Road
Suite 200
Philadelphia, PA 19116

John F. Kennedy Comm. MH/ MR Center Walk-In Clinic
112 Broad Street
Philadelphia, PA 19102

John F Kennedy Memorial Hospital Substance Abuse Services
Cheltenham Avenue and Langdon Street
Philadelphia, PA 19124

Kensington Hospital Alcohol and Drug Services
136 West Diamond Street
Philadelphia, PA 19122

Kensington Project
2907 Kensington Avenue
Philadelphia, PA 19134

Mercy Hospital of Philadelphia
5301 Cedar Avenue
Philadelphia, PA 19143

Methadone Maintenance
16th and Girard Avenue
Philadelphia, PA 19122

My Sisters Place
5601 Kingsessing Avenue
Philadelphia, PA 19143

Net
497 North 5th Street
Philadelphia, PA 19123

New Journeys in Recovery
2927 North 5th Street
Philadelphia, PA 19133

North Philadelphia Health System Girard Medical Center
Comprehensive Addictions
  Program
Dual Diagnosis Residential
Forensic Intensive Recovery
  Residence
Girard Avenue and 8 Street
Philadelphia, PA 19122

Northeast Treatment Centers Wharton Center
2205 Bridge Street
Philadelphia, PA 19125

NU Stop
2221-25 North Broad Street
2nd Floor
Philadelphia, PA 19132

Parkside Recovery
5000 Parkside Avenue
Philadelphia, PA 19131

Pennsylvania Hospital Hall Mercer Center
800 Spruce Street
Philadelphia, PA 19107-6192

Phase III Outpatient Counseling Services
555 East Indiana Avenue
Philadelphia, PA 19134

Philadelphia Consultation Center
313 South 16th Street
Philadelphia, PA 19102

Philadelphia Teen Challenge Women's Home
329 East Wister Street
Philadelphia, PA 19144

Presbyterian Medical Center
39th and Market Street
Philadelphia, PA 19104

R. W. Brown Community Center New Life Program
1701 North 8th Street
Philadelphia, PA 19122

Re-Enter, Inc.
3331 Powelton Avenue
Philadelphia, PA 19104

Rehab After Work
2821 Island Avenue, Suite 111
Philadelphia, PA 19153

15th Locust Street
Lewistower Building, Suite 201
Philadelphia, PA 19102

River's Bend Drug and Alcohol Unit
2401 Penrose Avenue
Philadelphia, PA 19145

Riverside House Inc
9549 Milnor Street
Philadelphia, PA 19114

Saint Gabriel's Hall Delasalle Aftercare
3509 Spring Garden Street
Philadelphia, PA 19104

Saint Gabriel System
117 South 17th Street
Suite 1701
Philadelphia, PA 19103

Saint Joseph Hospital
16th Street and Girard Avenue
Philadelphia, PA 19130

Self Help Movement, Inc.
2600 South Hampton Road
Philadelphia, PA 19116

Self, Inc.
121 North Broad Street
11th Floor
Philadelphia, PA 19107

Shalom, Inc.
311 South Juniper Street
Philadelphia, PA 19107

Sobriety Through Outpatient Inc
2221-25 North Broad Street
3rd Floor
Philadelphia, PA 19132

Teen Challenge Philadelphia Mens Home
156 West Schoolhouse Lane
Philadelphia, PA 19144

Therapeutic Center at Fox Chase
8400 Pine Road
Philadelphia, PA 19111

Veterans' Affairs Medical Center Alcohol/Drug Dependence Treatment Program
University and Woodland Avenues
Philadelphia, PA 19104

Wedge Medical Center
6701 North Broad Street
Philadelphia, PA 19126

1710 North 22nd Street
Philadelphia, PA 19122

2009 South Broad Street
Philadelphia, PA 19148

PHILIPSBURG

Quest Services
15th and Pine Streets
Philipsburg, PA 16866-9560

PHOENIXVILLE

Help Counseling Center
21 Gay Street
Phoenixville, PA 19460

PITTSBURGH

Abraxas Foundation, Inc.
Abraxas Center for Adolescent
  Females
437 Turrett Street
Pittsburgh, PA 15206

Abraxas III
936 West North Avenue
Pittsburgh, PA 15233

Addison Terrace Learning Center, Inc.
5937 Broad Street Mall
Suite 226-227
Pittsburgh, PA 15206

Alpha House
435 Shady Avenue
Pittsburgh, PA 15206

Alternative Program Associates, Inc.
6117 Broad Street
Pittsburgh, PA 15206

Center for Addiction Services Saint Francis Outreach
712 South Avenue
Pittsburgh, PA 15221

**Charter Behavioral Health
Systems Outpatient Recovery
Center**
2100 Wharton Street Birmingham
Towers Suite 120
Pittsburgh, PA 15203

**Circle C Specialized Group
Home for Chemically
Dependent Adolescents**
227 Seabright Street
Pittsburgh, PA 15214

Discovery House
1391 Washington Boulevard
Pittsburgh, PA 15206

Gateway Allegheny Valley
1385 Old Freeport Road
Pittsburgh, PA 15238

Gateway Greentree
2121 Noblestown Road Rear
Pittsburgh, PA 15205

Greenbriar Robinson Township
4955 Steubenville Street
Twin Towers, Suite 303
Pittsburgh, PA 15205

**Homewood/Brushton YMCA
Counseling Services**
7140 Bennett Street
Pittsburgh, PA 15208

House of the Crossroads
2012 Centre Avenue
Pittsburgh, PA 15219

**Ielase Institute Mon Yough
Corrections Program**
232 First Avenue, 3rd Floor
Pittsburgh, PA 15222

Mercy Behavioral Health
2100 Wharton Street Suite 200
Pittsburgh, PA 15203-1942

OUR House ARTP
735 North Highland Avenue
Pittsburgh, PA 15206

PBA, Inc. Second Step Program
1425 Beaver Avenue
Pittsburgh, PA 15233

**Pennsylvania Organization for
Women in Early Recover**
7445 Church Street
Pittsburgh, PA 15218

**Program for Female Offenders,
Inc. Allegheny County
Treatment Alternative
Program**
2410 5th Avenue
Pittsburgh, PA 15213

**Progressive Medical Specialists
Inc**
2900 Smallman Street
Pittsburgh, PA 15201

Saint Francis Medical Center
Center for Chemical Dependency
Treatment
6714 Kelly Street
Pittsburgh, PA 15208

Outpatient/Inpatient Detox
400 45th Street
Pittsburgh, PA 15201-1198

Uptown Center
1945 5th Avenue
Pittsburgh, PA 15219

Salvation Army
Harbor Light Center
865 West North Avenue
Pittsburgh, PA 15233

Public Inebriate Program
54 South 9th Street
Pittsburgh, PA 15203

Sojourner House
5460 Penn Avenue
Pittsburgh, PA 15206

**South Hills Health System
Counseling Center**
4129 Brownsville Road
Pittsburgh, PA 15227

Whale's Tale
Family Treatment Center
844 Proctor Way
Pittsburgh, PA 15210

Shadyside Office
250 Shady Avenue
Pittsburgh, PA 15206

Substance Abuse Treatment
Services
413 Evergreen Avenue
Pittsburgh, PA 15209

801 Wallace Avenue
Pittsburgh, PA 15221

**Veterans' Affairs Medical Center
Substance Abuse Treatment
Unit**
7180 Highland Drive
Unit 116A3/5
Pittsburgh, PA 15206

PITTSTON

**Wyoming Valley Alcohol and
Drug Services, Inc.**
49 South Main Street
Pittston, PA 18640

PORT ALLEGANY

**Alcohol and Drug Abuse
Services, Inc.**
118 Chestnut Street
Port Allegany, PA 16743

120 Chestnut Street
Port Allegany, PA 16743-1251

POTTSTOWN

**Addiction Counseling Services,
Inc.**
78 Savage Road
Pottstown, PA 19465

**Alternative Counseling
Associates**
438-440 High Street
Pottstown, PA 19464

Creative Health Services, Inc.
Drug and Alcohol Outpatient
365 High Street
Pottstown, PA 19464

Creative Health Systems, Inc.
101 King Street
Pottstown, PA 19464

Programs in Counseling
262 King Street Suite 320
Pottstown, PA 19464-5571

QUAKERTOWN

**Renewal Centers, Inc.
Quakertown Office**
2705 Old Bethlehem Pike
Quakertown, PA 18951

Saint Luke's Renewal Centers
2705 Old Bethlehem Pike
Quakertown, PA 18951

READING

Berks Counseling Center
700 Lancaster Street
Reading, PA 19602

Callowhill Family Therapy
244 North 5th Street
Reading, PA 19601

Center for Mental Health Drug and Alcohol Center
6 and Spruce Streets
Building J
Reading, PA 19611

Chor Youth and Family Services, Inc. Drug and Alcohol Center
1010 Centre Avenue
Reading, PA 19601

Hogar Crea Reading
302 South Fifth Street
Reading, PA 19602

Livengrin Counseling Center
Crestwood Street East
Hearthstone Court, Building 5
Reading, PA 19606

Pennsylvania Counseling Services
501 Washington Street, Suite 301
Reading, PA 19601

RED LION

Human Services Associates
424 South Pine Street
Red Lion, PA 17356

REHRERSBURG

Teen Challenge Training Center, Inc.
Teen Challenge Road
Rehrersburg, PA 19550

RIDGWAY

Nelson Behavioral Center
102 Center Street
Ridgway, PA 15853-1716

RURAL RIDGE

Teen Challenge of Western Pennsylvania
Lefever Hill Road
Rural Ridge, PA 15075

SAINT MARYS

Alcohol and Drug Abuse Services Saint Marys Unit
625 Maurus Street
Saint Marys, PA 15857

SALTSBURG

Adelphoi Village Keystone House
114 Washington Street
Saltsburg, PA 15681-1130

SAXTON

Twin Lakes Center for Drug and Alcohol Rehabilitation
805 Lower Main Street
Saxton, PA 16678

SCIOTA

Bethesda Day Treatment Center, Inc.
Business Route 209
Sciota, PA 18354

SCRANTON

A Better Today, Inc.
1339 North Main Avenue
Scranton, PA 18508

Drug and Alcohol Treatment Service, Inc. Outpatient Services
116 North Washington Avenue
3rd Floor
Scranton, PA 18503

Northeastern Pennsylvania Counseling Services
116 North Washington Avenue
Scranton, PA 18503

SELLERSVILLE

Community Service Foundation, Inc.
253 North Main Street
Sellersville, PA 18960

Penn Foundation, Inc. Recovery Center
807 Lawn Avenue
Sellersville, PA 18960

SHAMOKIN

Green Ridge Counseling Center Unit II
117 East Independence Street
Shamokin, PA 17872

SHARON

New Choices Sharon Regional Behavioral Health Services
740 East State Street
Sharon, PA 16146

SHARON HILL

Northwestern Human Services Delaware County/Life Guidance Division
800 Chester Pike
Sharon Hill, PA 19079

SHICKSHINNY

Clear Brook Lodge
RD 2
Shickshinny, PA 18655

SHIPPENSBURG

UHS PA Roxbury
601 Roxbury Road
Shippensburg, PA 17257

SHREWSBURY

Adams Hanover Counseling Services, Inc. Crossroads Counseling and Education Services
73 East Forest Avenue
Shrewsbury, PA 17361

SOMERSET

Twin Lakes Center for Drug/ Alcohol Rehabilitation
7 Byers Road
Somerset, PA 15501

SPARTANSBURG

Perseus House, Inc. Andromeda House II
39132 Mount Pleasant Road
Spartansburg, PA 16434

SPRING CITY

Creative Health Services, Inc.
1 Mennonite Church Road
Spring City, PA 19475

STATE COLLEGE

Counseling Alternatives Group
444 East College Avenue
Suite 300
State College, PA 16801

Counseling Service Drug and Alcohol Program
233 Easterly Parkway
State College, PA 16801

Lawrence T. Clayton and Counseling Associates, Inc.
230 South Fraser Street
State College, PA 16801

STROUDSBURG

Carbon/Monroe/Pike Drug/ Alcohol Commission Monroe County Clinic
Penn Square
724 Phillips Street, Suite A
Stroudsburg, PA 18360

SUNBURY

Green Ridge Counseling Center Unit V
1070 Market Street
Sunbury, PA 17801

Psychological Services Clinic
352 Arch Street
Sunbury, PA 17801

Valley Counseling Services
21 North 4th Street
Sunbury, PA 17801

TAMAQUA

Family Service Agency
37 West Broad Street
Tamaqua, PA 18252

TARENTUM

Saint Francis Medical Center
Office 3
400 Lock Street
Tarentum, PA 15084

TIONESTA

Forest/Warren Dept. of Human Services Alcohol and Drug Unit
Highland Street
Tionesta, PA 16353

TITUSVILLE

Crawford County Drug and Alcohol Executive Commission Incorporated
127 West Spring Street
Titusville, PA 16354

Deerfield Behavioral Health Network, Inc. Deerfield Centers of Addictions Treatment
605 North 1st Street
Titusville, PA 16354

TOWANDA

Mental Health Associates of North Central Pennsylvania/ Towanda
5 Lombard Street
Towanda, PA 18848

TREVOSE

Community Service Foundation, Inc.
3949 Brownsville Road
Trevose, PA 18901

TUNKHANNOCK

Catholic Social Services
Route 92
Tunkhannock, PA 18657

UNIONTOWN

Fayette County Drug and Alcohol Commission, Inc.
100 New Salem Road
Suite 106
Uniontown, PA 15401

UPPER DARBY

ChesPenn Health Services
20 South 69th Street, 2nd Floor
Upper Darby, PA 19082

Harwood House
9200 West Chester Pike
Upper Darby, PA 19082

VERONA

Whales Tale Penn Hills Office
6149 Saltsburg Road
Verona, PA 15147

WARMINSTER

Allegheny University Hospitals Bucks County
225 Newtown Road
Warminster, PA 18974

WARREN

Deerfield Behavioral Health of Warren Deerfield Centers of Addictions Treatment
414 Market Street
Warren, PA 16365

Forest/Warren Dept of Human Services Drug and Alcohol Program
27 Hospital Drive
Warren, PA 16365

WARRINGTON

Project Transition
1700 Street Road
Warrington, PA 18976

WASHINGTON

Abstinent Living at The Turning Point
199 North Main Street
Washington, PA 15301

Catholic Charities Diocese PGH Outpatient
331 South Main Street
Washington, PA 15301

Greenbriar Treatment Center
800 Manor Drive
Washington, PA 15301

Try Again Homes, Inc.
365 Jefferson Avenue
Washington, PA 15301-4245

WAVERLY

Marworth
Lily Lake Road
Waverly, PA 18471

WAYNESBORO

Roxbury Treatment Center
40 West North Street
Waynesboro, PA 17268-1257

WELLSBORO

Harbor Counseling
25 Water Street
Wellsboro, PA 16901

Laurel Behavioral Health
32-36 Central Avenue
Wellsboro, PA 16901

Laurel Health Center
15 Meade Street Suite L4/6
Wellsboro, PA 16901

Mental Health Associates of North Central Pennsylvania
68 Main Street
Wellsboro, PA 16901

WERNERSVILLE

Caron Foundation Treatment Services
Galen Hall Road
Wernersville, PA 19565

WEST CHESTER

Gaudenzia House
1030 South Concord Road
West Chester, PA 19382

Kindred House for Women and Children
1030 South Concord Road
West Chester, PA 19380

NHS Help Counseling Division
790 East Market Street, Suite 300
West Chester, PA 19382

WEST READING

Center for Mental Health Care
6th and Spruce Streets
Building 1C
West Reading, PA 19611

Jeter Counseling Services
529 Reading Avenue
West Reading, PA 19611

New Directions Treatment Services
20-22 North 6th Avenue
West Reading, PA 19611

WEXFORD

Mercy Behavioral Health
9983 Perry Highway
Wexford, PA 15090

WILKES-BARRE

Catholic Social Services
33 East Northampton Street
Wilkes-Barre, PA 18701

Clear Brook Lodge
1100 East Northampton Street
Wilkes-Barre, PA 18702

Family Service Association of Wyoming Valley
31 West Market Street
Wilkes-Barre, PA 18701

Ferrell and Associates, Inc.
111 North Franklin Street
Wilkes-Barre, PA 18701

First Hospital Wyoming Valley Adult II Dual Diagnosis
149 Dana Street
Wilkes-Barre, PA 18702

Veterans' Affairs Medical Center Substance Abuse Treatment Unit
1111 East End Boulevard
Wilkes-Barre, PA 18711

Wyoming Valley Alcohol and Drug Services, Inc.
437 North Main Street
Wilkes-Barre, PA 18705

WILLIAMSPORT

Crossroads Counseling, Inc.
2128 west 4th Street
Williamsport, PA 17701

Genesis House Inc Professional Counseling Services
1247 West 4th Street
Williamsport, PA 17701

Green Ridge Counseling Center Unit III
520 West 4 Street
Williamsport, PA 17701

White Deer Run of Williamsport
915 Vine Avenue
Williamsport, PA 17701

WILLOW GROVE

Health Care Options, Inc.
500 North Easton Road, 2nd Floor
Willow Grove, PA 19090

WYOMISSING

Caron Counseling Services
845 Park Road
Wyomissing, PA 19610

WYOMISSING HILLS

Pennsylvania Counseling Services
1733 Penn Avenue
Wyomissing Hills, PA 19609

YORK

Atkins House
313 East King Street
York, PA 17403

Colonial House Inc
1300 Woodbury Road
York, PA 17405

Craig and Associates
3550 Concord Road
York, PA 17402-8626

Family and Community Health Associates
810 Bonneview Road
York, PA 17402

1689 Kenneth Road, Suite 202
York, PA 17403

25 Monument Road
York, PA 17403

1030 Plymouth Road
York, PA 17402

New Insights, Inc.
707 Loucks Road
York, PA 17404

Stepping Stone Counseling and Education Services, Inc.
1776 South Queen Street
York, PA 17043

211 South George Street
York, PA 17403

Susquehanna Counseling
2300 East Market Street, Suite 4
York, PA 17402-2858

York Area Counseling Services
26 Mount Zion Road
York, PA 1740

RHODE ISLAND

CHARLESTOWN

South Shore Mental Health Center Addiction Program
4705A Old Post Road
Charlestown, RI 02813

CRANSTON

Addiction Services Comprehensive Community Action Program
311 Doric Avenue
Cranston, RI 02910

Eastman House, Inc.
1545 Pontiac Avenue
Cranston, RI 02920

SSTAR of Rhode Island, Inc. Birth
80 East Street
Cranston, RI 02920

EAST PROVIDENCE

East Bay Mental Health Center Substance Abuse Services
610 Wampanoag Trail
East Providence, RI 02914

EXETER

Marathon House
Exeter, RI 02822

JOHNSTON

Center for Behavioral Health
985 Plainfield Street
Johnston, RI 02919

Tri-Town Community Action Agency
1126 Hartford Avenue
Johnston, RI 02919-7130

MIDDLETOWN

Child and Family Services of Newport
19 Valley Road
Middletown, RI 02840

Newport County Community Mental Health Center
127 Johnnycake Hill Road
Middletown, RI 02842

NARRAGANSETT

Galilee Mission to Fishermen, Inc.
268 Kingstown Road
Narragansett, RI 02882

NEWPORT

New Visions of Newport County SSTAR
19 Broadway
Newport, RI 02840

NORTH KINGSTOWN

Meadows Edge
580 Ten Rod Road
North Kingstown, RI 02852-4220

SSTAR of Rhode Island Residential Alcohol/Drug Detox
1950 Tower Hill Road
North Kingstown, RI 02852

PASCOAG

Marathon, Inc. The Lodge at Wallum Lake
2198 Wallum Lake Road
Pascoag, RI 02859

Long-Term Care
2198 Wallum Lake Road
Pascoag, RI 02859

PAWTUCKET

Community Counseling Center, Inc.
101 Bacon Street
Pawtucket, RI 02860

Friends of Caritas House, Inc.
166 Pawtucket Avenue
Pawtucket, RI 02860

Robert J. Wilson House, Inc.
Outpatient Counseling Center
Residential
80 Summit Street
Pawtucket, RI 02860

Tri Hab House, Inc. Pawtucket Addictions Counseling Services
104 Broad Street
Pawtucket, RI 02860

PROVIDENCE

Alcohol and Drug Rehab Services, Inc.
Minority Alcohol Prog Outpatient
Counseling
66 Burnett Street
Providence, RI 02905

Butler Hospital Alcohol and Drug Treatment Service
345 Blackstone Boulevard
Providence, RI 02906

Discovery House South Providence Addiction Center
66 Pavillion Avenue
Providence, RI 02905

Discovery Program
520 Hope Street
Providence, RI 02906

Family Service Incorporated Substance Abuse Program
55 Hope Street
Providence, RI 02906

Marathon House, Inc.
Outpatient
131 Wayland Avenue
Providence, RI 02906

Multicultural Counseling Center
280 Broadway Street Suite 100
Providence, RI 02903

Providence Community Action
Division of Clinical Services
662 Hartford Avenue
Providence, RI 02909

Divison of Clinical Services
16 Borinquen Street
Providence, RI 02905

SSTAR of Rhode Island, Inc.
Residential Alcohol and Drug
Detox
Short Term Residential Program
for Pregnant Women
21 Peace Street
Providence, RI 02907

Talbot Residential Services
Talbot Outpatient
Womens Day Treatment
90 Plain Street
Providence, RI 02903

265 Oxford Street
Providence, RI 02905

WAKEFIELD

Marathon Sympatico
57 Columbia Street
Wakefield, RI 02879

WARWICK

Addiction Recovery Institute South
205 Helene Road Suite 102
Warwick, RI 02886

Kent County Mental Health Center Alcohol/Drug and Family Counseling
300 Centerville Road Suite 301-S
Warwick, RI 02886

Kent County Mental Health Center
50 Health Lane
Warwick, RI 02886

Kent House, Inc.
2020 Elmwood Avenue
Warwick, RI 02888

Mental Health Services Counseling and Intervention Services, Inc.
422-A Post Road
Warwick, RI 02886

WEST WARWICK

Directions
1071 Main Street
West Warwick, RI 02893

WOONSOCKET

Discovery House Woonsocket
1625 Diamond Hill Road
Woonsocket, RI 02895

Family Resources, Inc.
245 South Main Street
Woonsocket, RI 02895

Tri-Hab Counseling
58 Hamlet Avenue
Woonsocket, RI 02895

Tri-Hab House, Inc.
79 Asylum Street
Woonsocket, RI 02895

King House
80 Hamlet Avenue
Woonsocket, RI 02895

WYOMING

Friends of Caritas House, Inc. Corkery House
15 Baker Pines Road
Wyoming, RI 02898-1000

SOUTH CAROLINA

AIKEN

Aiken Center
1105 Gregg Highway
Aiken, SC 29801-0535

Aiken Regional Medical Center
Aurora Pavilion
655 Medical Park Drive
Aiken, SC 29801

ANDERSON

Anderson/Oconee Counties
Behavioral Health Services
226 McGee Road
Anderson, SC 29625

Patrick B. Harris Hospital
Substance Abuse Services
130 Highway 252
Anderson, SC 29621

BARNWELL

Axis I Center of Barnwell
2606 Jackson Avenue
Barnwell, SC 29812

BEAUFORT

Beaufort County Alcohol and
Drug Abuse Department
1905 Duke Street
Suite 270
Beaufort, SC 29902

Coastal Empire Community
Mental Health Center
Substance Abuse Services
1050 Ribaut Road
Beaufort, SC 29901

Joint Substance Abuse
Counseling Center
Marine Corps Air Station MCAS
Beaufort, SC 29904

MCRD Parris Island South
Carolina Substance Abuse
Counseling Center
Building 911
Beaufort, SC 29905-5001

BISHOPVILLE

Lee County Commission on
Alcohol and Drug Abuse
180 East Church Street
Bishopville, SC 29010

CAMDEN

Alpha Center
416 Rutledge Street
Camden, SC 29020

CHARLESTON

Columbia/Trident Behavioral
Health Services
9225 University Boulevard
Suite 2-E
Charleston, SC 29406

Department of Alcohol and
Other Drug Abuse Services of
Charleston County
615 Wesley Drive
Charleston, SC 29417-1398

Medical University of South
Carolina Drugs and Alcohol
Program
171 Ashley Avenue
Charleston, SC 29425

Roper North Treatment Center
2750 Speissegger Drive
Charleston, SC 29405

Veterans' Affairs Medical Center
Substance Abuse Treatment
Center
100 Bee Street
Charleston, SC 29401

CHESTER

Hazel Pittman Center
130 Hudson Street
Chester, SC 29706

CHESTERFIELD

Alpha Center/Chesterfield/
Kershaw/Lee Alcohol and
Drug Abuse Commission
141 West Main Street
Chesterfield, SC 29709

COLUMBIA

Columbia Area Mental Health
Center
1611 Devonshire Drive
Columbia, SC 29204

Earle E. Morris, Jr. Alcohol and
Drug Addiction Treatment
Center
610 Faison Drive
Columbia, SC 29203

Lexington/Richland Alcohol
and Drug Abuse Council
1325 Harden Street
Columbia, SC 29204

Richland Springs Psychiatric
Hospital
11 Medical Park
Columbia, SC 29203

CONWAY

Charter Sands Behavioral
Health System
152 Waccamaw Medical Park
Drive
Conway, SC 29526

Horry County Commission on
Alcohol and Drug Abuse
1004 Bell Street
Conway, SC 29526

DILLON

Dillon County Commission on
Alcohol and Drug Abuse
204 North Third Avenue
Dillon, SC 29536

FLORENCE

Bruce Hall
122 East Cedar Street
Florence, SC 29501

Palmetto Center
Florence, SC 29502

GAFFNEY

Cherokee County Commission on Alcohol and Drug Abuse
201 West Montgomery Street
Gaffney, SC 29341

GEORGETOWN

Georgetown County Alcohol and Drug Abuse Commission
1423 Winyah Street
Georgetown, SC 29440

GREENVILLE

Addcare Counseling, Inc.
11 Pointe Circle
Greenville, SC 29615

Addlife Addiction Services
701 Grove Road
Greenville, SC 29605

Don Foster and Associates, Inc.
104 Mills Avenue
Greenville, SC 29605

Greenville Metro Treatment Center
603 Arlington Avenue
Greenville, SC 29601

Greenville County Commission on Alcohol and Drug Abuse
3336 Buncombe Road
Greenville, SC 29609

Healthy Beginnings
730 South Pleasantburg Drive
Suite 109
Greenville, SC 29607

Holsmesview Center
Old Easley Bridge Road
Greenville, SC 29610

Rosewood House of Recovery, Inc.
9 Renrick Drive
Greenville, SC 29609

GREENWOOD

Faith Home Christian Alcohol and Drug Rehab
Buck Level Road
Greenwood, SC 29646

Greenwood/Edgefield/ McCormick Commission on Alcohol and Drug Abuse
1420 Spring Street
Greenwood, SC 29646

HAMPTON

New Life Center
First Street East
Second Floor, Annex Building
Hampton, SC 29924

LANCASTER

Springs Memorial Hospital Lancaster Recovery Center
800 West Meeting Street
Lancaster, SC 29720

LAURENS

Laurens Commission on Alcohol and Drug Abuse
Industrial Park Road
Laurens, SC 29360

MANNING

Clarendon County Commission on Alcohol and Drug Abuse
14 North Church Street
Manning, SC 29102

MARION

Marion County Alcohol and Drug Abuse Program
103 Court Street
Marion, SC 29571

MONCKS CORNER

Ernest E. Kennedy Center Alcohol and Drug Abuse Program
306 Airport Drive
Moncks Corner, SC 29461

NEWBERRY

ORANGEBURG

Westview Behavioral Health Services
800 Main Street
Newberry, SC 29108

Tri-County Commission on Alcohol and Drug Abuse
3190 Cook Road
Orangeburg, SC 29115

SALUDA

Saluda County Commission on Alcohol and Drug Abuse
204 Ramage Street
Saluda, SC 29138

Shaw Air Base 20th Medical Operations Squadron (SGOMH)
423 Lowry Avenue
Shaw AFB, SC 29152

SPARTANBURG

Spartanburg Area Mental Health Center Substance Abuse Services
149 East Wood Street
Spartanburg, SC 29303

Spartanburg County Commission on Alcohol and Drug Abuse
209 Catawba Street
Spartanburg, SC 29306

SUMMERVILLE

Dorchester County Commission on Alcohol and Drug Abuse
500 North Cedar Street
Summerville, SC 29483

UNION

Union County Commission on Alcohol and Drug Abuse
201 South Herndon Street
Union, SC 29379

WALTERBORO

Colleton County Commission on Alcohol and Drug Abuse
Walterboro, SC 29488

WEST COLUMBIA

Charter Rivers Hospital Alcohol and Drug Abuse Services
2900 Sunset Boulevard
West Columbia, SC 29169

Columbia Metro Treatment Center
421 Capital Square
West Columbia, SC 29169

WILLIAMSTON

Anmed Wellspring
313 William Street
Williamston, SC 29697

WINNSBORO

Fairfield County Substance Abuse Commission
200 Calhoun Street
Winnsboro, SC 29180

SOUTH DAKOTA

ABERDEEN

Northern Alcohol/Drug Referral and Information Center (NADRIC)
221 South First Street
Aberdeen, SD 57402

BELLE FOURCHE

Addiction Family Resources
608 5th Avenue
Belle Fourche, SD 57717

BERESFORD

Lutheran Social Services of South Dakota Woodfield Center
Beresford, SD 57004

BROOKINGS

East Central Mental Health Chemical Dependency Center
211 4 Street
Brookings, SD 57006

CANTON

Keystone Treatment Center
1010 East 2 Street
Canton, SD 57013

CHAMBERLAIN

Chamberlain Academy
211 West 16 Avenue
Chamberlain, SD 57325

HOT SPRINGS

Southern Hills Alcohol/Drug Referral Center
311 North River Street
Hot Springs, SD 57747

HURON

Community Counseling Services Alcohol and Drug Unit
1552 Dakota Street South
Huron, SD 57350

Our Home, Inc.
Rediscovery
360 Ohio Avenue NW
Huron, SD 57350

Inhalant Abuse Program
East Centennial Road
Huron, SD 57350

LEMMON

Three Rivers Chemical Dependency Center
11 East 4th Street
Lemmon, SD 57638

MADISON

Community Counseling Services
914 NE 3 Street
Madison, SD 57042

MITCHELL

Abbott House
909 Court Merrill Street
Mitchell, SD 57301-0700

Community Alcohol/Drug Center, Inc.
901 South Miller Street
Mitchell, SD 57301

PIERRE

Capital Area Counseling Service, Inc. Drug and Alcohol Unit
200 West Pleasant Street
Pierre, SD 57501

PLANKINTON

State Training School Alcohol and Drug Program
Plankinton, SD 57368

RAPID CITY

City/County Receiving and Referral Center
725 North Lacrosse Street
Rapid City, SD 57701

Focus, Inc.
114 Kinney Avenue
Rapid City, SD 57709

Youth and Family Counseling Services
924 North Maple Street
Rapid City, SD 57709

SIOUX FALLS

Carroll Institute
2nd Street Manor
826 West 2 Street
Sioux Falls, SD 57104

Outpatient Alcohol and Drug
 Center
310 South 1st Avenue
Sioux Falls, SD 57102

Arch Halfway House
Sioux Falls Detoxification Center
333 South Spring Avenue
Sioux Falls, SD 57104

**Communication Services for
The Deaf**
3520 Gateway Lane
Sioux Falls, SD 57106-1558

Counseling Resources
707 East 41st Street
Suite 205
Sioux Falls, SD 57105-6405

First Step Counseling Services
4320 South Louise Street
Sioux Falls, SD 57106

Glory House of Sioux Falls
4000 South West Avenue
Sioux Falls, SD 57105

**J. W. Doan and Associates
Behavioral Health Services**
625 South Minnesota Avenue
Suite 102
Sioux Falls, SD 57104-4872

Keystone Outreach Program
1908 West 42 Street
Sioux Falls, SD 57105

**McKennan Behavioral Health
Services Addiction Recovery
Program**
3926 South Western Avenue
Sioux Falls, SD 57101

**Sioux Valley Hospital
Behavioral Health Services**
2812 South Louise Avenue
Sioux Falls, SD 57106

**South Dakota State Penitentiary
Alcohol and Drug Program**
1600 North Drive
Sioux Falls, SD 57117

Turning Point
1401 West 51st Street
Sioux Falls, SD 57105

SISSETON

**Tetakwitha Adolescent
Treatment Center**
Rural Route 2
Sisseton, SD 57262

SPRINGFIELD

**Springfield State Prison
Chemical Dependency
Program**
Springfield, SD 57062

YSI/Springfield Academy
709 6th Street
Springfield, SD 57062

STURGIS

**Black Hills Special Services
Cooperative Chemical
Dependency Inpatient
Program**
1715 Lazelle Street
Sturgis, SD 57785

**Northern Hills Alcohol and
Drug Service**
950 Main Street
Sturgis, SD 57785

VALE

New Dawn Center
Rural Route 1
Vale, SD 57788

VERMILLION

**University of South Dakota
Student Counseling Center**
414 East Clark Street
Vermillion, SD 57069

WINNER

**Southern Plains Mental Health
Center Decision 1**
500 East 9 Street
Winner, SD 57580

**Winner Alcohol/Drug
Counseling Service**
223 South Main Street
Winner, SD 57580

YANKTON

**Adolescent Chemical
Dependency Program**
North Highway 81
Yankton, SD 57078

**South Dakota Human Services
Center**
Gateway Chemical Dependency
Treatment Center
3515 Broadway
Yankton, SD 57078

TENNESSEE

ASHLAND CITY

Centerstone Mental Health Centers Harriett Cohn Center/ Ashland City
197 Court Street
Ashland City, TN 37015

ATHENS

Volunteer Counseling Center Hiwassee
1805 Ingleside Avenue
Athens, TN 37303

BEAN STATION

Cherokee Health System
Highway 11 West
Bean Station, TN 37708

BLAINE

Cherokee Health System
180 Emory Road
Blaine, TN 37709

BOLIVAR

Quinco Mental Health Center Alcohol and Drug Services
10710 Highway 64
Bolivar, TN 38008

BRISTOL

Bristol Residential Counseling Center
26 Midway Street
Bristol, TN 37620

CASTALIAN SPRINGS

Pathfinders Residential Treatment Center
875 Highway 231 South
Castalian Springs, TN 37031

CENTERVILLE

Centerstone Mental Health Centers Family Counseling and Mental Health Center
1680 Highway 100
Centerville, TN 37033

CHATTANOOGA

Council for Alcohol and Drug Abuse Services
207 Spears Avenue
Chattanooga, TN 37405

911 Pineville Road
Chattanooga, TN 37405

Fortwood Center, Inc.
1028 East 3 Street
Chattanooga, TN 37403

Parkridge Hospital, Inc. DBA Columbia Valley Hospital
2200 Morris Hill Road
Chattanooga, TN 37421

Volunteer Treatment Center, Inc.
2347 Rossville Boulevard
Chattanooga, TN 37408

CLARKSVILLE

Harriett Cohn Mental Health Center
511 8 Street
Clarksville, TN 37040

CLEVELAND

Greenleaf Outpatient Services
2650 Executive Park North
Suite 2
Cleveland, TN 37312

Volunteer Behavioral Healthcare System
Hiwassee
1855 Executive Park NW
Cleveland, TN 37312-2747

Reality House
360 Worth Street
Cleveland, TN 37311

COLUMBIA

Centerstone Mental Health Centers Maury County Mental Health Center
1222 Medical Center Drive
Columbia, TN 38401

COOKEVILLE

Volunteer Behavioral Healthcare System
1200 South Willow Avenue
Cookeville, TN 38501

COVINGTON

Professional Counseling Services, Inc. Alcohol and Drug Abuse Services
1997 Highway 51 South
Covington, TN 38019

CROSSVILLE

Volunteer Behavioral Healthcare System
Cumberland Mountain Unit
Route 13
Crossville, TN 38555

DANDRIDGE

Cherokee Health System
809 Peal Street
Dandridge, TN 37725

DAYTON

Volunteer Behavioral Healthcare System RHEA County Mental Health Center
7200 Rhea County Highway
Dayton, TN 37321

DECATURVILLE

Quinco Mental Health Center Alcohol and Drug Services
Highway 100
Decaturville, TN 38329

DICKSON

Centerstone Mental Health Centers Southridge Psychological Services
721 Highway 46
Dickson, TN 37055

FAYETTEVILLE

Centerstone Mental Health Centers Highland Rim Mental Health Center
2241 Thornton Taylor Parkway
Fayetteville, TN 37334

GALLATIN

Cumberland Mental Health Services, Inc. Alcohol and Drug Program
528 East Main Street
Gallatin, TN 37066

GREENEVILLE

Frontier Health, Inc. Church Street Pavilion
616 East Church Street, Suite A
Greeneville, TN 37743

Nolachuckey/Holston Mental Health Center
401 Holston Drive
Greeneville, TN 37744

HARRIMAN

Ridgeview Psychiatric Hospital and Center Alcohol/Drug Abuse Program
221 Devonia Street
Harriman, TN 37748

HENDERSON

Quinco Mental Health Center Alcohol and Drug Services
925 East Main Street
Henderson, TN 38340

HENDERSONVILLE

Cumberland Mental Health Services, Inc. Alcohol and Drug Program
133 Indian Lake Road
Hendersonville, TN 37075

HOHENWALD

Buffalo Valley, Inc.
221 South Maple Street
Hohenwald, TN 38462

501 Park Avenue South
Hohenwald, TN 38462

511 Park Avenue South
Hohenwald, TN 38462

Centerstone Mental Health Centers
912 Summertown Highway
Hohenwald, TN 38462-0513

JACKSON

Aspell Manor
331 North Highland Avenue
Jackson, TN 38301

Charter Lakeside/Jackson
106 Stonebridge Boulevard
Jackson, TN 38305

Jackson Area Council on Alcoholism and Drug Dependency
900 East Chester Street
Jackson, TN 38301

Pathways Substance Abuse Treatment Center
238 Summar Drive
Jackson, TN 38301

JASPER

Volunteer Behavioral Healthcare System Marion City Mental Health Center
443 Browder Switch Road
Jasper, TN 37347-0610

JOHNSON CITY

Comprehensive Community Services
323 West Walnut Street
Johnson City, TN 37604

Frontier Health, Inc.
Fairview Associates
607 Baxter Street
Johnson City, TN 37604

Watauga Mental Health Center
106 East Watauga Avenue
Johnson City, TN 37605

Woodridge Hospital
403 State of Franklin Road
Johnson City, TN 37604

Recovery North Side Hospital Chemical Dependency Unit
401 Princeton Road
Johnson City, TN 37601

KINGSPORT

Frontier Health, Inc. Holston Children and Youth Services
2001 Stonebrook Place
Kingsport, TN 37660

Indian Path Hospital
2000 Pavilion Drive
Kingsport, TN 37660

KNOXVILLE

Agape, Inc. Halfway House
205-211-215 East Scott Avenue
Knoxville, TN 37917

Baptist Hospital of East Tennessee
137 Blount Avenue
Knoxville, TN 37920

Center Point Adult Services
3510 Ball Camp Pike
Knoxville, TN 37921

Cherokee Health System
10263 Kingston Pike
Knoxville, TN 37922

Child and Family Services Great Starts
2601 Keith Avenue
Knoxville, TN 37921

DRD Knoxville Medical Clinic
1501 Cline Street
Knoxville, TN 37921

E. M. Jellinek Center
130 Hinton Street
Knoxville, TN 37917

**Florence Crittenton Agency
Outpatient/Pregnant
Substance Abuse Program**
1531 Dick Lonas Road
Knoxville, TN 37909

**Helen Ross McNabb Center, Inc.
Alcohol and Drug Program**
1520 Cherokee Trail
Knoxville, TN 37920

1310 Oldham Avenue
Apartment 283
Knoxville, TN 37921

Outpatient
5310 Ball Camp Pike
Knoxville, TN 37921

Centerpointe
Adolescent Services
412 Citico Street
Knoxville, TN 37919

Knox County Detoxification
5908 Lyons View Drive
Knoxville, TN 37919

**Knoxville Knox County
Community Action Com.
Counseling and Recovery
Services**
2247 Western Avenue
Knoxville, TN 37921

Midway Rehabilitation Center
1715 Magnolia Avenue
Knoxville, TN 37927

**Overlook Center, Inc. Alcohol
and Drug Abuse Services**
3001 Lake Brook Boulevard
Knoxville, TN 37909

Peninsula Lighthouse
6800 Baum Drive NW
Knoxville, TN 37919

LAFAYETTE

**Volunteer Behavioral
Healthcare System Valley
Ridge Unit**
212 Public Square
Lafayette, TN 37083

LA FOLLETTE

**Ridgeview Psychiatric Hospital
and Center Alcohol/Drug
Abuse Program**
500 West Central Avenue
La Follette, TN 37766

LAWRENCEBURG

**Centerstone Mental Health
Centers Lawrence County
Counseling**
1090 Old Florence Road
Lawrenceburg, TN 38464

LEBANON

**Cumberland Mental Health
Services Drug and Alcohol
Program**
1404 Winter Drive
Lebanon, TN 37087

LEWISBURG

Buffalo Valley, Inc.
218 Martin Avenue South
Lewisburg, TN 37091

**Centerstone Mental Health
Centers Marshall County
Mental Health Center**
1221 Nashville Highway
Lewisburg, TN 37091

LEXINGTON

Turning Point
107 East Church Street
Lexington, TN 38351

LIVINGSTON

**Dale Hollow Mental Health
Center**
501 Spruce Street
Livingston, TN 38570

LOUISVILLE

**Peninsula Hospital Chemical
Dependency Program**
2347 Jones Bend Road
Louisville, TN 37777

MADISON

**Dede Wallace Center Alcohol
and Drug Program**
620 Gallatin Road South
Madison, TN 37115

MADISONVILLE

**Overlook Mental Health Center,
Inc. Alcohol and Drug Abuse
Services**
100 Main Street
Madisonville, TN 37354

MANCHESTER

**Bradford Health Services
Manchester Outreach**
1601 McArthur Street
Manchester, TN 37355

MARTIN

**Baptist Memorial Hospital
Behavioral Health Care**
1201 Bishop Street
Martin, TN 38261

MARYVILLE

**Blount Memorial Hospital
Mountain View Recovery
Center**
907 East Lamar Alexander
Parkway
Maryville, TN 37801

**Overlook Mental Health Center,
Inc. Alcohol and Drug Abuse
Services**
219 Court Street
Maryville, TN 37801

MAYNARDVILLE

Cherokee Health System
4330 Maynardville Highway
Maynardville, TN 37807

MCMINNVILLE

Cheer
120 Omni Drive
McMinnville, TN 37110

MEMPHIS

Baby Love
450 Pontotoc Street
Memphis, TN 38126

Charter Lakeside Behavioral Health System Dual Diagnosis Unit
2911 Brunsuick Road
Memphis, TN 38133-4199

Cocaine and Alcohol Awareness Program (CAAP)
1347 Ferguson Street
Memphis, TN 38106

Frayser/Millington Mental Health Center Alcohol and Drug Abuse Services
2150 Whitney Avenue
Memphis, TN 38127

Grace House, Inc.
329 North Bellevue Street
Memphis, TN 38105

Harbor House, Inc. Alcoholic Rehabilitation Center
1979 Alcy Road
Memphis, TN 38114

John A. Scott Sr. and Associates
5628 Murray Road, Suite 4
Memphis, TN 38119

Memphis Alcohol and Drug Council Prevention/Education
1430 Poplar Street
Memphis, TN 38104

Memphis City Schools Mental Health Center Substance Abuse Services
3782 Jackson Avenue
Room 102
Memphis, TN 38112

Memphis Mental Health Institute Substance Abuse Treatment Program
865 Poplar Avenue
Memphis, TN 38105

Memphis Recovery Centers, Inc.
219 North Montgomery Street
Memphis, TN 38104

1172 Vance Avenue
Memphis, TN 38104

Methodist Hospital
2009 Lamar Avenue
Memphis, TN 38114

Mid-Town Mental Health Center Alcohol and Drug Abuse Services
427 Linden Avenue
Memphis, TN 38126

New Directions, Inc.
642 Semmes Street
Memphis, TN 38111

Raleigh Professional Associates
2960-B Austin Peay Highway
Memphis, TN 38128

Saint Francis Hospital Addiction Treatment Program
5959 Park Avenue
Memphis, TN 38119

Serenity Houses Recovery Center
1094 Poplar Avenue
Memphis, TN 38105

Southeast Mental Health Center, Inc. Alcohol/Drug Abuse Program
3810 Winchester Road
Memphis, TN 38118

2579 Douglas Street
Memphis, TN 38114

3268 Summer Avenue
Memphis, TN 38122

Synergy Foundation, Inc.
2305 Airport Interchange
Memphis, TN 38132

Veterans' Affairs Medical Center Psychiatry Services/Alcohol/ Drug Dependency Treatment Program
1030 Jefferson Avenue
Memphis, TN 38104

Whitehaven/Southwest Mental Health Center Alcohol and Drug Abuse Program
1087 Alice Avenue
Memphis, TN 38116

MORRISTOWN

Cherokee Mental Health Center Substance Abuse Treatment Program
815 West 5 North Street
Morristown, TN 37814

MOUNTAIN CITY

Frontier Johnson Community Counseling Center
318 Donnelly Street
Mountain City, TN 37683

MOUNTAIN HOME

Quillen, James H., VAMC
Mountain Home, TN 37684

MURFREESBORO

Alvin C. York VA Medical Center Substance Abuse Rehabilitation Program
3400 Lebanon Road
Murfreesboro, TN 37130

Pathfinders, Inc. Murfreesboro Outpatient Center
815 South Church Street, Suite 100
Murfreesboro, TN 37130

NASHVILLE

Bradford Health Services Nashville Outreach
2525 Perimeter Place Drive
Suite 110
Greenbriar Business Park
Nashville, TN 37214

Centerstone Mental Health Centers Luton Mental Health Services
1921 Ransom Place
Nashville, TN 37217

**Cumberland Heights Alcohol
and Drug Treatment**
8283 River Road
Nashville, TN 37209

**Davidson County Sheriff's Office
New Avenues/Save**
5115 Harding Place
Nashville, TN 37201

**Life Challenge of Nashville
Women's Residence**
1017 Burchwood Avenue
Nashville, TN 37216

**Lloyd C. Elam Mental Health
Center Meharry Alcohol and
Drug Abuse Program**
1005 Dr. David B. Todd, Jr.,
Boulevard
Nashville, TN 37208

**Metro Health Department
Chemical Dependency
Program**
526 8th Avenue South
Nashville, TN 37203

Nashville Union Rescue Mission
129 7th Avenue South
Nashville, TN 37203

**Parthenon Pavilion CMC Dual
Treatment Program**
2401 Murphy Avenue
Nashville, TN 37203

**Psychiatric Hospital at
Vanderbilt**
1601 23rd Avenue South
Nashville, TN 37212

**Samaritan Recovery
Community, Inc.**
319 South 4th Street
Nashville, TN 37206

**Veterans Affairs Medical Center
Substance Abuse Treatment
Program**
1310 24th Avenue South
Nashville, TN 37212-2637

OAK RIDGE

Hope of East Tennessee, Inc.
171 Waddell Circle
Oak Ridge, TN 37830

**Methodist Medical Center
Turning Point Recovery
Center**
990 Oak Ridge Turnpike
Oak Ridge, TN 37830

**Ridgeview Psychiatric Hospital
and Center Alcohol/Drug
Abuse Program**
240 West Tyrone Road
Oak Ridge, TN 37830

NEWPORT

Cherokee Health System
132 West Broadway Street
Newport, TN 37821

NEW TAZEWELL

Cherokee Health System
606 Broad Street
New Tazewell, TN 37825

OLD HICKORY

Torch Counseling Services
1053 Donelson Avenue
Old Hickory, TN 37138

ONEIDA

**Scott County Hospital Recovery
Center**
Alberta Avenue
Oneida, TN 37841

PARIS

**Carey Counseling Center
Alcohol and Drug Abuse
Program**
408 Virginia Avenue
Paris, TN 38242

POWELL

Cherokee Health System
207 East Emory Road
Powell, TN 37849

RIPLEY

**Baptist Memorial Hospital of
Lauderdale County**
326 Asbury Road
Ripley, TN 38063

ROGERSVILLE

**Frontier Health, Inc. Hawkins
County Mental Health Clinic**
101 Lena Drive
Rogersville, TN 37857

SAVANNAH

**Care of Savannah, Inc. Jack
Gean Shelter for Women**
Route 3
Savannah, TN 38372

**Quinco Mental Health Center
Alcohol and Drug Services**
1105 Pickwick Road
Savannah, TN 38372

SELMER

**Quinco Mental Health Center
Alcohol and Drug Services**
641 East Poplar Street
Selmer, TN 38375

SEVIERVILLE

**Overlook Mental Health Center,
Inc. Alcohol and Drug Abuse
Services**
124 North Henderson Avenue
Sevierville, TN 37862

SEYMOUR

Cherokee Health System
10341 Chapman Highway, Suite 3
Seymour, TN 37865

SHELBYVILLE

**Centerstone Mental Health
Centers Highland Rim Mental
Health Center**
712 North Main Street
Shelbyville, TN 37160

Tony Rice Center, Inc.
1300 Railroad Avenue
Shelbyville, TN 37160

SMITHVILLE

**Wood, Deborah SM., and
Carlton G. Wood, Ph.D.**
Highway 70
Smithville, TN 37166

SNEEDVILLE

**Frontier Health, Inc. Hancock
County Mental Health Clinic**
Buck Valley Road
Sneedville, TN 37869

SPRINGFIELD

**Centerstone Mental Health
Centers Harriett Cohn Center/
Springfield**
713 Cheatharn Street
Springfield, TN 37172

TALBOTT

**Cherokee Health Systems
Substance Abuse Treatment
Program**
6350 West Andrew Johnson
Highway
Talbott, TN 37877

TAZEWELL

Cherokee Health System
1409 Old Tazewell Road
Tazewell, TN 37879

TENNESSEE RIDGE

**Centerstone Mental Health
Centers Ridgeview Residential
and Center Offices**
Route 1 Box 107
Main Street-Highway 147
Tennessee Ridge, TN 37178

TRENTON

Carey Counseling Center
200 East Eaton Street
Trenton, TN 38382

TULLAHOMA

**Highland Rim Mental Health
Center**
1803 North Jackson Street
Tullahoma, TN 37388

WAVERLY

**Centerstone Mental Health
Centers River Valley
Psychological Services**
811 East Railroad Street
Waverly, TN 37185

WAYNESBORO

**Centerstone Mental Health
Centers Wayne County Mental
Health Center**
Highway 135 South T
Waynesboro, TN 38485

WINCHESTER

**Centerstone Mental Health
Centers Highland Rim Mental
Health Center**
10 South Cedar Street
Winchester, TN 37398

TEXAS

ABILENE

**Abilene Regional MH/MR
Center Substance Abuse
Services**
2016 Clack Street, Suite 180
Abilene, TX 79603

Serenity Foundation of Texas
141 Mulberry Street
Abilene, TX 79601

Serenity Oak Tree Project
1533 North 3rd Street
Abilene, TX 79601

Serenity Women
1502 North 2nd Street
Abilene, TX 79601

ALICE

**Alice Counseling Center
Adolescent Supportive
Outpatient**
63 South Wright Street
Alice, TX 78333

**Bay Area Health Care Group,
Ltd. Columbia Counseling
Center of Alice**
1116 North Texas Boulevard
Alice, TX 78332

**Recovery Campuses of Texas,
Inc.**
160 FM 2507
Alice, TX 78333

Treatment Associates
1315 East Main Street, Suite 104
Alice, TX 78332

ALPINE

**Aliviane NO/AD, Inc. Project
AHDRA**
801 West Holland Street
Suite 102-A
Alpine, TX 79830

ALVIN

Alvin Counseling Services
304 Windsor Square
Alvin, TX 77511-4928

Bay Area Council
1111 West Adoue Street
Building C Suite 6
Alvin, TX 77511

**Gulf Coast Recovery Center
Alvin Recovery Program**
2426 South Gordon Street
Alvin, TX 77511

AMARILLO

Amarillo Alcoholic Women's Recovery Center The Haven
1308 South Buchanan Street
Amarillo, TX 79102

Amarillo Council on Alcohol and Drug Abuse
616 North Polk Street
Amarillo, TX 79107

Outpatient Services
710 North Polk, Suite 707
Amarillo, TX 79107

One Day at A Time Ministries
3418 Olsen Boulevard, Suite B
Amarillo, TX 79109-3074

Veterans' Affairs Medical Center Substance Abuse Treatment Program
6010 Amarillo Boulevard West
Ward 2-A
Amarillo, TX 79106

West Texas Counseling and Rehabilitation Program
2300 Line Avenue
Amarillo, TX 79106

ANGLETON

Door to Recovery/Brazoria County
108 East Magnolia Street
Angleton, TX 77515

Gulf Coast Center Substance Abuse Recovery Program
101 Tigner Street
Angleton, TX 77515

ARANSAS PASS

Charter Counseling Center
423 West Cleveland Street Suite 1
Aransas Pass, TX 78336

ARGYLE

Sante Center for Healing
914 Country Club Road
Argyle, TX 76226

ARLINGTON

Family Service, Inc. Addiction Services
401 West Sanford Street
Suite 2600
Arlington, TX 76011

Green Oaks Mental Health Services
3150 Matlock Road, Suite 409
Arlington, TX 76015

Tarrant Community Outreach, Inc.
711 East Lamar Boulevard
Suite 205
Arlington, TX 76011

Urban Behavioral Health Care Systems, Ltd.
711 East Lamar Street, Suite 112
Arlington, TX 76011

AUSTIN

Aeschbach and Associates Substance Abuse Services
2005 East Riverside Drive
Austin, TX 78741

American Institute for Learning Outpatient Program
422 Congress Avenue
Austin, TX 78701

Austin Family House, Inc.
2604 Paramount Avenue
Austin, TX 78704

Austin Recovery Center
1900 Rio Grande Street
Austin, TX 78705

Adolescent Outpatient
1900 East Oltorf Street, Suite 102
Austin, TX 78741

Men's Program Level II
1808 West Avenue
Austin, TX 78701

Outpatient Adult Center
1900 East Oltorf Street
Suites 102-3
Austin, TX 78705

Recovery Lodge/Girls Residential and Day Treatment
3207 Slaughter Lane
Austin, TX 78748-5707

Women's Program Level II
1900 Rio Grande Street Annex
Austin, TX 78705

Austin/Travis County MH/MR Center
Methadone Maintenance
1631-A East 2 Street
Austin, TX 78702

Oak Springs Treatment Center
3000 Oak Springs Drive
Austin, TX 78702

Charter Behavioral Health Systems
8402 Cross Park Drive
Austin, TX 78754

Cornerstone Counseling
2417 Ashdale Drive
Austin, TX 78757

Counseling Network
809 North Cuernavaca Drive
Austin, TX 78733-3217

La Haciendas Solutions
10435 Burnet Street, Suite 114
Austin, TX 78758

Northwest Counseling and Wellness Center
13740 Research Boulevard
Building 4
Austin, TX 78750

Phoenix House Academy
400 West Live Oak Street
Austin, TX 78704

Phoenix House Council for Drug Education
611 South Congress Avenue
Suite 225
Austin, TX 78704

Push-Up Foundations, Inc.
1700 East 2nd Street
Austin, TX 78702

Saint David's Pavilion Chemical Dependency Partial Program
1025 East 32nd Street
Austin, TX 78705

**Teen and Family Counseling
Center**
3536 Bee Caves Road
Suite 100
Austin, TX 78746

**Travis County Community
Justice Center Wakenhut
Corrections Corporation**
8101 FM 969
Austin, TX 78724

Trinity Therapeutic Options
1709 San Antonio Street
Austin, TX 78701-1224

Up to Me, Inc.
6222 North Lamar Street
Austin, TX 78752

BASTROP

**Bastrop Behavioral Health
Center**
106 Loop 150 West
Bastrop, TX 78602

Bastrop Recovery Center
1106 College Street, Suite B
Bastrop, TX 78602

BAYTOWN

**Community Council on Drugs
and Alcohol Just for You
Program**
616 Park Street
Baytown, TX 77520

BEAUMONT

**Beaumont Transitional
Treatment Center**
2495 Gulf Street
Beaumont, TX 77703

**Columbia Behavioral Health
Center Pinebrook Center**
3250 Fannin Street
Beaumont, TX 77701

Franklin House/North
5670 Concord Street
Beaumont, TX 77708

Jefferson County COADA
700 North Street
Beaumont, TX 77701

**Drug/Alcohol Abuse Recovery
Center (DAARC)**
2235 South Street
Beaumont, TX 77701

Land Manor, Inc.
Adams House/Adolescent
Residential
1970 Franklin Street
Beaumont, TX 77701

Graham House
1635 Avenue A
Beaumont, TX 77701

Melton Center
1785 Washington Boulevard
Beaumont, TX 77705

**Life Resource Substance Abuse
Program**
2750 South 8 Street
Beaumont, TX 77701

**New View Partial
Hospitalization Center**
4310 Dowlen Road, Suite 13
Beaumont, TX 77706

**Texas Youth Commission
Chemical Dependency
Treatment Programs**
Jefferson County State School
3890 FM 3514
Beaumont, TX 77705

BEDFORD

**Harris Methodist Springwood
Hospital Addiction Treatment
Center**
1608 Hospital Parkway
Bedford, TX 76022

BELTON

**Christian Farms/Treehouse, Inc.
Christian Farms Men's Center**
Route 3 Box 3852
Belton, TX 76513

**DAIRE Information Referral
Educational Services**
306 East Avenue C
Belton, TX 76513

BIG LAKE

**Permian Basin Rehabilitation
House, Inc. Clover House
Circuit Rider Annex**
3rd and Plaza Street
Big Lake, TX 76932

BIG SPRING

**Veterans' Affairs Medical Center
Substance Abuse Treatment
Program**
300 Veterans Boulevard
Big Spring, TX 79720

BONHAM

**Northeast Texas Council on
Alcohol and Drug Abuse
(NETCADA)**
107 East 16th Street
Bonham, TX 75418

**Sam Rayburn Memorial
Veterans Center Domiciliary
Substance Abuse Program**
9th and Lipscomb Streets
Bonham, TX 75418

BRADY

West Texas Recovery Center
116 West Main Street
Brady, TX 76825

BRECKENRIDGE

**Gateway Foundation Walker
Sayle Unit Breckenridge SAFP
Facility**
4176 Fm 1800
Breckenridge, TX 76424

BROWNSVILLE

**Cameron County Housing
Authority Recovery Center**
65 Castellano Circle
Brownsville, TX 78520

**Tropical Texas Center for MH/
MR Services**
5 Boca Chica Street
Suite 5
Brownsville, TX 78520

BROWNWOOD

Mid-Texas Council on Alcohol and Drug Abuse
901 Avenue B
Brownwood, TX 76801

Thomas R Havins Substance Abuse Felony Punishment Facility
500 FM 45 East
Brownwood, TX 76801

BRYAN

Brazos Valley Council on Alcohol Substance Abuse Adolescent Treatment
1103 Turkey Creek
Bryan, TX 77805

Mental Health/Mental Retardation Authority of Brazos Valley
Dual Diagnosis Treatment
804 South Texas Avenue
Bryan, TX 77805

Saint Joseph Adolescent Substance Abuse Program
2010 East Villa Maria Road
Bryan, TX 77802

Twin City Mission TTC
500 North Main Street
Bryan, TX 77803-3322

BUDA

Austin Recovery Center
1888 Wright Road
Buda, TX 78610

BUFFALO GAP

Shades of Hope Treatment Center, Inc.
402 A Mulberry Street
Buffalo Gap, TX 79508

BURLESON

Abide Inc
6436 Mark Drive
Burleson, TX 76028

BURNET

Gateway Foundation Burnet Substance Abuse Facility
800 Ellen Halbert Drive
Burnet, TX 78611

CANTON

Andrews Center
575 West Highway 243
Canton, TX 75103

Sundown Ranch, Inc.
Route 4
Canton, TX 75103

CARRIZO SPRINGS

South Texas Rural Health Services, Inc. Substance Abuse Program
709 North 3rd Street
Carrizo Springs, TX 78834

CARROLLTON

North Dallas Drug Rehabilitation Center
1606 South I-35
Suite 101
Carrollton, TX 75006

CENTER

Alcohol and Drug Abuse Council of Deep East Texas
114 Hurst Street
Center, TX 75935

CENTER CITY

Starlite Village Hospital Substance Abuse Services
Elm Pass Road
Center Point, TX 78010

CHILTON

Chilton House
4006 Street
Chilton, TX 76632

CLARKSVILLE

Northeast Texas Council on Alcohol and Drug Abuse
200 Walnut Road
Clarksville, TX 75426

CLEBURNE

Helping Open Peoples Eyes, Inc.
1800 Ridgemar Street
Cleburne, TX 76031

Outpatient
619 North Main Street
Cleburne, TX 76031-0162

Huguley Psychotherapy Clinic
214 North Caddo Street
Cleburne, TX 76031

Johnson/Ellis/Navarro MH/MR Services
1601 North Anglin Street
Cleburne, TX 76031

COLLEGE STATION

Scott and White Regional Clinic Alcohol and Drug Dependency Outpatient Treatment Program
702University Drive
Suite 100 D
College Station, TX 77840

COLORADO CITY

Permian Basin Rehabilitation House, Inc. Clover House Circuit Rider
Mitchell County Courthouse
349 Oak Street
Colorado City, TX 79512

COLUMBUS

Colorado County Youth/Family Servs Inc
1336 Fannin Street
Columbus, TX 78934

CONROE

Continuum Health Care Systems Texas Serenity Counseling Service
240 South Main Street
Conroe, TX 77301

Texas Serenity Whitehouse
3201 North Frazier Street
Conroe, TX 77301

CORPUS CHRISTI

Bay Area Health Care Group, Ltd. Columbia Counseling Center
6629 Woolridge Street
Corpus Christi, TX 78414

Charter Behavioral Health Systems
3126 Rodd Field Road
Corpus Christi, TX 78414

Coastal Bend Alcohol/Drug Rehab Center
25 North Country Club Place
Corpus Christi, TX 78407

Henderson House
38 North Country Club Place
Corpus Christi, TX 78407

Ivy House
41 North Country Club Place
Corpus Christi, TX 78407

Coastal Bend Outpatient Services
1201 Agnes Road
Corpus Christi, TX 78401

Corpus Christi Regional Center for
Addictions, Inc. Bay Area Care
5230 Kostoryz Road, Suite 5B
Corpus Christi, TX 78415

Counseling and Assistance Center
Naval Hospital
10651 East Street
Corpus Christi, TX 78419

Spohn Memorial Hospital Behavioral Medicine Department
2606 Hospital Boulevard
Corpus Christi, TX 78405-1818

Council on Alcohol and Drug Abuse/Coastal Bend
1201 3rd Street
Corpus Christi, TX 78404

CORSICANA

Corsicana State Home
West 2 Avenue
Corsicana, TX 75110

Helping Open Peoples Eyes, Inc.(HOPE)
300 West 3rd Street
Corsicana, TX 75110

Johnson/Ellis/Navarro MH/MR Services
800 North Main Street
Corsicana, TX 75110

COTULLA

South Texas Rural Health Services, Inc.
304 Nueces Street
Cotulla, TX 78014

CROCKETT

Community Rehabilitation Professional Services, Inc.
110 North 2nd Street
County Courthouse Annex
Crockett, TX 75835

DALHART

69th Judicial District CSCD
5th and Denver Street
Courthouse Annex, Suite 5
Dalhart, TX 79022

DALLAS

Adapt Behavioral Healthcare
4225 Office Parkway
Dallas, TX 75204

Addicare Group of Texas Zenith Program
4300 North Central Expressway
Suite G-100
Dallas, TX 75206

Addiction Counseling Associates
6220 Gaston Avenue, Suite 405
Dallas, TX 75214

Alameda Heights Outreach Center
2721 Lyola Street
Dallas, TX 75241

Alliance Life Centers
13999 Goldmark Street, Suite 343
Dallas, TX 75240

Baylor University Medical Center Baylor Center for Addictive Diseases
3500 Gaston Avenue
Collias Hospital
Dallas, TX 75246

Catholic Charities Adolescent and Family Services
325 West 12th Street
Dallas, TX 75208

Community Alcohol/Drug Aftercare Housing Program
3200 S Lancaster
Kiest Shopping Center, Suite 509
Dallas, TX 75216

Cornell Corrections
3606 Maple Avenue
Dallas, TX 75219

D/Boy Counseling Center
5215 Lawnview Avenue
Dallas, TX 75227

Dallas County Juvenile Department
2600 Lone Star Drive
Dallas, TX 75212

Dallas Inter/Tribal Center
209 East Jefferson Boulevard
Dallas, TX 75203

Daytop Dallas Drug Treatment Program
2345 Reagan Street
Dallas, TX 75219

East Dallas Counseling Center
4306 Bryan Street
Dallas, TX 75204

Ethel Daniels Foundation, Inc.
Outpatient Services
1900 North Prairie Street
Dallas, TX 75206

First Step Counseling Center
13610 Midway Road
Suite 421
Dallas, TX 75208

Gateway Foundation Help Is Possible Project
723 South Peak Street
Dallas, TX 75223

Green Oaks at Medical City
7808 Clodus Fields Drive
Dallas, TX 75251

Holmes Street Foundation, Inc.
Adolescent Residential
2719 Holmes Street
Dallas, TX 75209

Outpatient Program
2606 Martin Luther King Jr.
  Boulevard
Suite 202
Dallas, TX 75215

Homeward Bound, Inc. Trinity Recovery Center
233 West 10th Street
Dallas, TX 75215

La Sima Foundation
777 R. L. Thornton Freeway
Suite 106
Dallas, TX 75209

Miracle Network, Inc.
1266 East Ledbetter Drive
Dallas, TX 75216

New Place, The
4301 Bryan Street
Suite 120
Dallas, TX 75204

Nexus Recovery Center
Adult and Adolescent Specialized
  Female Residential Program
Women and Children Residential
  Program
8733 La Prada Drive
Dallas, TX 75228

Nexus Outreach Center
2519 Oaklawn Avenue
Dallas, TX 75219

North Texas Health Care System
4500 South Lancaster Road
Dallas, TX 75216

Oak Lawn Community Services
4300 MacArthur Street
Dallas, TX 75209

One Day At A Time Ministries Outpatient Counseling Center
2702 South Buckner Boulevard
Dallas, TX 75227

Our Brothers Keeper/NDUGU
4200 South Fitzhugh Street
Dallas, TX 75210

Permanente Medical Association of Texas Kaiser Permanente Chemical Dependency Treatment Program
9250 Amberton Parkway
Dallas, TX 75243

Phoenix Project, Inc.
201 South Tyler Street
Dallas, TX 75208

Recovery First
9202-B Markville Drive
Dallas, TX 75243

Recovery Healthcare Corporation
2530 Electronic Lane, Suite 707
Dallas, TX 75220

Right Alternatives for People, Inc.
401 Wynnewood Village
Suite 104
Dallas, TX 75224

Road to Recovery Chemical Dependency Program
8350 Meadow Road, Suite 268
Dallas, TX 75231

Saint Paul Medical Center Chemical Dependency Recovery Services
5909 Harry Hines Boulevard
Dallas, TX 75235

Salud Counseling Services
2760 West Davis Street
Dallas, TX 75211

Salvation Army Social Service Center Substance Abuse Services Program
5302 Harry Hines Boulevard
Dallas, TX 75235

Step Med
1705 Martin Luther King Jr.
  Boulevard
Suite E
Dallas, TX 75215-3222

Timberlawn Mental Health Systems
4600 Samuell Boulevard
Dallas, TX 75227

Turtle Creek Manor, Inc.
2707 Routh Street
Dallas, TX 75201

Outpatient Services
2506 Cedar Springs Street
Dallas, TX 75201

Welcome House, Inc.
921 North Peak Street
Dallas, TX 75204

DAYTON

Key Program Lonestar/Dempsey Henley Unit
Highway 321
5 Miles North of Dayton Street
Dayton, TX 77535

DEER PARK

Cenikor Foundation, Inc. Substance Abuse Program
4525 Glenwood Avenue
Deer Park, TX 77536

DEL RIO

Alliance Behavioral Health Services, Inc. Excel Adolescent Program
902 South Main Street, Suite G
Del Rio, TX 78840

DENISON

Drug Recovery Center
330 Highway 69-E
Denison, TX 75021

DENTON

Denton County MH/MR Center Intensive Outpatient Substance Abuse Treatment Program
2519 Scripture Street
Denton, TX 76201

Starting Over, Inc.
531 Londonderry Lane Suite 100
Denton, TX 76205

DE SOTO

Haven Behavioral Health System
800 Kirnwood Drive

Lakeview Southwest, Inc. DBA Cedars Hospital
2000 North Old Hickory Trail
De Soto, TX 75115

DICKINSON

Bay Area Recovery Center
4316 Washington Street
Dickinson, TX 77539

1807 Pine Drive
Dickinson, TX 77539

Omega/Alpha House Women's Center
1122 Farm Market Road
Suite 517
Dickinson, TX 77539

DRISCOLL

Coastal Bend Youth City Substance Abuse Program
2547 U.S. Highway 77
Driscoll, TX 78351

DUMAS

69th Judicial District CSCD
810 South Dumas Avenue
Suite 416
Dumas, TX 79029

DYESS AFB

Dyess Air Force Base Substance Abuse Program
7 MDOS/SGOMH
597 Hospital Loop
Dyess AFB, TX 79607-1442

EAGLE PASS

Alliance Behavioral Health Services, Inc. Excel Adolescent Program
2315 Hillcrest Street
Eagle Pass, TX 78852

EDINBURG

Areas Management Information Systems Amistad Alcohol and Drug Treatment
1401 South 9th Street
Edinburg, TX 78540

Rio Grande Valley Council on Alcohol and Drug Abuse
3511 West Alberta Street
Edinburg, TX 78539

Tropical Texas Center for MH/MR Outpatient Substance Abuse Services
1901 South 24 Street
Edinburg, TX 78539

ELGIN

Twin Oaks Adolescent Center, Inc.
701 North Highway 95
Elgin, TX 78621

EL PASO

Aliviane NO/AD, Inc.
7722 North Loop Street
El Paso, TX 79915

Adolescent Day Treatment
7580 Alameda Street
Building 1 Space 3
El Paso, TX 79915

Inner Resources Women's/ Children's Residential Center
11960 Golden Gate Road
El Paso, TX 79936

Inner Resources Recovery Center
10690 Socorro Road
El Paso, TX 79927

Outpatient Clinic
5160B El Paso Drive
El Paso, TX 79905

Alliance Behavioral Health Services, Inc. Excel Adolescent Program
4919 Hondo Pass
El Paso, TX 79903

Drug Abuse Service Center
5160 El Paso Drive
El Paso, TX 79905

El Paso Methadone Maintenance and Detox Treatment Center
5004 Alameda Avenue
El Paso, TX 79905

El Paso Psychiatric Association Alternatives Center
5001 Alabama Street
El Paso, TX 79930

Life Management Center for MH/MR Services
Casa Blanca Therapeutic Communities
600 Newman Street
El Paso, TX 79902

Ocotillo
5304 El Paso Drive
El Paso, TX 79905

Serenity Outpatient Services, Inc.
4625 Alabama Street
El Paso, TX 79930

Tigua Indian Reservation Ysleta del Sur Pueblo Substance Abuse Program
119 South Old Pueblo Drive
El Paso, TX 79907

Veterans' Affairs Substance Abuse Treatment Program
5001 North Piedras Street
El Paso, TX 79925

William Beaumont Army Medical Center Residential Treatment Facility
10 West 5005 Piedras Street
El Paso, TX 79920-5001

EULESS

American Indian Center
2219 West Euless Boulevard
Euless, TX 76040

FALFURRIAS

Alice Counseling Center Rural Youth Treatment
217 East Miller Street
Falfurrias, TX 78355

FLORESVILLE

Brush Country COADA Supportive Outpatient Program
3190 State Highway 97 East
Floresville, TX 78114

FORT BLISS

Alcohol and Drug Abuse and Control Program
1733 Pleasanton Road
Fort Bliss, TX 79916-6816

FORT DAVIS

Clover House, Inc. Circuit Rider
Jeff Davis County Courthouse
Court and Main Street
Fort Davis, TX 79734

FORT WORTH

All Saints Episcopal Hospital Recovery Place
1400 8th Avenue
Fort Worth, TX 76104

Cenikor Foundation, Inc. North Texas Facility
2209 South Main Street
Fort Worth, TX 76110

Family Service, Inc. Substance Abuse Treatment
1424 Hemphill Street
Fort Worth, TX 76104

North Texas Addiction Counseling, Inc.
909 West Magnolia Street, Suite 2
Fort Worth, TX 76104

Permanente Medical Association of Texas Kaiser Permanente Chemical Dependency Treatment Program
1300 South University Drive
Fort Worth, TX 76104

Phoenix Associates Counseling Services
3001-A West 5th Street
Fort Worth, TX 76107

Salvation Army
First Choice Program
2110 Hemphill Street
Fort Worth, TX 76110

Santa Fe Counseling Center, Inc. Adolescent Services
3122 East Rosedale Street
Fort Worth, TX 76105

Tarrant County Medical Education and Research Foundation
Outpatient
904 Southland Avenue
Fort Worth, TX 76104

Volunteers of America Northern Texas, Inc.
2710 Avenue J
Fort Worth, TX 76105

Gemini House South
4700 South Riverside Street
Fort Worth, TX 76119

Western Clinical Health Services Pennsylvania Avenue Clinic
514 Pennsylvania Avenue
Fort Worth, TX 76104

FREEPORT

Brazoria County Alcohol Recovery Center Brazos Place
11034 North Avenue H
Freeport, TX 77541

GAINESVILLE

Cooke County Mental Health Center
301 West Main Street
Gainesville, TX 76240

Texas Youth Commission
Gainesville State School
4701 East Farm Road
Suite 678
Gainesville, TX 76240

GALVESTON

Alcohol and Drug Abuse Women's Center, Inc.
201 1st Street
Galveston, TX 77550

Dual Recovery
Galveston, TX 77550

Family Opportunity Resources
6000 Broadway Street Suite 106-R
Galveston, TX 77551

Galveston Recovery Program
123 Rosenberg Street
Galveston, TX 77550

Gulf Coast Center
123 Rosenberg Street, Suite 6
Galveston, TX 77550

New Horizons Center
728 Church Street
Galveston, TX 77550

Recovery Campuses of Texas, Inc.
2216 Avenue O
Galveston, TX 77550

Recovery Center, Inc.
3205 Avenue O
Galveston, TX 77550-6861

Turning Point
801 37th Street
Galveston, TX 77550

GARLAND

D. Gonzalez and Associates
2848 West Kingsley Road
Suite B
Garland, TX 75041

Garland Community Hospital
Behavioral Medicine Services
2696 West Walnut Street
Garland, TX 75042

Wellness Center
2636 West Walnut Street
Garland, TX 75042

Garland Treatment Center
6246 Broadway Street, Suite 102
Garland, TX 75043

GATESVILLE

Gateway Foundation Texas Hackberry SAFP Facility
1401 State School Road
Gatesville, TX 76528

GEORGETOWN

Center for Addiction Recovery and Education
107 Halmar Cove
Georgetown, TX 78628

Cornerstone Counseling
504-B Leander Road
Georgetown, TX 78628

GOODFELLOW AFB

Goodfellow Air Force Base Substance Abuse Program
17 MDOS/SGOKB
143 Ft Lancaster Avenue
Building 143
Goodfellow AFB, TX 76908

GRAPEVINE

Charter Grapevine Behavioral Health System
2300 William D Tate Street
Grapevine, TX 76051

GREENVILLE

Glen Oaks Hospital
301 East Division Street
Greenville, TX 75401

Green Villa
733 IH 30 East
Greenville, TX 75401

Tarrant Community Outreach, Inc. Faces of Reality Counseling Center
2901 Lee Street
Greenville, TX 75403-1097

HARLINGEN

Rio Grande Valley Council on Alcohol and Drug Abuse
2308 South 77 Sunshine Strip
Harlingen, TX 78550

Tropical Texas Center for Mental Health/Mental Retardation Services
1242 North 77 Sunshine Strip
Harlingen, TX 78550

HEBRONVILLE

Stop Child Abuse and Neglect, Inc. Stand Outpatient Program
707 South Smith Street
Hebbronville, TX 78361

HEMPSTEAD

Brazos Valley Council on Alcohol and Drug Abuse
Walker County Corrections
925 5th Street
Hempstead, TX 77445

HENDERSON

Sabine Valley Center
Regional Substance Abuse
Recovery Center
209 North Main Street
Henderson, TX 75652

HOUSTON

Association for the Advancement of Mexican Americans (AAMA)
Region 6 Youth COADA
6001 Gulf Freeway Building C-1
Houston, TX 77023

AAMA/Campus
4514 Lyons Avenue
Houston, TX 77020

Better Way Inc
4802 Caroline Street
Houston, TX 77004

Bay Area Council on Drugs and Alcohol
1300 Bay Area Boulevard
Houston, TX 77058

Bayon City Medical Center South Campus Psychiatric Services
6700 Bellaire Boulevard
Houston, TX 77074

Best Recovery Health Care
9211 South Main Street
Houston, TX 77025

Blues Management, Inc. Dapa Recovery Program
7447 Harwin Street, Suite 212-B
Houston, TX 77036

Boundaries Counseling Center
9725 1/2 Lou Edd Street
Houston, TX 77070

Browns Education and Recovery
9000 West Bellfort Street
Suite 325
Houston, TX 77031

**Career and Recovery Alternative
Drug Abuse Treatment
Program**
2525 San Jacinto Street
Houston, TX 77002

Center for Recovering Families
2620 Fountain View Drive
Suite 480
Houston, TX 77057-7621

Cheyenne Center
9100 Dodson Street
Houston, TX 77093-7148

**Chicano Family Center
Substance Abuse Program**
7524 Avenue E
Houston, TX 77012

**Child and Adolescent
Development, Inc. Adolescent
Residential**
2505 Southmore Street
Houston, TX 77004

Clear Lake Counseling Services
17000 El Camino Real Street
Suite 104-C
Houston, TX 77058

**Cornell Corrections Ben A. Reid
Facility**
10950 Beaumont Highway
Houston, TX 77078

**Cypress Creek Hospital
Substance Abuse Services**
17750 Cali Street
Houston, TX 77090

De Pelchin Children's Center
Montgomery County Satellite
100 Sandman Street
Houston, TX 77007

Outpatient Services
3214 Austin Street
Houston, TX 77004

Door to Recovery
4910 Dacoma Street
Houston, TX 77092

2005 Jacquelyn Drive
Houston, TX 77055

7605 Denton Street
Houston, TX 77028

Intensive Residential Unit
638 Harbor Road
Houston, TX 77092

**Dr. Crismon and Associates,
Inc.**
4625 North Freeway, Suite 150
Houston, TX 77022-2913

Easy Does It, Inc.
6630 Harwin Street, Suite 225
Houston, TX 77036

Extended Aftercare, Inc.
5002 North Shepard Street
Houston, TX 77018

**Families Under Urban and
Social Attack**
2206 Dowling Street Suite 201
Houston, TX 77288-0107

6719 West Montgomery Street
Houston, TX 77091

Family Service Center
4615 Lillian Street
Suite 101
Houston, TX 77087

**Forest Springs Residential
Treatment Center**
1120 Cypress Station
Houston, TX 77090

**Fulfillment Foundation Prospect
House**
309 West 27th Street
Houston, TX 77008

Gulf Shores Academy, Inc.
11300 South Post Oak Street
Suite 1
Houston, TX 77038

**Harris County Dual Disorders
Project**
2627 Caroline Street
Houston, TX 77004

New Directions Women's Program
2502 Fannin Street
Houston, TX 77002

Houston Aftercare, Inc.
407 Welch Street
Houston, TX 77006-1307

2004 Crocker Street
Houston, TX 77006

**Houston Maintenance Clinic,
Inc.**
4900 Fannin Street, Suite 201
Houston, TX 77004

Houston New Start Inc
9219 Katy Freeway Suit 291
Houston, TX 77024

Houston Substance Abuse Clinic
7428 Park Place Boulevard
Houston, TX 77087

Journey Program Inc
9219 Katy Freeway, Suite 291
Houston, TX 77024

Lifeway
6251 Corporate Drive
Houston, TX 77036-3411

Mac House, Inc.
3903 Hartsdale Street
Houston, TX 77063

Make Ready, Inc.
2405 Smith Street
Houston, TX 77006

**Memorial Hospital Southwest
Parkside Recovery Center**
7600 Beechnut Street, 10th Floor
Houston, TX 77074

Montrose Counseling Center
701 Richmond Avenue
Houston, TX 77006

Narcotics Withdrawal Center
4800 West 34th Street
Suite B3
Houston, TX 77092

New Directions Club, Inc.
607 Thornton Street
Houston, TX 77018

Odyssey House Texas, Inc.
5629 Grapevine Street
Houston, TX 77085

Oxford Counseling Center
4101 North Freeway
Suite 100
Houston, TX 77022

Pain Care Center
4543 Post Oak Place, Suite 106
Houston, TX 77027

Passages, Inc.
7722 Westview Drive
Houston, TX 77055

**Pollux House Addictions
    Foundation, Inc.**
4728 Gunter Street
Houston, TX 77020

Recovery Foundation, Inc.
4312 Crane Street
Houston, TX 77026-4802

**Recovery Houston Institute
    Choices Program**
10525 Eastex Freeway
Houston, TX 77093

Rehab Mission, Inc.
1701 Jacquelyn Street
Houston, TX 77055

Riverside Campus
4514 Lyons Avenue
Houston, TX 77020-5237

Riverside General Hospital
2905 Elgin Street
Houston, TX 77004

Jones Healthcare Center
7655 Bellfort Street
Houston, TX 77061

Total Care/Detox Unit
3204 Ennis Street
Houston, TX 77004

**S and S Counseling Services
    and Associates Incorporated**
9000 West Bellfort Street Suite
    570
Houston, TX 77031

Santa Maria Hostel, Inc.
807 Paschall Street
Houston, TX 77009

Set Free DAT Center
3333 Fannin Street, Suite 106
Houston, TX 77004

Sunrise Recovery Program
2611 Fm 1960 West
Houston, TX 77090

**Texas Alcoholism Foundation,
    Inc.**
Texas House Treatment Program
2208 West 34 Street
Houston, TX 77213

Texas Clinic/Fulton Street
6311 Fulton Street
Houston, TX 77022

Westview Drive
9320 Westview Drive
Suite 10
Houston, TX 77055

**Texas Serenity Counseling
    Service**
250 Meadow Fern Road Suite 100
Houston, TX 77067

Texas Treatment Center
4800 West 34th Street Suite B-3
Houston, TX 77092

Texas Treatment Center South
1050 Edgebrook Drive Suite 2
Houston, TX 77034

Toxicology Associates
530 North Belt Street
Suite 311
Houston, TX 77060

Turning Point
3600 South Gessner Street
Suite 248
Houston, TX 77063

**University of Texas Health
    Science Center**
Houston Recovery Campus
4514 Lyons Avenue
Houston, TX 77020

Substance Abuse Research Center
1300 Moursund Street
Houston, TX 77030

**Unlimited Visions Aftercare,
    Inc.**
5528 Lawndale Street
Houston, TX 77023

**Veterans' Affairs Substance
    Abuse Program**
2002 Holcombe Boulevard
Houston, TX 77030

Volunteers of America
Rogers Street Recovery Center
308 East Rogers Street
Houston, TX 77022

2141 Bingle Street
Houston, TX 77001

**West Oaks Hospital, Inc.
    Chemical Dependency
    Services**
6500 Hornwood Drive
Houston, TX 77074

HUMBLE

**Door to Recovery Montgomery
    County**
1220 Stone Hollow Drive
Humble, TX 77339

HUNT

La Hacienda Treatment Center
FM 1340
Hunt, TX 78024

HUNTSVILLE

**Dual Diagnosis Treatment
    Program**
21016 South Sam Houston Street
Huntsville, TX 77340

Gateway Foundation
Estelle Unit/SAFP Facility
Huntsville, TX 77340

Jester Unit 1
1600 Financial Plaza, Suite 370
Huntsville, TX 77340

**Hunstville Alcohol/Drug Abuse
    Program**
115 North Highway 75
Huntsville, TX 77340

Hunstville Clinic, Inc.
829 10th Street
Huntsville, TX 77340

**Montgomery/Walker County
COADA Right Start Youth**
526 11th Street
Huntsville, TX 77340

HURST

**Tarrant County MH/MR
Services Addiction Recovery
Center**
129 Harmon Road
Hurst, TX 76053

HUTCHINS

**Volunteers of America Northern
Texas, Inc. Perry F Bradley
Center**
800 West Wintergreen Road
Hutchins, TX 75141

IRVING

New Vision Teen Center
220 West Irving Boulevard
Irving, TX 75060

**Irving Christian Counseling
Centers**
2621 West Airport Freeway
Suite 124
Irving, TX 75062-6069

**Remedy Addictions Counselors
(RAC), Inc.**
317 East Airport Freeway
Irving, TX 75062

West Texas Counseling of Irving
2001 West Airport Freeway
Suite 113
Irving, TX 75062

JACKSONVILLE

**Community Rehabilitation
Professional Services, Inc.**
514 East Commerce Street
Jacksonville, TX 75766

**Sabine Valley Center The
Beginning/Regional Substance
Abuse Recovery Center**
903 South Jackson Street
Jacksonville, TX 75766

KELLY AFB

**Alcohol and Drug Abuse
Prevention and Treatment
Program**
76 AMDS/SGPH
1014 Billy Mitchell Boulevard
Suite 2
Kelley AFB, TX 78241-5604

**Kelly Air Force Base Substance
Abuse Program**
76 MDOS-SGOMH
144 Armistad Circle, Suite 2
Kelly AFB, TX 78241-5846

KERRVILLE

**Hill Country Independence
House**
976 Barnett Street
Kerrville, TX 78028

Kimberlite Cottage
324 Clay Street
Kerrville, TX 78028

**South Texas Veterans Health
Care System Substance Abuse
Treatment**
3600 Memorial Boulevard
Kerrville, TX 78028

Treatment Associates
712 Barnett Street
Kerrville, TX 78028-4520

KINGWOOD

**Charter Hospital of Kingwood
Inpatient Unit**
2001 Ladbrook Drive
Kingwood, TX 77339

KOUNTZE

Life Resource/Hardin County
Highway 326
Kountze, TX 77625

KYLE

**Wackenhut Corrections
Corporation New Vision**
701 South IH 35
Kyle, TX 78640

LACKLAND AFB

**Lackland AFB Alcohol and
Drug Abuse Prevention and
Treatment Program**
59 MDW/MMCNS
2220 Berguist Drive, Suite 1
Lackland AFB, TX 78236-5300

**Wilford Hall Medical Center
Substance Abuse Services/
MMPWS**
2289 McChord Street
Building 1355
Lackland AFB, TX 78236-5300

LAKE JACKSON

**Brazosport Memorial Hospital
Alpha Center**
100 Medical Drive
Lake Jackson, TX 77566

LA MARQUE

**Bay Area Council on Drugs and
Alcohol, Inc.**
1101 Delmar Street, Suite 9
La Marque, TX 77568

Toxicology Associates
2411 Franklin Street
La Marque, TX 77568

LAMESA

**Permian Basin Rehabilitation
House, Inc. Clover House
Circuit Rider**
609 North 1st Street
Lamesa, TX 79331

LAREDO

**Association for the
Advancement of Mexican
Americans**
Buena Salud
2305 Ventura Street
Laredo, TX 78040

Concilio Hispano Libre
1205 East Hillside Street
Laredo, TX 78041

Mi Tierra South Texas Council on Alcohol/Drug Abuse
2520 Lane Street
Laredo, TX 78040

South Texas COADA
1502 Laredo Street, Suite 2
Laredo, TX 78040

Stop Child Abuse and Neglect, Inc.
Raices Residential Program
4600 South Zapata Highway
Laredo, TX 78042

Stand Outpatient Program
1901 La Pita Mangana Road
Laredo, TX 78043

2387 East Sanders Street
Laredo, TX 78041-5434

LAUGHLIN AFB

Laughlin Air Force Base Substance Abuse Program
47 MDOS/SGOMH
590 Mitchell Boulevard
Laughlin AFB, TX 78840-5244

LEAGUE CITY

Devereux Texas Treatment Network
Devereux Intensive Outpatient Chemical Dependency Program
1150 Devereux Drive
League City, TX 77573

Neurobehavioral Institute of Texas
Helena House
2605 Austin Street
League City, TX 77573

LEWISVILLE

Medical City Dallas, Inc. Columbia Green Oaks Behavioral Health Services
475 West Elm Street Suite 100
Lewisville, TX 75057

LIVERPOOL

Door to Recovery III on the Bayou
638 Harbor Road
Liverpool, TX 77577

LIVINGSTON

Alcohol and Drug Abuse Council of Deep East Texas
Courthouse
Livingston, TX 77351

LOCKHART

Hayes Caldwell Council on ADA
216 West San Antonio Street
Lockhart, TX 78644-2807

LONGVIEW

East Texas Clinic
201 Pine Tree Road
Longview, TX 75604

Kirkpatrick Family Center
1411 North 10th Street, Suite 1
Longview, TX 75601

Woodbine Treatment Center
9111 Pegues Place
Longview, TX 75608

LUBBOCK

Canyon Lakes Residential Treatment Center, Inc. Supportive Adolescent Services
2402 Canyon Lake Drive
Lubbock, TX 79415

Charter Plains Behavioral Health Services
801 North Quaker Avenue
Lubbock, TX 79416

Lubbock Faith Center, Inc.
Center Recovery Program
2809 Clovis Road
Lubbock, TX 79415

Lubbock Regional MH/MR Center
Billy Meeks Addiction Center
1601 Vanda Avenue
Lubbock, TX 79401

Lubbock Regional MH/MR Center Project Hope
1202 Main Street
Lubbock, TX 79401

Methadone Clinic
14 Briercroft Office Park
Lubbock, TX 79402

The Ranch
3201 East Kent Street
Lubbock, TX 79403

Managed Care Center for Addictive and Other Disorders
1705 North Farm Market Road 179
Lubbock, TX 79416

1926 34th Street
Lubbock, TX 79411

Texas Tech University Health Sciences Center Southwest Institute for Addictive Diseases
Department of Psychiatry
3601 4th Street
Lubbock, TX 79410

Walker House
1614 Avenue K
Lubbock, TX 79401

LUFKIN

Alcohol and Drug Abuse Council of Deep East Texas
304 North Raguet Street
Lufkin, TX 75901

Burke Center
Peavy Switch Recovery Center
Route 5
Lufkin, TX 75901

Adolescent Center
2303 North Raguet Street
Lufkin, TX 75901

LYTLE

Las Manos Community Mental Health Center
18325 IH-35 South
Lytle, TX 78052

MARSHALL

Azleway, Inc.
Azleway Boys Ranch
411 West Burleson Street
Marshall, TX 75670

**Choices Adolescent Treatment
Center**
4521 Karnack Highway
Marshall, TX 75670

Grove/Moore Center
401 North Grove Street
Marshall, TX 75670

Oak Haven Recovery Center
Highway 154
Marshall, TX 75670

MCALLEN

**Charter Palms Behavioral
Health Services**
1421 East Jackson Avenue
McAllen, TX 78503

**Kids in Development Services,
Inc. Pasos at Taylor Ranch**
4 1/2 Miles North Taylor Road
McAllen, TX 78501

**Rio Grande Valley Family
Recovery Center**
5401 North 10th Street, Suite 128
McAllen, TX 78504-2759

Treatment Associates
805 East Esperanza Street
McAllen, TX 78501

MCKINNEY

Collin County MH/MR Center
825 North McDonald Street
McKinney, TX 75069

MENARD

**West Texas Recovery Center
Menard County Courthouse**
210 East San Saba Street
Menard, TX 76859

MIDLAND

**Court Residential Treatment
Center**
215 West Industrial Avenue
Midland, TX 79702

Desert Springs Medical Center
3300 South FM 1788
Midland, TX 79711

Palmer Drug Abuse Program
413 North Baird Street
Midland, TX 79701

**Permian Basin Community
Centers for Mental Health/
Mental Retardation**
Project Proud
606 North Weatherford Street
Midland, TX 79701

**West Texas Counseling and
Rehabilitation Program**
1802 West Wall Street
Midland, TX 79701

MINEOLA

**Andrews Center Substance
Abuse Services**
703 West Patton Street
Mineola, TX 75773

MINERAL WELLS

Helping Open Peoples Eyes, Inc.
319 North Oak Street
Mineral Wells, TX 76068

MOUNT PLEASANT

**Sabine Valley Center The
Beginning/Regional Substance
Abuse Recovery Center**
107 East 11th Street
Mount Pleasant, TX 75455

NACOGDOCHES

**Alcohol and Drug Abuse
Council of Deep East Texas**
1329 North University Drive
Nacogdoches, TX 75961

**Community Rehabilitation
Professional Services, Inc.**
206 West Pillar Street
Nacogdoches, TX 75961

ODESSA

Permian Basin Rehab
406 North Texas Street
Odessa, TX 79761

700 North Dixie Street
Odessa, TX 79761

Project Elizabeth
620 South Grant Street
Odessa, TX 79761

TTC Circuit Rider
300 North Jackson Street
Odessa, TX 79761

Turning Point
2000 Maurice Road
Odessa, TX 79763

ORANGE

**Life Resource/A CMHC
Substance Abuse Services**
4303 North Tejas Parkway
Orange, TX 77630

PALESTINE

**Daytop Pine Mountain
Residential**
Route 3
Palestine, TX 75801

PALO PINTO

Helping Open Peoples Eyes, Inc.
503 Oak Street
Palo Pinto, TX 76484

PAMPA

Genesis House, Inc.
Administrative Unit
615 West Buckler Street
Pampa, TX 79066

Genesis House for Boys
600 West Browning Street
Pampa, TX 79065

Genesis House for Girls
420 North Ward Street
Pampa, TX 79066

PARIS

Northeast Texas Council on Alcohol and Drug Abuse Bright Futures Integrated Treatment Program
136 Grand Avenue
Paris, TX 75460

Saint Josephs Hospital and Health Center Behavioral Medicine Services
820 Clarksville Street
Paris, TX 75460

PASADENA

Bay Area Council on Drugs and Alcohol
1149 West Elsworth Street
Suite 145
Pasadena, TX 77501

Houston Substance Abuse Clinic
5825 Spencer Highway
Pasadena, TX 77505

PHARR

Self and Family Empowerment Zone
1899 North Cage Street, Suite B-2
Pharr, TX 78577

PLAINVIEW

Central Plains Center for MH/MR and Substance Abuse
2700 Yonkers Street
Plainview, TX 79072

Institute for Adolescent Addictions
404 Floydada Street
Plainview, TX 79072

Plainview Women's Center
700 Borger Street
Plainview, TX 79072

W. W. Allen Treatment Center
715 Houston Street
Plainview, TX 79072

Methodist Hospital Plainview Lonetree Recovery Center
2601 Dimmitt Road
Plainview, TX 79072

Serenity Center, Inc.
806 El Paso Street
Plainview, TX 79072

PLANO

Collin County MH/MR Center Plano Clinic
3920 Alma Drive
Plano, TX 75023

Green Oaks Behavior Healthcare
3801 West 15th Street, Suite 320
Plano, TX 75075

New Place, The
221 West Parker Road, Suite 510
Plano, TX 75023

Presbyterian Hospital of Plano
Seay Behavioral Healthcare Center
6110 West Parker Road
Plano, TX 75093

PLEASANTON

Brush Country COADA Supportive Outpatient Program
1085 FM 3006
Pleasanton, TX 78064

PORT ARTHUR

Best Recovery Health Care, Inc.
509 9th Avenue
Port Arthur, TX 77642

Life Resource South County Alcohol and Drug Treatment
3401 57th Street
Port Arthur, TX 77640

PORT NECHES

Patch of Jefferson County, Inc.
1227 Dallas Street
Port Neches, TX 77651

PRESIDIO

Clover House, Inc. Circuit Rider
Court House Annex
O Riley Street
Presidio, TX 79845

RANDOLPH AFB

Randolph Air Force Base ADAPT Program
12 MDOS/SGOMH
221 3rd Street West
Randolph AFB, TX 78150

RANKIN

Permian Basin Rehabilitation House, Inc. Clover House
205 East 10th Street
Rankin, TX 79778

RICHARDSON

Baylor/Richardson Medical Center Mental Health Services
401 West Campbell Road
Richardson, TX 75080

Paul Meier New Life Clinic
2071 North Collins Boulevard
Richardson, TX 75080

Turning Point Counseling Center
1701 North Greenville Avenue
Suite 701
Richardson, TX 75081-1852

RIO GRANDE CITY

STCADA Outpatient Level IV
105 Lopez Street
Rio Grande City, TX 78582

Stop Child Abuse and Neglect, Inc. Stand Outpatient Program
102 North Lopez Street
Rio Grande City, TX 78582

SAN ANGELO

Court Residential Treatment Center
3398 McGill Street
San Angelo, TX 76905

River Crest Hospital
1636 Hunters Glen Street
San Angelo, TX 76901

Shannon Medical Center
2018 Pulliam Street
San Angelo, TX 76905

West Texas Counseling and Rehabilitation Program
601 South Irving Street, Suite 4
San Angelo, TX 76903

West Texas Recovery Center
232 West Beauregard Road
Suite 101
San Angelo, TX 76903

SAN ANTONIO

Alamo Area Dual Diagnosis Expansion Project The Center for Health Care Services
3031 IH 10 West
San Antonio, TX 78201

Alamo Mental Health Group, Inc. Spectrum
5115 Medical Drive
Building G
San Antonio, TX 78229

Alamo Recovery Center
1018 Grayson Street
San Antonio, TX 78208

2821 Guadalupe Street, Suite 108
San Antonio, TX 78207

Alpha Home, Inc.
300 East Mulberry Avenue
San Antonio, TX 78212

Baptist Medical Center Baptist Recovery Center
111 Dallas Street
San Antonio, TX 78205

Brooks Air Force Base Counseling Services
8005 Lindbergh Drive
San Antonio, TX 78235

Center for Health Care Services
IH 10 West Unit
3031 IH 10 West
San Antonio, TX 78201

Charter Behavioral Health System
8550 Huebner Road
San Antonio, TX 78240

City of San Antonio Metropolitan Health District
332 West Commerce Street
San Antonio, TX 78210-3845

Community Counseling Center
MCHE 5YA Building
142 Stanley Road
San Antonio, TX 78234-6327

Drug Dependence Associates
3701 West Commerce Street
San Antonio, TX 78207

Inman Christian Center
Residential Treatment Center
18952 Redland Road
San Antonio, TX 78259

Youth Counseling Center
1014 South San Jacinto Street
San Antonio, TX 78207

Lackland Air Force Base Substance Abuse Clinic
Building 1355
San Antonio, TX 78236

Mission Vista Behavioral Health System
14747 Jones Maltsberger Street
San Antonio, TX 78247-3713

Patrician Movement
263 Felisa Street
San Antonio, TX 78210

Site 1/Residential
222 East Mitchell Street
San Antonio, TX 78210

Site 3/Outpatient Treatment Program
215 Claudia Street
San Antonio, TX 78210

Site 5/Outpatient Treatment Program
528 South Polaris Street
San Antonio, TX 78203

River City Rehabilitation Center, Inc.
680 Stonewall Street
San Antonio, TX 78214

San Antonio Regional Hospital Chemical Dependency Program
8026 Floyd Curl Drive
San Antonio, TX 78229

South Texas Veterans Health Care System Substance Abuse Treatment
7400 Merton Minter Boulevard
San Antonio, TX 78284

Southwest Mental Health Center
2939 West Woodlawn Avenue
San Antonio, TX 78228

Tejas Recovery and Counseling Services
7418 West Military Drive
San Antonio, TX 78227-2949

Treatment Associates of San Antonio
410 South Main Street, Suite 202
San Antonio, TX 78204

SAN DIEGO

Key Program Lonestar/ Glossbrenner Unit
623 South Fm 1329
San Diego, TX 78384

SAN MARCOS

Counseling Network
174 South Guadalupe Street
Suite 200
San Marcos, TX 78666

Hays Caldwell Council on Alcohol and Drug Abuse
101 Uhland Road, Suite 113
San Marcos, TX 78666

SEGUIN

Guadalupe Valley Hospital Teddy Buerger Center for Alcohol/Drug Abuse
1215 East Court Street
Seguin, TX 78155

Treatment Associates of Seguin
504 North River Street
Seguin, TX 78155-4739

SHEPPARD AFB

Sheppard Air Force Base Substance Abuse Program
82 MDOS/SGOHA
149 Hart Street, Suite 5
Sheppard AFB, TX 76311-3482

SHERMAN

Alliance Life Centers
209 South Travis Street
Sherman, TX 75090

SINTON

Coastal Bend Regional Substance Abuse Treatment Facility
800 North Vineyard Street
Sinton, TX 78387

SMITHVILLE

Austin Recovery Center
Park Road Suite 1-C
Smithville, TX 78957

SPRING

Jamies House, Inc.
15919 Stuebner Airline Street
Spring, TX 77379

SPUR

Permian Basin Rehabilitation House, Inc.
Clover House White River Lindsey Place
HCR 2, Box 123
White River Lake
Spur, TX 79370

STAFFORD

Depelchin Children's Center
10435 Greenbough Street
Building 200
Stafford, TX 77477

STEPHENVILLE

Helping Open Peoples Eyes, Inc. (HOPE)
586 East Washington Street
Stephenville, TX 76402

Summer Sky, Inc. Chemical Dependency Treatment Center
1100 McCart Street
Stephenville, TX 76401

SULPHUR SPRINGS

Northeast Texas Council on Alcohol and Drug Abuse Outpatient Unit
954 Main Street
Sulphur Springs, TX 75482

TAFT

Shoreline, Inc.
1220 Gregory Street
Taft, TX 78390

TEMPLE

CEN/TEX Alcoholic Rehabilitation Center
2500 South General Bruce Drive
Temple, TX 76504

Central Texas Veterans Healthcare System Psychiatry Service
1901 South First Street
Temple, TX 76504

Christian Farms/Treehouse, Inc. Treehouse Women's Center
3804 Riverside Trail
Temple, TX 76502

Scott and White Santa Fe Center Alcohol and Drug Dependence Treatment Program
600 South 25 Street
Temple, TX 76503

TERRELL

Alliance Life Centers
809 West Nash Street
Terrell, TX 75160

Training andDevelopment Center of Terrell Employee Support Systems Company of Texas
211 East Moore Street
Terrell, TX 75160

TEXARKANA

Bowie County Addiction Counseling
1414 New Boston Road, Suite 101
Texarkana, TX 75501

Edge of Texas Recovery Center
519 Oak Street
Texarkana, TX 75501

Hazel Street Recovery Center
1217 Hazel Street
Texarkana, TX 75501

Red River Council on Alcohol and Drug Abuse
Dowd House
2101 Dudley Avenue
Texarkana, TX 75502

Sabine Valley Center The Beginning/Regional Substance Abuse Recovery Center
911 North Bishop Street
Texarkana, TX 75501

TEXAS CITY

Alcohol Drug Abuse Women's Center, Inc.
712 5 Avenue North
Texas City, TX 77590

Gulf Coast Center Mainland Recovery Program
8900 Emmett Lowry Expressway
Suite 103
Texas City, TX 77591-2103

TOMBALL

Tomball College Counseling Institute Substance Abuse Services
30555 Tomball Parkway
Tomball, TX 77375

TULIA

Driskill Halfway House
1202 Highway 87 North
Tulia, TX 79088

TYLER

Azleway Inc.
1203 North Broadway
Tyler, TX 75702

Azleway Boys Ranch
15892 County Road 26
Tyler, TX 75707

Beginning, The
4717 Troup Highway
Tyler, TX 75701

East Texas Medical Center Behavioral Health Center
4101 University Boulevard
Tyler, TX 75701

Fister Counseling Services First Step Recovery Program
215 Winchester Drive
Tyler, TX 75701

UNIVERSAL CITY

Behavorial Health Clinic ADAPT Program
1985 First Street West, Suite 1
Universal City, TX 78150

UVALDE

South Texas Rural Health Services, Inc.
1024 Garner Field Road
Uvalde, TX 78801

VAN HORN

Aliviane NO/AD, Inc. Project Ahora
1801 West Broadway, Suite 105
Van Horn, TX 79855

VERNON

Vernon State Hospital Adolescent Forensics
4730 College Drive
Vernon, TX 76384

VICTORIA

Bay Area Health Care Group, Ltd. Columbia Counseling Center
1403 North Wheeler Street
Victoria, TX 77901

Best Recovery Health Care, Inc.
1708 Laurent Street
Victoria, TX 77901

Columbia Counseling Center
2001 Sabine Street Suite 104
Victoria, TX 77901-5953

Steps to Recovery
1402-B Villagee Drive
Victoria, TX 77901

Treatment Associates
107 Cozzi Circle
Victoria, TX 77901

VINTON

Alliance Behavioral Health Services Excel Adolescent Program
431-B East Vinton Road
Vinton, TX 79821

WACO

Lake Shore Center for Psychological Services Better Way Chemical Dependency Treatment Program
4555 Lake Shore Drive
Waco, TX 76710

Manna House
926 North 14th Street
Waco, TX 76707

Freeman Center
Dear Unit
1619 Washington Avenue
Waco, TX 76703

Doris Goodrich Jones House
326 North 14th Street
Waco, TX 76703

Men's Residential
1401 Columbus Avenue
Waco, TX 76701

Outpatient Unit
2505 Washington Avenue
Waco, TX 76703

Residential Unit
1515 Columbus Avenue
Waco, TX 76701

Women's Residential
1425 Columbus Avenue
Waco, TX 76703

Washington House
2200 Washington Avenue
Waco, TX 76708

WAXAHACHIE

Alliance Life Centers
201 East Franklin Street
Waxahachie, TX 75165

Johnson/Ellis/Navarro MH/MR Services
116 North Rogers Street
Waxahachie, TX 75165

WESLACO

Texson Management Group, Inc. Valley Transitional Treatment Center
617 1/2 South International Street
Weslaco, TX 78596

WHITE OAK

Sabine Valley Center Dear Recovery Center
2000 U.S. Highway 80
White Oak, TX 75693

WICHITA FALLS

Red River Detox and Recovery Center
4411 Henry S Grace Freeway
Wichita Falls, TX 76302

Red River Drug and Alcohol Treatment Center Adolescent Inpatient Program
1505 8th Street
Wichita Falls, TX 76301

Rose Street Clinics
1800 Rose Street
Wichita Falls, TX 76301

Serenity Foundation of Texas Intensive Outpatient/ Outpatient
3100 5th Street, Suite 12
Wichita Falls, TX 76309

510 Lamar Street
Wichita Falls, TX 76301

WILMER

Cornell Corrections
200 Greene Road
Wilmer, TX 75172

WOODVILLE

Alcohol and Drug Abuse Council of Deep East Texas
100 Courthouse Street, Room 303
Woodville, TX 75979

Stop Child Abuse and Neglect, Inc. Stand Outpatient Program
800 Block Highway 83
Zapata, TX 78076

UTAH

BEAVER

Southwest Center
757 North Main Street
Beaver, UT 84713

BLANDING

San Juan Substance Abuse Services
356 East Main Street
Blanding, UT 84511

BOUNTIFUL

Bountiful Outpatient
470 East Medical Drive
Bountiful, UT 84010

Columbia Lake View Hospital Behavioral Medicine Unit
630 East Medical Drive
Bountiful, UT 84010

Utahs, Inc. of Davis County
48 East 400 South, Suite C
Bountiful, UT 84010

BRIGHAM CITY

New Choices Substance Abuse Treatment
245 West 1100 South
Brigham City, UT 84302

CASTLE DALE

Four Corners Mental Health Center
45 East 100 South
Castle Dale, UT 84513

CEDAR CITY

Paiute Tribe Behavioral Health Dept
600 North 100 East Paiute Drive
Cedar City, UT 84720

Southwest Center
91 North 1850 West
Cedar City, UT 84720

Horizon House Chemical Dependency Center
54 North 200 East
Cedar City, UT 84720

CLEARFIELD

Davis County Mental Health
Addictions Treatment Unit
904-A South State Street
Clearfield, UT 84015

Alcohol and Drug Center
860 South State Street
Clearfield, UT 84015

Women's Recovery Center
904-B South State Street
Clearfield, UT 84015

DELTA

Central Utah Counseling Center
51 North Center Street
Delta, UT 84624

DUCHESNE

Northeastern Counseling Center
27 South 100 West
Duchesne, UT 84021

DUGWAY

Alcohol and Drug Abuse Prevention and Control Program
Dugway Proving Ground
Building 5124, Room 210
Dugway, UT 84022

EAST CARBON

Four Corners Mental Health Center
305 Center Street
East Carbon, UT 84520

EPHRAIM

Central Utah Counseling Center
390 West 100 North
Ephraim, UT 84627

ESCALANTE

Southwest Center
100 East 100 North
Escalante, UT 84726

FARMINGTON

Davis County Mental Health Center
291 South 200 West
Farmington, UT 84025

FILLMORE

Central Utah Counseling Center
65 West Center
Fillmore, UT 84631

FORT DUCHESNE

Ute Indian Tribe Adult Alcohol Program
550 South 6777 East
Fort Duchesne, UT 84026

GREEN RIVER

Four Corners Mental Health Center
110 Medical Drive
Green River, UT 84525

HEBER CITY

Wasatch County Alcohol and Drug Treatment and Prevention Program
32 West 200 South
Heber City, UT 84032

HILL AFB

75 Medical Group/SGOHS Substance Abuse Program
6068 Aspen Avenue
Bldg 1295, Room 8
Hill AFB, UT 84056-5401

HURRICANE

Southwest Center
25 South Main Street
Hurricane, UT 84737

KANAB

Southwest Center
310 South 100 East, Suite 11
Kanab, UT 84741

KOOSHAREM

Sorenson's Ranch School, Inc.
410 North 100 East
Koosharem, UT 84744

LOGAN

Bear River Health Department New Choices Substance Abuse Treatment Program
95 South 100 West, Suite 300
Logan, UT 84321

Logan Regional Hospital Dayspring
1400 North 500 East
Logan, UT 84321

MIDVALE

Family Counseling Center
46 East 7200 South
Midvale, UT 84047

MOAB

Four Corners Mental Health Center MOAB Clinic
198 East Center
Moab, UT 84532

MOUNT PLEASANT

Central Utah Counseling Center
125 South State Street
Mount Pleasant, UT 84647

MATR
Mount Pleasant, UT 84647

NEPHI

Central Utah Counseling Center
656 North Main Street
Nephi, UT 84648

NORTH SALT LAKE

Life Line Inc
1130 West Center Street
North Salt Lake, UT 84054

OGDEN

Blue Skies Recovery Center, Inc.
727 24th Street
Ogden, UT 84102

Columbia Ogden Regional Medical Center
5475 South 500 East
Ogden, UT 84405

McKay/Dee Hospital Dayspring Chemical Dependency Unit
5030 Harrison Boulevard
Ogden, UT 84403

New Horizons Education Treatment and Consulting
205 26th Street, Suite 14
Ogden, UT 84401

Professional Services Corporation
533 26 Street
Suite 100
Ogden, UT 84401

Rocky Mountain Consultants
727 24th Street
Ogden, UT 84401

Weber Human Services
2650 Lincoln Avenue
Ogden, UT 84401

ORDERVILLE

Southwest Center
425 East State Street, Suite 11
Orderville, UT 84758

OREM

Addiction and Psychological Services
224 North Orem Boulevard
Orem, UT 84057

Assessment and Psychotherapy Assoc Inc
1411 North State Street, Suite 7
Orem, UT 84058

Utah County Council on Drug Abuse Rehabilitation (UCCODAR)
251 East 1200 South
Orem, UT 84058

PANGUITCH

Southwest Center
609 North Main Street
Panguitch, UT 84759

PARK CITY

Aspen Therapy Center
700 Bitner Road
Park City, UT 84098

Valley Mental Health Summit County Unit
1753 Sidewinder Drive
Park City, UT 84060

PAYSON

Columbia Mountain View Hospital Pavilion
1000 East Highway 6
Payson, UT 84651

PRICE

Four Corners Mental Health Center
276 South Carbon Avenue
Price, UT 84501

Price Clinic
575 East 100 South
Price, UT 84501

PROVO

Affiliated Family Treatment Center
1675 North Freedom Boulevard
Provo, UT 84604

Project Reality Utah County Site
150 East Center Street, Suite 1100
Provo, UT 84606

Provo Canyon School Substance Abuse Services
4501 North University Avenue
Provo, UT 84603

Heritage Center
5600 North Heritage School Drive
Provo, UT 84604

Utah County Human Services
1726 South Buckley Lane
Provo, UT 84606

RICHFIELD

Central Utah Counseling Substance Abuse Center
255 South Main Street
Richfield, UT 84701

Sevier County Alcohol and Drug Program
835 East 300 North
Richfield, UT 84701

ROOSEVELT

Northeastern Counseling Center
510 West 200 North
Roosevelt, UT 84066

SAINT GEORGE

Brightway at Saint George
115 West 1470 South
Saint George, UT 84770

Kolob Therapeutic Services, Inc.
437 South Bluff Street, Suite 202
Saint George, UT 84770

Southwest Center
354 East 600 South
Suite 202
Saint George, UT 84770

Reach Alcohol and Drug Outpatient
321 North Mall Drive, Suite 101
Saint George, UT 84770

Youth Services
628 South 300 East
Saint George, UT 84770

SALT LAKE CITY

Asian Association of Utah
1588 South Major Street 30 East
Salt Lake City, UT 84115

Assessment and Psychotherapy Association, Inc.
2114 East Fort Union Boulevard
Salt Lake City, UT 84121

Catholic Community Services
2570 West 1700 South
Salt Lake City, UT 84104

Center for Behavioral Health
1073 East 3300 South
Salt Lake City, UT 84106

Cornerstone Counseling Center
660 South 200 East
Suite 308
Salt Lake City, UT 84111

Drug Free Community
3646 South Redwood Road
Suite 1-A
Salt Lake City, UT 84119

England and Associates
5821 South Beaumont Drive
Salt Lake City, UT 84121

Family Counseling Center
807 East South Temple Street
Suite 350
Salt Lake City, UT 84102

First Step House
411 North Grant Street
Salt Lake City, UT 84116

Gateway to Recovery
320 West 200 South, Suite 230-B
Salt Lake City, UT 84101

Haven, The
974 East South Temple
Salt Lake City, UT 84102

Highland Ridge Hospital Substance Abuse Services
4578 Highland Drive
Salt Lake City, UT 84117

Latter-Day Saints Hospital Intermountain Health Care Dayspring Program
C Street and 8 Avenue
Salt Lake City, UT 84143

Neo Genesis
744 South 500 East
Salt Lake City, UT 84102

Northwest Passage, Inc.
432 North 300 West
Salt Lake City, UT 84103

Odyssey House, Inc.
Adolescent Facility
607 East 200 South
Salt Lake City, UT 84102

Adult Treatment Program
68 South 600 East
Salt Lake City, UT 84102

Intensive Outpatient Program
623 South 200 East
Salt Lake City, UT 84102

Women and Children's Program
42 South 500 East
Salt Lake City, UT 84102

Parents Helping Parents DBA Turnabout
2738 South 2000 East
Salt Lake City, UT 84109

Positive Adjustments Corporation
2480 South Main Street, Suite 108
Salt Lake City, UT 84115

Professional Services Corporation Substance Abuse Services
4667 South Halladay Boulevard
Salt Lake City, UT 84117

Project Reality
150 East 700 South
Salt Lake City, UT 84111

Residential Unit
1416 South State Street
Salt Lake City, UT 84115

Rocky Mountain Consultants
5278 Pinemount Drive
Suite A-120
Salt Lake City, UT 84107

Saint Mary's Home for Men
1206 West 200 South
Salt Lake City, UT 84104

Salt Lake County Division of Youth Services
177 West Price Avenue
Salt Lake City, UT 84115

Salvation Army Alcohol Rehabilitation Program
252 South 500 East
Salt Lake City, UT 84102

Sequoia Counseling Center
20738 South 2000 East, Suite B
Salt Lake City, UT 84109

University of Utah Alcohol and Drug Abuse Clinic
50 North Medical Drive
Room 1R52
Salt Lake City, UT 84132

University of Utah Neuropsychiatric Institute
501 Chipeta Way
Salt Lake City, UT 84108

Utah Alcoholism Foundation Combined Facilities
2880 South Main Street
Suite 210
Salt Lake City, UT 84115

House of Hope
1006 East 100 South, Suite 210
Salt Lake City, UT 84102

Progress Home
21 I Street
Salt Lake City, UT 84103

Utah Child and Youth Guidance Center
1414 East 4500 South, Suite 4
Salt Lake City, UT 84117

Valley Mental Health
East Valley Unit
1141 East 3900 South
Suite A-160
Salt Lake City, UT 84124

Forensic Unit
530 East 500 South, Suite 10
Salt Lake City, UT 84102

Alcohol and Drug Treatment Unit
5965 South 900 East, Suite 240
Salt Lake City, UT 84121

Veterans' Affairs Medical Center Substance Abuse Treatment Units
500 East Foothill Boulevard
Salt Lake City, UT 84148

Volunteers of America Alcohol and Drug Detoxification Center
252 West Brooklyn Avenue
Salt Lake City, UT 84101

Wasatch Canyons
Intermountain Health Care
5770 South 1500 West
Salt Lake City, UT 84123

Wasatch Youth Support Systems
3392 West 3500 South
Salt Lake City, UT 84120

SANDY

Positive Adjustments Corporation
870 East 9400 South, Suite 103-C
Sandy, UT 84094

SAINT GEORGE

Desert Hills Therapeutic Services, Inc.
1240 East 100 South, Suite 18-B
St George, UT 84790

TOOELE

Valley Mental Health Center
305 North Main Street
Tooele, UT 84074

TREMONTON

New Choices SAT Program
125 South 100 West
Tremonton, UT 84337

VERNAL

Mountain Valley Counseling
365 West 50 North, Suite W-1
Vernal, UT 84078

Uintah Basin Counseling Vernal Office
559 North 1700 West
Vernal, UT 84078

WASHINGTON

Counseling Services of Southern Utah
293 East Telegraph Road
Suite 35
Washington, UT 84780

WOODS CROSS

Benchmark Behavioral Health Services
592 West 1350 South
Woods Cross, UT 84087

VERMONT

BELLOWS FALLS

Healthcare and Rehab Services of Southeast Vermont
1 Hospital Court, Suite 410
Bellows Falls, VT 05101

BENNINGTON

United Counseling Service of Bennington County, Inc.
Ledge Hill Drive
Bennington, VT 05201

BRATTLEBORO

Alcohol/Drug Treatment
5 Fairview Street
Brattleboro, VT 05301

Brattleboro Retreat Adult Alcohol and Substance Abuse Program
75 Linden Street
Brattleboro, VT 05301

Families in Recovery
75 High Street
Brattleboro, VT 05301

Marathon Behavioral Treatment Services
101 Western Avenue
Brattleboro, VT 05301

Youth Services Incorporated
11 Walnut Street
Brattleboro, VT 05301

BURLINGTON

Act One
184 Pearl Street
Burlington, VT 05401

Champlain Drug and Alcohol Services
45 Clarke Street
Burlington, VT 05401

Howard Center for Human Services Pine Street Counseling Center
855 Pine Street
Burlington, VT 05401

Spectrum Youth and Family Services
31 Elmwood Avenue
Burlington, VT 05401

HUNTINGTON

Marathon, Inc. Mountain View Treatment Center
609 Delfrate Road
Huntington, VT 05462

MIDDLEBURY

Counseling Service of Addison County Substance Abuse Treatment Unit
89 Main Street
Middlebury, VT 05753

MONTPELIER

Dawnland Center
119 Barre Street
Montpelier, VT 05601

Washington County Youth Service Bureau
38 Elm Street
Montpelier, VT 05602

MORRISVILLE

Lamoille County Mental Health Services Substance Abuse Treatment Unit
520 Washington Highway
Morrisville, VT 05661

NEWPORT

Northeast Kingdom Mental Health Tri-County Substance Abuse Services
343 Main Street
Newport, VT 05855

RANDOLPH

Clara Martin Center Substance Abuse Treatment Unit
11 Main Street
Randolph, VT 05060

RUTLAND

Rutland Mental Health Service Evergreen Center for Alcohol/Drug Services
7 Court Square
Rutland, VT 05701

SAINT ALBANS

Northwestern Counseling and Support Services, Inc. Outpatient Treatment Unit
8 Ferris Street
Saint Albans, VT 05478

SAINT JOHNSBURY

Tri-County Substance Abuse Services
297 Summer Street
Saint Johnsbury, VT 05819-1605

SOUTH BURLINGTON

Adolescent Family Services
595 Dorset Street, Suite 6
South Burlington, VT 05403

Fletcher Allen Day One
200 Twin Oaks Terrace, Suite 6
South Burlington, VT 05403

UNDERHILL

Maple Leaf Farm Associates, Inc.
10 Maple Leaf Road
Underhill, VT 05489

WALLINGFORD

Recovery House
12 Church Street
Wallingford, VT 05773

WHITE RIVER JUNCTION

Health Rehabilitation Services of Southeastern Vermont
195 North Main Street, Suite 2
White River Junction, VT 05001-7044

Veterans Affairs Medical Center Substance Abuse Treatment Services
215 North Main Street
White River Junction, VT 05009

WILDER

Quitting Time
Depot Street
Wilder, VT 05088

WINOOSKI

Centerpoint
81 West Canal Street
Winooski, VT 05404-2111

VIRGINIA

ABINGDON

Highlands Community Services Substance Abuse Intensive Treatment Program
432 East Main Street, Suite A
Abingdon, VA 24210

ALEXANDRIA

Alexandria Community Services Board Substance Abuse Services
2355-A Mill Road
Alexandria, VA 22314

Franconia Road Treatment Center
6015 Bush Hill Drive
Alexandria, VA 22310

Living Free Alcohol and Chemical Dependence Program
6391 Little River Turnpike
Alexandria, VA 22312

Second Genesis, Inc.
1001 King Street
Alexandria, VA 22314

ANANDALE

Fairfax Methadone Treatment Center
7008-G Little River Turnpike
Annandale, VA 22003

ARLINGTON

Arlington County Alcohol and Drug Program
1725 North George Mason Drive
Arlington, VA 22205

Columbia Arlington Hospital
Addiction Treatment Program
1701 North George Mason Drive
Arlington, VA 22205

Northern Virginia Community Hospital
601 South Carlin Springs Road
Arlington, VA 22204

The Women's Home, Inc.
1628 North George Mason Drive
Arlington, VA 22205

Vanguard Services, Ltd. Phoenix Program
506 North Pollard Street
Arlington, VA 22203

ASHLAND

Hanover County Community Services Board
12300 Washington Highway
Ashland, VA 23005

BLACKSBURG

New River Valley Community Services Montgomery Clinic
700 University City Boulevard
Blacksburg, VA 24060-2706

CARTERSVILLE

Human Resources, Inc. Willow Oaks
2123 Cartersville Road
Cartersville, VA 23027

CEDAR BLUFF

Cumberland Mental Health Center Substance Abuse Services
Route 19
Cedar Bluff, VA 24609

CHARLOTTESVILLE

University of Virginia Hospitals North Ridge Hosp Addictions Treatment Program
2955 Ivy Road, Suite 210
Charlottesville, VA 22903

CHESAPEAKE

Chesapeake Substance Abuse Program
524 Albermarle Drive
Chesapeake, VA 23320

Virginia Beach Group at Chesapeake
300 Medical Parkway Suite 306
Chesapeake, VA 23320-4985

CHESTERFIELD

Chesterfield Substance Abuse Services
6801 Lucy Corr Court
Rogers Building
Chesterfield, VA 23832

CLINTWOOD

Dickenson County Community Services Substance Abuse Services
McClure Avenue Clinical Services Building
Clintwood, VA 24228

COLONIAL HEIGHTS

Behavior and Stress Management
3236 B Boulevard
Colonial Heights, VA 23834

COVINGTON

Allegheny Highlands Community Services Board Substance Abuse Services
305 South Monroe Avenue
Covington, VA 24426

CULPEPER

Pinebrook Psychiatric Center Substance Abuse Services
501 Sunset Lane
Culpeper, VA 22701

DANVILLE

Alcoholic Counseling Center, Inc. Hope Harbor
1021 Main Street
Danville, VA 24541

Associates in Mental Health Services
108 Holbrook Street, Suite 203
Danville, VA 24541

Interventions Counseling and Consulting Services
105 South Union Street, Suite 800
Danville, VA 24541

FAIRFAX

Dominion Hospital
11200 Waples Mill Road, Suite 100
Fairfax, VA 22030

Fairfax/Falls Church Community Services Board Alcohol and Drug Services
3900 Jermantown Road
Suite 200
Fairfax, VA 22030

Life Line Addictions Program
10565 Lee Highway
Suite 100
Fairfax, VA 22030

FALLS CHURCH

Ethos Foundation, Inc.
5201 Leesburg Pike
Suite 100
Falls Church, VA 22041

Innova Comprehensive Addiction Treatment Services (CATS)
3300 Gallows Road
Falls Church, VA 22046

FARMVILLE

Crossroads Community Services Board
Highway 460
Farmville, VA 23901

FISHERSVILLE

Recovery Choice Program at Augusta Medical Center
96 Medical Center Way
Fishersville, VA 22939

FORT EUSTIS

Fort Eustis Community Counseling Center Army Substance Abuse Program
515 Sternberg Avenue
Fort Eustis, VA 23604-5548

FORT LEE

Fort Lee Alcohol and Drug Community Counseling Center
Kenner Clinic
Building 12000
Fort Lee, VA 23801

FORT MONROE

Community Counseling Center Alcohol and Drug Prevention Control Office
Building T-194
Fort Monroe, VA 23651

FREDERICKSBURG

Rappahannock Area Community Services Board Alcohol and Drug Outpatient Services
600 Jackson Street
Fredericksburg, VA 22401

Serenity Home, Inc. Substance Abuse ICF and Halfway Treatment Services
514 Wolfe Street
Fredericksburg, VA 22401

Snowden at Fredericksburg
1200 Sam Perry Boulevard
Fredericksburg, VA 22401

FRONT ROYAL

Northwestern Community Services Board Substance Abuse Service
209 West Criser Road
Front Royal, VA 22630

GALAX

Galax Treatment Center, Inc. Life Center of Galax
112 Painter Street
Galax, VA 24333

GLEN ALLEN

Henrico Area MH/MR Services
10299 Woodman Road
Glen Allen, VA 23060

GLOUCESTER

Middle Peninsula/Northern Neck Counseling Center
9228 George Washington Memorial Highway
Gloucester, VA 23061

GOLDVEIN

Deep Run Lodge
13259 Blackwells Mill Road
Goldvein, VA 22720

GOOCHLAND

Goochland/Powhatan Community Services
3058 River Road West
Goochland, VA 23063

HAMPTON

Hampton Roads Clinic
2236 West Queen Street
Hampton, VA 23666

Langley Air Force Base Substance Abuse Program
Building 74
Hampton, VA 23665

Peninsula Behavioral Health Center
2244 Executive Drive
Hampton, VA 23666

Substance Abuse Treatment Program
100 Emancipation Road
Suite 116-A
Hampton, VA 23667

HARRISONBURG

Family Life Resource Center
250 East Elizabeth Street, Suite 102
Harrisonburg, VA 22801

Harrisonburg/Rockingham Community Services Board
1241 North Main Street
Harrisonburg, VA 22801

HOPEWELL

Columbia John Randolph Behavioral Health Center
504 North 3rd Street
Hopewell, VA 23860

LEESBURG

Graydon Manor Psychiatric Hospital
801 Childrens Center Road
Leesburg, VA 20175

Loudoun County Mental Health Center Substance Abuse Program
102 Heritage Way NE, Suite 302
Leesburg, VA 20176

LYNCHBURG

Community Services Board of Central Virginia Substance Abuse Services
2235 Landover Place
Lynchburg, VA 24501

Virginia Baptist Hospital Pathways Treatment Center
3300 Rivermont Avenue
Lynchburg, VA 24503

MANASSAS

Center for Psychiatric and Addiction Treatment
8700 Sudley Road
Manassas, VA 22110

MARION

Mount Rogers Transitions Substance Abuse Services
115 North Church Street
Marion, VA 24354

Southwestern Virginia Mental Health Institute Medical Detox Unit
502 East Main Street
Marion, VA 24354

MARTINSVILLE

Memorial Hospital of Martinsville and Henry County Psychiatric Services
320 Hospital Drive
Martinsville, VA 24115-4788

Passages
817 Starling Avenue
Martinsville, VA 24112

Patrick Henry Drug and Alcohol Council Crossroads/Intensive Outpatient Program
24 Clay Street
Martinsville, VA 24114

MECHANICSVILLE

Hanover Community Service Board Gail Taylor/LCSW
8157 Old Calvary Drive, Suite 102
Mechanicsville, VA 23111

MIDLOTHIAN

Rockwood Counseling Associates
10128 Hull Street Road
Midlothian, VA 23112

NEW KENT

Cumberland Hospital for Children and Adolescents
9407 Cumberland Road
New Kent, VA 23124

NEWPORT NEWS

CAPO Center Detox
2351 Terminal Avenue
Newport News, VA 23607

Comprehensive Outpatient Services Peninsula Alcoholism Services
11832 Canon Boulevard, Suite C
Newport News, VA 23606

Riverside New Foundations
610 Thimble Shoals Boulevard
Building 5, Suite 100-A
Newport News, VA 23606

Woodside Hospital LLC
17579 Warwick Boulevard
Newport News, VA 23603

NORFOLK

ARD/CAAC NAB LCREK AMPHIB Base
Building 3007
Norfolk, VA 23521-5000

Naval Alcohol Rehabilitation Center
1650 Gilbert Street
Norfolk, VA 23511

New Bridges
Bridges Outpatient Rehabilitation Center
6330 Newtown Road, Suite 200
Norfolk, VA 23502

Norfolk Community Services Board Substance Abuse Services
1150 East Little Creek Road
Suite 302
Norfolk, VA 23518

Rehabilitation Services, Inc.
300 West 20 Street
Norfolk, VA 23517

**Sentara Norfolk General
   Hospital**
600 Gresham Drive
Norfolk, VA 23507

NORTON

Saint Mary's Family Center
910 Virginia Avenue
Norton, VA 24273

PETERSBURG

**District 19 Substance Abuse
   Services**
20 West Bank Street
Petersburg, VA 23803

**Poplar Springs Hospital
   Chemical Dependency
   Program**
350 Poplar Drive
Petersburg, VA 23805

PILOT

Serenity House
Fisher's View
Pilot, VA 24138

PORTSMOUTH

T. W. Neumann and Associates
720 Rodman Avenue
Portsmouth, VA 23707

QUANTICO

**Consolidated Substance Abuse
   Counseling Center**
Marine Corps Base Quantico
2034 Barnett Avenue
Quantico, VA 22134-5012

RADFORD

**Saint Albans Psychiatric
   Hospital Substance Abuse
   Services**
Route 11 West
Radford, VA 24143

RICHMOND

Chippenham Medical Center
Johnston Willis Hospital
Tucker Pavilion
7101 Jahnke Road
Richmond, VA 23225

**Deaf and Hard of Hearing
   Community Counseling
   Services**
8917 Fargo Road
Richmond, VA 23229

Human Resources' Inc.
Division of Addiction Services/
   Drug Free Unit
2926 West Marshall Street
Richmond, VA 23230

Outpatient Methadone Program
15 West Cary Street
Richmond, VA 23220

MCC Behavioral Care
7501 Boulders View, Suite 400
Richmond, VA 23225

**Richmond Aftercare, Inc. Men's
   and Women's Program**
1109 Bainbridge Street
Richmond, VA 23224

Saint Marys Hospital
Outpatient Services
2006 Bremo Road, Suite 102-A
Richmond, VA 23226

Psychiatric Unit Substance Abuse
   Services
5801 Bremo Road, 7th Floor
Richmond, VA 23226

**Veterans' Affairs Medical Center
   Substance Abuse Treatment
   Program**
1201 Broad Rock Boulevard
Richmond, VA 23249

Virginia Health Center
2203 East Broad Street
Richmond, VA 23223

**Williamsburg Place of
   Richmond**
10049 Midlothian Turnpike, Suite
   B-2
Richmond, VA 23235

ROANOKE

**Bethany Hall Women's Recovery
   Home Chemical Dependency
   Treatment**
1109 Franklin Road SW
Roanoke, VA 24016

Walnut Avenue Clinic
16 Walnut Avenue SW
Roanoke, VA 24016

SALEM

**Lewis Gale Medical Center
   Center for Recovery**
1902 Braeburn Drive
Salem, VA 24153

**Veterans Affairs Medical Center
   Substance Abuse Treatment
   Program**
1970 Roanoke Boulevard
Psychiatry 116A-4
Salem, VA 24153

SOUTH BOSTON

**Southside Community Services
   Board Substance Abuse
   Treatment Services**
424 Hamilton Boulevard
South Boston, VA 24592

STAUNTON

**Shenandoah Counseling
   Associates**
1048 West Beverley Street
Staunton, VA 24401

**Valley Alcohol Safety Action
   Program**
Holiday Court
Suite B
Staunton, VA 24401

STEPHENSON

Shalom Et Benedictus, Inc.
1160 Jordan Springs Road
Stephenson, VA 22656

SUFFOLK

Psychiatric Care Center Dr. Richard Key
1900 North Main Street, Suite 207
Suffolk, VA 23434

Western Tidewater Mental Health Center Substance Abuse Department
157 North Main Street
Suffolk, VA 23434

SURRY

District 19 MH/MR Substance Abuse Services Surry Counseling Service
474 Colonial Trail West
Surry, VA 23883

VIRGINIA BEACH

Addiction Rehabilitation Department Counseling and Assistance Center
Building 531 NAS Oceana
Virginia Beach, VA 23460

Atlantic Psychiatric Services
780 Lynnhaven Parkway, Suite 220
Virginia Beach, VA 23452

Crisis Intervention Home
811 13th Street
Virginia Beach, VA 23451

First Hospital Corp Recovery Place and Serenity Lodge at the Beach
1100 First Colonial Road
Virginia Beach, VA 23454

Virginia Beach Substance Abuse Services
Pembroke Six Street
Suite 126
Virginia Beach, VA 23462

WARRENTON

Family Focus Counseling Service
20-B John Marshall Street
Warrenton, VA 20186

Rappahannock/Rapidan CSB
Fauquier Family Guidance
340 Hospital Drive
Warrenton, VA 20186

WILLIAMSBURG

Bacon Street, Inc.
247 McLaws Circle
Williamsburg, VA 23185

Colonial Services Board Substance Abuse Services
1657 Merrimac Trail
Williamsburg, VA 23185

Williamsburg Place
5447 Mooretown Road
Williamsburg, VA 23185

WINCHESTER

First Step
129 Youth Develpment Court
Winchester, VA 22602

Lord Fairfax Community, Inc. Council on Alcoholism
512 South Braddock Street
Winchester, VA 22601

Winchester Medical Center Choices Detox
1890 Amherst Street
Winchester, VA 22601

WOODSTOCK

Northwestern Community Services Board
441 North Main Street
Woodstock, VA 22664

WASHINGTON

ABERDEEN

Grays Harbor Community Hospital Eastcenter Recovery
1006 H Street
Aberdeen, WA 98520

Social Treatment Opportunity Programs (STOP)
2700 Simpson Avenue
Aberdeen, WA 98520

ANACORTES

Follman Agency
1004 7th Street, Suite 207
Anacortes, WA 98221

SKAGIT Recovery Center
1010-A 6th Street
Anacortes, WA 98221

ARLINGTON

Focus
436 West Avenue North
Arlington, WA 98223

M K Standish and Associates, Inc.
16404 Smokey Point Boulevard
Suite 109
Arlington, WA 98223

Stillaguamish Tribe Substance Abuse Services
3439 Stoluckguamish Lane
Arlington, WA 98223

AUBURN

Future Visions (FVP Enterprises) DBA Social Treatment Opportunity Programs
620 M Street NE
Auburn, WA 98002

Lakeside Milam Recovery Centers
1833 Auburn Way North, Suite A
Auburn, WA 98002

Muckleshoot Tribal Alcohol and Drug Program
39015 172nd Avenue South East
Auburn, WA 98092-9763

BAINBRIDGE ISLAND

Bainbridge Island Recovery Center, Inc.
600 Winslow Way East, Suite 135
Bainbridge Island, WA 98110

BELLEVUE

C and P Counseling
1200 112th Avenue NE
Suite C-179
Bellevue, WA 98004

Coastal Treatment Services
12443 Bel Red Road
Building 300, Suite 320
Bellevue, WA 98005

Group Health Behavioral Health Services
13451 SE 36th Street
Bellevue, WA 98006

Open Door Behavioral Health Services
2840 Northup Way
Bellevue, WA 98004

Youth Eastside Services (YES)
16150 NE 8th Street
Bellevue, WA 98008

BELLINGHAM

Belair Clinic
1130 North State Street
Bellingham, WA 98225

Chambers and Wells Counseling
1130 North State Street
Bellingham, WA 98225

Lummi Care Program
1790 Bayon Road
Bellingham, WA 98226

Pacific Recovery Healing Center
2502 Cedarwood Avenue, Suite 3
Bellingham, WA 98225-1464

Saint Joseph Hospital Recovery Center Inpatient and Outpatient
809 East Chestnut Street
Bellingham, WA 98225-5298

Saint Josephs Recovery House
1209 Girard Street
Bellingham, WA 98225

Sea Mar Substance Abuse Program
2209 Elm Street, Suite AZC
Bellingham, WA 98225

Sehome Behavioral Health, Inc.
1116 Key Street
Bellingham, WA 98225-5224

BOTHELL

Alpha Center for Treatment, Inc.
10614 Beardslee Boulevard
Suite D
Bothell, WA 98011

Residence XII
14506 Juanita Drive NE
Bothell, WA 98011

BREMERTON

Agape Unlimited
5464 Kitsap Way
Bremerton, WA 98312

Group Health Adapt/Bremerton
5002 Kitsap Way
Suite 202
Bremerton, WA 98312

Kitsap Mental Health Services Youth MICA Program
5455 Almira Drive
Bremerton, WA 98312

Kitsap Recovery Center
1975 NE Fuson Road
Bremerton, WA 98310

Navy Alcohol Treatment Department
1400 Farragut Avenue
Building 491, 2nd Floor
Bremerton, WA 98314-5001

Olympic Educational Services District 114/Youth Recovery Program
105 National Avenue North
Bremerton, WA 98312

Right Choice Counseling Service
1740 Northeast Riddell Road
Suite 314
Bremerton, WA 98310

Tara Counseling Center, Inc.
3627 Wheaton Way, Suite F
Bremerton, WA 98310

BURIEN

South King County Recovery Centers
15025 4th Avenue SW
Burien, WA 98166-2301

BURLINGTON

Follman Agency
127 South Spruce Street
Burlington, WA 98233

CASTLE ROCK

Drug Abuse Prevention Center
2232 South Silverlake Road
Castle Rock, WA 98611

CATHLAMET

Wahkiakum Chemical Dependency Services
42 Elochoman Valley Road
Cathlamet, WA 98612

CENTRALIA

New Directions Counseling
1000 Kresky Road, Suite G
Centralia, WA 98531

Omni Program
20311 Old Highway 9 SW
Centralia, WA 98531-9699

CHEHALIS

Eugenia Center
249 NW Chehalis Avenue
Chehalis, WA 98532-1371

Green Hill School Day Treatment Program
375 SW 11th Street
M-S S21-5
Chehalis, WA 98532

Right Step, Inc.
118 North Market Boulevard
Chehalis, WA 98532

CHELAN

Riverview Recovery
219 West Gibson Avenue
Chelan, WA 98816

CHEWELAH

**Stevens County Counseling
    Services**
East 301 Clay Street, Room 210
Chewelah, WA 99109

COLVILLE

**Stevens County Counseling
    Services**
165 East Hawthorne Avenue
Colville, WA 99114

CONCRETE

Sunlight Again, Inc.
310 Dillard Avenue
Concrete, WA 98237-9643

DAVENPORT

**Lincoln County Alcohol/Drug
    Center**
518 Morgan Street
Davenport, WA 99122

DAYTON

**Columbia County Services
    Substance Abuse Program**
221 East Washington Street
Dayton, WA 99328

DEER PARK

Deer Park Recovery
South 22 Vernon Street, Suite 4
Deer Park, WA 99006

**Salvation Army Drug Abuse
    Outpatient**
West 110 Crawford Street
Deer Park, WA 99006

DES MOINES

Sea Mar Treatment Center
24215 Pacific Highway South
Des Moines, WA 98198

EDMONDS

New Spirit Recovery Program
22617 76th Avenue W, Suite 1001
Edmonds, WA 98026

Lakeside Milam Recovery North
7935 Lake Ballinger Way
Edmonds, WA 98026

ELLENSBURG

**Alcohol/Drug Dependency
    Service**
507 Nanum Street
Room 111
Ellensburg, WA 98926

**Kittitas Valley Recovery
    Services**
103 East 4th Street, Suite 204
Ellensburg, WA 98926

**Parke Creek Chemical
    Dependency Program**
11042 Parke Creek Road
Ellensburg, WA 98926

ELMA

**Northwest Indian Treatment
    Center**
Elma, WA 98541

ENUMCLAW

Dotters Counseling Service, Inc.
847 Blake Street
Enumclaw, WA 98022

**South King County Recovery
    Centers**
1325 Cole Street
Enumclaw, WA 98022

EVERETT

**Catholic Community Services
    Lifeline Recovery Program**
1918 Everett Avenue
Everett, WA 98201

Everett Treatment Services
7207 Evergreen Way, Suite M
Everett, WA 98203

Evergreen Manor, Inc.
Outpatient Services
Recovery House/Detox Services
2601 Summit Avenue
Everett, WA 98201

**Family Counseling DBA
    Northwest Alternatives**
9930 Evergreen Way
Everett, WA 98208

Focus
909 SE Everett Mall Way
Suite C-364
Everett, WA 98204

**Lakeside/Milam Recovery
    Centers, Inc.**
2731 Wetmore Avenue, Suite 402
Everett, WA 98201

**North Sound Assesment and
    Counseling Service**
1316 Wall Street, Suite 1-B
Everett, WA 98201

Pacific Treatment Alternatives
1114 Pacific Avenue
Everett, WA 98201

**Sea Mar Community Health
    Center**
8625 Evergreen Way, Suite 255
Everett, WA 98201

EVERSON

Nooksack Tribes Genesis II
6750 Mission Road
Everson, WA 98247

FAIRCHILD AIR FORCE BASE

**Fairchild Air Force Base Mental
    Health Services**
200 North Chennault Street
Fairchild AFB, WA 99011

FEDERAL WAY

Federal Way Youth and Family Services
1411 Dash Point Road SW
Federal Way, WA 98023

Intercept Associates
30620 Pacific Highway South
Suites 107
Federal Way, WA 98003

Lakeside Milam Recovery Centers
28621 Pacific Highway South
Federal Way, WA 98003

Sundown M Ranch
720 South 333rd Street, Suite 105
Federal Way, WA 98003-6399

Valley Cities Counseling and Consultation
33301 1st Way South, Suite C-115
Federal Way, WA 98003

Western Clinical Health Services
2025 South 341st Place
Federal Way, WA 98003

FERNDALE

Jerry F. Starr Memorial Foundation Avalon Counseling and Treatment Services
5778 2nd Avenue, Suite B
Ferndale, WA 98248

FORKS

West End Outreach Services Forks Community Hospital
550 5th Street
Forks, WA 98331

FORT LEWIS

Alcohol and Drug Abuse Prevention and Control Program
HQ I Corps/Fort Lewis
Building 2006 Room 206
Fort Lewis, WA 98433

FRIDAY HARBOR

San Juan Community Alcoholism Center
955 Guard Street
Friday Harbor, WA 98250

GIG HARBOR

Center Peninsula
7116 Pioneer Way
Gig Harbor, WA 98335

Gig Harbor Counseling and Recovery Center
5112 Olympic Drive NW
Gig Harbor, WA 98335

GOLDENDALE

Goldendale Branch White Salmon Counseling
777 East Broadway Street, Suite 1
Goldendale, WA 98620

Kick/It Counseling
104 East Main Street
Goldendale, WA 98620-9005

GRANDVIEW

Phoenix Addiction Counseling Services
242 Division Street
Grandview, WA 98930

HOQUIAM

Evergreen Chemical Dependency Program
804 Levee Street
Hoquiam, WA 98550

Grays Harbor Crisis Clinic Detox Unit
615 8th Street
Hoquiam, WA 98550

ISSAQUAH

Friends of Youth Issaquah
414 Front Street
Issaquah, WA 98027

Lakeside/Milam Issaquah Outpatient
98 North East Gilman Street
Suite 200
Issaquah, WA 98027

KELSO

Drug Abuse Prevention Center
214 North Pacific Avenue
Kelso, WA 98626

First Place Inc
309 Oak Street
Kelso, WA 98626

KENMORE

Residence XII
14506 Juanita Drive NE
Kenmore, WA 98028

KENNEWICK

Action Chemical Dependency Center
552 North Colorado Street
Suite 114
Kennewick, WA 99336

Advocates for Wellness
120 Vista Way
Kennewick, WA 99336

Discovery Substance Abuse Services
5219 West Clearwater Avenue
Suite 9
Kennewick, WA 99336

Life Changes Chemical Dependency Agency
313 North Morain Street
Kennewick, WA 99336

KENT

Comprehensive Alcohol Services
1609 South Central Avenue
Suite 1
Kent, WA 98032

Hope Recovery Services
10820 South Kent-Kangley Road
Kent, WA 98031

Kent Youth and Family Services
232 South 2 Avenue
Suite 201
Kent, WA 98032

South King County Recovery Centers
505 South Washington Avenue
Kent, WA 98032

KINGSTON

Port Gamble Klallam Recovery Center
32272 Little Boston Road NE
Kingston, WA 98346

KIRKLAND

Lakeside Milam Recovery Centers
10422 NE 37th Circle, Suite B
Kirkland, WA 98033

10322 NE 132nd Street
Kirkland, WA 98034

McClure and Associates Counseling
11416 Slater Avenue NE, Suite 202
Kirkland, WA 98033

Youth Eastside Services Lake Washington
13009 85th Street
Kirkland, WA 98033

LAKEWOOD

Moms and Women's Recovery Center
9609 Bristol Street
Lakewood, WA 98499

LA PUSH

Quileute Family and Health Services
560 Quileute Heights Road
La Push, WA 98350

LONGVIEW

Chance for Change
828 12th Avenue, Suite B
Longview, WA 98632

Starting Point, Inc.
1315 Hemlock Street
Longview, WA 98632

LYNDEN

The Center
310 5th Street
Lynden, WA 98264-1911

LYNNWOOD

Crosby Enterprises, Inc.
3924 204 Street SW
Lynnwood, WA 98036

Family Counseling Service DBA Northwest Alternatives
4230 198th Street SW, Suite 100
Lynnwood, WA 98036-672

Options Treatment and Evaluations
15620 Highway 99, Suite 10
Lynnwood, WA 98037

Pacific Treatment Alternatives
19324 40 Avenue West
Suite A
Lynnwood, WA 98036

MAPLE VALLEY

Cedar Hills Treatment Center
15900 227 Avenue SE
Maple Valley, WA 98038

MARYSVILLE

Northwest Alternatives
1410 7th Street
Marysville, WA 98270

Tulalip Tribal Alcoholism Program
6700 Todum Road
Marysville, WA 98271

Tulalip Tribes Recovery Home
2821 Mission Hill Road
Marysville, WA 98271

MCCHORD AIR FORCE BASE

62 MDG/SGOHA Alcohol and Drug Abuse Prevention and Treatment
Building 100, Room 3012
McChord AFB, WA 98438

MEDICAL LAKE

Pine Lodge Pre-Release
751 Pine Street
Medical Lake, WA 99022

MONROE

Alpha Center for Treatment, Inc.
18962 South Route 2, Suite A
Monroe, WA 98272

Drug Abuse Council of Snohomish County
909 West Main Street, Suite 9
Monroe, WA 98272

Family Counseling DBA Northwest Alternatives
18962 State Road 2, Suite A
Monroe, WA 98272

Valley General Hospital Alcohol and Drug Recovery Center
14701 179 Street SE
Monroe, WA 98272

MONTESANO

Healthy Risk Counseling Center
330 Pioneer Avenue West
Montesano, WA 98563

MOSES LAKE

Grant County Alcohol and Drug Center
510 West Broadway
Moses Lake, WA 98837

MOUNT VERNON

Skagit Community Mental Health Center
916 South 3rd Street
Mount Vernon, WA 98273

Skagit Recovery Center John King Recovery House
1905 Continental Place
Mount Vernon, WA 98273

NASELLE

Naselle Youth Camp Bridge
11 Youth Camp Lane
Naselle, WA 98638

NESPELEM

Colville Tribal Alcohol Drug Program
Confederated Tribes of Colville
Street
Nespelem, WA 99155

NEWPORT

Pend Oreille County Mental Health
325 South Spokane Street
Newport, WA 99156

OAK HARBOR

Recovery Center Island County
231 SE Barrington Drive
Suite 209
Oak Harbor, WA 98277

OAKVILLE

Tsapowum Chehalis Tribal Chemical Dependency Program
420 Howanut Drive
Oakville, WA 98568

OLALLA

Olalla Recovery Center
12851 Lala Cove Lane SE
Olalla, WA 98359

OLYMPIA

BHR Recovery Services
317 East 4th Avenue
Olympia, WA 98501

Group Health Cooperative Behavioral Health Services
700 North Lilly Road NE
Olympia, WA 98506

Northwest Resources
2742 Pacific Avenue
Olympia, WA 98506

Olympic Counseling Services/ Tamarc
1625 Mottman Road SW
Olympia, WA 98502

Recovery Associates
317 Fourth Avenue East
Olympia, WA 98501

Right Step, Inc.
3929 Martin Way East
Suites A and B
Olympia, WA 98506

OMAK

Okanogan County Counseling Services Chemical Dependency Programs
307 South Main Street
Omak, WA 98841

OTHELLO

Adams County Community Counseling Service Alcohol/ Drug Abuse Program
165 North First Street
Suite 120
Othello, WA 99334

PARKLAND

Moms and Women's Recovery Center
12108 Pacific Avenue
Parkland, WA 98444

PASCO

Benton Franklin Detox Services
1020 South 7th Street
Pasco, WA 99301

Unity Counseling Services
303 North 20 Street
Pasco, WA 99301

POMEROY

Rogers Counseling Center
856 Main Street
Pomeroy, WA 99347

PORT ANGELES

Healthy Families of Clallam County
1914 West 18th Street
Port Angeles, WA 98363

Lower Elwha Chemical Dependency Program
22 Kwitsen Drive
Port Angeles, WA 98362

Peninsula Community Mental Health Center Substance Abuse Services
118 East 8 Street
Port Angeles, WA 98362

Woodlands
1225 East Front Street
Port Angeles, WA 98362

PORT ORCHARDS

Olympic Educational Services/ District 114
1962 Hoover Avenue SE
Port Orchard, WA 98366

Port Orchard Counseling Recovery Center
1950 Pottery Avenue
Port Orchard, WA 98366

West Sound Treatment Center
120 Bethel Avenue
Port Orchard, WA 98366

PORT TOWNSEND

Jefferson County Community Recovery Center
1200 Sims Way
Port Townsend, WA 98368

Safe Harbor Recovery Center
686 Lake Street, Suite 400
Port Townsend, WA 98368-2272

PULLMAN

Abstemious Outpatient Clinic
10525 East Main Street, Suite P
Pullman, WA 99206

Whitman County Alcohol Center
NE 340 Maple Street
Room 2
Pullman, WA 99163

PUYALLUP

Counselor
315 39 Avenue SW
Suite 11
Puyallup, WA 98373

Horizon Treatment Services
11212 94th Avenue East, Suite B
Puyallup, WA 98373-3656

Lakeside Recovery Center
12812 101st Avenue, Suite 103
Puyallup, WA 98373

Shared Health Services
10116 116th Street East
Suite 202 and 102
Puyallup, WA 98373

REDMOND

**Group Health Cooperative
    Alcohol and Drug Abuse Unit**
2700 152 Avenue NE
Redmond, WA 98052

Square One Redmond
7811 159th Place NE
Redmond, WA 98052-7301

RENTON

**Lakeside/Milam Recovery
    Centers, Inc. South**
1000 SW 7th Street
Renton, WA 98055

**Renton Area Youth Services
    (RAYS)**
1025 South 3 Street
Renton, WA 98055

Valley Medical Recovery Center
400 South 43 Street
Renton, WA 98055

REPUBLIC

**Change Point of Ferry County
    Community Services**
42 North Klondike Road
Republic, WA 99166

RICHLAND

Carondelet/Lourdes ADTP
1175 Carondelet Drive
Richland, WA 99352

Choices and Changes, Inc.
1236 Columbia Drive SE
Richland, WA 99352

SEATTLE

Addiction Recovery Systems
720 Broadway
Seattle, WA 98125

Alternatives
1530 Eastlake Avenue East
Suite 305
Seattle, WA 98109

Associated Behavioral Health
120 Northgate Plaza
Northgate Medical Building
Suite 355
Seattle, WA 98125

Bissell Institute
22620 7th Avenue South
Seattle, WA 98198

Catholic Community Services
100 23rd Avenue South
Seattle, WA 98144

Central Seattle Recovery Center
464 12th Avenue Suite 300
Seattle, WA 98122

Detoxification Unit
1309 Summit Avenue
Seattle, WA 98101

**Central Youth and Family
    Services**
1901 Martin Luther King Jr. Way
    South
Seattle, WA 98144

Chrysalis Recovery Inc
816 North 38th Street
Seattle, WA 98103

Circle of Recovery
1207 North 200th Street
Seattle, WA 98133

**Cocaine Outreach and Recovery
    Programs**
1509 East Madison Street, Suite
    101
Seattle, WA 98122

**Consejo Counseling and
    Referral Services**
3808 South Angeline Street
Seattle, WA 98118

**Dykeman, Ruth Youth and
    Family Service**
15001 8 Avenue SW
Seattle, WA 98166

Evergreen Treatment Services
1700 Airport Way South
Seattle, WA 98134-1618

1740 Airport Way South
Seattle, WA 98134-1618

Genesis House
621 34 Avenue
Seattle, WA 98122

Group Health/Behavioral Health
1730 Minor Avenue
Suite 1400
Seattle, WA 98101

Guardian Recovery Program
4812 Aurora Avenue North
Seattle, WA 98121

Highline West
2600 SW Holden Street
Seattle, WA 98126-3505

Iwasil Youth Program
102 Prefontaine Place
Seattle, WA 98104

Milam Recovery Program
12845 Ambaum Boulevard SW
Seattle, WA 98146

Perinatal Treatment Services
1005 East Jefferson Street
Seattle, WA 98122

Praxis
1319 Dexter Avenue North, Suite
    290
Seattle, WA 98109

2825 Eastlake Avenue East
Suite 305
Seattle, WA 98102

Professional Health Associates
610 NW 44th Street
Seattle, WA 98107-4431

Recovery Options Northwest
2150 North 107th Street
Suite 200
Seattle, WA 98133-9009

Ryther Child Center
Adolescent Alcohol and Substance
   Abuse Program
2400 NE 95th Street
Seattle, WA 98115-2499

Safeco Safe House
11729 1/2 36th Avenue NE
Seattle, WA 98125

Schick Shadel Hospital
   Substance Abuse Program
12101 Ambaum Boulevard SW
Seattle, WA 98146

Seadrunar
Phase I/Georgetown
976 South Harney Street
Seattle, WA 98108

Queenanne
200 West Comstock Street
Seattle, WA 98119

Seattle Indian Health Board
   Alcohol/Drug Outpatient
611 12 Avenue South
Seattle, WA 98144

Shamrock Group, Inc.
8535 Phinney Avenue North
Seattle, WA 98103

Shared Health Services
14900 Interurban Avenue South
Suite 215
Seattle, WA 98168

Stonewall Recovery Services
430 Broadway East
Seattle, WA 98107

Sunrise Centers
12650 First Avenue South
Seattle, WA 98168

Swedish Medical Center
Addiction Recovery Program
5300 Tallman Street NW
Seattle, WA 98104

Therapeutic Health Services,
   Inc. Midvale Treatment
   Center
1116 Summit Avenue
Seattle, WA 98101

Thunderbird Treatment Center
9236 Renton Avenue South
Seattle, WA 98118

Trexam Program
1530 Eastlake Avenue East
Suite 203
Seattle, WA 98102

Veterans' Affairs Medical Center
   Addiction Treatment Center
1660 Columbian Way South
Seattle, WA 98108

Virginia Mason Chemical
   Dependency Program
1100 Olive Way
Metro Park West Tower
Suite 1000
Seattle, WA 98101

Washington Asian Pacific
   Islander Families
606 Maynard Avenue South
Suite 106
Seattle, WA 98104-2957

Women's Recovery Center
4649 Sunnyside Avenue North
Suite 200
Seattle, WA 98103

SEDRO WOOLLEY

Pioneer Center North
2275 Thompson Drive
Sedro Woolley, WA 98284

Safe Passage NPO
2268 Hub Drive
Sedro Woolley, WA 98284

United Northwest Recovery
   Center, Inc.
605 B Sunset Park Drive
Sedro Woolley, WA 98284-1578

SEQUIM

Jamestown S. Klallam Chemical
   Dependency Program
1032 Old Blyn Highway
Sequim, WA 98382

Safe Harbor Recovery Center
271 South 7th Avenue, Suite 23
Sequim, WA 98382-3633

SHELTON

Olympic Counseling Services/
   Tamarc
615 Alder Street
Shelton, WA 98584

Recovery Associates
110 West K Street
Shelton, WA 98584

Skokomish Tribe Alcohol/Drug
   Program Hope
North 80 Tribal Center Road
Shelton, WA 98584

Squaxin Island Health Clinic
70 Squaxin Lane SE
Shelton, WA 98584

Right Step, Inc.
111 East Railroad Avenue
Shelton, WA 98584

SHORELINE

Center for Human Services
17018 15th Avenue NE
Shoreline, WA 98155

Therapeutic Health Services
17962 Midvale Avenue North,
   Suite 150
Shoreline, WA 98133-4922

SILVERDALE

Cascade Recovery Center
   Silverdale
9095 McConnell Avenue
Silverdale, WA 98383

SNOQUALMIE

Echo Glen Children's Center Exodus
33010 SE 99 Street
Snoqualmie, WA 98065

SPOKANE

Abstemious Outpatient Clinic, Inc.
1007 West Francis Avenue
Spokane, WA 99205

Addiction Recovery Systems, Inc.
West 601 Francis Avenue
Spokane, WA 99205

American Behavioral Health Systems, Inc.
3400 West Garland Street
Spokane, WA 99205

Behavioral Health Services
2703 North Pittsburgh Street
Spokane, WA 99209

Colonial Clinic
N 910 Washington Street
Suite 210
Spokane, WA 99204

Community Detox Services of Spokane
165 South Howard Street
Spokane, WA 99204

Daybreak of Spokane
11707 East Sprague, Suite D4
Spokane, WA 99206

Intensive Inpatient Program for Youth
Outpatient Treatment
628 South Cowley
Spokane, WA 99223

Deaconess Medical Center Chemical Dependency Unit
800 West 5th Avenue
Spokane, WA 99210

Group Health Northwest Chemical Dependency Program
322 West North River Drive
Spokane, WA 99201

Healing Lodge of The Seven Nations Youth Treatment Center
5600 East 8th Avenue
Spokane, WA 99212

Isabella House
West 2308 3 Avenue
Spokane, WA 99204

Lakeside Recovery Centers
601 West Mallon Avenue, Suite C
Spokane, WA 99201

Native Project
1803 West Maxwell Street
Spokane, WA 99201

New Horizon Counseling Services
West 2317 3 Avenue
Spokane, WA 99204

Spokane Addiction Recovery Centers (SPARC)
1509 West 8 Avenue
Spokane, WA 99204

1508 West 6th Avenue
Spokane, WA 99204

West 1403 7th Avenue
Spokane, WA 99204

Spokane Regional Health District
1101 West College Avenue
Spokane, WA 99201

Stepps/YFA Connections
901 East 2nd Avenue Suite 100
Spokane, WA 99202-2257

Sun Ray Court
518 South Browne Street
Spokane, WA 99202

Veterans' Affairs Medical Center Substance Abuse Treatment Program
4815 North Assembly Street
Spokane, WA 99205

STEVENSON

Skamania County Counseling Center
683 SW Rock Creek Drive
Stevenson, WA 98648

SUMNER

Moms and Women's Recovery Center
930 Alder Street
Sumner, WA 98390

Prosperity Counseling and Treatment Services, Inc.
1723 Bonney Avenue, Suite A
Sumner, WA 98390

The Center East
1110 Fryar Avenue
Sumner, WA 98390

SUNNYSIDE

Merit Resource Services
702 East Franklin Street
Sunnyside, WA 98944

SUQUAMISH

Suquamish Wellness Program
18465-A Augusta Avenue
Suquamish, WA 98392

TACOMA

Action Association Counseling Services
923 Martin Luther King Jr. Way
Tacoma, WA 98405-4149

Affirmation Counseling Services
4301 South Pine Street
Suite 30
Tacoma, WA 98409

Crossroads Treatment Center
6403 Lakewood Drive West
Tacoma, WA 98467

Griffin and Griffin EAP, Inc.
4218 South Steele Street
Suite 304
Tacoma, WA 98409

Health Department Methadone Treatment Program
3629 South D Street MS-049
Tacoma, WA 98408

Horizon Treatment Services
2607 Bridgeport Way West
Suite 2-J
Tacoma, WA 98466

Lakeside/Milam Recovery Centers, Inc.
535 Dock Street, Suite 104
Tacoma, WA 98402

Moms and Women's Recovery Center
2367 Tacoma Avenue South
Tacoma, WA 98402

Pierce County Alliance
510 Tacoma Avenue South
Tacoma, WA 98402

Puyallup Tribal Treatment Center
2209 East 32 Street
Tacoma, WA 98402

Reflections Recovery and Learning Center
8907-C Gravelly Lake Drive SW
Tacoma, WA 98499-3109

Remann Hall Alcohol and Drug Development Program (RHADD)
5501 6th Avenue
Tacoma, WA 98406-2697

Serenity Counseling Services
4410 East 20th Street
Tacoma, WA 98424

Shared Health Services
9112 Lakewood Drive SW
Suite 208
Tacoma, WA 98499

Social Treatment Opportunity Programs (STOP)
4301 South Pine Street, Suite 112
Tacoma, WA 98409

Tacoma Detoxification Center
721 Fawcett Avenue
Room 100
Tacoma, WA 98402

The Center MDC
721 South Fawcett Street
Suite 203
Tacoma, WA 98402

The Center South
10510 Gravelly Lake Drive SW
Tacoma, WA 98498

Transitions Limited
1004 72nd Street
Tacoma, WA 98445

Upper Tacoma Treatment Service
2367 South Tacoma Avenue
Tacoma, WA 98402

Western Washington Alcohol Center, Inc.
504 South 112th Street
Suite 214
Tacoma, WA 98409

TAHOLAH

Quinault Indian Nation Alcoholism Treatment Program
116 Quinault Street
Taholah, WA 98587

TOKELAND

Shoalwater Bay Tribe Counseling Chemical Dependency Program
4138 Shoalwater Bay Drive
Tokeland, WA 98590

TOPPENISH

Merit Resource Services
307 Asotin Street
Toppenish, WA 98948

Phoenix Support Services, Inc.
304 Monroe Street
Toppenish, WA 98948

USK

Kalispel Tribe Social Services Alcohol Program
Usk, WA 99180

VANCOUVER

Clark County Council on Alcohol and Drugs 8th Street Branch
509 West 8 Street
Vancouver, WA 98660

Columbia Treatment Services
7017 NE Highway 99, Suite 114
Vancouver, WA 98665

John Owen Recovery House
1950 Fort Vancouver Way
Vancouver, WA 98663

Rivercrest Treatment Center
1815 D Street
Vancouver, WA 98663

Starting Point
2703 East Mill Plain Boulevard
Vancouver, WA 98661

Western Psychological and Counseling Services
5305 East 18th Street
Suite A-East
Vancouver, WA 98661-6582

WALLA WALLA

Chemical Dependency Treatment Program DVAMC
77 Wainwright Drive
Suite 112-MH
Walla Walla, WA 99362

WAPATO

Merit Resource Services
312 West 2 Street
Wapato, WA 98951

WELLPINIT

Spokane Tribe of Indians Tribal Alcoholism and Drug Abuse Program
Old School Lane
Wellpinit, WA 99040

WENATCHEE

Center for Alcohol and Drug Treatment Casa, Inc.
327 Okanogan Avenue
Wenatchee, WA 98801

Olympic Counseling Services
766 South Mission Street
Wenatchee, WA 98801-3052

Quality Resources
6 First Street, Suite 6
Wenatchee, WA 98801

WHITE SALMON

White Salmon Counseling
1000 Jewett Boulevard, Suite 4
White Salmon, WA 98672

WOODINVILLE

Motivations
17311 135 Avenue NE
Suite C-400
Woodinville, WA 98072

YAKIMA

A J Alcohol and Drug Services
32 North 3 Street
Room 310
Yakima, WA 98901

Barth Clinic
414 North 2nd Street
Suite 2
Yakima, WA 98901

**Central Washington
  Comprehensive Mental Health
  Drug Program**
321 East Yakima Avenue
Yakima, WA 98901

**James Oldham Treatment
  Center**
308 North 4th Street
Yakima, WA 98907

Riel House
1408 West Yakima Avenue
Yakima, WA 98902

Sundown M Ranch
2280 SR 821
Yakima, WA 98901

**Triumph Treatment Services,
  Inc. Community Drug and
  Alcohol Center**
102 South Naches Avenue
Yakima, WA 98901

**Yakima Human Services DBA
  Dependency Health Services**
315 Holton Avenue, Suite B-1
Yakima, WA 98902

Detox Unit
401 South 5th Avenue
Yakima, WA 98902

YELM

Resolution A Counseling Service
10501 Creek Street SE
Suite 4
Yelm, WA 98597

WEST VIRGINIA

BARBOURSVILLE

Cedar Ridge Group Home
55 Bass Avenue
Barboursville, WV 25504

BECKLEY

**FMRS Mental Health Council,
  Inc.**
Public Inebriate Shelter
101 South Eisenhower Drive
Beckley, WV 25801

**Southern West Virginia
  Fellowship Home, Inc.**
201 Woodlawn Avenue
Beckley, WV 25801

**Veterans' Affairs Medical Center
  Substance Abuse Treatment
  Program**
200 Veterans Avenue
Beckley, WV 25801

BERKELEY SPRINGS

Eastridge Health Systems
404 South Green Street
Berkeley Springs, WV 25411

BUCKHANNON

**Appalachian Community Health
  Center, Inc. Upshur County
  Office**
27 South Kanawha Street
Buckhannon, WV 26201

**Saint Josephs Hospital Center
  Behavioral Health Unit**
Amalia Drive
Buckhannon, WV 26201

CHARLESTON

**Alliance Behavioral Services,
  Inc.**
3508 Staunton Avenue, Suite 300
Charleston, WV 25304-1477

**Behavioral Health Services
  Charleston Area Medical
  Center**
Brooks and Morris Streets
Charleston, WV 25302

**Behavioral Health Services
  Substance Abuse Services**
501 Morris Street
Charleston, WV 25301

Hopemont
State Route 1 Box 223
Charleston, WV 25304

PEERS
600 Broad Street
Charleston, WV 25301

Shawnee Hills, Inc.
DUI Safety Treatment Program
Adult Outpatient Services
600 North Broad Street, 2nd Floor
Charleston, WV 25301

Southway Treatment Center
4605 Maccorkle Avenue SW
Charleston, WV 25309

CHARLES TOWN

Eastridge Health Systems
114 West Liberty Street
Charles Town, WV 25414

CHATTAROY

Logan/Mingo Area Mental Health, Inc. Mingo County Office
Buffalo Creek Road
Chattaroy, WV 25667

CLARKSBURG

United Summit Center Adult Intensive Outpatient Program
6 Hospital Plaza
Clarksburg, WV 26301

Veterans' Affairs Medical Center Substance Abuse Services
Medical Center Drive
Clarksburg, WV 26301

CROSS LANES

Viewpoint
5405 Alpine Drive
Cross Lanes, WV 25313

DANVILLE

Shawnee Hills, Inc.
DUI Safety Treatment Program
Adult Outpatient Services
2 Human Services Complex
Danville, WV 25053

ELKINS

Appalachian Community Health Center
725 Yokum Street
Elkins, WV 26241

Public Inebriate/Detainee Shelter
Gorman and Main Streets
Elkins, WV 26241

FAIRMONT

Fairmont General Hospital Addiction Treatment
1325 Locust Avenue
Fairmont, WV 26554

Valley Comprehensive Community Mental Health Center, Inc.
Alpha Chemical Dependency Treatment Unit
100 Crosswind Drive
Fairmont, WV 26554

Marion County Office
28 Oakwood Road
Fairmont, WV 26554

New Beginnings Program for Women
202 Columbia Street
Fairmont, WV 26554

Crossroads Treatment Program for Adolescents
28 Oakwood Road
Fairmont, WV 26554

FAYETTEVILLE

FMRS Mental Health Council Fayette County Office
209 West Maple Avenue
Fayetteville, WV 25840

GRAFTON

Valley Comprehensive Community Mental Health Center Taylor County Office
501 North Pike Street
Grafton, WV 26354

GYPSY

Rainbow House
158 Main Street
Gypsy, WV 26361

HARRISVILLE

Westbrook Health Services
605 North Street
Harrisville, WV 26362-1205

HUNTINGTON

Area Psychiatric and Psychotherapy Group
1326 6th Avenue
Huntington, WV 25701-2100

Columbia Riverpark Hospital
1230 6th Avenue
Huntington, WV 25701

Innerchange/Prestera River Park Hospital
1230 6th Avenue
Huntington, WV 25701

Laurelwood
432 6th Avenue
Huntington, WV 25701

PARC Way Assessment Center
1530 Norway Avenue
Huntington, WV 25709

PARC West
318 West 14th Street
Huntington, WV 25701

Prestera Center for Mental Health Services, Inc.
1420 Washington Avenue
Huntington, WV 25705

Saint Mary's Hospital Substance Abuse Unit
2900 First Avenue
Huntington, WV 25701

Veterans Affairs Medical Center Outpatient Treatment Program
1540 Spring Valley Drive
Huntington, WV 25704

KINGWOOD

Olympic Center/Preston Adolescent Treatment Program
Route 7
Kingwood, WV 26537

Preston Addiction Treatment Center
300 South Price Street
Kingwood, WV 26537

Valley Comprehensive Community Mental Health Center, Inc. Preston County Office
202 Tunnelton Street Garden Towers
Kingwood, WV 26537

LOGAN

Logan/Mingo Area Mental Health Substance Abuse Services
Route 10
3 Mile Curve
Logan, WV 25601

MARLINGTON

Seneca MH/MR Council, Inc. Pocahontas County Office
704 3rd Avenue
Marlinton, WV 24954

MARTINSBURG

CAT 5/Substance Abuse Services
Route 9 South
Martinsburg, WV 25401

City Hospital, Inc. Gateway Behavioral Health Services
Dry Run Road
Martinsburg, WV 25401

Eastridge Health Systems Eastridge Addiction Treatment Center
125 West Martin Street
Martinsburg, WV 25401

MORGANTOWN

Valley Comprehensive CMHC Main Unit
301 Scott Avenue
Morgantown, WV 26505

MOUNDSVILLE

Northwood Health Systems
10 Ash Avenue
Moundsville, WV 26041

MULLENS

Southern Highlands Community Mental Health Center, Inc.
Wyoming County Office/Mullens Clinic
102 Howard Avenue
Mullens, WV 25882

NEW MARTINSVILLE

Evergreen Behavioral Health
240 North Street
New Martinsville, WV 26155-0247

Northwood Health Systems Wetzel County Office
747 2nd Street
New Martinsville, WV 26155

PARKERSBURG

Saint Josephs Hospital Center for Behavioral Medicine
1824 Murdoch Avenue
Parkersburg, WV 26101

Westbrook Health Services Amity Center
1011 Mission Drive
Parkersburg, WV 26101

Worthington Center, Inc.
3199 Core Road
Parkersburg, WV 26104

PARSONS

Appalachian Community Health Center, Inc. Tucker County Office
601 Walnut Street
Parsons, WV 26287

PETERSBURG

Potomac Highlands Guild, Inc.
1 Virginia Avenue
Petersburg, WV 26847

PHILIPPI

Appalachian Community Health Center, Inc. Barbour County Office
227 Garnett Avenue
Philippi, WV 26416

POINT PLEASANT

Prestera Center for Mental Health Services, Inc. Mason County Office
715 Main Street
Point Pleasant, WV 25550

PRINCETON

Mercer/McDowell/Wyoming Mental Health Council, Inc. Mentoring Program
200 12th Street Extension
Princeton, WV 24740

Southern Highlands Community Mental Health Center, Inc.
200 12 Street Extension
Princeton, WV 24740

RAINELLE

Seneca MH/MR Council, Inc.
645 Kanawha Avenue Suite A
Rainelle, WV 25962

RIPLEY

Westbrook Health Services Jackson County Office
6003 Church Street
Ripley, WV 25271

SOUTH CHARLESTON

Thomas Memorial Hospital Southway Outpatient Program
4825 MacCorkle Avenue SW
Suite B
South Charleston, WV 25309

SPENCER

Westbrook Health Services Roane County Office
227 Clay Road
Spencer, WV 25276

SUMMERSVILLE

Seneca MH/MR Council, Inc.
1 Stevens Road
Summersville, WV 26651

SUTTON

Braxton County Fellowship Home
72 South Stone Wall Street
Suite 2
Sutton, WV 26601

TERRA ALTA

Shawnee Hills, Inc.
Rehabilitation Unit
Substance Abuse Treatment
State Route 1
Terra Alta, WV 26764

UNION

**FMRS Mental Health Council
  Monroe County Office**
Monroe County Health Center
Union, WV 24983

VIENNA

Westbrook Health Services
1907 Grand Central Avenue
Lower Level
Vienna, WV 26105

WAYNE

**Prestera Center for Mental
  Health Services, Inc.**
145 Kenova Avenue
Wayne, WV 25570

WEBSTER SPRINGS

**Seneca MH/MR Council, Inc.
  Webster County Office**
70 Parcoal Road
Webster Springs, WV 26288

WEIRTON

Healthways, Inc.
501 Colliers Way
Weirton, WV 26062

WELCH

**Southern Highlands Community
  Mental Health Center, Inc.
  McDowell County Office**
787 Virginia Avenue
Welch, WV 24801

WHEELING

**Northwood Health Systems First
  Step Program**
111 19th Street
Wheeling, WV 26003

New Hope
304 North East Street
Wheeling, WV 26003

WISCONSIN

ALGOMA

**Kewaunee County Community
  Programs Alcohol and Drug
  Abuse Treatment Program**
522 4 Street
Algoma, WI 54201

ALMA

Gundersen Lutheran
Alma, WI 54610

AMERY

Cottonwood Group Homes, Ltd.
773 Rustic Road
Amery, WI 54001

ANTIGO

Langlade Health Care Center
1225 Langlade Road
Antigo, WI 54409

APPLETON

Casa Clare, Inc.
310 North Durkee Street
Appleton, WI 54911

**Health Assessment and
  Counseling Services**
1531 South Madison Street
Madison Center, Suite 530
Appleton, WI 54915

Lutheran Social Services
1412 North Rankin Street
Appleton, WI 54913

Meridian House
1308 North Leona Street
Appleton, WI 54913

Saint Elizabeth Hospital
Alcohol/Drug Program (ADP)
1506 South Oneida Street
Appleton, WI 54915

**The Mooring Halfway House,
  Inc.**
607 West 7th Street
Appleton, WI 54911

ARCADIA

**Franciscan Skemp Healthcare
  Emergency Room Substance
  Abuse Services**
464 South Saint Joseph Avenue
Arcadia, WI 54612

ASHLAND

**Ashland County Information
  and Referral Center**
206 6th Avenue West
Room 213
Ashland, WI 54806

**Memorial Medical Center, Inc.
  Behavioral Health Services**
1635 Maple Lane
Ashland, WI 54806

**New Horizons North Community
  Support Services**
511 West Main Street Suite 1
Ashland, WI 54806

BARABOO

**Saint Clare Hospital Saint Clare
  Center**
707 14th Street
Baraboo, WI 53913

**Sauk County Dept of Human
  Services Alcoholism and Drug
  Abuse Outpatient Services**
505 Broadway Street
Baraboo, WI 53913

BAYFIELD

Red Cliff Tribe AODA Program
Old Dump Road Off Blueberry
   Road
Bayfield, WI 54814

BEAVER DAM

Psychiatric Associates
200 Front Street
Beaver Dam, WI 53916

BELOIT

**Beloit Inner City Council
   Substance Abuse Services**
1435 Wisconsin Avenue
Beloit, WI 53511

**Mercy Options Addiction
   Treatment Services**
2825 Prairie Avenue
Beloit, WI 53511

BERLIN

**Berlin Memorial Hospital
   Emergency Detoxification**
225 Memorial Drive
Berlin, WI 54923

BLACK RIVER FALLS

**Franciscan Skemp Behavioral
   Health**
208 Main Street
Black River Falls, WI 54615-1747

**Ho Chunk Nation Dept of Social
   Services Alcohol/Drug
   Program Services**
1 North 2nd Street
Black River Falls, WI 54615

Kruhn Clinic
610 West Adams Street
Black River Falls, WI 54615

BOSCOBEL

**Memorial Hospital of Boscobel
   Substance Abuse Services**
205 Parker Street
Boscobel, WI 53805

BOWLER

**Stockbridge/Munsee Health
   Center Tribal Alcoholism
   Treatment Program**
N8705 Moh-He-Con-Nuck Road
Bowler, WI 54416

BROOKFIELD

**Elmbrook Memorial Hospital
   Alcohol and Drug Treatment
   Center**
19333 West North Avenue
Brookfield, WI 53045

BURLINGTON

Transition House
501 McHenry Street
Burlington, WI 53105

CHILTON

**Calumet County Human Service
   Dept. Alcohol and Other Drug
   Abuse Unit**
206 Court Street
Courthouse
Chilton, WI 53014

CHIPPEWA FALLS

**L. E. Phillips Libertas Center
   for the Chemically Dependent**
2661 County Road I
Chippewa Falls, WI 54729

**Serenity House, Inc.
   Transitional Living Program**
205 East Grand Avenue
Chippewa Falls, WI 54729

Transitus House
1830 Wheaton Street
Chippewa Falls, WI 54729

CRANDON

**Forest County Potawatomi
   Alcohol and Drug Program**
Crandon, WI 54520

**Koller Behavioral Health
   Services**
213 East Madison Street
Crandon, WI 54520

CUMBERLAND

**Cumberland Memorial Hospital
   Emergency Detoxification**
1110 7 Avenue
Cumberland, WI 54829

**Northern Pines Unified Service
   Center Board Chemical
   Dependency Service**
1066 8 Avenue
Cumberland, WI 54829

DARLINGTON

**Lafayette County Department of
   Human Services/AODA
   Program**
627 Main Street
Darlington, WI 53530

**Memorial Hospital of Lafayette
   County**
800 Clay Street
Darlington, WI 53530

DODGEVILLE

**Unified Counseling Services
   Dodgeville Outpatient Clinic**
410 North Union Street
Dodgeville, WI 53533

EAGLE RIVER

**Eagle River Memorial Hospital
   Emergency Room Substance
   Abuse Services**
201 Hospital Road
Eagle River, WI 54521

**Koller Behavioral Health
   Services**
150 Hospital Road
Eagle River, WI 54521

EAU CLAIRE

Eau Claire Academy
550 North Dewey Street
Eau Claire, WI 54701

Fahrman Center
3136 Craig Road
Eau Claire, WI 54701

First Things First Counseling and Consulting, Ltd.
2125 Heights Drive, Suite 2-D
Eau Claire, WI 54701

Luther Midelfort Behavioral Health
1221 Whipple Street
Eau Claire, WI 54702

Lutheran Social Services
3136 Craig Road
Eau Claire, WI 54701

Sacred Heart Hospital Substance Abuse Services
900 West Clairemont Avenue
Eau Claire, WI 54701

Triniteam, Inc. Treatment Alternative Program
202 Graham Avenue
Eau Claire, WI 54701

ELKHORN

Walworth County Department of Human Services Center
County Highway NN
Elkhorn, WI 53121

ELLSWORTH

Pierce County Dept. of Human Services Alcohol and Other Drug Abuse Services
412 West Kinne Street
Ellsworth, WI 54011

ELROY

Franciscan Skemp Healthcare Community Services Pinecrest Center
1510 Academy Street
Elroy, WI 53929

FOND DU LAC

Beacon House
166 South Park Avenue
Fond Du Lac, WI 54935

Blandine House, Inc.
25 North Park Avenue
Fond du Lac, WI 54935

Robert E. Berry Halfway House
178 6th Street
Fond du Lac, WI 54935

Saint Agnes Hospital Behavioral Health Services
430 East Division Street
Fond du Lac, WI 54935

FORT ATKINSON

Fort Atkinson Memorial Health Services
611 East Sherman Avenue
Fort Atkinson, WI 53538

FRIENDSHIP

Adams County Dept. of Community Programs
108 East North Street
Friendship, WI 53934

GREEN BAY

Brown County Mental Health Center Alcohol and Other Drug Abuse Services
2900 Saint Anthony Drive
Green Bay, WI 54311

Family Service Association Outpatient AODA Program
300 Crooks Street
Green Bay, WI 54301

Jackie Nitschke Center, Inc.
630 Cherry Street
Green Bay, WI 54301

Libertas Treatment Center
1701 Dousman Street
Green Bay, WI 54303

Oneida Tribal Social Services Counseling Services
2640 West Point Road
Green Bay, WI 54304

GREEN LAKE

Green Lake County Human Services Dept. Community Services Unit
500 Lake Steel Street
Green Lake, WI 54941

GRESHAM

Maehnowesekiyah Treatment Program
N 4587 County Highway G
Gresham, WI 54128

HALES CORNERS

Cedar Creek Family Counseling
9415 West Forest Home Avenue, Suite 108
Hales Corners, WI 53130

HAYWARD

Hayward Area Memorial Hospital Substance Abuse Services
Route 3
Hayward, WI 54843

Lac Courte Oreilles Alcohol/ Drug and Mental Health Program
Route 2
Hayward, WI 54843

NOO/JII/MOO/WII/MIES Halfway House
Round Lake Township
Hayward, WI 54843

Sawyer County Council on AODA Hill House
County Hill Road
Hayward, WI 54843

Sawyer County Information and Referral Center on Alcohol and Other Drug Abuse
105 East 4th Street
Hayward, WI 54843

HERTEL

Saint Croix Family Resource Center
Hertel, WI 54845

HUDSON

Burkwood Residence
615 Old Mill Road
Hudson, WI 54016

Hudson Medical Center
  Chemical Health Recovery
  Center
400 Wisconsin Street
Hudson, WI 54016

HURLEY

Iron County Council on Alcohol
  and Drug Abuse
408 Silver Street
Hurley, WI 54534

JANESVILLE

Alcohab, Inc.
New Dawn Residential Primary
  Treatment
430 North Jackson Street
Janesville, WI 53545

River Commons
786 South Main Street
Janesville, WI 53545

Associates in Psychotherapy
  Affected Family Member
  Program
1519 Primrose Lane
Janesville, WI 53545

Crossroads Counseling Center
301 East Milwaukee Street
Janesville, WI 53545

Lutheran Social Services/Rock
  County Alcohol and Drug
  Treatment Unit
205 North Main Street
Suite 102
Janesville, WI 53545

Mercy Options Addiction
  Treatment Services
1000 Mineral Point
Janesville, WI 53545

Rock County Psychiatric
  Hospital Substance Abuse
  Services
3530 North County Trunk Street
Suite F
Janesville, WI 53545

Rock Valley Community
  Program, Inc. Treatment
  Alternative Program
203 West Sunny Lane Road
Janesville, WI 53546

JUNEAU

Dodge County Dept. of Human
  Services Chemical
  Dependency Services
199 Home Road
Juneau, WI 53039

KENOSHA

Addiction Consulting Associates
611 56th Street
Kenosha, WI 53140

Alcohol and Drug Consultants
7543 17 Avenue
Kenosha, WI 53143

Covenant Behavioral Health
6021 56th Avenue, Suite 6
Kenosha, WI 53144

Gateway House Group Home
460 56th Avenue
Kenosha, WI 53144

Interventions
6755 14th Avenue
Kenosha, WI 53140

Oakwood Clinical Associates,
  Ltd.
4109 67th Street
Kenosha, WI 53140

Professional Services Group Inc
6233 39th Avenue
Kenosha, WI 53142

Saint Catherine's Hospital
  Behavioral Services
3556 7th Avenue
Kenosha, WI 53140

3734 7th Avenue Dominican
  Building, Suite 3
Kenosha, WI 53140

KESHENA

Menominee County Human
  Services Dept. Alcohol and
  Other Drug Abuse Program
Highway 55 and 47
Keshena, WI 54135

KEWASKUM

Exodus Transitional Care
  Facility, Inc.
1421 Fond Du Lac Avenue
Kewaskum, WI 53040

LAC DU FLAMBEAU

Family Resource Center
  Chippewa Health Center
450 Old Abe Road
Lac du Flambeau, WI 54538

LA CROSSE

Coulee Youth Center, Inc.
231 Copeland Avenue
La Crosse, WI 54602

La Crosse County Human
  Service Dept. Clinical
  Services Section
300 North 4th Street
La Crosse, WI 54601

Farrell and Wissing Alternatives
505 King Street, Suite 38
La Crosse, WI 54601

Franciscan Skemp Behavioral
  Healthcare
212 South 11th Street
La Crosse, WI 54601

Intensive Residential Adult
  Chemical Dependency Program
620 South 11th Street
La Crosse, WI 54601

FSH Behavioral Health
  Residential Services
LAAR House
1022 Division Street
La Crosse, WI 54601

Scarseth House
535 South 17th Street
La Crosse, WI 54601

Gundersen Lutheran
1312 5th Avenue
La Crosse, WI 54601

Unity for Women
1922 Miller Street
La Crosse, WI 54601

**Hoffe/Cassel Counseling
Services LLC**
La Crosse, WI 54601

LADYSMITH

**Rusk County Memorial Hospital
Substance Abuse Services**
900 College Avenue West
Ladysmith, WI 54848

LANCASTER

Unified Counseling Services
210 South Washington Street
Lancaster, WI 53813

MADISON

ARC Community Services, Inc.
Arc House
202 North Paterson Street
Madison, WI 53703

ARC Center for Women and
Children
1409 Emil Street
Madison, WI 53713

Capitol Square Associates
660 West Washington Avenue,
Suite 305
Madison, WI 53703

Hope Haven, Inc.
Colvin Manor
425 West Johnson Street
Madison, WI 53703

North Bay Lodge
3602 Memorial Drive
Madison, WI 53704

Lutheran Social Services
5 Odana Court
Madison, WI 53713

**Mendota Mental Health Institute
Substance Abuse Services**
301 Troy Drive
Madison, WI 53704

**Mental Health Center of Dane
County Alcohol and Drug
Treatment Unit**
625 West Washington Avenue
Madison, WI 53703

Meriter Hospital/New Start
New Start East
1310 Mendota Street
Suite 110
Madison, WI 53714

New Start West
1015 Gammon Lane
Madison, WI 53719

Washington Avenue Unit
309 West Washington Avenue
Madison, WI 53703

**Schwert AODA Treatment
Center**
3501 Kipling Drive
Madison, WI 53704

Tellurian UCAN, Inc.
Adult Residential Program (ARP)
300 Femrite Drive
Madison, WI 53716

Day Treatment Program
1250 Fermrite Drive
Madison, WI 53716

Detoxification Unit
2914 Industrial Drive
Madison, WI 53713

Thoreau House
1102 Spaight Street
Madison, WI 53703

MANITOWOC

**Holy Family Memorial Medical
Center**
2300 Western Avenue
Manitowoc, WI 54220

**Manitowoc County Human
Services Dept. Counseling
Center**
927 South 8th Street
Manitowoc, WI 54220

Marco
1114 South 11th Street
Manitowoc, WI 54220

MARINETTE

Bay Area Medical Center
3100 Shore Drive
Marinette, WI 54143

**Marinette County Human
Services Adapt**
2400 Hall Avenue
Marinette, WI 54143

MAUSTON

**Juneau County Human Service
Center**
220 East La Crosse Street
Mauston, WI 53948

MEDFORD

**Taylor County Human Services
Department**
540 East College Street
Medford, WI 54451

MENASHA

**Family Service Association of
Fox Valley**
1488 Kenwood Center
Menasha, WI 54952

**Theda Clark Center for
Recovery**
324 Nicolet Boulevard
Menasha, WI 54952

MENOMONIE

**Arbor Place Alcohol and Other
Drug Abuse Program**
320 21st Street North
Menomonie, WI 54751

**Saint Mary's Behavioral
Medicine**
13111 North Port Washington
Road
Mequon, WI 53097

MERRILL

**Lincoln Health Care Center
Merrill Office**
503 South Center Avenue
Merrill, WI 54452

Sacred Heart Outpatient Clinic Oasis Recovery Program
807 East 1st Street
Merrill, WI 54452

MILWAUKEE

American Indian Council on Alcoholism
2240 West National Avenue
Milwaukee, WI 53204

Aro Counseling Center, Inc.
4325 South 60th Street, Suite 3
Milwaukee, WI 53220-3508

Cedar Creek Counseling Center
6815 West Capitol Drive, Suite 301
Milwaukee, WI 53216-2070

Children and Family Service, Inc.
4365 North 27th Avenue
Milwaukee, WI 53218

Council for the Spanish Speaking Salud de la Familia
614 West National Street
Milwaukee, WI 53204

Genesis Behavioral Services, Inc.
Milwaukee Outpatient Clinics
2040 West Wisconsin Avenue, Suite 560
Milwaukee, WI 53201

Genesis Detoxification Center
1218 West Highland Boulevard
Milwaukee, WI 53233

Holton Youth Center AODA YMCA
510 East Burleigh Street
Milwaukee, WI 53202

Horizon House
2511 West Vine Street
Milwaukee, WI 53205

Ivanhoe Treatment, Inc.
2203 East Ivanhoe Place
Milwaukee, WI 53202

Lutheran Social Services of Wisconsin and Upper Michigan, Inc.
6101 West Vliet Street, Suite 100
Milwaukee, WI 53213

10401 West Lincoln Avenue
Suite 209
Milwaukee, WI 53227

Matt Talbot Recovery Center
2613 West North Avenue
Milwaukee, WI 53205

Milwaukee Health Services System
4383 North 27 Street
Milwaukee, WI 53216

2778 South 35th Street
Milwaukee, WI 53215

Milwaukee Women's Center Behavioral Health Clinic
611 North Broadway
Suite 230
Milwaukee, WI 53202

Multi-Cultural Counseling Services DBA Renew Counseling Services
1225 West Mitchell Street
Suite 223
Milwaukee, WI 53204

2014 West North Avenue
Milwaukee, WI 53233

Northwest General Hospital Substance Abuse Services
5310 West Capitol Drive
Milwaukee, WI 53216

Pathways Counseling Center
2645 North Mayfair Road
Suite 230
Milwaukee, WI 53226

Reach, Inc. Comprehensive Mental Health Clinic Substance Abuse
6001 West Center Street
Suite 9711
Milwaukee, WI 53210

Relapse Prevention Service
8112 West Bluemound Road
Suite 106
Milwaukee, WI 53213

Riverwest North Meta House
2626 North Bremen Street
Milwaukee, WI 53212

SAFE Group Services, Inc.
3500 North Sherman Boulevard
Suite 302
Milwaukee, WI 53216

Saint Michael's Hospital Mental Health Center
2400 West Villard Avenue
Milwaukee, WI 53209

Sinai Samaritan Medical Center Substance Abuse Services
2000 West Kilbourn Avenue
Milwaukee, WI 53233

United Community Center New Beginning Clinic
1028 South 9 Street
Milwaukee, WI 53204

Wisconsin Cipe, Inc.
1915 West Hampton Avenue
Milwaukee, WI 53209

Wisconsin Correctional Service (WCS)
152 West Wisconsin Avenue
Milwaukee, WI 53203

Wisconsin Midwest Clinical Services
2200 North Mayfair Road
Milwaukee, WI 53226

Zablocki VA Medical Center
5000 West National Avenue
Milwaukee, WI 53295

MINOCQUA

Koller Behavioral Health Services
415 Menominee Street
Minocqua, WI 54548

MONROE

Green County Human Services Alcohol/Other Drug Abuse Services
N3152 State Highway 81
Monroe, WI 53566

MONTELLO

Marquette Chemical Dependency Service
Highway 22 South
Montello, WI 53949

MUKWONAGO

Norris Adolescent Center
Center Drive
Route 5 W247 S10395
Mukwonago, WI 53149

NEILLSVILLE

Clark County Community Services Alcohol and Other Drug Abuse Program
517 Court Street
Neillsville, WI 54456

NEW LONDON

New London Family Medical Center Emergency Room Substance Abuse Services
1405 Mill Street
New London, WI 54961

NEW RICHMOND

Saint Croix County Health and Human Services
1445 North 4th Street
New Richmond, WI 54017

NIAGARA

Adapt Human Services
1201 Jackson Street
Niagara, WI 54151

OCONTO

Oconto County Dept. of Human Services Clinical Services Division/Substance Abuse Unit
501 Park Avenue
Oconto, WI 54153

ODANAH

Bad River Alcohol/Drug Program
Bad River Community Center
Odanah, WI 54861

ONEIDA

Oneida Group Homes Kuthani Yosta
453 Country Court
Oneida, WI 54155

OSHKOSH

Mercy Medical Center Counseling Service
515 Washburn Boulevard
Oshkosh, WI 54901

Nexus House Lutheran Social Services
2002 Algoma Boulevard
Oshkosh, WI 54901

Summit House
2501 Harrison Street
Oshkosh, WI 54901

Nova Treatment Center
Horizon House
111 Josslyn Street
Oshkosh, WI 54901

Terra House
105 Josslyn Street
Oshkosh, WI 54901

United Behavioral Health Services
1750 West Pointe Drive
Oshkosh, WI 54901

PHILLIPS

Counseling and Personal Development AODA Treatment Program
171 Chestnut Street
Phillips, WI 54555

PLATTEVILLE

Unified Counseling Services Platteville Outpatient Clinic
6057 South Chestnut Street
Platteville, WI 53818

PLYMOUTH

Sheboygan Counseling and Development Center
710 Eastern Avenue
Plymouth, WI 53073

PORTAGE

Divine Savior Hospital Emergency Room Substance Abuse Detox Services
1015 West Pleasant Street
Portage, WI 53901

Pauquette Center for Psychological Services
304 West Cook Street
Portage, WI 53901

PORT EDWARDS

Entrance/Exit Program
1351 Wisconsin River Drive
Port Edwards, WI 54469

PORT WASHINGTON

Ozaukee County Dept. of Community Programs Ozaukee County Counseling Center
121 West Main Street
Port Washington, WI 53074

POYNETTE

Poynette Counseling and Psychotherapy Associates, Inc.
415 North Main Street
Poynette, WI 53955

PRAIRIE DU CHIEN

FSH Behavioral Health Residential Services Villa Succes
121 South Prairie Street
Prairie du Chien, WI 53831

PRAIRIE DU SAC

Pathway Clinic
50 Prairie Avenue
Prairie Du Sac, WI 53578

RACINE

All Saints Behavioral Health Services
1320 Wisconsin Avenue
Racine, WI 53403

Charter Counseling Center
6021 Durand Avenue
Racine, WI 53406

Covenant Behavioral Health
1055 Prairie Drive
Racine, WI 53406

Crisis Center of Racine, Inc.
1925 Washington Street
Racine, WI 53403

Genesis Behavioral Services
5200 Washington Avenue
Suite 105
Racine, WI 53406

Durand Home
4606 Durand Avenue
Racine, WI 53406

Saint Clair House
4107-4109 Saint Clair Street
Racine, WI 53402

Spring Place Manor Residential
   Facility
1725-27 Spring Place
Racine, WI 53401

Racine Psychological Services
840 Lake Avenue
Racine, WI 53403

RHINELANDER

Koinonia Residential Treatment Center
1991 Winnebago Drive
Rhinelander, WI 54501

Koller Behavioral Health Services
622 Mason Street
Rhinelander, WI 54501

RICE LAKE

Parkview Center
1107 East Orchard Beach Lane
Rice Lake, WI 54868

RICHLAND CENTER

Richland County Community Programs
1000 Highway 14 West
Richland Center, WI 53581

RIVER FALLS

Kinnic Falls Alcohol and Drug Abuse Services
900 South Orange Street
River Falls, WI 54022

SAINT CROIX FALLS

Saint Croix Valley Memorial Hospital Chemical Dependency Center
204 South Adams Street
Saint Croix Falls, WI 54024

SHAWANO

Shawano County Department of Community Programs
504 Lakeland Road
Shawano, WI 54166

Shawano Medical Center
309 North Bartlette Street
Shawano, WI 54166

Shawano County Community Programs Professional Services Center
125 North Main Street
Shawano, WI 54166

SHEBOYGAN

Counseling and Development Center
2205 Erie Avenue
Sheboygan, WI 53081

Kettle Moraine/Genesis
503 Wisconsin Avenue
Sheboygan, WI 53081

Rebos Manor
908 Jefferson Street
Sheboygan, WI 53081

Sheboygan County Human Services Outpatient Services
1011 North 8th Street
Sheboygan, WI 53081

Sheboygan Memorial Medical Center Chemical Dependency Services
2629 North 7th Street
Sheboygan, WI 53083

SHELL LAKE

Indianhead Residential Care Facility, Inc.
122 5th Avenue West
Shell Lake, WI 54871

SPARTA

Monroe County Department Human Service
14301 County Highway B, Box 19
Sparta, WI 54656-4509

SPOONER

Spooner Community Memorial Hospital Substance Abuse Detox
819 Ash Street
Spooner, WI 54801

STEVENS POINT

Community Alcohol and Drug Abuse Center
209 Prentice Street North
Stevens Point, WI 54481

Oakside Residential Living Facility
201 North Prentice Street
Stevens Point, WI 54481

Saint Michael's Hospital Emergency Room Substance Abuse Services
900 Illinois Avenue
Stevens Point, WI 54481

STOUGHTON

Lutheran Social Services Home Programs/Serenity Unit
209 North Division Street
Stoughton, WI 53589

STURGEON BAY

Door County Department of Community Programs
421 Nebraska Street
Sturgeon Bay, WI 54235

SUPERIOR

Recovery Center, Inc.
2231 Catlin Avenue
Suite 2 East
Superior, WI 54880

TOMAH

Gundersen Lutheran
321 Butts Avenue
Tomah, WI 54660

Veterans' Affairs Medical Center Alcohol/Drug Dependence Treatment Program
500 East Veterans Street
Tomah, WI 54660

TOMAHAWK

Lincoln Health Care Center Tomahawk Office/Substance Abuse Services
310 West Wisconsin Avenue
Tomahawk, WI 54487

Oasis Recovery Program
216 North 7th Street
Tomahawk, WI 54487

VIROQUA

Pierzina Counseling Services
210 Airport Road, Suite 103-B
Viroqua, WI 54665-1160

Vernon Memorial Hospital Emergency Detoxification
507 South Main Street
Viroqua, WI 54665

WASHBURN

Lutheran Social Services
320 Superior Avenue
Washburn, WI 54891

WATERTOWN

Directions Counseling Center
129 Hospital Drive
Watertown, WI 53094

WAUKESHA

Aro Counseling Center Incorporated
400 West Moreland Boulevard
Waukesha, WI 53188

Century House
1130 Northview Road
Waukesha, WI 53188

Genesis House
1002 Motor Avenue
Waukesha, WI 53188

La Casa de Esperanza AODA Prevention/Education
410 Arcadian Avenue
Waukesha, WI 53186

Lutheran Social Services
325 Sentinel Drive
Waukesha, WI 53186

Southeastern Youth and Family Services NOAH House
West 222 South 3210 Racine Avenue
Waukesha, WI 53186

WAUPACA

Waupaca County Dept. of Human Services Outpatient Treatment Services
811 Harding Street
Waupaca, WI 54981

WAUSAU

Center for Well Being, Inc.
2801 North Seventh Street
Suite 400
Wausau, WI 54401

North Central Health Care Facilities
1100 Lake View Drive
Wausau, WI 54401

WAUTOMA

Alcoholism and Drug Abuse Services of Waushara County
310 South Scott Street
Wautoma, WI 54982

WAUWATOSA

Associated Women Psychotherapist
10625 West North Avenue, Suite 208
Wauwatosa, WI 53226

Milwaukee Psychiatric Hospital Chemical Dependency Services
1220 Dewey Avenue
Wauwatosa, WI 53213

WEST ALLIS

Charter Counseling Center
2323 South 109th Street
Suite 175
West Allis, WI 53227

Genesis Behavioral Services, Inc.
1126 South 70th Street
West Allis, WI 53214

WINNEBAGO

Anchorage
Winnebago, WI 54985

Winnebago Mental Health Institute Gemini
Main Butler Avenue
Winnebago, WI 54985

WISCONSIN RAPIDS

Riverview Hospital Emergency Inpatient Detox
410 Dewey Street
Wisconsin Rapids, WI 54494

Wood County Unified Services
2611 South 12th Street
Wisconsin Rapids, WI 54494

WYOMING

BASIN

Big Horn County Counseling
220 South 4 Street
Basin, WY 82410

BUFFALO

Northern Wyoming Mental Health Center Substance Abuse Services
521 West Lott Street
Buffalo, WY 82834

CASPER

Casper Psychological Services
136 South Washington Street
Casper, WY 82601

Sunrise Recovery Center Wyoming Medical Center
255 South Jackson Street
Casper, WY 82601

The Prairie Institute, Inc.
309 North McKinley Street
Casper, WY 82601

Wyoming Behavioral Institute
2521 East 15th Street
Casper, WY 82609

CHEYENNE

Behavioral Health Services
United Medical Center East Building
2600 East 18th Street
Cheyenne, WY 82001

Cheyenne Community Drug Abuse Treatment Council, Inc. Pathfinder
121 west Carlson Street
Cheyenne, WY 82001

Southeast Wyoming Mental Health Center
Chemical Health Services
2526 Seymour Avenue
Cheyenne, WY 82003

Cheyenne Alcohol Receiving Center
Halfway House
Transitions Residential Program
2310 East 8th Street
Cheyenne, WY 82001

Veterans Affairs Medical Center Substance Abuse Treatment Program
2360 East Pershing Boulevard
Cheyenne, WY 82001

CODY

Cedar Mountain Center at West Park Hospital
707 Sheridan Avenue
Cody, WY 82414

DOUGLAS

Eastern Wyoming Mental Health Center Substance Abuse Services
1841 Madora Avenue
Douglas, WY 82633

EVANSTON

Cornerstone
195 Featherway Street, Suite 1
Evanston, WY 82930

Wyoming State Hospital
831 Highway 150
Evanston, WY 82930

GILLETTE

Powder River Chemical Dependency, Inc.
400 South Kendrick Avenue
Suite 101
Gillette, WY 82716

Wyoming Regional Counseling Center
900 West 6th Street
Gillette, WY 82716

GLENROCK

Eastern Wyoming Mental Health Center
925 West Birch Street
Glenrock, WY 82637

JACKSON

Curran/Seeley Foundation
610 West Broadway
Suite L-1
Jackson, WY 83001

LARAMIE

Ivinson Memorial Hospital
255 North 30th Street
Laramie, WY 82072

Southeast Wyoming Mental Health Center Substance Abuse Services
710 Garfield Street
Suite 320
Laramie, WY 82070

Wyoming Counseling and Outreach Services
901 South 3rd Street
Laramie, WY 82070

LOVELL

Big Horn County Counseling
441 Montana Avenue
Lovell, WY 82431

LUSK

Eastern Wyoming Mental Health Center Substance Abuse Services
905 South Main Street
Lusk, WY 82225

NEWCASTLE

Northern Wyoming Mental Health Center Substance Abuse Services
420 Deanne Avenue
Newcastle, WY 82701

PINEDALE

Sublette Community Counseling Services
41 1/2 South Franklin Street
Pinedale, WY 82941

RAWLINS

Carbon County Counseling Center
721 West Maple Street
Rawlins, WY 82301

RIVERTON

Fremont Counseling Service
511 North 12th West
Riverton, WY 82501

ROCK SPRINGS

Southwest Counseling Service
1414 North 12th Street East
Rock Springs, WY 82901

SHERIDAN

Northern Wyoming Mental Health Center Substance Abuse Services
1221 West 5 Street
Sheridan, WY 82801

Piedmont Psychological Practice
425 West Loucks Street
Sheridan, WY 82801

Sheridan House, Inc.
1003 Saberton Street
Sheridan, WY 82801

Veterans' Affairs Medical Center Substance Abuse Treatment Program
1898 Fort Road
Sheridan, WY 82801

THERMOPOLIS

Hot Springs County Counseling Service
121 South 4th Street
Thermopolis, WY 82443

TORRINGTON

Southeast Wyoming Mental Health Center Substance Abuse Services
1942 East D Street
Torrington, WY 82240

WHEATLAND

Southeast Wyoming Mental Health Center Substance Abuse Services
103 Park Avenue
Wheatland, WY 82201

WORLAND

Washakie County Mental Health Services
509 Big Horn Avenue
Worland, WY 82401

U.S Territories and Affiliated States

FEDERATED STATES OF MICRONESIA

POHNPEI

Department of Health Services Community Mental Health Center
Pohnpei, FM 96941

YAP

Yap Memorial Hospital Department of Health Services
Yap, FM 96943

GUAM

TAMUNING

Department of Mental Health and Substance Abuse
Substance Abuse Drug and Alcohol Prevention Program
790 Governor Carlos G. Camacho Road
Tamuning, GU 96911

PUERTO RICO

AGUADILLA

Centro de Salud Mental (SITA)
First Floor Hospital Regional
Aguadilla, PR 00605

Hogar Crea Aguadilla
Carretera 2 Interior 110 Km 1180
Barrio Ceiba Baja
Aguadilla, PR 00605

Teen Challenge de Aguadilla
Carretera 107 KM 3.5
Sector Playuela Barrio Borinquen
Aguadilla, PR 00603

AIBONITO

Hogar Crea Aibonito Adolescentes
Calle Alfredo Marrero 68
Aibonito, PR 00705

ANASCO

Hogar Crea Anasco Varones
Carretera 109 Kilometro 42 Barrio Espino
Anasco, PR 00610

Hogar Jesus Inc
Street 406 Kilometro 22 Barrio Casey
Anasco, PR 00610

ARECIBO

Centro de Tratamiento de Menores Libre de Drogas de Arecibo
Carretera 129 Arecibo Alares Antiguo Hospital de Distrito
Arecibo, PR 00612

Centro de Tratamiento Para Adultos de Arecibo
Antiguo Hospital de Distrito
Arecibo, PR 00612

Hogar Crea Arecibo Adolescentes
Carretera 682 Kilometro 59
Barrio Garrochales
Arecibo, PR 00612

Hogar Crea Arecibo Adultos
Carretera 129 Kilometro 412
Barrio Hato Arriba
Arecibo, PR 00612

Mision Rescate Drug Abuse Treatment Rehabilitation Center
Carretera 651 Km 27
Int Hato Arriba Sector Combate
Arecibo, PR 00612

BARRANQUITAS

Hogar Crea Barranquitas
Calle Principal 14
Barranquitas, PR 00794

BAYAMON

Hogar Crea Vista Alegre
Calle La Liga Esquina C
Barriada Vista Alegre
Bayamon, PR 00959

Hogar Crea Bayamon Adolescentes
Calle la Liga Esquina Barriada Vista Alegre
Bayamon, PR 00959

Hogar Crea Districto de Bayamon
Carretera 852 Kilometro 02
Bayamon, PR 00961

Ministerios Jehova/Justicia Nuestra
Calle A-CC-16 Bayamon Gardens
Bayamon, PR 00957

New Life for Girls de Puerto Rico
Carretera 830 Km 57 Barrio Santa Olaya Sector Los Llanos
Bayamon, PR 00956

Renovados en Cristo
Carr 812 KM 6.4 Camino Los Ponos
Bo Guaraguao Sector La Pena
Bayamon, PR 00956

Teen Challenge of Puerto Rico Inc
Carretera 2 Kilometro 77 Barrio Juan Domingo
Bayamon, PR 00957

CAGUAS

Hogar Crea Cabo Rojo
Carr 311 Kilometro 31
Interior Camino Los Ascencios
Cabo Rojo, PR 00623

**Adm Servicios Salud Mental y
Contra Adicion Centro
deTratamiento Menores**
Centro Tratamiento a Menores
Apartado 9150
Caguas, PR 00726

**Caguas Substance Abuse
Treatment Center**
Calle Gautier Benitez 162
Edificio Angora San Alfonso Plaza
Caguas, PR 00725

Hogar Crea De Caguas
Calle Padia Final Barrio
Bairoa La 25 Carretera 796
Caguas, PR 00725

Hogar Resurreccion
Carretera 175 KM 3 HM O
Bo San Antonio
Caguas, PR 00725

Hogar Crea Canovanas
Carretera 188 Kilometro 13
Barrio San Isidro
Canovanas, PR 00729

Hogar Crea La Central
Barrio Torrecilla Alta
Canovanas, PR 00729

CAROLINA

Hogar Crea Carolina
Carretera 887 Kilometro 14
Barrio Martin Gonzalez
Carolina, PR 00987

Hogar El Buen Samaritano, Inc.
Unit 2
Carr 857 KM 9.5
Barrio Carruzo Sector Filipinas
Carolina, PR 00628

CAYEY

Hogar Crea Cayey
Avenida Antonio R. Barzelo
al lado del Cuartel de la Policia
Cayey, PR 00737

CIDRA

First Hospital Panamerica
Carretera 787 Kilometro 15
Cidra, PR 00739

COMERIO

**Hogar Crea Comerio
Adolescente Barrio Palomas
Abajo**
Sector El 26
Carretera 156 Kilometro 33 Hm 8
Comerio, PR 00782s

COROZAL

Hogar Crea Corozal
Hectometro 02 Barrio Dos Bocas
Carretera 159 Km 124
Corozal, PR 00783

DORADO

Hogar Crea Dorado
Calle A Bloque C-48
Costa de Oro
Dorado, PR 00646

EL SENORIAL/RIO PIEDRAS

**Puerto Rico Addiction Medical
Services**
6 Street South 7-2
Villas de Parana
El Senorial/Rio Piedras, PR 00960

FAJARDO

Hogar Crea Arturo Nieves
Calle 3 Barrio Jerusalem
Fajardo, PR 00738

GUANICA

Hogar Crea Guanica
Carretera Ochoa Km 19 Bda
Esperanza
Finca 5 Hermanos
Guanica, PR 00653

GUAYAMA

Hogar Crea Guayama
Barrio Linea
Capo 13 Carretera 15
Guayama, PR 00785

Hogar Nuevo Camino
Sector Villodas
Carretera 713 Kilometro 0.3
Guayama, PR 00784

GUAYNABO

Centro Renancer, Inc.
Carretera 834 Km 42
Barrio Sonadora Sector Las
Parcelas
Guaynabo, PR 00970

**Hogar Crea Guaynabo
Adolescentes**
Calle Vanda Numero 1
Urbanizacion Torrimar
Guaynabo, PR 00966

Hogar Crea Guaynabo Adultos
Calle Union 3 Sector Montalvo
Camino Alejandrino Kilometro 05
Guaynabo, PR 00965

Hogar Crea Sabana
Calle Maritima 410
Barrio Sabana
Guaynabo, PR 00965

Hogar de Ayuda El Refugio, Inc.
Avenida Ponce de Leon
Esquina Santa Rosa De Lima 17A
Guaynabo, PR 00965

GURABO

Hogar El Buen Samaritano, Inc.
Carretera 941 KM 5 HM 0
Barrio Jaguas
Gurabo, PR 00778

**Hogar Intermedio De Dama En
Gurabo**
Calle Santiago Final
Carretera 943 Km2
Gurabo, PR 00778

Hogar Nueva Vida
Carretera 181 Ramal 944
Bo Celada
Gurabo, PR 00778

Hogar Nueva Vida Oseli
Barrio Calabasas, Carretera 182
Gurabo, PR 00778

HATO REY

**Hogar Crea Jovenes Y Adultos
Quisqueya Proyecto Especial**
Calle Quisqueya 207
Hato Rey, PR 00917

HUMACAO

Hogar Crea Humacao
Carretera 908 Kilometro 2 Hm 7
Barrio Tejas
Humacao, PR 00791

Proyecto Hombre
Calle Antonio Lopez 116
Humacao, PR 00792

ISABELA

**Hogar Crea Isabela
Adolescentes**
Carretera 472 Kilometro 32
Barrio Bejucos
Isabela, PR 00662

Hogar Crea Juana Diaz Adultos
Carretera 14 Kilometro 169
Sector Tijera
Juana Diaz, PR 00795

**Proyecto Especial para
Adolecentes De Juana Diaz**
Barrio Caoitanejo
Kilometro 115-2 Carrtera 1
Juana Diaz, PR 00795

JUNCOS

Hogar Crea Juncos
Carretera 185 Kilometro 20
Hectometro 0
Barrio Las Pinas
Juncos, PR 00777

Hogar Nuevo Pacto
Carretera 31 KM 19
Bo Caimito 1
Juncos, PR 00777

LAS MARIAS

Hogar Crea Las Marias
Carretera 119 Kilometro 261
Barrio Maravilla Norte
Las Marias, PR 00670

LOIZA

Hogar Crea Loiza
Calle San Patricio Final 16
Loiza, PR 00772

LUQUILLO

Hogar Crea Luquillo
Calle 14 Barrio Hato Viejo
Fortuna
Luquillo, PR 00773

MANATI

**Centro Tratamiento
Ambulatorio Centro
Tratamiento Adultos**
Obrero 15-A Esquina Quinones
Box 583
Manati, PR 00674-0583

Hogar Crea Manati Adultos
Carretera 2 Kilometro 48
Barrio Cotto Norte
Manati, PR 00674

Hogar Crea Manati Damas
Carretera 616 Kilometro 2
Barrio Tierras Nuevas Sector
Cantitos
Manati, PR 00674

MAYAGUEZ

**Centro SITA Tratamiento A
Sustancias (Drogas)**
Avenida Hostos 11
Mayaguez Medical Center
Mayaguez, PR 00680

**Centro Tratamiento A Menores
Mayaguez**
Avenida Eugenio Maria de Hostos
Carreterra 2 - Hospital Betances
Mayaguez, PR 00681

**Hogar Crea Modulo Crea/Centro
Detencion Oeste**
Carretera 105 Kilometro 18
Mayaguez, PR 00680

**Hogar Crea/Posada Fe Y
Esperanza**
Calle Comercio 242
Mayaguez, PR 00680

**Mision Rescate, Inc. Drug Abuse
Treatment**
Road 104 Kilometro 1.7
Barrio Algarrobo
Mayaguez, PR 00680

MOROVIS

**Hogar Crea Morovis
Adolescentes**
Carretera 159 Kilometro 16
Barrio Montellano Sector La
Fabrica
Morovis, PR 00687

NAGUABO

Hogar Crea Naguabo
Carretera 3 Kilometro 63 H4
Barrio Daguao
Naguabo, PR 00718

NARANJITO

Hogar Crea Naranjito
Carretera 164 Kilometro 05
Barrio Nuevo
Naranjito, PR 00719

OROCOVIS

Hogar Crea Orocovis
Barrio Sabana Sector La Pista
Orocovis, PR 00720

PONCE

**Centro de Tratamiento Para
Adultos de Ponce**
Carretera Num 14 Barrio
Machuelo
Facilidades de Centro Medico
Ponce, PR 00731

**Desintoxicacion Para Menores
Cede Ponce**
Carretera 14 Centro Medico
Barrio Machuelo
Ponce, PR 00731

Hogar Crea Distrito de Ponce
Calle Central 13
Barrio Machuelo
Ponce, PR 00731

Hogar Crea Ponce Adolescente
Calle 1 Numero 4
Urbanizacion Villa Flores
Ponce, PR 00733

Hogar Crea Ponce Mercedita
Carretera 1 Kilometro 119 Hm .9
Barrio Buyones
Ponce, PR 00731

**Hogar Crea Ponce Playa Posada
Fe Y Esperanza**
Avenida Los Meros 45
Playa Ponce
Ponce, PR 00733

**Institucion Regional del Sur
Jovenes Adultos Tratamiento
Sicosocial**
Bo El Tuque Sector Las Cucharas
Ponce, PR 00731

Mision Refugio Incorporado
Bo Maraquez KM 4 HM 2
Ponce, PR 00731

**Ponce Alcoholism Treatment
Program**
Ponce Medical Center
Ponce, PR 00731

**Programa Ayuda y Consejeria
Empleado PACE ASSMCA**
Centro Medico Carreterra 14
Barrio Machuelo
Ponce, PR 00731

**Hogar Crea Quebradillas
Adultos**
Carretera 478 Kilometro .5
Barrio San Antonio
Quebradillas, PR 00678

Hogar Crea Quebradillas Ninos
Carretera 113 Kilometro 141
    Interior
Barrio San Antonio
Quebradillas, PR 00678

RIO PIEDRAS

Hogar Crea Rio Grande Damas
Carretera 956 Kilometro 04
Barrio Guzman
Rio Grande, PR 00745

**Centro Quimioterapia San Juan
Barrio Monacillos/Facilidades
Centro**
Rio Piedras, PR 00928

**Emergency Alcoholism Detox
Unit**
Casa De Salud Medical Center
Rio Piedras, PR 00935

**Puerto Rico Addiction Medical
Services**
Carretera 21
Rio Piedras, PR 00928

Hogar Crea Sabana Grande
Carretera 368 Kilometro 38
Barrio Machuchal
Sabana Grande, PR 00637

**Mission Rescate Drug Abuse
Treatment and Rehabilitation**
Carretera 328 Kilometro 57
Intersection Barrio Rayo Guara
Sabana Grande, PR 00637

Hogar Crea San German
Carretera 318 Kilometro 08
Barrio Maresua
San German, PR 00683

SAN JUAN

ASEM
Pabellon J. Terrenos Centro
    Medico
Barrio Monacillos
San Juan, PR 00925-2129

**ASSMCA Centro Tratmiento
Drogas y Alcohol**
Pabellon G Centro Medico
San Juan, PR 00918

Bayamon Quimioterapia
414 Avenida Barbosa
San Juan, PR 00928

Casa La Providencia
Calle Norzagaray Street 200
Old San Juan
San Juan, PR 00902

Cede San Juan
Pabellon B Calle Maga
Barrio Monacillos
San Juan, PR 00925

**Centro de Rehabilitacion Dr
Fumero**
Fernadez Juncos Station
San Juan, PR 00910

**Hogar Crea Districto De San
Juan I**
Avenida Ponce De Leon
1955 Parada 26 1/2
San Juan, PR 00915

**Hogar Crea Centro Madres Con
Ninos Hogar Crea San Jose**
Calle Urdiales Esquina Burgos
    Embalse
San Jose
San Juan, PR 00928

**Hogar Crea Ciudad Modelo
Damas**
Calle Hoare No. 716 Parada 15
San Juan, PR 00907

Hogar Crea Country Club
Calle Lola Rodriguez de Tio 794
2da Extencion Country Club RP
San Juan, PR 00928

Hogar Crea Las Americas
Calle Teniente Cesar Gonzalez
1105 Villa Nevarez
San Juan, PR 00927

**Hogar Crea Parcelas Falu
Proyecto Especial**
Calle 36 Final Parcelas Falu
San Juan, PR 00928

Hogar Crea Park Gardens
Calle Tortosa Final P-15
Villa Andalucia
San Juan, PR 00926

Hogar Crea Puerta de Tierra
Paseo Covadonga Numero 110
Puerta de Tierra
San Juan, PR 00907

Hogar Crea Sabana Llana
Calle Lealtad Esquina Libertad
    1012
Urbanizacion Victoria
San Juan, PR 00924

Hogar Crea San Jose
Calle Urdiales Esquina Burgos
Embalse San Jose
San Juan, PR 00928

Hogar Crea Taft
Calle Leon Acuna 1702
San Juan, PR 00911

Hogar Crea Tortugo
Carretera 873 Kilometro 195
Barrio Tortugo
San Juan, PR 00926

Hogar Crea Venezuela
Calle Guadacanal Final
Barrio Venezuela
San Juan, PR 00926

Hogar Crea Villa Palmeras
Calle Tapia 453
San Juan, PR 00915

Remanso De Paz Inc
Carretera 842 Km 4.2
Camino Pablo Diaz Barrio Caimito
    Alto
San Juan, PR 00926

**Residencial Mujeres Adultas
    San Juan**
Pabellon B. Calle Maga Centro
    Medico
San Juan, PR 00935

**Rio Piedras Psychiatric
    Hospital Rio Piedras
    Alcoholism Program**
Building G Centro Medico
San Juan, PR 00925

**Veterans' Affairs Medical Center
    Drug Dependence Treatment
    Program**
San Juan, PR 00927

SAN LORENZO

Hogar Crea San Lorenzo
Carretera 181 Kilometro 30.6
Barrio Quebrada
San Lorenzo, PR 00754

SAN SEBSTIAN

Hogar Crea San Sebastian
Carretera 448 Kilometro 18
Barrio Guajataca
San Sebastian

SANTA ISABEL

Hogar Crea Santa Isabel
Carretera 1 Kilometro 107
Barrio Jaucal
Santa Isabel, PR 00757

SAINT JUST

**Hogar Crea Inc Posada De La
    Esperanza Centro De Madres
    Con Ninos**
Carretera 848 Km 09
Esq Calle Urano Urbanizacion
    Wonderville
Saint Just, PR 00978

TOA ALTA

Hogar Crea Toa Alta
Barrio Galateo Centro
Carretera 804 Kilometro 17
Toa Alta, PR 00953

Hogar Posada la Victoria, Inc.
C/Principal 165 KM 4 Hect 9
Parcela
52 Barrio Galateo Hoyo
Toa Alta, PR 00953

TRUJILLO ALTO

**Hogar Crea Damas El
    Conquistador**
Carretera 175 Kilometro 90
Barrio Carraizo
Trujillo Alto, PR 00976

Hogar Crea Damas Central
Carretera 848 Kilometro 10
Avenida Saint Just
Trujillo Alto, PR 00976

**Hogar Crea La Quinta Carlos
    Quevedo Estrada**
Carretera 848 Kilometro 13
Barrio Saint Just
Trujillo Alto, PR 00976

**Hogar Crea Ninas Adolescentes
    Hogar Crea Central Damas**
Carretera 848 Kilometro 07 Saint
    Just
Trujillo Alto, PR 00976

Hogar Crea Trujillo Pueblo
Carretera 175 Kilometro 133
Trujillo Alto, PR 00976

VEGA ALTA

Hogar Crea Modulo Vega Alta
Kilometro 8
Barrio Sabana Hoyo
Vega Alta, PR 00692

Hogar Crea Vega Alta
Carretera 159 Kilometro .05
Vega Alta, PR 00692

VEGA BAJA

Hogar Crea Vega Baja
Carr 686 Km 37
Barrio Cabo Caribe
Vega Baja, PR 00693

**Hogar El Camino Barrio
    Puguado Afuera**
Carr 155 Km 61.5 Izquierda
Carr 673
Sector El Palmar
Vega Baja, PR 00693

Silo Mision Cristiana Inc
Carretera 2 Kilometro 426
Barrio Algarrobo
Vega Baja, PR 00693

YABUCOA

Hogar Crea Yabucoa
Kilometro 15
Barrio Aguacate Carretera 906
Yabucoa, PR 00767

YAUCO

Hogar Crea Yauco
Barrio Jacanas Carretera
127 Kilometro 1 Hectometro 5
Yauco, PR 00698

REPUBLIC OF PALAU

PALAU

Ministry of Health
Palau, PW 96940-0504

VIRGIN ISLANDS

CHRISTIANSTED

**Village/Virgin Islands Partners
in Recovery**
1 Sion Hill
Christiansted, VI 00823

SAINT CROIX

**Mental Health Alcoholism and
Drug Dependency Services**
3500 Richmond Christiansted
Street
Saint Croix, VI 00820

SAINT THOMAS

**Council on Alcoholism and
Drug Dependence**
4B-5-6A Norre Gade Street
Saint Thomas, VI 00802

APPENDIX IV

Bureau of Justice Statistics

INTRODUCTION

The Bureau of Justice Statistics is an agency of the U.S. Department of Justice, Washington, DC. In a 1993 report entitled *Drugs, Crime, and the Justice System*, the bureau presented an overview of how the U.S. justice system attempts to combat illegal drugs.

Many areas of society are included in the overview. Here we present summarized data in easy to review format, with new, post–1990 information provided by Mark Kleiman and Thai Ishizuka-Capp, both from the Drug Policy Analysis Program, School of Public Policy and Social Research, University of California, Los Angeles. Much of the information offered here is fully discussed throughout the alphabetical entries of the encyclopedia—in Volumes 1, 2, and 3. Consult the Index at the end of this volume for references to items of further interest.

POLICIES, STRATEGIES, AND TACTICS USED TO CONTROL THE ILLEGAL DRUG PROBLEM

POLICIES

Prohibition is the ban on the distribution, possession, and use of specified substances made illegal by legislative or administrative order and the application of criminal penalties to violators.

Regulation is control over the distribution, possession, and use of specified substances. Regulations specify the circumstances under which substances can be legally distributed and used. Prescription medications and alcohol are the substances most commonly regulated in the U.S.

STRATEGIES

Demand reduction strategies attempt to decrease individuals' tendency to use drugs. Efforts provide information and education to potential and casual users about the risks and adverse consequences of drug use, and treatment to drug users who have developed problems from using drugs.

Supply reduction focuses diplomatic, law enforcement, military, and other resources on eliminating or reducing the supply of drugs. Efforts focus on foreign countries, smuggling routes outside the country, border interdiction, and distribution within the U.S.

User accountability emphasizes that all users of illegal substances, regardless of the type of drug they use or the frequency of that use, are violating criminal laws and should be subject to penalties. It is closely associated with zero tolerance.

Zero tolerance holds that drug distributors, buyers, and users should be held fully accountable for their offenses under the law. This is an alternative to policies that focus only on some violators such as sellers of drugs or users of cocaine and heroin while ignoring other violators.

TACTICS

Criminal justice activities include enforcement, prosecution, and sentencing activities to apprehend, convict, and punish drug offenders. Although thought of primarily as having supply reduction goals, criminal sanctions also have demand reduction effects by discouraging drug use.

Prevention activities are educational efforts to inform potential drug users about the health, legal, and other risks associated with drug use. Their goal is to limit the number of new drug users and dissuade casual users from continuing drug use as part of a demand reduction strategy.

Taxation requires those who produce, distribute, or possess drugs to pay a fee based on the volume or value of the drugs. Failure to pay subjects violators to penalties for this violation, not for the drug activities themselves.

Testing individuals for the presence of drugs is a tool in drug control that is used for safety and monitoring purposes and as an adjunct to therapeutic interventions. It is in widespread use for employees in certain jobs such as those in the transportation industry and criminal justice agencies. New arrestees and convicted offenders may be tested. Individuals in treatment are often tested to monitor their progress and provide them an incentive to remain drug free.

Treatment (therapeutic interventions) focus on individuals whose drug use has caused medical, psychological, economic, and social problems for them. The interventions may include medication, counseling, and other support services delivered in an inpatient setting or on an outpatient basis. These are demand reduction activities to eliminate or reduce individuals' drug use.

HISTORIC MILESTONES IN EARLY U.S. DRUG CONTROL EFFORTS

Drugs of abuse have changed since the 1800s—most rapidly over the past quarter century. Problems with opiate addiction date from widespread use of patent medicines in the 1800s. The range of drugs included opium, morphine, laudanum, cocaine, and, by the turn of the century, heroin. The tonics, nostrums, and alleged cures that contained or used such drugs were sold by itinerant peddlers, mail order houses, retail grocers, and pharmacists. There also was unrestricted access to opium in opium-smoking dens and to morphine through retailers.

When morphine was discovered in 1806, it was thought to be a wonder drug. Its use was so extensive during the Civil War that morphine addiction was termed the "army disease." The availability of the hypodermic syringe allowed nonmedicinal use of morphine to gain popularity among veterans and other civilians. After 1898, heroin was used to treat respiratory illness and morphine addiction in the belief that it was nonaddicting.

In the 1880s coca became widely available in the U.S. as a health tonic and remedy for many ills. Its use was supported first by the European medical community and later by American medical authorities. In the absence of restrictive national legislation, its use spread. Initially cocaine was offered as a cure for opiate addiction, an asthma remedy (the official remedy of the American Hay Fever Association), and an antidote for toothaches.

By 1900, in the face of an estimated quarter of a million addicts, State laws were enacted to curb drug addiction. The major drugs of abuse at the time were cocaine and morphine.

Major Federal legislation and international conventions

Opium importation, domestic cultivation, manufacture, and trafficking limited/prohibited (1887-1890)

Pharmacy Act of 1868 required registration of those dispensing drugs

Executive branch initiatives:

Natural conditions, moods, attitudes and activities; state and local legislation and regulation

San Francisco and numerous Western States prohibit opium dens (1875-90)

Cocaine introduced (mainly as a wine) as a substitute for opium and a cure for asthma and toothaches

Morphine and syringe availability in the Civil War created the "army disease"

Concern with Nation's cocaine epidemic surfaces

1860

1900

Major national events   Civil War

10 years = 13/16 inches

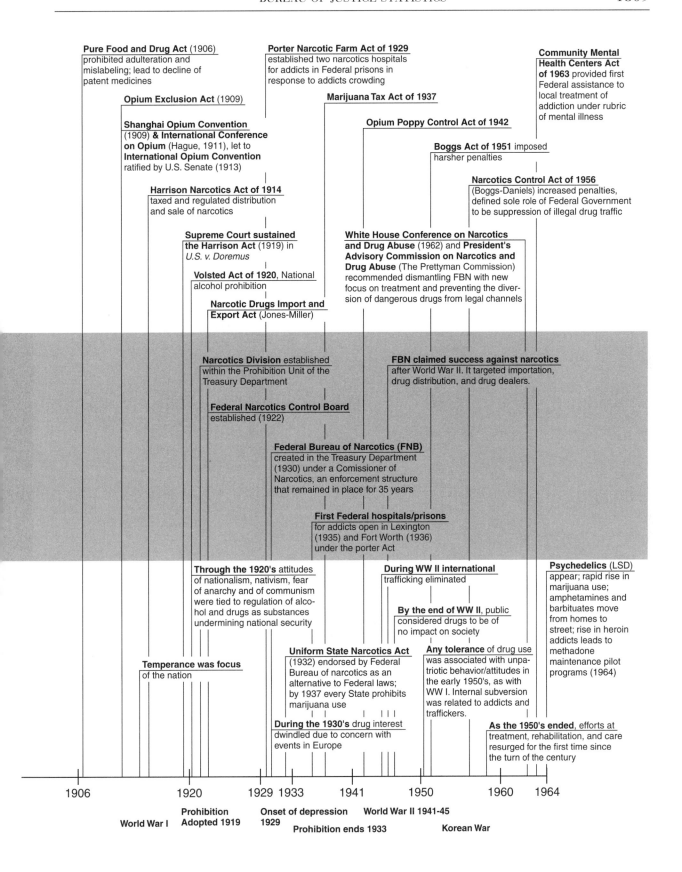

Pure Food and Drug Act (1906) prohibited adulteration and mislabeling; lead to decline of patent medicines

Opium Exclusion Act (1909)

Shanghai Opium Convention (1909) **& International Conference on Opium** (Hague, 1911), let to **International Opium Convention** ratified by U.S. Senate (1913)

Harrison Narcotics Act of 1914 taxed and regulated distribution and sale of narcotics

Supreme Court sustained the Harrison Act (1919) in *U.S. v. Doremus*

Volsted Act of 1920, National alcohol prohibition

Narcotic Drugs Import and Export Act (Jones-Miller)

Narcotics Division established within the Prohibition Unit of the Treasury Department

Federal Narcotics Control Board established (1922)

Federal Bureau of Narcotics (FNB) created in the Treasury Department (1930) under a Comissioner of Narcotics, an enforcement structure that remained in place for 35 years

First Federal hospitals/prisons for addicts open in Lexington (1935) and Fort Worth (1936) under the porter Act

Porter Narcotic Farm Act of 1929 established two narcotics hospitals for addicts in Federal prisons in response to addicts crowding

Marijuana Tax Act of 1937

Opium Poppy Control Act of 1942

Boggs Act of 1951 imposed harsher penalties

Narcotics Control Act of 1956 (Boggs-Daniels) increased penalties, defined sole role of Federal Government to be suppression of illegal drug traffic

White House Conference on Narcotics and Drug Abuse (1962) and **President's Advisory Commission on Narcotics and Drug Abuse** (The Prettyman Commission) recommended dismantling FBN with new focus on treatment and preventing the diversion of dangerous drugs from legal channels

FBN claimed success against narcotics after World War II. It targeted importation, drug distribution, and drug dealers.

Community Mental Health Centers Act of 1963 provided first Federal assistance to local treatment of addiction under rubric of mental illness

Through the 1920's attitudes of nationalism, nativism, fear of anarchy and of communism were tied to regulation of alcohol and drugs as substances undermining national security

Temperance was focus of the nation

Uniform State Narcotics Act (1932) endorsed by Federal Bureau of narcotics as an alternative to Federal laws; by 1937 every State prohibits marijuana use

During the 1930's drug interest dwindled due to concern with events in Europe

During WW II international trafficking eliminated

By the end of WW II, public considered drugs to be of no impact on society

Any tolerance of drug use was associated with unpatriotic behavior/attitudes in the early 1950's, as with WW I. Internal subversion was related to addicts and traffickers.

As the 1950's ended, efforts at treatment, rehabilitation, and care resurged for the first time since the turn of the century

Psychedelics (LSD) appear; rapid rise in marijuana use; amphetamines and barbituates move from homes to street; rise in heroin addicts leads to methadone maintenance pilot programs (1964)

| 1906 | 1920 | 1929 | 1933 | 1941 | 1950 | 1960 | 1964 |

Prohibition Adopted 1919

World War I

Onset of depression 1929

Prohibition ends 1933

World War II 1941-45

Korean War

**Major Federal legislation and
international conventions**

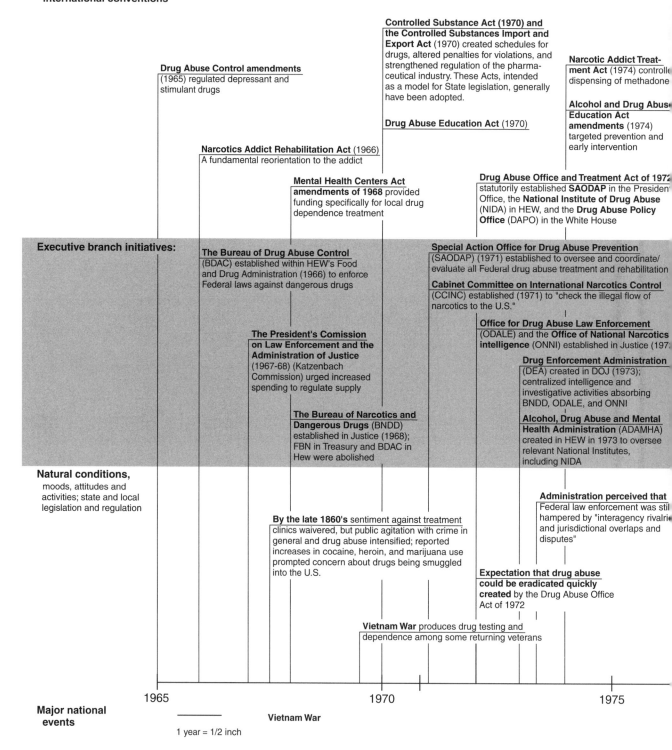

Drug Abuse Control amendments
(1965) regulated depressant and
stimulant drugs

**Controlled Substance Act (1970) and
the Controlled Substances Import and
Export Act** (1970) created schedules for
drugs, altered penalties for violations, and
strengthened regulation of the pharmaceutical industry. These Acts, intended
as a model for State legislation, generally
have been adopted.

Drug Abuse Education Act (1970)

**Narcotic Addict Treat-
ment Act** (1974) controll
dispensing of methadone

**Alcohol and Drug Abuse
Education Act
amendments** (1974)
targeted prevention and
early intervention

Narcotics Addict Rehabilitation Act (1966)
A fundamental reorientation to the addict

**Mental Health Centers Act
amendments of 1968** provided
funding specifically for local drug
dependence treatment

Drug Abuse Office and Treatment Act of 1972
statutorily established **SAODAP** in the Presiden
Office, the **National Institute of Drug Abuse**
(NIDA) in HEW, and the **Drug Abuse Policy
Office** (DAPO) in the White House

Executive branch initiatives:

The Bureau of Drug Abuse Control
(BDAC) established within HEW's Food
and Drug Administration (1966) to enforce
Federal laws against dangerous drugs

Special Action Office for Drug Abuse Prevention
(SAODAP) (1971) established to oversee and coordinate/
evaluate all Federal drug abuse treatment and rehabilitation

Cabinet Committee on International Narcotics Control
(CCINC) established (1971) to "check the illegal flow of
narcotics to the U.S."

**The President's Comission
on Law Enforcement and the
Administration of Justice**
(1967-68) (Katzenbach
Commission) urged increased
spending to regulate supply

Office for Drug Abuse Law Enforcement
(ODALE) and the **Office of National Narcotics
intelligence** (ONNI) established in Justice (197.

Drug Enforcement Administration
(DEA) created in DOJ (1973);
centralized intelligence and
investigative activities absorbing
BNDD, ODALE, and ONNI

**The Bureau of Narcotics and
Dangerous Drugs** (BNDD)
established in Justice (1968);
FBN in Treasury and BDAC in
Hew were abolished

**Alcohol, Drug Abuse and Mental
Health Administration** (ADAMHA)
created in HEW in 1973 to oversee
relevant National Institutes,
including NIDA

Natural conditions,
moods, attitudes and
activities; state and local
legislation and regulation

Administration perceived that
Federal law enforcement was stil
hampered by "interagency rivalri
and jurisdictional overlaps and
disputes"

By the late 1860's sentiment against treatment
clinics waivered, but public agitation with crime in
general and drug abuse intensified; reported
increases in cocaine, heroin, and marijuana use
prompted concern about drugs being smuggled
into the U.S.

**Expectation that drug abuse
could be eradicated quickly
created** by the Drug Abuse Office
Act of 1972

Vietnam War produces drug testing and
dependence among some returning veterans

1965   1970   1975

**Major national
events**

——————   **Vietnam War**

1 year = 1/2 inch

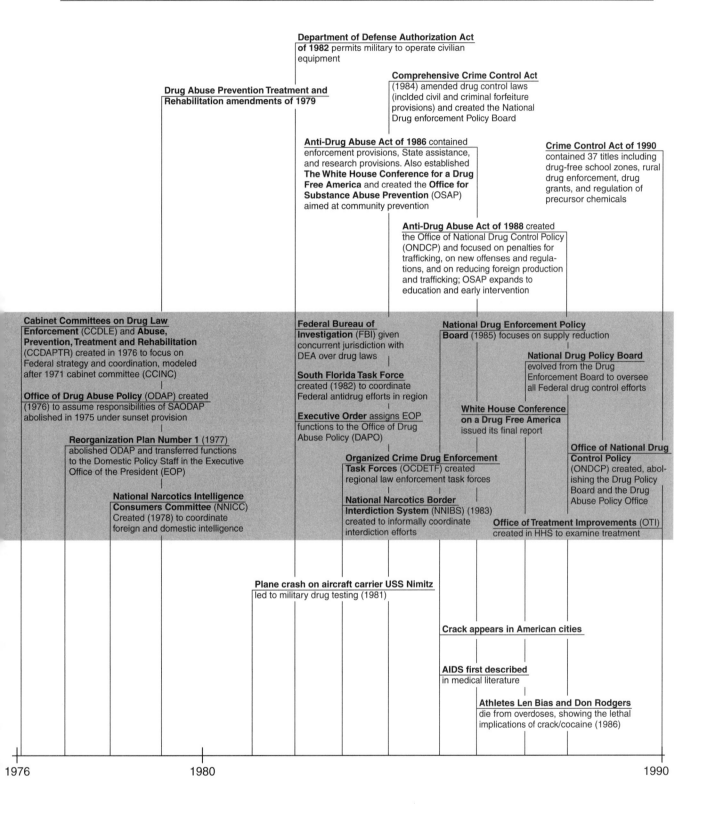

Department of Defense Authorization Act of 1982 permits military to operate civilian equipment

Drug Abuse Prevention Treatment and Rehabilitation amendments of 1979

Comprehensive Crime Control Act (1984) amended drug control laws (inclded civil and criminal forfeiture provisions) and created the National Drug enforcement Policy Board

Anti-Drug Abuse Act of 1986 contained enforcement provisions, State assistance, and research provisions. Also established **The White House Conference for a Drug Free America** and created the **Office for Substance Abuse Prevention** (OSAP) aimed at community prevention

Crime Control Act of 1990 contained 37 titles including drug-free school zones, rural drug enforcement, drug grants, and regulation of precursor chemicals

Anti-Drug Abuse Act of 1988 created the Office of National Drug Control Policy (ONDCP) and focused on penalties for trafficking, on new offenses and regulations, and on reducing foreign production and trafficking; OSAP expands to education and early intervention

Cabinet Committees on Drug Law Enforcement (CCDLE) and **Abuse, Prevention, Treatment and Rehabilitation** (CCDAPTR) created in 1976 to focus on Federal strategy and coordination, modeled after 1971 cabinet committee (CCINC)

Office of Drug Abuse Policy (ODAP) created (1976) to assume responsibilities of SAODAP abolished in 1975 under sunset provision

Reorganization Plan Number 1 (1977) abolished ODAP and transferred functions to the Domestic Policy Staff in the Executive Office of the President (EOP)

National Narcotics Intelligence Consumers Committee (NNICC) Created (1978) to coordinate foreign and domestic intelligence

Federal Bureau of Investigation (FBI) given concurrent jurisdiction with DEA over drug laws

South Florida Task Force created (1982) to coordinate Federal antidrug efforts in region

Executive Order assigns EOP functions to the Office of Drug Abuse Policy (DAPO)

Organized Crime Drug Enforcement Task Forces (OCDETF) created regional law enforcement task forces

National Narcotics Border Interdiction System (NNIBS) (1983) created to informally coordinate interdiction efforts

National Drug Enforcement Policy Board (1985) focuses on supply reduction

National Drug Policy Board evolved from the Drug Enforcement Board to oversee all Federal drug control efforts

White House Conference on a Drug Free America issued its final report

Office of National Drug Control Policy (ONDCP) created, abolishing the Drug Policy Board and the Drug Abuse Policy Office

Office of Treatment Improvements (OTI) created in HHS to examine treatment

Plane crash on aircraft carrier USS Nimitz led to military drug testing (1981)

Crack appears in American cities

AIDS first described in medical literature

Athletes Len Bias and Don Rodgers die from overdoses, showing the lethal implications of crack/cocaine (1986)

1976   1980   1990

**Major Federal legislation and
international conventions**

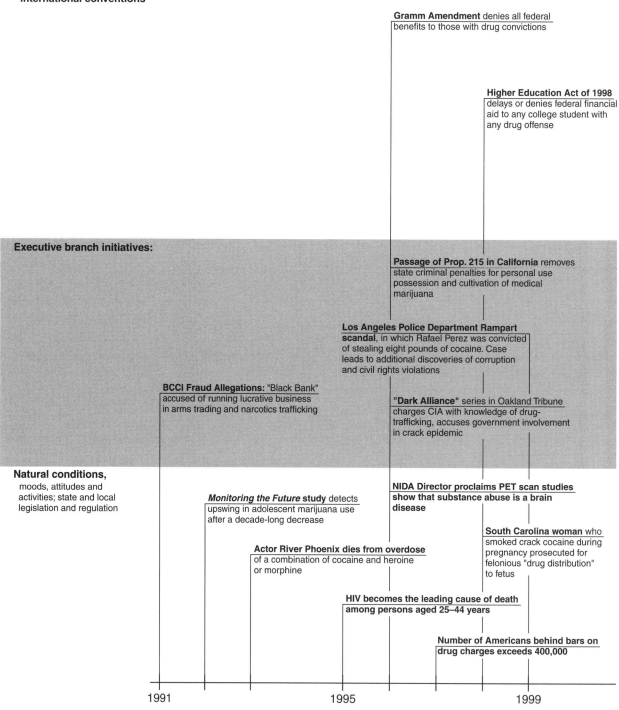

Gramm Amendment denies all federal benefits to those with drug convictions

Higher Education Act of 1998 delays or denies federal financial aid to any college student with any drug offense

Executive branch initiatives:

Passage of Prop. 215 in California removes state criminal penalties for personal use possession and cultivation of medical marijuana

Los Angeles Police Department Rampart scandal, in which Rafael Perez was convicted of stealing eight pounds of cocaine. Case leads to additional discoveries of corruption and civil rights violations

BCCI Fraud Allegations: "Black Bank" accused of running lucrative business in arms trading and narcotics trafficking

"Dark Alliance" series in Oakland Tribune charges CIA with knowledge of drug-trafficking, accuses government involvement in crack epidemic

Natural conditions,
moods, attitudes and
activities; state and local
legislation and regulation

Monitoring the Future **study** detects upswing in adolescent marijuana use after a decade-long decrease

NIDA Director proclaims PET scan studies show that substance abuse is a brain disease

South Carolina woman who smoked crack cocaine during pregnancy prosecuted for felonious "drug distribution" to fetus

Actor River Phoenix dies from overdose of a combination of cocaine and heroine or morphine

HIV becomes the leading cause of death among persons aged 25–44 years

Number of Americans behind bars on drug charges exceeds 400,000

1991   1995   1999

1 year = 1/2 inch

MAJOR FEDERAL ANTIDRUG BILLS, ENACTED 1984–2000

The 1984 Crime Control Act—

- expanded criminal and civil asset forfeiture laws
- amended the Bail Reform Act to target pretrial detention of defendants accused of serious drug offenses
- established a determinate sentencing system
- increased Federal criminal penalties for drug offenses

The 1986 Anti-Drug Abuse Act—

- budgeted money for prevention and treatment programs, giving the programs a larger share of Federal drug control funds than previous laws
- restored mandatory prison sentences for large-scale distribution of marijuana
- imposed new sanctions on money laundering
- added controlled substances' analogs (designer drugs) to the drug schedule
- created a drug law enforcement grant program to assist State and local efforts
- contained various provisions designed to strengthen international drug control efforts.

The 1988 Anti-Drug Abuse Act—

- increased penalties for offenses related to drug trafficking, created new Federal offenses and regulatory requirements, and changed criminal procedures
- altered the organization and coordination of Federal antidrug efforts
- increased treatment and prevention efforts aimed at reduction of drug demand
- endorsed the use of sanctions aimed at drug users to reduce the demand for drugs
- targeted for reduction drug production abroad and international trafficking in drugs

The Crime Control Act of 1990—

- doubled the appropriations authorized for drug law enforcement grants to States and localities
- expanded drug control and education programs aimed at the Nation's schools
- expanded specific drug enforcement assistance to rural States
- expanded regulation of precursor chemicals used in the manufacture of illegal drugs
- provided additional measures aimed at seizure and forfeiture of drug trafficker assets
- sanctioned anabolic steroids under the Controlled Substances Act
- included provisions on international money laundering, rural drug enforcement, drug-free school zones, drug paraphernalia, and drug enforcement grants.

"Smoke a Joint, Lose your License" Bill (passed as Public Law 101-516) of 1990—

- required that each State must either: enact laws that mandate suspending or revoking for six months the driver's license of any person convicted of controlled substance violations; or pass a resolution in both houses of the State legislature, accompanied by a written certification from the Governor acknowledging his agreement, that the State does not wish to enact the law
- failure to do one of these results in a 10% loss of the State's federal highway funds.

Gramm Amendment (Senate Amendment 4935 to the Welfare Reform package) in 1996—

- denied for life Federal assistance-based cash aid and food stamps to anyone convicted of felony drug charges
- applied to future felony drug convictions, and States have the ability to opt out of the program if they enact legislation to do so

Higher Education Act of 1998—

- delayed or denied Federal financial aid eligibility to any individual convicted of a State or Federal drug offense
- established that drug possession convictions result in ineligibility for one year (first offense), two years (second offense), or indefinitely (third offense), and that drug sale convictions result in ineligibility for two years (first offense) or indefinitely (second offense)
- provided that students may receive early restoration of benefits by completing a treatment program that fulfills yet-to-be-announced Dept. of Education regulations
- specified that ineligibility applies to all forms of Federal financial aid, including grants, student loans, and work-study

Civil Asset Forfeiture Reform Act of 1999 (effective August 23, 2000)—

- established that in order to seize assets, the government must prove that property is related to a crime, as opposed to property owners' having to prove that their property is "innocent"
- created an "innocent owner defense," whereby property owners who are either unaware of or unsuccessfully try to stop criminal activity on their property can recover the property

- eliminated the cost-bond requirement, which previously required property owners to pay $5,000 or 10 percent of the seized property's value to contest seizure in court

- provided compensation for property damage caused by federal agents and extended the time for filing a claim to contest a forfeiture

APPENDIX V

Illicit and Licit Drugs of Abuse— Schedules of Controlled Substances

INTRODUCTION

U.S. legislation called the Controlled Substances Act of 1970 has ranked and categorized drugs according to their effects, medical use, and potential for abuse. Ongoing research may reclassify drugs from one category to another, as has happened in the past.

At the federal level. Schedule I is the most strictly controlled—with the highest abuse potential; Schedule V is the least strictly controlled—drugs sold with or without prescription by mail and in shops, with instructions for use, dosages, and warnings about effects and side effects printed on the packaging of over-the-counter (OTC) medications. The schedules shown below in simplified form are followed by extensive schedules (which are discussed fully in Volume 1, in the article entitled Controls: Scheduled Drugs/Drug Schedules, U.S.). A discussion of the Controlled Substances Act of 1970 precedes it.

Drugs are scheduled under federal law according to their effects, medical use, and potential for abuse

DEA Schedule	Abuse Potential	Examples of Drugs Covered	Some of the Effects	Medical Use
I	highest	heroin, LSD, hashish, marijuana, methaqualone	unpredictable effects, severe psychological or physical dependence, or death	no accepted use; some are legal for limited research use only
II	high	morphine, PCP, cocaine, methadone, methamphetamine	may lead to severe psychological or physical dependence	accepted use with restrictions
III	medium	codeine with aspirin or Tylenol®, some barbiturates, anabolic steroids	may lead to moderate or low physical dependence or high psychological dependence	accepted use
IV	low	Darvon®, Talwin®, Equanil®, Valium®, Xanax®	may lead to limited physical or psychological dependence	accepted use
V	lowest	over-the-counter or prescription cough medicines with codeine	may lead to limited physical or psychological dependence	accepted use

SOURCE: Adapted from Drug Enforcement Administration, *Drugs of abuse (1996) and Schedules of Controlled Substances*, Revised as of April 1, 1998.

SCHEDULES OF U.S. CONTROLLED DRUGS

CRITERIA FOR U.S. DRUG SCHEDULING

Schedule	Potential for:		Medical Use & Safety
	Abuse	Dependence	
I	+ + + +	+ + + +	No
II	+ + + +	+ + + +	Yes
III	+ + +	+ + +	Yes
IV	+ +	+ +	Yes
V	+	+	Yes

LIST OF CONTROLLED DRUGS

SCHEDULE I

Opiates		Opium Derivatives	Hallucinogens	Depressants	Stimulants
Accty-alpha-methylfentanyl	Hydroxypethidine	Acetorphine	Alpha-ethyltryptamine	Mecloqualone	Aminorex Cathinone
Acetylmethadol	Ketobemidone	Acetyldihydrocodeine	4-bromo-2.5-DMA	Methaqualone	Fenethylline
Allylprodine	Levomoramide	Benzylmorphine	Alpha-desmethyl DOB		Methcathinone
Alphameprodine	Levophenacylmorphan	Codeine methylbromide	2.5-DMA		(±) cis-4-methylam-
Alphamethadol	3-methylfentanyl	Codeine-N-Oxide	DOET		inorex
Alpha-methylfentanyl	3-methylthiofentanyl	Cyprenorphine	PMA		N-ethylamphetamine
Alpha-methylthiofentanyl	Morpheridine	Desomorphine	5-methoxy-3,4-mdthylene-		N,N-dimethyl-am-
Benzethidine	MPPP	Dihydromorphine	dioxyamphetamine		phetamine
Betacetylmethadol	Noracymethadol	Drotebanol	MMDA		
Beta-hydroxyfentanyl	Norlevorphanol	Etorphine (except HCI salt)	DOM, STP		
Beta-hydroxy-3-methylfentanyl	Normethadone	Heroin	MDA		
Betameprodine	Norpipanone	Hydromorphinol	MDMA		
Betamethadol	Para-fluorofentanyl	Methyldesorphine	MDEA		
Betaprodine	PEPAP	Methyldihydromorphine	N-hydroxy MDA		
Clonitazene	Phenadoxone	Morphine methylbromide	3,4,5-trimethoxy		
Dextromoramide	Phenampromide	Morphine methylsulfonate	amphetamine		
Diampromide	Phenomorphan	Morphine-N-Oxide	Bufotenine		
Diethylthiambutene	Phenoperidine	Myrophine	DET		
Difenoxin	Piritramide	Nicocodeine	DMT		
Dimenoxadol	Proheptazine	Nicomorphine	Ibogaine		
Dimepheptanol	Properidine	Normorphine	LSD		
Dimethylthiambutene	Propiram	Pholcodine	Marihuana		
Dioxaphetyl butyrate	Racemoramide	Thebacon	Mescaline		
Dipipanone	Thiofentanyl		N-ethyl-3-peperidyl		
Ethylmethylthiambutene	Tilidine		benzilate		
Etonitazene	Trimeperidine		N-methyl-3-piperidyl-		
Etoxeridine			benzilate		
Furethidine			Peyote		
			Pheneyelidine analogs		
			PCE, PCPy, TCP,		
			TCPy		
			Psilocybin		
			Psilocyn		
			Tetrahydrocannabinols		

Temporary listing of substances subject to emergency scheduling:
Benzlyfentanyl
Thenylfentanyl

LIST OF CONTROLLED DRUGS

SCHEDULE II

Opiates	Opium & Derivatives	Hallucinogens	Depressants	Stimulants	Others
Alfentanil	Raw opium	Dronabinol	Amobarbital	Amphetamine	Opium poppy
Alphaprodine	Opium extracts	Nabilone	Glutethimide	Methamphetamine	Poppy straw
Anileridine	Opium fluid		Pentobarbital	Phenmetrazine	Coca leaves
Bezitramide	Powdered opium		Phencyclidine	Methylphenidate	Immediate precursors to:
Bulk dextropro-	Granulated opium		Secobarbital		Amphetamine
phene	Tincture of opium				Methamphetamine
Carfentanil	Codeine				Phencyclidine
Dihydrocodeine	Ethylmorphine				
Diphenoxylate	Etorphine hydrochloride				
Fentanyl	Hydrodone				
Isomethadone	Hydromorphone				
Levo-alphacetylmethadol	Metopon				
Levomethorphan	Morphine				
Levorphanol	Oxycodone				
Metazocine	Oxymorphone				
Methadone	Thebaine				
Methadone-Intermediate					
Moramide-Intermediate					
Pethidine					
Pethidine-Intermediate-A					
Pethidine-Intermediate-B					
Pethidine-Intermediate-C					
Phenazocine					
Piminodine					
Racemethorphan					
Racemorphan					
Remifentanil					
Sufentanil					

LIST OF CONTROLLED DRUGS

SCHEDULE III

Narcotics	Depressants	Stimulants	Others
Limited quantities of:	Mixtures of	Limited mixtures	Nalorphine
Codeine	Amobarbital	of Schedule II	All anabolic steroids
Dihydrocodeinone,	Secobarbital	amphetamines	
Dihydrocodeine,	Pentobarbital	Benzphetamine	
Ethylmorphine,	Derivatives of	Chlorphentermine	
Opium, and	barbituric acid	Clortermine	
Morphine	Chlorhexadol	Phendimetrazine	
in combination	Lysergic acid		
with nonnarcotics.	Lysergic acid amide		
	Methyprylon		
	Sulfondiethylmethane		
	Sulfonethylmethane		
	Sulfonmethane		
	Tiletamine		
	Zolazepam		

LIST OF CONTROLLED DRUGS

SCHEDULE IV

Narcotics	Depressants		Stimulants	Others
Limited quantity of difenoxin in combination with atropine sulfate	Alprazolam	Loprasolam	Cathine	Butorphanol
	Barbital	Lorazepam	Diethylpropion	Fenfluramine
	Bromazepam	Lormetazepam	Fencamfamin	Pentazocine
Dextropropoxyphere	Camazepam	Mebutamate	Fenproporex	
	Chloral betaine	Medazepam	Mazindol	
	Chloral hydrate	Meprobamate	Mefenorex	
	Chlordiazepoxide	Methohexital	Pemoline	
	Clobazam	Methylphenobarbital	Phentermine	
	Clorazepate	Nimetazepam	Pipradrol	
	Clotiazepam	Nitrazepam	Sibutramine	
	Cloxazolam	Nordiazepam	SPA	
	Delorazepam	Oxazepam		
	Diazepam	Oxazolam		
	Estazolam	Paraldehyde		
	Ethchlorvynol	Petrichloral		
	Ethinamate	Phenobarbital		
	Ethyl loflazepate	Pinazepam		
	Fludiazepam	Prazepam		
	Flunitrazepam	Quazepam		
	Flurazepam	Temazepam		
	Halazepam	Tetrazepam		
	Haloxazolam	Triazolam		
	Ketazolam	Zolpidem		

LIST OF CONTROLLED DRUGS

SCHEDULE V

Narcotics	Stimulants
Buprenorphine	Pyrovalcrone
Limited quantities (less than Schedules III & IV) of:	
Codeine,	
Dihydrocodeine,	
Ethylmorphine,	
Diphenoxylate, Opium, and Difenoxin in combination with nonnarcotics	

Index

during pregnancy, *893–897*
punishment schedule research and, 1004, *1005*
Antibodies, immunoassays and, 626–627
Anticonvulsants
  barbiturates as, 159–160, 163–164
  benzodiazepines as (*See* Benzodiazepines)
  THC as, 1084
Antidepressants, **135–136**
  for ADHD, 156
  for alcoholism, 1155–1156, 1251
  for anxiety, 139–140
  for cocaine addiction, 271, 1169, 1170, 1254–1255
  elderly, alcohol and, 60–61
  serotonin uptake inhibitors as (*See* Serotonin uptake inhibitors)
  tricyclic (*See* Tricyclic antidepressants)
  withdrawal from, 1352–1353
Antidiabetic agents, 61
Antidiarrheals, 805, 820–821
  laudanum, 681–682
  morphine as, 742, 743
  paregoric, 835–836
Antidipsotropics, 74, 1252
  calcium carbimide as, 215–216, 411, 1152–1153
  disulfiram as, 410–412, 970, 1152
  metronidazole as, 411
Antidiuretic hormone, 295–296
Antidotes, **136–137**, 723, 1363
Antiemetics, *cannabis* as, 705, 706, 1084
Antihelmintics, 184
Antihistamines
  driving and, 15
  elderly and, 58–60
  as sedative, 1021
Antilles, 264–265
Antineoplastic agents, 220
Antipsychotics, **137**, **771**
  chemical structure of, *137*
  for cocaine addiction, 1170, 1254
  elderly, alcohol and, 60–61
  for hallucinations, 586
  for schizophrenia, 1016
  withdrawal from, 1353
Antisocial personality disorder, **137–139**, 844
  aggression and, 525–526
  alcoholism genetic link, 53
  conduct disorder and, 347, 348–349
  substance abuse and, 327–328
  suicide and, 1064–1066
Anxiety disorders, **139–140**. *See also specific anxiety disorders*, e.g., Panic disorder
  alcohol treatment and, 1156
  antianxiety agents for (*See* Antianxiety agents)
  rebound, from benzodiazepines, 1344
  substance abuse and, 329
Anxiolytics. *See* Antianxiety agents
APA. *See* American Psychiatric Association
APHA. *See* American Public Health Association
Aphrodisiacs, **140**
Apnea, neonatal. *See* Neonatal apnea
Apomorphine, 1252
Appetite suppressants. *See* Anorectic agents
Aquatic accidents. *See* Water accidents
Aquavit, 407–408
Arab countries. *See* Middle East
Arawak culture, 872–874
ARC. *See* Addiction Research Center
Areca catechu. See Betel nut
Arecoline, 183

Aredaidine, 183
Argot, **141**. *See also* Slang and jargon
Aromatic hydrocarbon solvents, 643
Arrestee Drug Abuse Monitoring, **141–142**, 365
  amphetamines and, 368
  cannabis and, 368
  cocaine and, 367
  coerced treatment and, 276
  opioids and, 366–367
Arterial injection. *See* Intravenous route of administration
Arts. *See* Creativity and drug use
ARU (Addiction Research Unit), **18–19**
Arylcyclohexylamines. *See* Ketamine; Phencyclidine
ASAM. *See* American Society of Addiction Medicine
ASAM News, 108
ASAM Principles of Addiction Medicine, Second Edition, 108
ASAP. *See* Alcohol Safety Action Project
ASI. *See* Addiction Severity Index
Asia, **142–146**, *143. See also specific countries*, e.g., China
  alcohol and, 80, 233
  betel nut use in, 182–183
  cannabis use in, 221, 664–665
  ginseng use in, 578
  opium use in, 665–666, 833, 876
  as source country
    cocaine, 875
    methamphetamines, 119
    opium, 146, 813
  tea use in, 874
  terrorism in, 1081
  variations among subgroups of, 508–509
Asian Americans
  alcohol and, 254
  cultural considerations for, 505
Aspartate, 777–779
Aspirin. *See also* Analgesics
  with alcohol, *59*, 60
  for pain, 829–831
  poisoning, 448
  propoxyphene used with, 937
Assembly of Specialized Accrediting Bodies, 933
Assertiveness training. *See* Cognitive-behavior therapy
Assessment of Public Health and Social Problems Associated with the Use of Psychotropic Drugs, 1365
Assessment of substance abuse. *See* Diagnosis of substance abuse
Asset forfeiture, **151–153**
  DEA and, 1273
  prosecutors and, 446
Asset Forfeiture Fund, 1273, 1298
Association for Medical Education and Research in Substance Abuse, **153–154**
Association for the Study of Inebriety, 936
Association of the Relatives and Friends of the Mentally Ill, 1110
AST. *See* Liver enzymes
Asthma
  caffeine for, 210, 213
  drug-induced, 105–106
Asylum tradition, 1118–1120
Ataractics. *See* Sedative-hypnotics
Atarax. *See* Hydroxyzine
ATF. *See* Bureau of Alcohol, Tobacco and Firearms
Atherosclerosis, 290

Athletes and drug use. *See* Sports and drug use
Ativan. *See* Lorazepam
ATPase. *See* Adenosinetriphosphatase
Atropa belladonna. See Scopolamine
Atropine, **1017**
  acetylcholine and, 183
  in jimsonweed, 675
Attention deficit/hyperactivity disorder, **154–157**
  amphetamines for, 111
  conduct disorder and, 347
  methylphenidate for, 725
  pemoline for, 840
  rate-dependency theory and, 1003
  stimulants for, 242
  substance abuse and, 329
Australia
  as cocaine source, 875
  St. Vincent's Hospital, 1246–1247
Automobile accidents. *See* Motor vehicle accidents
Autonomic effects of hallucinogens, 590–591
Availability, regulation of, 683–685
AVE. *See* Abstinence violation effect
Aventyl. *See* Nortriptyline
Aversion therapy, 238, **1227–1229**, 1257–1258. *See also* Classical conditioning
  for alcoholism, 1148
  for tobacco addiction, 1210–1211
Aviation accidents, alcohol-related, 76–77
Avoidant personality disorder, 844
Axons, 774, 775, 776, 777
  synapses and, 1071
Ayahuasca, **157**
Azaspirodecadiones
  for alcoholism, 1251–1252
AZT. *See* Zidovudine
Aztec civilization
  beer use in, 77–78, 80–81
  chocolate use in, 255–256
  peyote use in, 845

B

B cells. *See* Leukocytes
Babies, addicted. *See* Addicted babies
Babor, Thomas, 399
Baby boomers, 616–617, 884
BAC. *See* Blood alcohol concentration
BACCHUS. *See* Boosting Alcohol Consciousness Concerning Health of University Students
Bacchus (Roman deity), 77–79
Bachman, Jerald, 600
Back pain, 174–175
Baclofen, 1160, 1353
Bacon, Seldon, 1013
Baeyer, Adolf von, 159
Bagwell, Jeff, 1105
Bahamas, 1112
Banisteriopsis caapi. See Ayahuasca
Bank Secrecy Act of 1970, 740–741
Banks, 740–741
Bantron. *See* Lobeline
Barbital, 159, *160*
Barbiturates, **159–163**, 1021
  with alcohol, *59*
  for alcohol withdrawal, 1251
  allergic response to, 105
  vs. benzodiazepines, 171–174
  British system and, 204
  chemical structure of, *160*
  vs. chloral hydrate, 255
  complications from, **163–164**

alcohol and (*See* Fetal alcohol syndrome)
cocaethylene and, 267
cocaine and, 898–899
drugs effect on, **537–543**
opioids and, 898
tobacco and, 302
Fifth Amendment. *See* Exclusionary rule
Fiji, 677
Filipino Americans and alcohol, 254
Fillmore, Kaye Middleton, 672
Financial Action Task Force, 740–741
Financial analysis, **443–444**
in Colombia, 284, 660
Customs Service and, 1304
Fire. *See* Burns and fire
First-order elimination kinetics, 856–858
Fischer, Emil Hermann, 159
5-HT. *See* Serotonin
5-hydroxytryptamine. *See* Serotonin
Flagyl. *See* Metronidazole
Flashbacks, 293, 693, 1024
Flay, Brian R., 918–919
Fleischl-Marxow, Ernst von, 548
Fleming, Robert, 1124
Florida
as Colombia smuggling route, 285
Operation PAR, 1137–1138
tobacco lawsuit, 46–47, 785
Fluid intake
animal research on, 29–30, 978
motivation and, 984
Flumazenil, 174, 711, 941, 1021
Flunitrazepam. *See* Rohypnol
Fluorescein, 628
Fluorescence polarization immunoassays,
626, 628–629
Fluorodeoxyglucose, 623–624
Fluoxetine, 1026, 1027
alcohol and, 970, 1156, 1251
for cocaine addiction, 1254–1255
for depression, 136
for weight control, 1108
Flupenthixol, 1170, 1196–1197
Flurazepam
as hypnotic, *173*, 174, 178, 1020
residual effects of, 175
Flushing reaction (Alcohol), 72
Fluvoxamine, 1027, 1251
Fly agaric, 145, **543**, *543*
Follicle-stimulating hormone, 295, 296
Food
animal research on, 977–978, 1002–1003
BAC and, 188
motivation and, 984
Food and Drug Act (Canada), 218
Food and Drug Act of 1906. *See* Pure Food
and Drugs Act of 1906
Food and Drug Administration
alcohol advertising and, 39
on amphetamines distribution, 115
clinical testing and, 965, 966–967, 1277
drug advertising and, 42–43, 44, 45
fenfluramine and, 902
ibogaine and, 622, 623
LAAM approval, 681
methadone and, 716
on tobacco, 684, 685, 1204–1205
Ford, Gerald R.
cabinet committees and, 1284
ODAP and, 1279, 1287
treatment policy and, 1127
Foreign Assistance Act, 1055
Foreign policy (U.S.), **543–546**
DEA and, 1272
Department of State and, 1274

Forfeiture Act. *See* Comprehensive Drug
Abuse Prevention and Control Act
of 1970
Forfeiture of assets. *See* Asset forfeiture
Formula grants. *See* Block grants
Forth Worth, Texas, Public Health Service
Hospital. *See* U.S. Public Health
Service Hospitals
Fourteenth Amendment. *See* Exclusionary
rule
Fourth Amendment. *See* Exclusionary rule
Fox, Ruth, 107–108, 759
Fox, Vicente, 725
FPIA. *See* Fluorescence polarization
immunoassays
France
heroin processing in, 655
HIV discovery in, 1060
Le Patriarche, 686–687
wine use in, 79
Franklin, Benjamin, 101–102
Free radicals and alcohol, 75
Freebasing, **546–548**
of cocaine, 269, 354
of methamphetamines, 118–119
Freon. *See* Chlorofluorocarbon propellants
Freud, Sigmund, *548*, 938–939
cocaine and, 13, **548–549**
on gambling, 560
on Jews and alcohol, 673
Friends Don't Let Friends Drive Drunk
campaign, 409
Frontal cortex, 192, 193–195, 196
Frontal lobe, 192
FTC. *See* Federal Trade Commission
Functional tolerance, 25
Funding. *See also* Government funding
of parent prevention groups, 838
for research, 964–965
social cost estimates and, 1049
for treatment, **1115–1116**

G

G-proteins, 780–781, 952
GA. *See* Gamblers Anonymous
GABA. *See* Gamma-aminobutyric acid
Gabon, 622
Gacha, Rodrigo, 285–286
Galan, Luis Carlos, 285–286
Galen, 813–814
Gam-Anon, 554, 560
The Gambler, 560
Gamblers Anonymous, 551, 554, 557–558,
560, 563
Gambling addiction, *559*, **559–564**
assessment of, **551–555**
epidemiology of, **555–559**
progression of, *554*
Gaming industry. *See* Gambling addiction
Gamma-aminobutyric acid, **564–565**
alcohol and, 71, 75, 233, 1155
alcohol-related aggression and, 53
barbiturates and, 160, *161*
benzodiazepines and, 172–174, 177–178
depressants and, 464–465
flunitrazepam and, 1008
memory and, 710, 711
muscimol as agonist for, 543
neurotransmission and, 777–779,
780–781
reinforcement and, 196
Gamma-hydroxybutyrate
as date rape drug, 264, 1009
for polydrug addiction, 1196–1197
Gangs, *565*, **565–574**

Ganja, **575**. *See also Cannabis sativa*
Gap junctions, 777
Garagiola, Joe, 1105
Garriott, James C., 646–647
Gas chromatography methods, *456*, 457,
584
Gasoline as inhalant, 644
Gastrointestinal disorders
alcohol and, 219–220, 304–308, 322
caffeine-related, 213, 214
Cryptosporidium parvum, 835
elderly and, 55, 57–58, 60
oral route of administration and, 340–341
varices, cirrhosis and, 310–311
Gateway drugs
adolescents and, 33, 34
alcohol as, 318
cannabis as, 702, 706
Gateway Foundation, 1136
Gautier, Theophile, 592–593
Gaviria, Cesar, 285, 286, 658–660
Gay-Lussac, Joseph Louis, 533
Gazeau, Charles, 301
Gender, **575–576**. *See also* Women and
substance abuse
adolescent substance abuse and, 607–608
antisocial personality disorder and, 138
DAWN records and, 430
gang roles and, 565–566
Latin-American differences, 611, 612–613
vulnerability and, 509, **1319–1322**,
1355–1359
genetics, 232, 1323
Gendreau, Mary Ann, *718*
Gene regulation, **577**
General Accounting Office, 190
General Assistance welfare program, 1337
Generalized anxiety disorder, 139
Genes, **577**. *See also* Genetics
Genetics, **577**
addiction, violence and, 53–54
ADHD and, 155, 329
as alcoholism factor, 36–38
animal research and, 988
antisocial personality disorder and, 138
chromosomes and, 256
cloning and (*See* Cloning)
enzyme polymorphism and, 447
gambling and, 553
gene regulation, **577**
genome project, 577
Jews, alcohol and, 673
marijuana addiction and, 1188
NIAAA research on, 1293
obesity and, 793
vs. psychological factors, 239
vulnerability and, **232–234**, 1316, 1318,
1322–1324
Genome project, **578**
Genotoxic carcinogens, 219
Genung, Don, 1137
Georgia
first boot-camp prison, 1028–1029
paraphernalia laws and, 836, 837, 924
Germany, beer use in, 166–167
Gerontology. *See* Elderly
GHB. *See* Gamma-hydroxybutyrate
Gin, 407–408
Ginseng, *578*, **578**
Giordano, Henry L., 133
Glasser, Ira, 449
Glaucoma and THC, 706, 1084–1085
Gleaton, Thomas "Buddy," 837, 918
Glide Memorial Methodist Church, 504
GLU. *See* Glutamate
Glucagon, 297